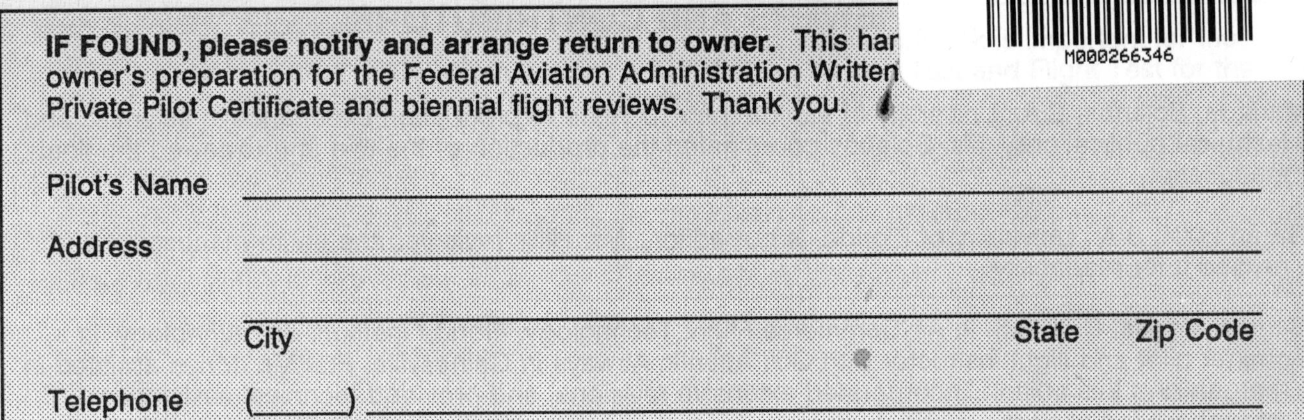

**IF FOUND, please notify and arrange return to owner.** This han[illegible] owner's preparation for the Federal Aviation Administration Written [illegible] Private Pilot Certificate and biennial flight reviews. Thank you.

Pilot's Name ______________________________

Address ______________________________

______________________________
City State Zip Code

Telephone (_____) ______________________________

Additional copies of *Private Pilot Handbook* are available from

Gleim Publications, Inc.
P.O. Box 12848
University Station
Gainesville, Florida 32604
(904) 375-0772
(800) 87-GLEIM

The price is $12.95 (subject to change without notice). Orders must be prepaid. Use the order form on page 374. Shipping and handling charges will be added to telephone orders. Add applicable sales tax to shipments within Florida.

Gleim Publications, Inc. guarantees the immediate refund of all resalable materials returned within 30 days. Shipping and handling charges are nonrefundable.

**ALSO AVAILABLE FROM GLEIM PUBLICATIONS, INC.**

*ORDER FORM ON PAGE 374.*

*PRIVATE PILOT/RECREATIONAL PILOT FAA WRITTEN EXAM*
*PRIVATE PILOT FAA PRACTICAL TEST PREP*
*RECREATIONAL PILOT FLIGHT MANEUVERS*

***Advanced Pilot Training Books***

*INSTRUMENT PILOT FAA WRITTEN EXAM*
*INSTRUMENT PILOT FAA PRACTICAL TEST PREP*

*COMMERCIAL PILOT FAA WRITTEN EXAM*
*COMMERCIAL PILOT FAA PRACTICAL TEST PREP*

*FLIGHT/GROUND INSTRUCTOR FAA WRITTEN EXAM*
*FUNDAMENTALS OF INSTRUCTING FAA WRITTEN EXAM*
*FLIGHT INSTRUCTOR FAA PRACTICAL TEST PREP*

*AIRLINE TRANSPORT PILOT FAA WRITTEN EXAM*

**AVAILABLE JUNE 1993**

***Aviation Weather and Aviation Weather Services*** is a rewrite in outline format of *Aviation Weather* AC 00-6A and *Aviation Weather Services* AC 00-45D. Use this easy-to-understand book to save you time and effort.

# REVIEWERS AND CONTRIBUTORS

Maria M. Bolanos, B.A., University of Florida, has 10 years of production experience in scientific and technical publications. Ms. Bolanos coordinated the production of the text and reviewed the final manuscript.

Gillian Hillis, B.A., University of Florida, is our editor. Ms. Hillis reviewed the entire manuscript and revised it for readability.

Barry A. Jones, CFII, B.S. in Air Commerce/Flight Technology, Florida Institute of Technology, is a charter pilot and flight instructor with Gulf Atlantic Airways in Gainesville, FL. Mr. Jones assisted in reorganizing this edition, incorporated extensive revisions, and provided technical assistance throughout the project.

Heiko E. Kallenbach, ATP, CFII, MEI, MFA, Carnegie Mellon University, is a flight instructor in single and multiengine airplanes, and is a ShandsCair pilot with Kenn-Air Corporation in Gainesville, FL. Mr. Kallenbach reviewed the manuscript, assisted in editing the text, and provided technical assistance.

John F. Rebstock, CIA, is a graduate of the Fisher School of Accounting at the University of Florida. Mr. Rebstock reviewed the entire edition and composed the page layout.

The many FAA employees who helped, in person or by telephone, primarily in Gainesville, FL; Jacksonville, FL; Orlando, FL; Oklahoma City, OK; and Washington, DC.

The many CFIs, pilots, and student pilots who have provided comments and suggestions about *Private Pilot Written Exam*, *Private Pilot FAA Practical Test Prep* and *Private Pilot Handbook* during the past 12 years.



# A PERSONAL THANKS

This manual would not have been possible without the extraordinary effort and dedication of Jim Collis and Connie Steen, who typed the entire manuscript and all revisions, as well as prepared the camera-ready pages.

The author also appreciates the proofreading assistance of Mike Amideo, Alison Barrett, Laura David, Kim Houellemont, Gregory Mullins, and Steve Palasay.

Finally, I appreciate the encouragement, support, and tolerance of my family throughout this project.

## FOURTH EDITION

# PRIVATE PILOT handbook

by Irvin N. Gleim, Ph.D., CFII

**ABOUT THE AUTHOR**

Irvin N. Gleim earned his private pilot certificate in 1965 from the Institute of Aviation at the University of Illinois, where he subsequently received his Ph.D. He is a commercial pilot and flight instructor (instrument) with multiengine and seaplane ratings, and is a member of the Aircraft Owners and Pilots Association, American Bonanza Society, Civil Air Patrol, Experimental Aircraft Association, and Seaplane Pilots Association. He is also author of Practical Test Prep books for the private, instrument, commercial, and flight instructor certificates/ratings, and study guides for the private, instrument, commercial, flight/ground instructor, fundamentals of instructing, and airline transport pilot FAA written tests.

Dr. Gleim has also written articles for professional accounting and business law journals, and is the author of the most widely used review manuals for the CIA exam (Certified Internal Auditor), the CMA exam (Certified Management Accountant), and the CPA exam (Certified Public Accountant). He is Professor Emeritus, Fisher School of Accounting, University of Florida, and is a CIA, CMA, and CPA.

**Gleim Publications, Inc.**
P. O. Box 12848
University Station
Gainesville, Florida 32604
(904) 375-0772
(800) 87-GLEIM

Library of Congress Catalog Card No. 93-70241

ISBN 0-917539-38-9



The author is indebted to Cessna Aircraft Corporation for permission to reproduce various checklists, diagrams, and charts from the Cessna-152 Pilot Operating Handbook, © 1980. These are reprinted **for academic illustration/training purposes only**. FOR FLIGHT, use your *Pilot's Operating Handbook* or *FAA-Approved Airplane Flight Manual*.

The author is indebted to Jeppesen Sanderson, Inc. for permission to reproduce illustrations from *Aviation Fundamentals*, Copyright 1976 and 1988.

**HELP !!**

This is one book in a series of three books designed specifically for potential pilots, student pilots, and private pilots. Please send any corrections and suggestions for subsequent editions to the author, c/o Gleim Publications, Inc. The last page in this book has been reserved for you to make comments and suggestions. It can be torn out and mailed to me.

Also, please bring this book to the attention of flight instructors, fixed base operators, and others interested in flying. Wide distribution of this series of books and increased interest in flying depend on your assistance and good word. Thank you.

# TABLE OF CONTENTS

# PREFACE

The primary purpose of this handbook is to organize all FAA material available on topics relevant to private pilot ground schools. This includes the Federal Aviation Regulations, Pilot's Handbook of Aeronautical Knowledge, Flight Training Handbook, Aviation Weather, Aviation Weather Services, and many other FAA books, pamphlets, circulars, etc. The objective was to get all ground school textual information into one usable book for student, private, and other pilots.

The secondary purpose of this study aid is to present the material in an easy-to-use and easy-to-understand format. The outline format helps readers organizationally. It also facilitates understanding and learning.

The third purpose is to assist pilots in preparing for their biennial flight review (BFR). Appendix A is designed for this purpose. As appropriate, you are referred back to specific topics in this book from Appendix A.

Most books create additional work for the user. In contrast, this handbook facilitates your effort. It is easy to use. The outline format, type styles, and spacing are designed to improve readability. Concepts are often presented as phrases rather than as complete sentences.

Read Chapter 1, How to Obtain a Private Pilot Certificate, carefully. Also, recognize that this study manual is concerned with airplane flight training, rather than balloon, glider, or helicopter training. I am confident this manual will also be very useful after you become a private pilot. It will help keep you current and be an invaluable study aid to prepare for your biennial review. I wish you the very best as you complete your private pilot certification, in subsequent flying, and in obtaining additional ratings and certificates.

I encourage your suggestions, comments, and corrections for future editions. The last page of this book has been designed to help you note corrections and suggestions throughout your study process. It can be torn out and mailed to me. Thank you.

Enjoy Flying -- Safely!

*Irvin N. Gleim*

April 1993

# CHAPTER ONE
# HOW TO OBTAIN A PRIVATE PILOT CERTIFICATE



To enable you to fly (pilot) an airplane, the U.S. Federal Aviation Administration (FAA) requires a formal training program, i.e., flight lessons. Learning to fly and getting a pilot certificate are fun. Begin today! The purpose of this chapter is to acquaint you with the requirements, procedures, costs, etc., to obtain your private pilot certificate.

## 1.1 WHAT IS A PRIVATE PILOT CERTIFICATE?

A private pilot certificate is much like an ordinary driver's license. A private pilot certificate will allow the pilot to fly an airplane and carry passengers and baggage, although not for compensation or hire. However, operating expenses may be shared with other travelers in the airplane. The certificate, which is a piece of paper similar to a driver's license, is sent to you by the FAA upon satisfactory completion of your training program, a written test, and a practical test comprised of an oral exam and a flight test. A sample certificate is reproduced below.

Front

I. UNITED STATES OF AMERICA XI.
Department of Transportation · FEDERAL AVIATION ADMINISTRATION
THIS CERTIFIES IV.
THAT V. LARRY NELSON MCALEXANDER
1101 NW 39TH AVENUE K70
GAINESVILLE FL 32601

| DATE OF BIRTH | HEIGHT IN. | WEIGHT | HAIR | EYES | SEX | NATIONALITY VI. |
|---|---|---|---|---|---|---|
| 01-18-48 | 75 | 220 | BROWN | BLUE | M | USA |

IX. HAS BEEN FOUND TO BE PROPERLY QUALIFIED TO EXERCISE THE PRIVILEGES OF
II. PRIVATE PILOT III. CERT. NO. 222208771
RATINGS AND LIMITATIONS
XII. AIRPLANE SINGLE ENGINE LAND

XIII.
VII. SIGNATURE OF HOLDER X. Donald D. Engen
X. DATE OF ISSUE 09-15-90 VIII. ADMINISTRATOR
AC Form 8060-2 (5-81)

Back

**DURATION**

This certificate is of such duration as is provided in the currently effective Federal Aviation Regulations, unless sooner suspended or revoked. Airmen is not authorized to exercise privileges of any class or ratings issued in error. Return immediately for correction. Certificate should be returned to address below within 30 days of death of Airman.

FEDERAL AVIATION ADMINISTRATION
AIRMAN CERTIFICATION BRANCH
P. O. BOX 25082
OKLAHOMA CITY, OKLAHOMA 73125

**REPAIRMAN OPERATIONAL RESTRICTION**

The holder hereof shall not perform or approve alterations, repairs or inspections of aircraft except in accordance with the applicable airworthiness requirements of the Federal Aviation Regulations, or such method, techniques, and practices found acceptable to the Administrator.

**WARNING**: Alteration of this certificate is subject to a fine of not exceeding $1,000 or imprisonment not exceeding three years, or both. (U.S. Code, Title 49, Sec. 1472(b)).

## 1.2 WHAT IS A RECREATIONAL PILOT CERTIFICATE?

The FAA added a recreational pilot certificate in 1989 for those who want to fly locally for fun, i.e., recreation. The objective is to provide only the flight training required for those **NOT** aspiring to fly on trips, at night, with more than one passenger, or to airports with an operating control tower or other airspace requiring ATC (air traffic control) communication. A recreational pilot certificate will take you less time and money to obtain, but your flying privileges will be restricted. The recreational pilot certificate is, however, upgradable to a private pilot certificate. The recreational pilot certificate is similar in appearance to the private pilot certificate, except it reads "Recreational Pilot," not "Private Pilot." Author's Note: This has not been a successful program in that fewer than 100 people have obtained recreational pilot certificates since its inception.

## 1.3 REQUIREMENTS TO OBTAIN A PRIVATE PILOT CERTIFICATE

A. **Obtain an FAA medical certificate.**

1. You must undergo a routine medical examination which may only be administered by FAA-designated doctors called aviation medical examiners.
2. The medical certificate necessary for a private (or recreational) pilot certificate is called a third-class medical. It is valid for 2 years and expires on the last day of the month issued (when another medical examination is required).
3. Even if you have a physical handicap, medical certificates can be issued in many cases. Operating limitations may be imposed depending upon the nature of the disability.
4. Your flight instructor or FBO (Fixed Base Operator) will be able to recommend an aviation medical examiner.
    a. FBO is an airport business that offers flight lessons, sells aviation fuel, rents and repairs airplanes, etc.
    b. Also, the FAA publishes a directory that lists all authorized aviation medical examiners by name and address. Copies of this directory are kept at all FAA Flight Standards District Offices, Air Traffic Control facilities, and Flight Service Stations.
5. Although you may begin your flight lessons with an instructor before obtaining your medical certificate, your author recommends that you see an aviation medical examiner and obtain a combined medical certificate/student pilot certificate before spending money on flight lessons.
    a. This combined certificate becomes valid once you and the aviation medical examiner sign it.
    b. To obtain this combined certificate, you must be at least 16 years of age and be able to read, speak, and understand the English language.
        1) Alternatively, a separate student pilot certificate can be obtained from an FAA-designated pilot examiner, FAA inspector, or an FAA Flight Standards District Office.
            a) This would be necessary if your aviation medical examiner issued you a medical certificate instead of the combined medical certificate/student pilot certificate.

c. The only substantive difference between a regular medical certificate and a medical certificate/student pilot certificate is that the back of the medical certificate/student pilot certificate provides for flight instructor signatures.

   1) Note that the back of the student pilot certificate must be signed by your flight instructor prior to solo flight (flying by yourself).

d. The front and back of a sample FAA medical certificate/student pilot certificate are reproduced below.

UNITED STATES OF AMERICA
DEPARTMENT OF TRANSPORTATION
FEDERAL AVIATION ADMINISTRATION

BB-5342031

MEDICAL CERTIFICATE 3rd CLASS
AND STUDENT PILOT CERTIFICATE

THIS CERTIFIES THAT *(Full name and address)*
Richmond, Kane Everett
1771 Coral Way
N. Ft. Myers, FL. 33903

| DATE OF BIRTH | HEIGHT | WEIGHT | HAIR | EYES | SEX |
|---|---|---|---|---|---|
| 1/30/67 | 5'9" | 110 | Brn. | Brn. | M |

has met the medical standards prescribed in Part 67 Federal Aviation Regulations for this class of Medical Certificate, and the standards prescribed in Part 61 for a Student Pilot Certificate.

LIMITATIONS: STUDENT PILOTS ARE PROHIBITED FROM CARRYING PASSENGERS.
None

DATE OF EXAMINATION: 3/15/92
EXAMINER'S SERIAL NO.: 11967-1

EXAMINER — SIGNATURE: [signature]
TYPED NAME: E.W. Williams II, D.O.

AIRMAN'S SIGNATURE: Kane E. Richmond

FAA FORM 8420-2 (10-73) SUPERSEDES PREVIOUS EDITION

Front

CONDITIONS OF ISSUE: This certificate shall be in the personal possession of the airman at all times while exercising the privileges of his airman certificate. As a medical certificate, it is temporary for a period of 60 days; as a student pilot certificate, it is temporary for a period of 90 days. If no notice to the contrary is received within such periods, it will remain in effect until the expiration dates as provided in Sections 61.19 and 61.23 of the Federal Aviation Regulations, unless modified or recalled by proper authority. The holder of this certificate is governed by the provisions of FAR Secs 61.53, 63.19, and 65.49(d) relating to physical deficiency.

CERTIFICATED INSTRUCTOR'S ENDORSEMENTS FOR STUDENT PILOTS

I certify that the holder of this certificate has met the requirements of the regulations and is competent for the following:

| | DATE | MAKE AND MODEL OF AIRCRAFT | INSTRUCTOR'S SIGNATURE | INSTRUCTOR'S CERTIFICATE NO | EXP DATE |
|---|---|---|---|---|---|
| A. TO SOLO THE FOLLOWING AIRCRAFT | 9/15/92 | C-152 | [signature] | [illegible] | 9/93 |
| | | | | | |
| | | AIRCRAFT CATEGORY | | | |
| B. TO MAKE SOLO CROSS-COUNTRY FLIGHTS | | AIRPLANE | | | |
| | | GLIDER | | | |
| | | ROTOCRAFT | | | |

NOTICE: Any alteration of this certificate is punishable by a fine not exceeding $1,000, or imprisonment not exceeding 3 years, or both

Back

B. **Pass a written test with a score of 70% or better.**

1. Most FAA written tests are administered by FAA-designated written test examiners. This test is administered at some Flight Standards District Offices (FSDOs) and certain airport FBOs. After you take your written test at one of these facilities, your answer sheet is sent to the FAA's Aeronautical Center in Oklahoma City. It takes 4 to 6 weeks for the FAA to process your answer sheet and return an FAA written test report (Form 8080-2) to you. Thus, you should take your written test about 2 months before you anticipate taking your practical test.

   a. The FAA has contracted with several computer testing services to administer FAA written tests. The advantage is that you get an immediate test report on completion of the computer test. Thus, you do not have to wait to have your written test sent to the FAA in Oklahoma City for grading and then have the results mailed to you.

      1) Below are telephone numbers for three computer testing services which have testing centers throughout the country. You register by calling an 800 number. There are others; contact your local FAA FSDO for names and telephone numbers. Call the following testing services for information regarding

         a) The location of their testing center most convenient to you,
         b) The time allowed, and
         c) The cost to take their private pilot (airplane) written test.

| | |
|---|---|
| DRAKE | (800) 359-3278 |
| PLATO | (800) 869-1100 |
| SYLVAN | (800) 967-1100 |

      2) Note that the FAA corrects (redoes) defective questions on the computer tests, which it cannot do in the written test books. Thus, it is important to carefully study questions that are noted to have no correct answer in test prep books such as Gleim's *Private Pilot and Recreational Pilot FAA Written Exam*. On the pencil and paper test, you will get credit for these defective questions, but on the computer tests, the questions will probably have been rephrased.

   b. The FAA permits FAR Part 141 schools to develop, administer, and grade their own written tests as long as they use the FAA written test books, i.e., those with the same questions as in Gleim's FAA Written Exam books. The FAA does not provide the correct answers to the 141 schools and the FAA only reviews the 141 school test question selection sheets. Thus, some of the answers used by 141 test examiners may not agree with the FAA or those in Gleim's FAA Written Exam books. This may explain why you miss a question in a 141 written test using an answer presented in Gleim's FAA Written Exam books.

      1) Also, about 20 Part 141 schools use the AVTEST computer testing system, which is very similar to the computer testing services described above.

   c. Gleim has **FAA Test Prep** software which is tutorial software to help you prepare for your FAA written tests. The software has a study mode and a test mode.

      1) The study mode permits you to select the topics you wish to study. As you answer questions, you receive explanations of correct and incorrect answers.

      2) The test mode simulates AVTEST, DRAKE, PLATO, or SYLVAN and permits you to take practice tests and provides feedback on your proficiency by subject matter.

d. Gleim's *Private Pilot and Recreational Pilot FAA Written Exam* book is also an easy-to-use, effective means of preparing to pass the FAA written test. It converts the preparation process from a memorization marathon to a learning and understanding experience.

2. The written or computerized test consists of 60 multiple-choice questions selected from the 710 airplane-related questions in the FAA's *Recreational Pilot and Private Pilot Written Test Book.*

   a. Each of the FAA's airplane questions is reproduced in *Private Pilot and Recreational Pilot FAA Written Exam* by Irvin N. Gleim with complete explanations to the right of each question. The questions test the following topics:

      Introduction to Airplanes and Aerodynamics
      Airplane Performance
      Airplane Instruments, Engines, and Systems
      Airports and Air Traffic Control
      Weight and Balance
      Weather
      Federal Aviation Regulations
      Navigation Charts
      Other Navigational Publications
      Navigation
      Flight Physiology
      Cross-Country Flying

3. You are required to satisfactorily complete a ground instruction or home-study course prior to taking the written test. See page 375 for a standard authorization form which can be completed, signed by a flight instructor or ground instructor, torn out, and taken to the examination site.

4. FAR 61.105 provides the following description of private pilot ground school topics:

   *(1) The accident reporting requirements of the National Transportation Safety Board and the Federal Aviation Regulations applicable to private pilot privileges, limitations, and flight operations for airplanes, the use of the "Airman's Information Manual," and FAA advisory circulars;*

   *(2) VFR navigation using pilotage, dead reckoning, and radio aids;*

   *(3) The recognition of critical weather situations from the ground and in flight, the procurement and use of aeronautical weather reports and forecasts.*

   *(4) The safe and efficient operation of airplanes including high-density airport operations, collision avoidance precautions, and radio communication procedures;*

   *(5) Basic aerodynamics and the principles of flight which apply to airplanes; and*

   *(6) Stall awareness, spin entry, spins, and spin recovery techniques.*

5. You must be at least 15 years of age to take either the Recreational or Private Pilot written test.

C. **Obtain required flight experience (FAR 61.109).**

1. A total of at least 40 hr. of flight instruction and solo flight time. The requirements include
   a. 20 hr. of flight instruction from an authorized flight instructor, including at least
      1) 3 hr. of cross-country, i.e., to other airports.
      2) 3 hr. at night, including 10 takeoffs and landings for applicants seeking night flying privileges.
      3) 3 hr. in airplanes in preparation for the private pilot flight test within 60 days prior to that test.
   b. 20 hr. of solo flight time, including at least
      1) 10 hr. in airplanes (some could be in a glider, etc.).
      2) 10 hr. of cross-country flights
         a) Each flight with a landing more than 50 NM from the point of departure.
         b) One flight of 300 NM, with landings at three points, one of which is more than 100 NM from the point of departure.
      3) Three solo takeoffs and landings to a full stop at an airport with an operating control tower.
2. FAA-certificated pilot schools (Part 141) may obtain approval of a private pilot (airplane) training course providing for a total of 35 hr. of flight and other special instruction time.
   a. These programs are known as Part 141 programs because they are authorized by Part 141 of the Federal Aviation Regulations (FARs) issued by the FAA.
   b. All other regulations concerning certification of pilots are found in Part 61 of the FARs.

D. **Obtain required flight instruction.**

1. FAR 61.107 specifies instruction in the following 10 areas:

   *(1) Preflight operations, including weight and balance determination, line inspection, and airplane servicing;*

   *(2) Airport and traffic pattern operations, including operations at controlled airports, radio communications, and collision avoidance precautions;*

   *(3) Flight maneuvering by reference to ground objects;*

   *(4) Flight at slow airspeeds with realistic distractions, and the recognition of and recovery from stalls entered from straight flight and from turns;*

   *(5) Normal and crosswind takeoffs and landings;*

   *(6) Control and maneuvering an airplane solely by reference to instruments, including descents and climbs using radio aids or radar directives;*

   *(7) Cross-country flying, using pilotage, dead reckoning, and radio aids, including one 2-hour flight;*

   *(8) Maximum performance takeoffs and landings;*

   *(9) Night flying, including takeoffs, landings, and VFR navigation; and*

   *(10) Emergency operations, including simulated aircraft and equipment malfunctions.*

E. **Successfully complete a practical (flight) test.**

1. You must be at least 17 years of age to take the Private Pilot (or Recreational Pilot) Practical Test.
2. Both an oral exam and a flight test will be given by an FAA inspector or a designated examiner. The test is prescribed by the FAA's Private Pilot Practical Test Standards. Refer to Gleim's *Private Pilot FAA Practical Test Prep* for everything you need to know.
   a. FAA inspectors are FAA employees and do not charge for their services. They administer very few private practical tests. Primarily, they administer flight instructor practical tests.
   b. FAA-designated examiners are proficient, experienced flight instructors who are authorized by the FAA to conduct flight tests. They do charge a fee.
3. The FAA's Practical Test Standards (PTSs) are reproduced in Gleim's *Private Pilot FAA Practical Test Prep* for the private pilot practical test and in Gleim's *Recreational Pilot Flight Maneuvers* for the recreational pilot practical test.

## 1.4 QUESTIONS FREQUENTLY ASKED BY THE BEGINNING STUDENT

The following questions and answers were compiled by the FAA based on a survey of flight schools and flight instructors. They are the questions most frequently asked by new student pilots.

1. Is it difficult to fly an airplane?

   No. It is not particularly difficult. You will do most of the actual flying from the beginning -- handling the controls of the airplane yourself.

2. When can I begin to fly?

   Immediately. However, you will need to apply for certain certificates, as described in this book, in preparation for your solo flight.

3. Is there a set number of flight instructional hours I will receive before I solo?

   No, your instructor will not solo you until you have learned to perform the maneuvers taught you, including, of course, safe takeoffs and landings. You must be able to maintain positive control of the airplane at all times!!

4. If engine failure occurs, what would happen?

   Aircraft engines are very reliable and complete failure is a rare occurrence. If the improbable does happen, however, you will not "fall out of the sky." You just do what your instructor will have you practice during your lessons; select a good landing area and land.

5. Is flying safe?

   A well-built and well-maintained airplane flown by a competent and prudent pilot makes flying safer than many other forms of transportation.

### MEDICAL AND STUDENT PILOT CERTIFICATES

6. When do I need a medical certificate?

   Prior to solo flight.

7. When do I need a student pilot certificate?

   Prior to solo flight.

8. How do I get a medical certificate?

   By passing a physical examination designed for pilots and administered by a doctor who is an authorized FAA aviation medical examiner.

9. How do I obtain a student pilot certificate?

A combination medical certificate and student pilot certificate will be issued, at your request, by the medical examiner upon the satisfactory completion of your physical examination. Student pilot certificates may be issued by FAA inspectors, designated pilot examiners, or the nearest Flight Standards District Office (FSDO) if you already possess a valid medical certificate. Applicants who fail to meet certain requirements or who have physical disabilities which might limit, but not prevent, their acting as pilots should contact the nearest FSDO.

10. What are the requirements for a student pilot certificate (airplane)?

Applicants must be (a) 16 years of age; (b) able to read, speak, and understand the English language; and (c) hold at least a third-class medical certificate. Operating limitations may be imposed in lieu of requirement (b).

11. Where do I get my medical certificate?

From any aviation medical examiner. There are approximately 7,500 doctors authorized by the FAA as aviation medical examiners.

12. Where can a list of FAA-authorized aviation medical examiners be found?

The FAA publishes a directory which lists all authorized aviation medical examiners by name and address. Copies of this directory are kept at all FAA Flight Standards District Offices, Air Traffic Control facilities, and Flight Service Stations. Airport FBOs may also be able to supply this information.

13. What class of medical certificate is required for a student pilot?

Third-class, although any class will suffice. Medical certificates are designated as first-, second-, or third-class. Generally, the first-class is designed for the airline transport pilot; the second-class for the commercial pilot; and the third-class for the student, recreational, and private pilot.

14. If I have a physical handicap, is there any provision for obtaining a medical certificate?

Yes. Medical certificates can be issued in many cases where physical disabilities are involved. Operating limitations may be imposed, depending upon the certificate held and nature of disability. If there are any questions, you should check with a medical examiner prior to beginning flight training. The wearing of eyeglasses or contacts is not considered a physical handicap.

15. For how long a period is my medical and student pilot certificate valid?

The student pilot and third-class medical certificates expire at the end of the 24th month after the month in which it was issued. (For example, a certificate issued on December 2, 1992, would expire at midnight on December 31, 1994.)

16. Can my student pilot certificate be renewed?

No, but a new one may be issued by the medical examiner upon completion of the required examination, or by an inspector or pilot examiner if you already hold a valid medical certificate.

17. If my original student pilot certificate has been endorsed for solo, do I lose this endorsement on my new certificate?

Endorsements will not be transferred to the new medical and student pilot certificate by the medical examiner. You should retain your old certificate as a record of these endorsements.

**18. Should my flight instructor endorse my student pilot certificate prior to or after my first solo flight?**

The endorsement on the student pilot certificate certifying that the holder is competent to solo must be made by the flight instructor prior to the first solo flight. The recurring endorsement follows each 90 days thereafter.

**19. If I solo in more than one make and model of aircraft, must I have an endorsement for each on my student pilot certificate? By whom?**

Yes. A flight instructor must make this endorsement for each make and model of aircraft prior to the first solo flight in each make and model of aircraft.

**20. Does the endorsement to solo permit me to make solo cross-country flights?**

No. The student pilot certificate must be specifically endorsed for solo cross-country flights by the flight instructor.

**21. Must I carry my student pilot certificate on my person when I am piloting an aircraft in solo flight?**

Yes.

**22. Must I carry my medical certificate on my person when I am piloting an aircraft in solo flight?**

Yes.

**23. Is there a charge for the student pilot certificate?**

Not when the student pilot certificate is issued by an FAA Flight Standards District Office. An FAA-designated pilot examiner is allowed to charge a reasonable fee for issuing student pilot certificates, and executing the necessary reports. The aviation medical examiner will charge a fee for the physical examination in connection with issuing the combination medical and student pilot certificate.

## STUDENT PILOT TRAINING

**24. Where can I obtain my flight and ground school training?**

Most airport operators (FBOs) can furnish this information, or you can contact your nearest FAA Flight Standards District Office.

**25. What must I know about the Federal Aviation Regulations prior to my first solo?**

The flight instructor will determine that you are familiar with appropriate portions of FAR Part 61 and the general and visual flight rules of FAR Part 91, and will administer you a written test prior to solo endorsement. The presolo written test will also include questions on flight characteristics and operational limitations of the make and model of aircraft to be flown.

**26. After my student pilot certificate is endorsed for solo, may I fly solo any time I wish?**

Yes, so long as your logbook has also been appropriately endorsed for solo by an authorized flight instructor and you operate within the limitations of the endorsement.

**27. What does an appropriate logbook endorsement for solo mean?**

It means an endorsement by an authorized flight instructor showing that on the date specified the student was given dual instruction and found competent to make solo flights.

**28. When is such an endorsement required?**

A student pilot must have such an endorsement dated within 90 days prior to any solo flight.

**29.** Does a student pilot automatically have the privilege of flying cross-country alone after soloing?

No. An instructor must have reviewed the pilot's preflight planning and preparation for each solo cross-country flight to determine that the flight can be made safely under the known circumstances and conditions. A one-time endorsement must be made on the student pilot certificate for solo cross-country flights for each category of aircraft to be flown. The instructor must also endorse the student pilot's logbook prior to each cross-country flight stating the pilot is considered competent to make the flight.

**30.** Am I permitted to carry passengers with me prior to receipt of my private pilot certificate?

No!

**31.** May I operate an aircraft for compensation or hire, or in the furtherance of a business?

No!

**32.** Where can I take the flight (practical) test?

The FAA has designated many flight instructors as pilot examiners, i.e., your flight instructor or FBO can usually help you schedule your flight test with an FAA inspector or an FAA-designated examiner that they know and can recommend to you. The FAA Flight Standards District Offices, which are usually located on or adjacent to an airport, also conduct flight tests for pilot certification.

**33.** Is there any charge for taking the flight (practical) test?

You must provide the airplane. FAA inspectors (FAA employees) will not charge you. FAA-designated examiners who are not FAA employees will charge you approximately $100 to $150.

**34.** May I fly as a private pilot immediately after passing my flight test or must I wait until I receive the actual private pilot certificate?

The inspector or examiner will issue you a 120-day temporary private pilot certificate which is effective immediately. This will serve as your official certificate until the permanent certificate is issued by mail.

**35.** Once I have a license, how do I keep it current?

To stay current, you must complete a flight review every 2 years with a flight instructor and obtain a medical exam every 2 years. Also, you must perform three takeoffs and landings every 90 days to be able to carry passengers. These must be at night if the intended flight is to be at night.

## 1.5 COSTS TO OBTAIN YOUR PRIVATE PILOT CERTIFICATE

A. The price of instruction varies across the country and also from FBO to FBO. Fuel, maintenance, and airplane cost play a major role in determining airplane rental rates. Just as with any sizable purchase, you should shop around to make sure you are buying what you want at a fair price.

B. Some FBOs use regulated Part 141 programs which use a very structured syllabus that must be approved by the FAA. The advantage to the FBO is a mass production potential based on the structured syllabus.

   1. Usually, both the ground school and the flight training are based on the building block method. That is, each new concept or maneuver builds and relies on the previous concept or maneuver (building block).

      a. Student pilots do not progress to the next concept or maneuver until the previous concept or maneuver is mastered.

2. The advantage to the student pilot is that only 35 hr. of flight are required for completion of the program.
   a. Also, the flight test is administered by the FBO's chief pilot (with whom the student pilot may have flown previously) at schools with examining authority.
3. The general consensus, however, is that few persons complete the program in less than 40 hr.

C. Listed below is an example cost estimate at the middle of the cost range of $2,500 to $4,000. Your total cost will depend on the FBO, equipment, local cost factors, competition, etc., and the amount of training in excess of 40 hr. Fortunately, most flight schools require that cash outlays be made as time progresses, lesson by lesson, instead of all at once.

| | | |
|---|---|---|
| Medical Exam | $ 40.00 | |
| Books and Supplies (a) | 100.00 | (assuming self-study) |
| Written Test Fee (b) | 50.00 | |
| 25 Hr. of Dual (c) | 1,750.00 | |
| 20 Hr. of Solo (d) | 1,000.00 | |
| Rental of Aircraft for Flight Test | 50.00 | |
| Examiner's Fee | 150.00 | |
| TOTAL | $3,140.00 | |

1. NOTE: The above may be a low estimate based on a recent survey indicating the national average of total hours for student pilots is close to 60 hr. (which could add over $1,000 to the above estimate).
   a. Books and Supplies, $100. Assuming a course of self-study, *Private Pilot Handbook, Private Pilot and Recreational Pilot FAA Written Exam, Private Pilot FAA Practical Test Prep*, a plotter, a flight computer, a sectional chart, and a pilot logbook are all you need, at a cost of about $100. Plotters, flight computers, and sectional charts are used to navigate, i.e., determine how to get to your destination on long trips. If you want a hand-held aviation calculator computer rather than a slide rule computer, you will spend at least another $50. Enrolling in a formal ground school may cost you up to several hundred dollars, depending on the school.
   b. Written Test Fee, $50. This fee is the typical charge by most FBOs to administer the FAA written test. There is no charge if you take the test at an FAA Flight Standards District Office (FSDO). However, you may spend more than $50 in gas and time getting to and from the nearest FSDO. Computerized testing centers also charge about $50 for administering the written test.
   c. 25 Hr. of Dual, $1,750. This is based on $50 per hour for the aircraft and $20 per hour for your instructor.
   d. 20 Hr. of Solo, $1,000 based on $50 per hour for airplane rental.
   e. Some FBOs sell blocks of time (e.g., 10 or 20 hr.) at a discount of perhaps 10%, if paid in advance.

(f) Do not be upset if you have to fly more than 40 hr. prior to your flight test. Most people require more than 50 hr. of flight time. Thus, you should be prepared to spend several hundred dollars more than your original minimum estimate. Conversely, there are still a few flight schools at which you can obtain a private certificate for about $2,500.

## 1.6 TIME REQUIRED TO OBTAIN YOUR PRIVATE PILOT CERTIFICATE

A. While only 40 hr. of flight instruction are required, the total process usually takes several months and hundreds of hours due to commuting, ground instruction, aircraft preflight, canceled lessons due to bad weather, etc.

   1. Private pilot certificates can be obtained in as little time as a month with near full-time effort. A more realistic, relaxed, and efficient timetable is 3 to 4 months.

B. In conjunction with flight instruction, you must also prepare to take the FAA written test, which consists of 60 multiple-choice questions.

   1. Ground schools teaching the material are offered by some flight schools (especially in conjunction with flight instruction).

      a. A typical instruction course would be 1 evening a week (3 hr. long) for 6 to 8 weeks.

   2. Also, several audio-visual instruction programs (i.e., Part 141 programs) are available through FBOs.

   3. This book, however, in conjunction with *Private Pilot and Recreational Pilot FAA Written Exam*, is a "home study program" which will provide you with the necessary background and knowledge to take and earn a high score on the FAA written test.

## 1.7 HOW TO GET STARTED

A. **Talk to several people who have recently obtained their private pilot certificate.** Visit your local airport and ask for the names of several people who have just completed their private pilot training. When you locate one person, (s)he can usually refer you to another. How did they do it?

   1. *Flight training:* Airplane? CFI? What period of time? Cost? How structured was the program?
   2. *Ask for their advice.* How would they do it differently? What do they suggest to you?
   3. *What difficulties did they encounter?*

B. **Talk to several CFIs.** Tell them you are considering becoming a private pilot. Evaluate each as a prospective instructor.

   1. *What do they recommend?*
   2. *Ask to see their flight syllabus. How structured is it?*
   3. *What are their projected costs?*
   4. *What is the rental cost for their training aircraft, solo and dual?*
   5. *Ask for the names and phone numbers of several persons who recently obtained private pilot certificates under their direction.*
   6. *Does the flight instructor's schedule and the schedule of available aircraft fit your schedule?*
   7. *Where will they recommend you take your flight test? What is its estimated cost?*

C. Once you have made a preliminary choice of flight instructor and/or FBO, **sit down with your CFI and plan a schedule of flight instruction.**

   1. When and how often you will fly.
   2. When you will take the FAA written test.
   3. When you should plan to take your practical (flight) test.
   4. When and how payments will be made for your instruction.
   5. Review, revise, and update the total cost to obtain your private certificate (see opposite page).

D. **Prepare a tentative written time budget and a written expenditure budget.**

| | |
|---|---|
| Hours Solo: ____ hours x $_____ . . . . . . . . . . . . . . . . . . . . . . . . . . . . . . | $__________ |
| Hours Dual with CFI: ____ hours x $______ . . . . . . . . . . . . . . . . . . . . . . . . | $__________ |
| Written or Computerized Test Cost . . . . . . . . . . . . . . . . . . . . . . . . . . . . . . | $__________ |
| Flight Test (Examiner) . . . . . . . . . . . . . . . . . . . . . . . . . . . . . . . . . . . . . | $__________ |
| Flight Test (Airplane) . . . . . . . . . . . . . . . . . . . . . . . . . . . . . . . . . . . . . | $__________ |
| Medical Exam . . . . . . . . . . . . . . . . . . . . . . . . . . . . . . . . . . . . . . . . . . | $__________ |
| This book . . . . . . . . . . . . . . . . . . . . . . . . . . . . . . . . . . . . . . . . . . . . | $ 12.95 |
| Gleim's *Private Pilot and Recreational Pilot FAA Written Exam* . . . . . . . . . . . . | $ 12.95 |
| Gleim's *Private Pilot FAA Practical Test Prep* . . . . . . . . . . . . . . . . . . . . . . | $ 16.95 |
| Gleim's *Private Pilot FAA Written Test Prep* software . . . . . . . . . . . . . . . . . | $ 25.00 |
| Other books and supplies: | |
| *Airman's Information Manual* . . . . . . . . . . . . . . . . . . . . . . . . . . . . . . | $__________ |
| One or more Sectional Chart(s) . . . . . . . . . . . . . . . . . . . . . . . . . . . . . | $__________ |
| FAR Book . . . . . . . . . . . . . . . . . . . . . . . . . . . . . . . . . . . . . . . . . . | $__________ |
| Information Manual for your training airplane . . . . . . . . . . . . . . . . . . . | $__________ |
| Flight Computer and Navigation Plotter . . . . . . . . . . . . . . . . . . . . . . . | $__________ |
| TOTAL . . . . . . . . . . . . . . . . . . . . . . . . . . . . . . . . . . . . . . . . . . . . . . | $__________ |

E. Schedule and take your flight physical to receive your combined medical/student pilot certificate.

F. **Consider purchasing an airplane (yourself, or through joint ownership) or joining a flying club.** Frequently, shared expenses through joint ownership can reduce the cost of flying.

1. Inquire about local flying clubs.
2. Call a member and learn about the club's services, costs, etc.

## 1.8 ADDITIONAL FLIGHT CERTIFICATES

After you earn your private pilot certificate for single-engine land airplanes, you may pursue additional certificates and ratings. Most pilots obtain an instrument rating after 125 flight hr. and a commercial certificate after 250 flight hr.

A. Certificates

1. Commercial -- This certificate requires significantly more training and will allow the pilot to carry passengers and/or cargo for compensation or hire. You are required to have 250 flight hr. and 50 hr. of cross-country flight as pilot in command before you may obtain this certificate.
2. Flight instructor (CFI) -- This certificate gives the commercial pilot teaching privileges. You are required to have a commercial pilot certificate.
3. Airline transport pilot (ATP) -- This certificate is the top of the aviation industry. It is necessary before flying as captain on a scheduled airline. You are required to have 1,500 flight hr. and 500 hr. of cross-country flight as pilot in command and to be at least 23 years old before you may obtain this certificate.

B. Ratings that can be added to any certificate:

1. Aircraft category:
   a. Rotorcraft
   b. Glider
   c. Lighter-than-air
2. Airplane classes:
   a. Single-engine land (generally, this is the first rating you will earn)
   b. Multiengine land
   c. Single-engine sea
   d. Multiengine sea
3. Instrument -- The instrument rating, which may be added to any certificate, will allow the pilot to operate in less than VFR weather conditions. It shows that the pilot is competent when flying solely by reference to the aircraft's instruments. You are required to have 125 flight hr. and 50 hr. of cross-country flight as pilot in command before you can obtain this rating.
4. Aircraft type -- In order to act as pilot in command of an aircraft with a gross weight in excess of 12,500 lb., an aircraft that is turbojet powered, or an aircraft specified by the FAA, a type rating is necessary showing proficiency in operation of that particular type of aircraft.

# CHAPTER TWO
# INTRODUCTION TO AIRPLANES AND AERODYNAMICS



The purpose of this chapter is to introduce you to the parts of the airplane and to aerodynamics, i.e., the forces acting on the airplane in flight. As you study this and subsequent chapters, write all new terms, definitions, etc., on a separate sheet of paper. At the end of each study session, review these new concepts to make sure you understand them.

If you become bored or confused by the detail, skim the chapter to obtain an overview. Then later, as you study related sections of *Private Pilot and Recreational Pilot FAA Written Exam* and *Private Pilot FAA Practical Test Prep*, you can return to study (and learn) the material in this chapter as needed. Also, this chapter will make more sense after you have experienced several flights.

## 2.1 DEFINITIONS

A. Airfoils

1. *Airfoil* -- any surface, such as an airplane wing, designed to obtain reaction such as lift from the air through which it moves. The diagram below is a cross-section of a wing.

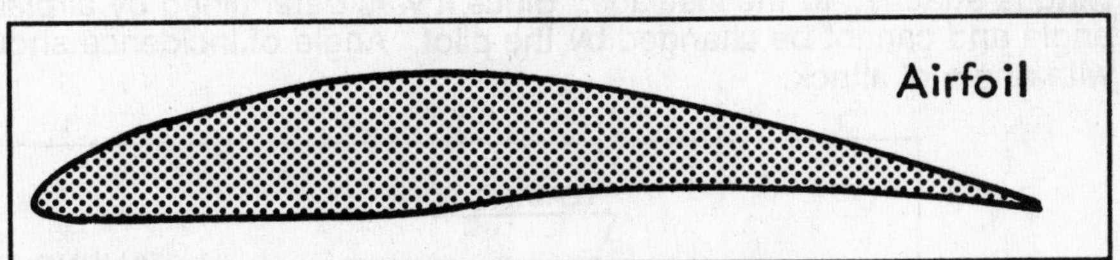

2. *Camber* -- the curvature of the airfoil (e.g., the wing) from the leading edge to the trailing edge. In the diagram below, positive camber refers to the curvature of the upper surface. Negative camber refers to the curvature of the lower surface. Mean camber refers to the line which is equidistant at all points between the upper and lower surfaces.

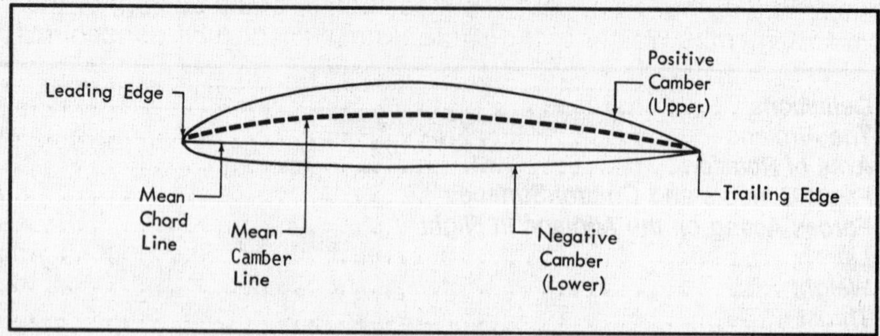


3. *Chord* -- an imaginary straight line drawn from the leading edge to the trailing edge of a cross section of an airfoil. See the diagram at the bottom of this page.

B. Aerodynamics

1. *Angle of Attack* -- the acute angle between the chord line of the wing and the flight path. The angle of attack is always based on the flight path, not the ground, as shown in the diagram below.

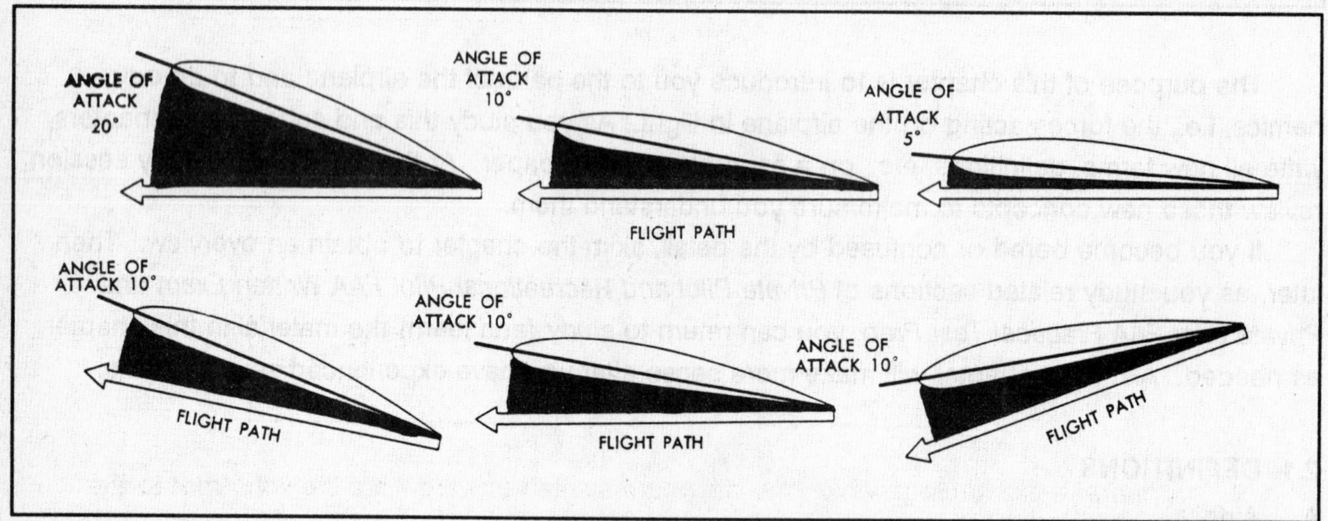


2. *Angle of Incidence* -- the acute angle formed by the chord line of the wing and the longitudinal axis of the airplane, as shown in the diagram below. It is the angle at which the wing is attached to the fuselage. Since it was determined by airplane design, it is a fixed angle and cannot be changed by the pilot. Angle of incidence should not be confused with angle of attack.

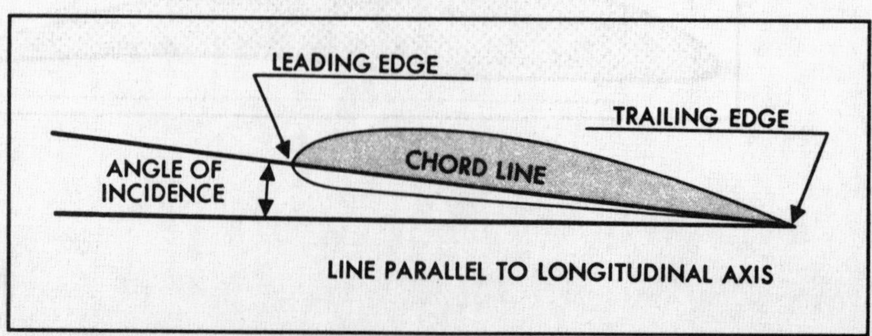

3. *Attitude* -- the relationship of the airplane to the horizon, i.e., its pitch angle (nose up or down) and its bank angle (left or right). It is measured in number of degrees of both pitch and bank.
4. *Center of Gravity* -- the point about which an aircraft would balance if it were possible to suspend it at that point. It is the mass center of the aircraft, or the theoretical point at which the entire weight of the aircraft is assumed to be concentrated.

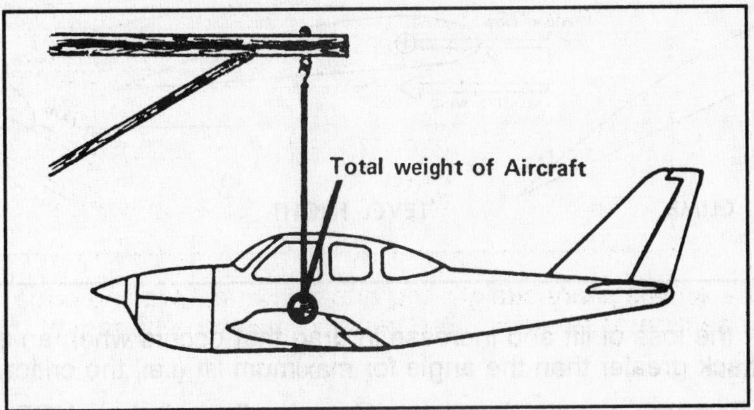


5. *Center of Pressure* -- the point along the chord line of a wing where the lift force is considered to be concentrated. Also called the center of lift.

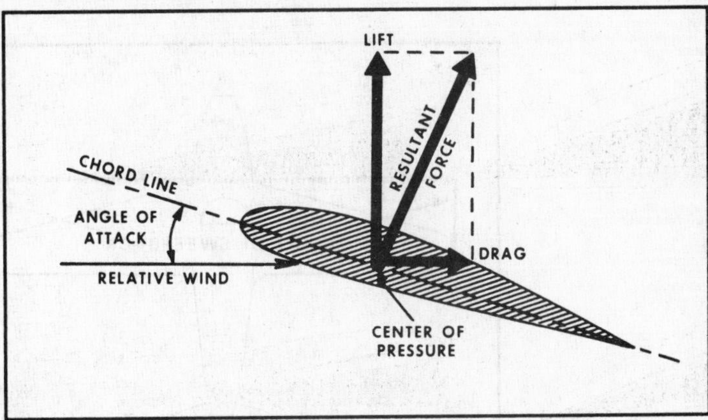


6. *Dihedral* -- the angle at which the wings are slanted upward from the wing root to the wingtip.

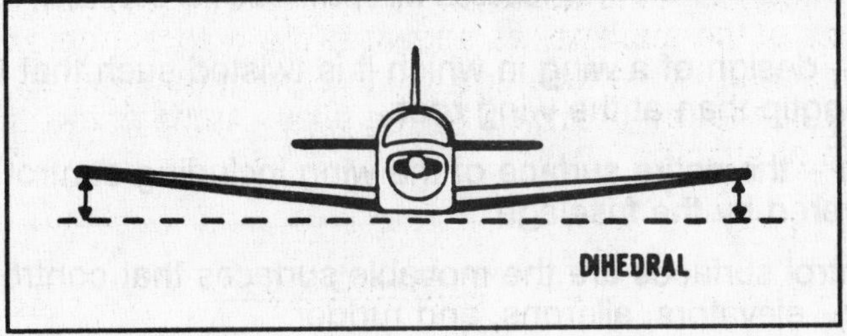

7. *Relative Wind* -- the direction of the airflow produced by an object moving through the air. The relative wind for an airplane in flight flows parallel with and opposite to the direction of flight. Therefore, the actual flight path of the airplane determines (is the opposite of) the direction of the relative wind, as shown below.

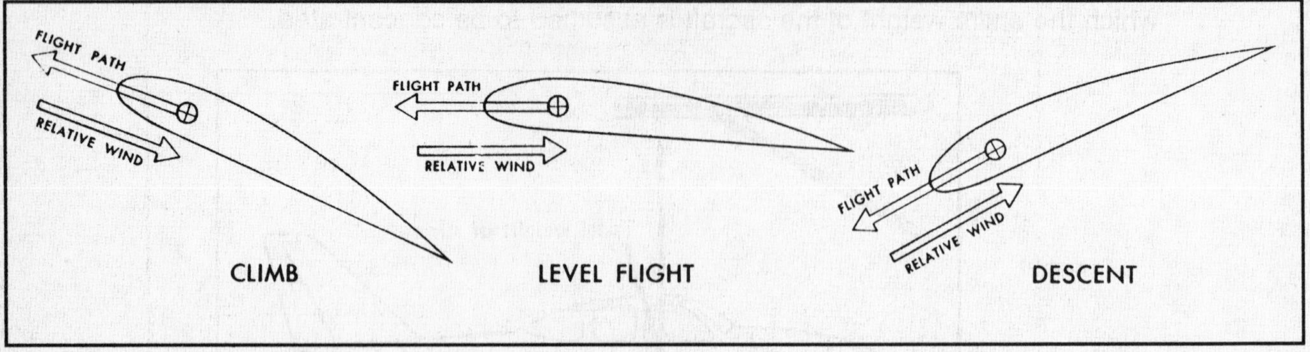


8. *Stall* -- the loss of lift and increase in drag that occurs when an aircraft is flown at an angle of attack greater than the angle for maximum lift (i.e., the critical angle of attack).
   a. Remember, a stall is an aerodynamic effect. It does NOT mean the engine has stopped.
9. *Sweepback* -- the angle at which the wings are slanted rearward from the wing root to the wingtip.

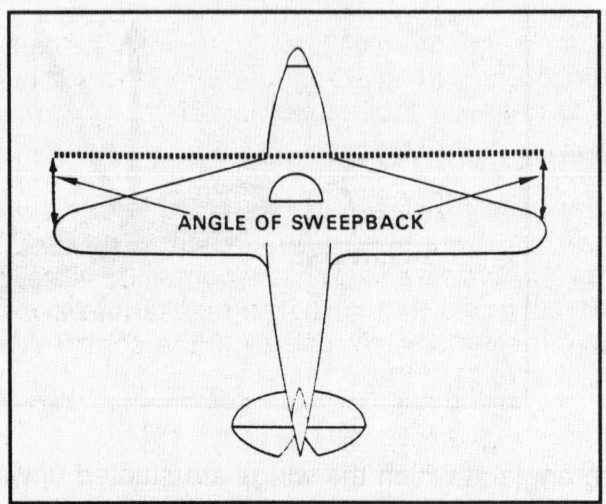




10. *Washout* -- design of a wing in which it is twisted such that the angle of incidence is less at the wingtip than at the wing root.
11. *Wing Area* -- the entire surface of the wing including control surfaces. It may include wing area covered by the fuselage.
    a. Control surfaces are the movable surfaces that control the attitude of the airplane, e.g., elevators, ailerons, and rudder.

12. *Wing Planform* -- the shape or form of a wing as viewed from above. It may be long and tapered, short and rectangular, or various other shapes. See the diagram below.

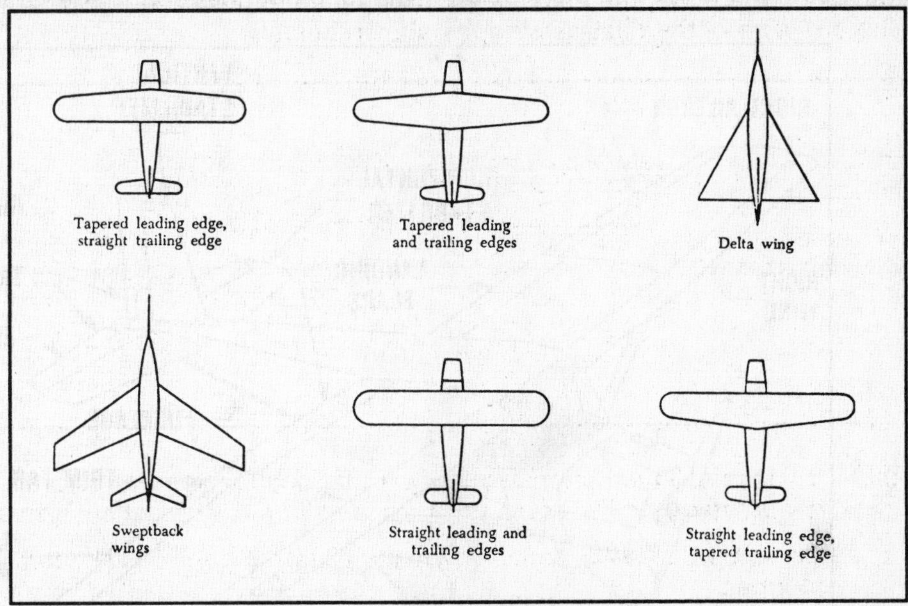


13. *Wingspan* -- the maximum distance from wingtip to wingtip.

C. Speed and Velocity

1. *Acceleration* -- a change of velocity per unit of time. It means changing speed and/or changing direction, including starting from rest (positive acceleration) and stopping (deceleration or negative acceleration).
2. *Speed* -- the distance traveled in a certain time.
3. *Vector* -- the graphic representation of a force. It is drawn as a straight line with direction indicated by an arrow and magnitude indicated by its length. When an object is being acted upon by two or more forces, the combined effect of these forces may be represented by a resultant vector. The resultant vector may then be measured to determine the direction and magnitude of the combined forces, as shown below.

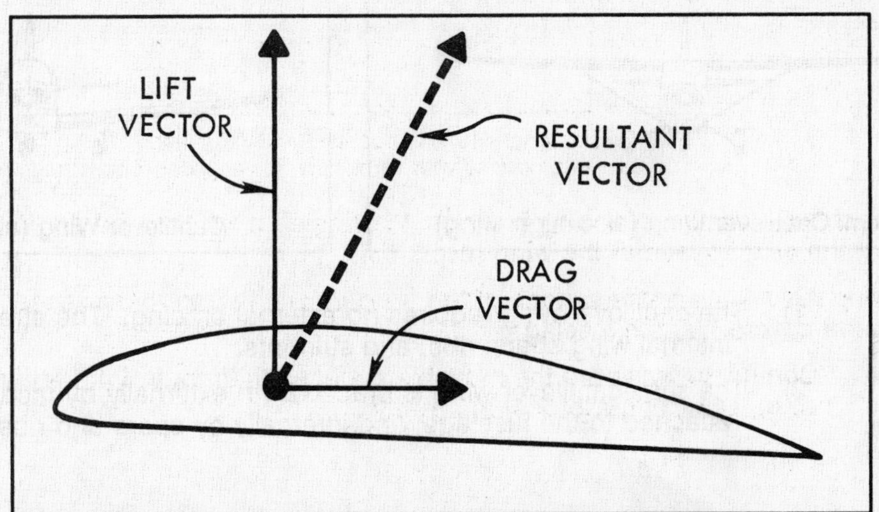


4. *Velocity* -- the speed or rate of movement in a certain direction.

## 2.2 THE AIRPLANE

A. The diagram below illustrates the basic components of the airplane. The structural units of any conventional airplane include the fuselage, wings, empennage, and the landing gear.

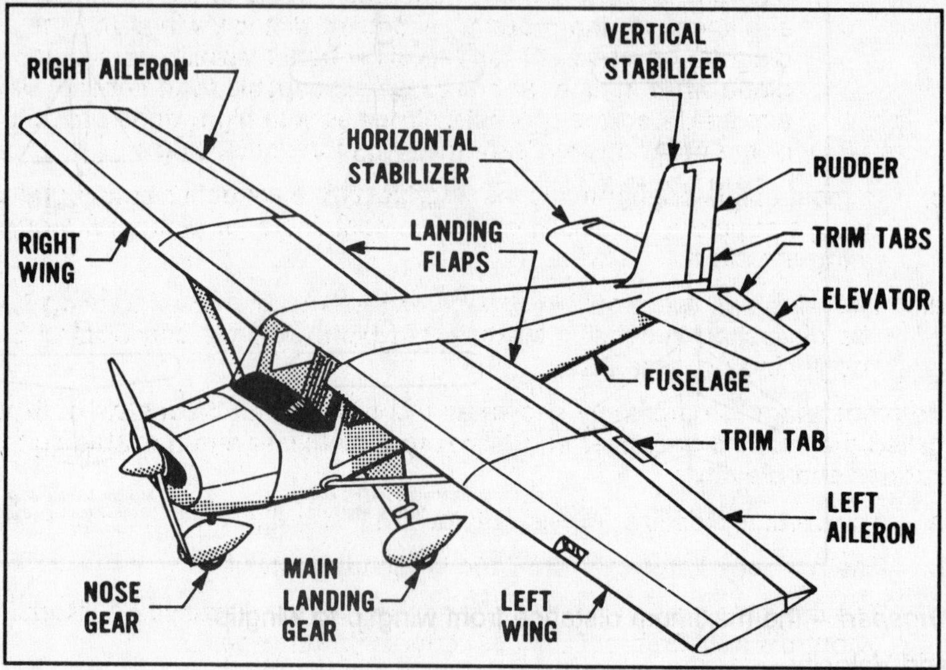


1. The **fuselage** is the main component of the airplane. It serves as the common attachment point for the other major structural units of the airplane. It also houses the crew, passengers, cargo, instruments, and other essential equipment.
2. **Wings** are airfoils attached to each side of the fuselage and are the main lifting surfaces which support the airplane in flight. Numerous wing designs, shapes, and sizes are used by various manufacturers.
   a. Wings are of two main types -- cantilever and semi-cantilever, as shown below.

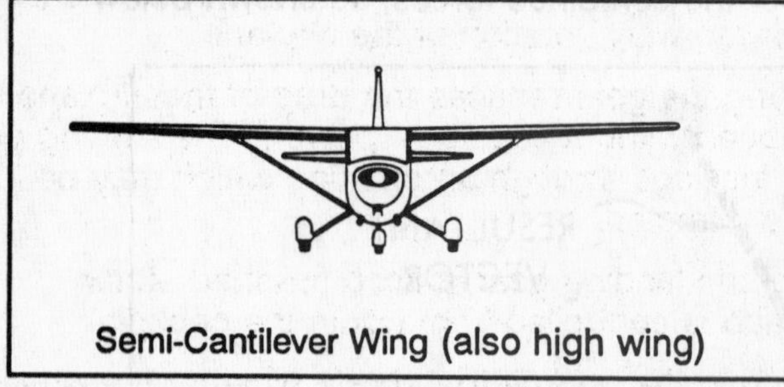
Semi-Cantilever Wing (also high wing)

Cantilever Wing (also low wing)

1) The cantilever wing requires no external bracing. The stress is carried by internal wing spars, ribs, and stringers.

2) The semi-cantilever wing is braced both externally by means of wing struts attached to the fuselage, and internally by spars and ribs.

b. Wings may be attached at the top, middle, or lower portion of the fuselage. These designs are called high, mid, and low wing, respectively.

1) High Wing vs. Low Wing -- Airplanes with high wings (on the left in the diagram on page 20) are more susceptible to the effects of wind while the airplane is on the ground. Airplanes with low wings (on the right in the diagram on page 20) tend to allow better visibility above and around the plane while in flight and are less susceptible to the effects of wind while the airplane is on the ground. Airplanes with high wings provide better visibility of the ground when airborne, e.g., for sightseeing.

c. In most single-engine airplanes, the fuel tanks are either an integral part of the wing's structure or consist of flexible containers (or bladders) mounted inside the wing structure.

d. The wing has two movable surfaces known as **ailerons** and **wing flaps**. These will be discussed in detail in Module 2.4, Flight Controls and Control Surfaces, beginning on page 23.

3. The empennage is commonly known as the tail section. It consists of fixed surfaces called the **vertical stabilizer** and **horizontal stabilizer** and movable surfaces called the **rudder** and **elevator**.

a. The vertical stabilizer provides directional stability.

b. The horizontal stabilizer provides longitudinal stability.

c. The movable portions of the empennage will be discussed in Module 2.4, Flight Controls and Control Surfaces, beginning on page 23.

4. The landing gear supports the airplane during the landing and when the airplane is on the ground. It consists of the main landing gear and either a nosewheel or a tailwheel.

a. The main landing gear consists of two main wheels and struts. Each main strut is attached to the primary structure of the fuselage or the wing.

b. Nosewheel (tricycle) vs. Tailwheel (conventional). Nosewheel airplanes have the third wheel in front of the main landing gear (i.e., under the nose). Tailwheel airplanes have the third wheel under the tail.

1) The **nose gear** (or tailwheel) is designed to steer the airplane on the ground. It is not stressed for excessive impacts or loads. It is designed to carry only the weight of the forward (or rearward) portion of the airplane.

c. Retractable Landing Gear. Retracting the gear reduces the drag of the airplane in flight, and thus increases the airspeed without additional power. The landing gear normally retracts into the wing or fuselage through an opening which may be covered by doors after the gear is retracted.

1) The retraction or extension of the landing gear is accomplished either electrically or hydraulically and is controlled from within the cockpit.

2) Indicators are usually provided in the cockpit to indicate whether the wheels are extended and locked, or retracted.

3) In nearly all airplanes equipped with retractable landing gear, a system is provided for emergency gear extension in the event that the primary landing gear mechanisms fail to lower the gear.

## 2.3 AXES OF ROTATION

A. The airplane has three axes of rotation around which it moves.

1. Lateral (pitch) axis -- an imaginary line from wingtip to wingtip.
   a. Rotation about the lateral axis is called pitch and is controlled by the elevators. This rotation is referred to as longitudinal control or longitudinal stability. This may seem confusing, but consider that as the airplane rotates about the lateral axis, the longitudinal axis (the front to rear axis) moves up and down.

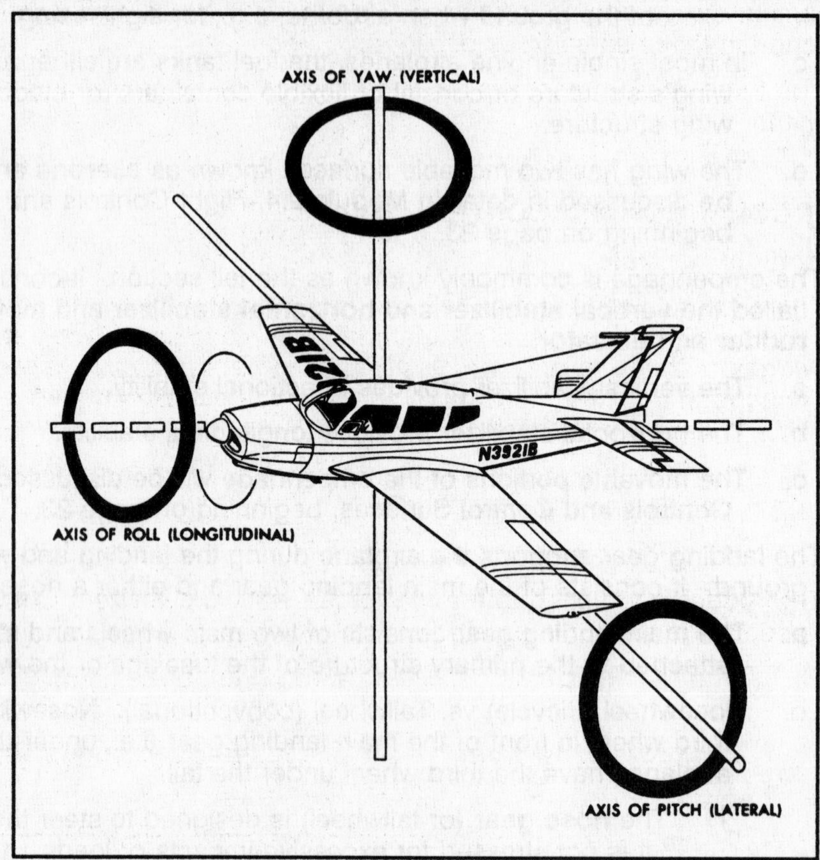


   b. The rotation is similar to a seesaw. The bar holding the seesaw is the lateral axis but the rotation is longitudinal.
2. Longitudinal (roll) axis -- an imaginary line from the nose to the tail.
   a. Rotation about the longitudinal axis is called roll and is controlled by the ailerons. This rotation is referred to as lateral control or lateral stability. This may seem confusing, but consider that, as the airplane rotates about the longitudinal axis (i.e., rolls), the lateral axis (the line through the wingtips) moves up and down.
   b. The rotation is similar to a barbecue rotisserie, where the spit is the longitudinal axis but the rotation is lateral.

3. Vertical (yaw) axis -- an imaginary line extending vertically through the intersection of the lateral and longitudinal axes.
   a. Rotation about the vertical axis is called yaw and is controlled by the rudder. This rotation is referred to as directional control or directional stability.
   b. The rotation is similar to a weathervane, where the post holding the vane is the vertical axis but the rotation is directional.

B. The airplane can rotate around one, two, or all three axes simultaneously. Think of these axes as imaginary axles around which the airplane turns, much as a wheel would turn around axles positioned in these same three directions.
   1. The three axes intersect at the airplane's center of gravity and each is perpendicular to the other two.

## 2.4 FLIGHT CONTROLS AND CONTROL SURFACES

A. **Primary flight controls**
   1. The airplane's attitude (i.e., rotation about the three axes) is controlled by deflection of the primary flight controls. These are hinged, movable surfaces attached to the trailing edges of the wing and vertical and horizontal stabilizers. When deflected, these surfaces change the camber (curvature) and angle of attack of the wing or stabilizer, and thus, its lift and drag characteristics.
      a. The pilot operates the flight controls through connecting linkage to the rudder pedals and the control yoke.
         1) The control yoke may be either a wheel or a stick.
   2. The rudder is attached to the rear of the vertical stabilizer. Controlled by the rudder pedals, the rudder is used to control yaw (i.e., rotation about the airplane's vertical axis).
      a. When the rudder is deflected to one side (left or right), it protrudes into the airflow, causing a horizontal force to be exerted in the opposite direction.
      b. This pushes the tail of the airplane in that direction and yaws the nose in the desired direction.

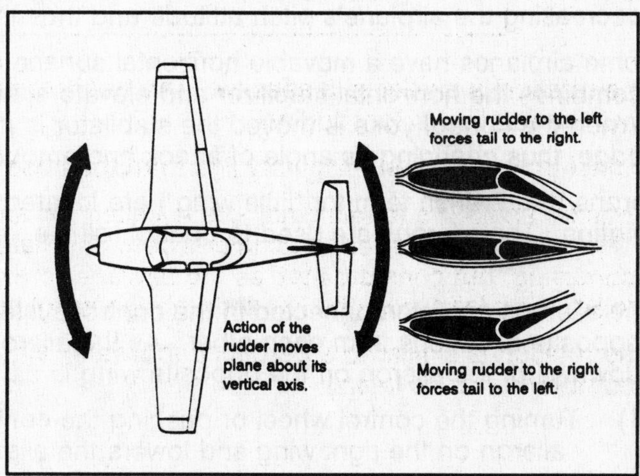


      c. The primary purpose of the rudder in flight is to counteract the effect of adverse yaw and to help provide directional control of the airplane.
      d. When only the rudder is used for steering during ground taxiing, the propeller slipstream provides the force to yaw or turn the airplane in the desired direction.

3. The elevators are attached to the rear of the horizontal stabilizer. The elevators are used to control pitch (i.e., rotation about the airplane's lateral axis). They are controlled by pushing or pulling the control yoke.
   a. You adjust the angle of attack of the entire horizontal stabilizer by raising or lowering the elevators.
   b. Applying back pressure on the control yoke (i.e., pulling the yoke toward you) raises the elevators. The raised elevators increase the horizontal stabilizer's negative angle of attack and consequently increase the downward tail force. This forces the tail down, increasing the airplane's pitch attitude and thus the angle of attack of the wings.

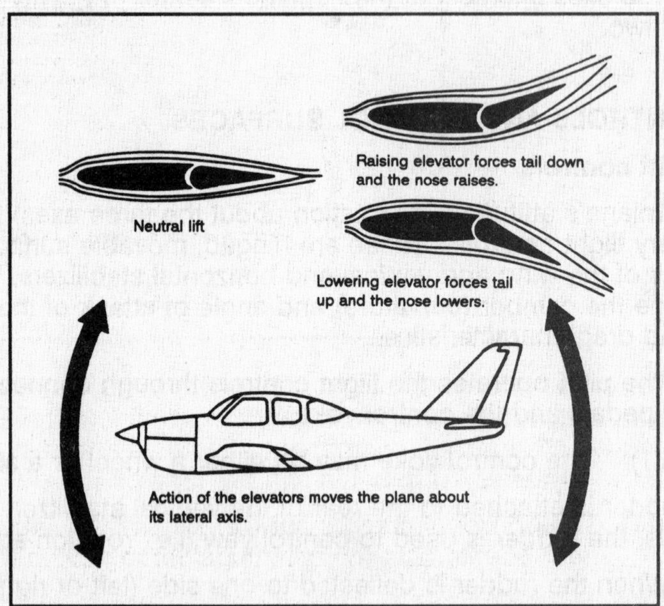


   c. Applying forward pressure to the control yoke (i.e., pushing it forward) lowers the elevators. The lowered elevators decrease the horizontal stabilizer's negative angle of attack and consequently decrease the downward force on the tail. The tail rises, decreasing the airplane's pitch attitude and thus the angle of attack of the wings.
   d. Some airplanes have a movable horizontal surface called a stabilator, which combines the horizontal stabilizer and elevators, such as on the Piper Cherokee. When the control yoke is moved the stabilator is moved to raise or lower its leading edge, thus changing its angle of attack and amount of lift.
4. The ailerons (the French term for "little wing") are located on the rear of each wing near the wingtips. The ailerons are used to control roll (i.e., rotation about the longitudinal axis).
   a. The ailerons are interconnected in the control system to operate simultaneously in opposite directions from each other. As the aileron on one wing is deflected downward, the aileron on the opposite wing is deflected upward.
      1) Turning the control wheel or pushing the control stick to the right raises the aileron on the right wing and lowers the aileron on the left wing.
      2) Turning the control wheel or pushing the control stick to the left raises the aileron on the left wing and lowers the aileron on the right wing.

b. When an aileron is lowered, the angle of attack on that wing is increased, which increases the lift. When an aileron is raised, the angle of attack is decreased, which decreases the lift. This permits rolling (banking) the airplane to any desired bank angle.

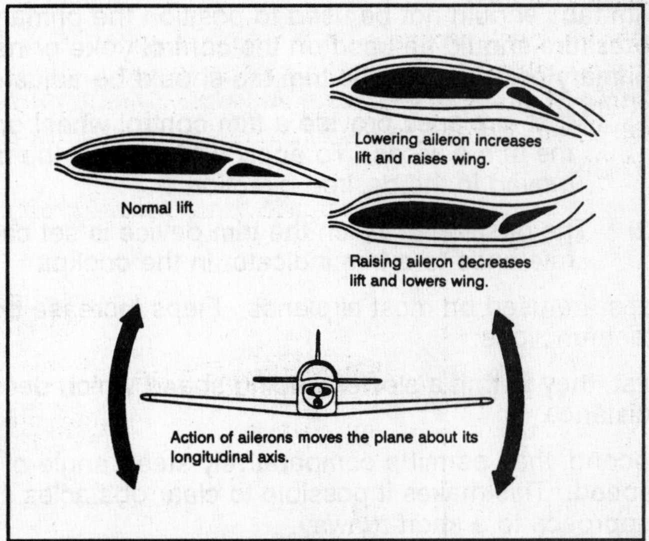


c. The airplane turns primarily due to banking of the wings, which produces horizontal lift. With wings level, all lift is perpendicular to the Earth. With wings banked, the lift has a horizontal component as well as a vertical component. (See Module 2.12, How Airplanes Turn, beginning on page 36.)

1) The horizonal component (i.e., when the wings are lifting sideways as well as up) counteracts the centrifugal force pulling the airplane straight ahead.

2) The rudder is used in conjunction with the ailerons as explained in Module 2.12, How Airplanes Turn, beginning on page 36.

B. **Secondary Flight Controls**

1. In addition to the primary flight controls, there is a group termed "secondary controls." These include trim devices of various types, wing flaps, leading edge devices, and spoilers.

2. Trim devices are commonly used to relieve you of the need to maintain continuous pressure on the primary controls. Thus, you can retrim at each power setting, airspeed, and/or flight attitude to neutralize control pressure.

   a. These devices are small airfoils attached to, or recessed into, the trailing edge of the primary control surfaces (i.e., elevator, aileron, and/or rudder).

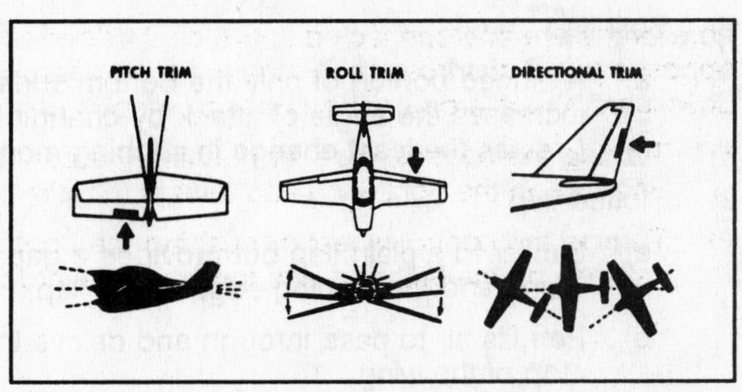

b. Trim tabs are moved in a direction opposite to the direction in which pressure is being applied on the control yoke.

   1) If the elevator requires a constant up deflection, the back pressure on the control yoke can be relieved by deflecting the trim tab down.

c. Trim tabs should not be used to position the primary control. Rather, control pressure should be used on the control yoke or rudder pedals to position the primary control, then the trim tab should be adjusted to relieve the control pressure.

   1) Most airplanes provide a trim control wheel or electric switch for adjustment of the trim devices. To apply a trim force, the trim wheel or switch must be moved in the desired direction.

   2) The position in which the trim device is set can usually be determined by reference to a trim indicator in the cockpit.

3. Wing flaps are used on most airplanes. Flaps increase both lift and drag and have three important functions:

   a. First, they permit a slower landing speed which decreases the required landing distance.

   b. Second, they permit a comparatively steep angle of descent without an increase in speed. This makes it possible to clear obstacles safely when making a landing approach to a short runway.

   c. Third, they may also be used to shorten the takeoff distance and provide a steeper climb path.

   d. Types of wing flaps

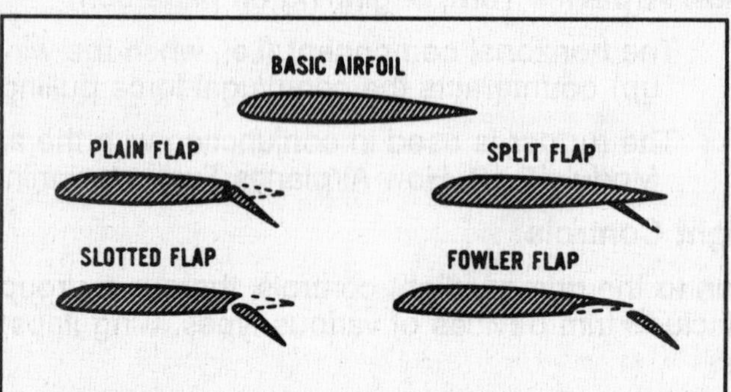


      1) Plain flap

         a) Is a portion of the trailing edge of the wing on a hinged pivot which allows the flap to be moved downward.

         b) This changes the chord line, angle of attack, and camber of the wing.

      2) Split flap

         a) A hinged portion of only the bottom surface of the wing
         b) Increases the angle of attack by changing the chord line.
         c) Creates the least change in pitching moment.

      3) Slotted flap

         a) Similar to a plain flap but provides a gap between the trailing edge of the wing and the leading edge of the flap.

         b) Permits air to pass through and delays the airflow separation along the top of the wing.

4) Fowler flap

a) Not only tilts downward but also slides rearward on tracks.

b) Increases the angle of attack, wing camber, and wing area.

c) Provides additional lift without significantly increasing drag.

d) Fowler flap provides the greatest amount of lift with the least amount of drag, which creates the greatest change in pitching moment.

e. Most wing flaps are hinged near the trailing edges of the wings, inboard of the ailerons.

1) They are controllable by the pilot either manually, electrically, or hydraulically.

2) When they are in the up (retracted) position, they fit flush with the wings and serve as part of the wing's trailing edge.

3) When in the down (extended) position, the flaps pivot downward from the hinge points to various angles ranging up to 30° to 40° from the wing.

4. Leading edge devices are used on many larger airplanes.

a. High-lift leading edge devices are applied to the leading edge of the airfoil.
b. Fixed slots direct airflow to the upper wing surface.

1) This allows for smooth airflow over the wing at higher angles of attack, and delays the airflow separation.

2) Does not increase the wing camber.

3) Stalls are delayed to a higher angle of attack.

c. A slat is a leading edge segment which is free to move on tracks.

1) At low angles of attack the slat is held flush against the leading edge.

2) At high angles of attack, either a low pressure area at the wing's leading edge or pilot operated controls force the slat to move forward.

a) This opens a slot and allows the air to flow smoothly over the wing's upper surface, delaying the airflow separation.

5. Spoilers, found only on certain airplane designs and most gliders, are mounted on the upper surface of each wing. Their purpose is to "spoil" or disrupt the smooth flow of air over the wing, reducing the wing's lifting force. It is a means of increasing the rate of descent without increasing the airplane's speed.

## 2.5 FORCES ACTING ON THE AIRPLANE IN FLIGHT

A. Among the aerodynamic forces acting on an airplane during flight, four are considered to be basic because they act upon the airplane during all maneuvers. These basic forces in relation to straight-and-level, unaccelerated flight are:

1. Lift -- the upward-acting force which opposes weight. It is produced by the dynamic effect of the air acting on the wing and acts perpendicular to the flight path through the wing's center of lift.

2. Weight -- the combined load of the airplane itself, the crew, the fuel, and the cargo or baggage. Weight pulls the airplane downward because of the force of gravity. It opposes lift and acts vertically downward through the airplane's center of gravity.

3. Thrust -- the forward force produced by the engine/propeller. It opposes or overcomes the force of drag. As a general rule, it is said to act parallel to the longitudinal axis.

4. Drag -- the rearward, retarding force which is caused by disruption of airflow by the wing, fuselage, and other protruding objects. Drag opposes thrust, and acts rearward and parallel to the relative wind.

B. While in steady (unaccelerated) flight, the attitude, direction, and speed of the airplane will remain constant until one or more of the basic forces changes in magnitude.

1. In steady flight, the opposing forces are in equilibrium.

   a. That is, the sum of all upward forces equals the sum of all downward forces, and the sum of all forward forces equals the sum of all rearward forces.

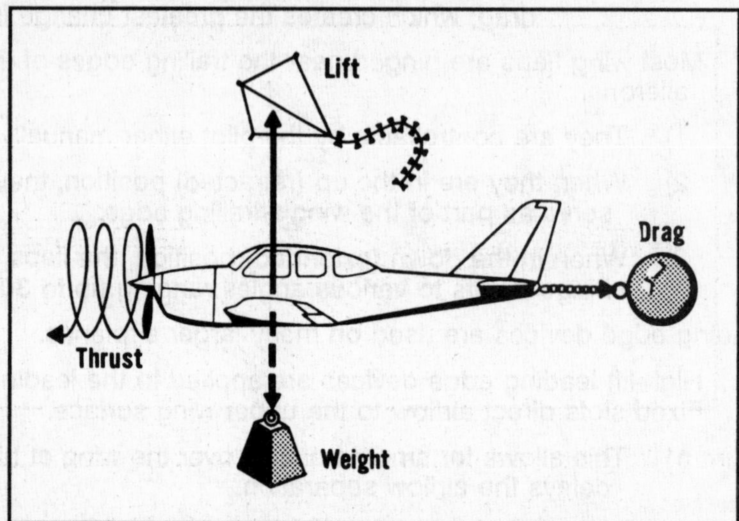


C. When pressure is applied to one or more of the airplane controls, one or more of the basic forces change in magnitude and become greater than the opposing force, causing the airplane to move in the direction of the applied force(s).

1. EXAMPLE: If power is applied (increasing thrust) and altitude is maintained, the airplane will accelerate. As speed increases, drag increases until a point is reached at which drag again equals thrust. Then the airplane will continue in steady flight at a higher speed.

D. Airplane designers make an effort to increase the performance of the airplane by increasing the efficiency of the desirable forces of lift and thrust while reducing, as much as possible, the undesirable forces of weight and drag.

## 2.6 LIFT

A. Lift is the force created by an airfoil when it is moved through the air. Although lift may be exerted to some extent by many external parts of the airplane, the three principal airfoils on an airplane are:

1. The wing
2. The propeller
3. The horizontal and vertical tail surfaces

B. Bernoulli's Principle states in part that "the internal pressure of a fluid (liquid or gas) decreases at points where the speed of the fluid increases." In other words, high speed flow is associated with low pressure, and low speed flow is associated with high pressure.

1. This principle is applicable to an airplane wing because it is designed and constructed with a curve or camber. When air flows along the upper wing surface it travels a greater distance in the same period of time (i.e., faster) than the airflow along the lower wing surface.

2. Therefore, the pressure above the wing is less than it is below the wing. This generates a lift force over the upper curved surface of the wing.

C. At the same time, the lower surface of the wing, by its shape, deflects the air downward. Since for every action there is an equal and opposite reaction (Newton's Third Law of Motion), additional upward force is generated.

1. Thus, both the development of low pressure above the wing and reaction to the force and direction of air being deflected from the wing's lower surface contribute to the total lift. See the illustration below.

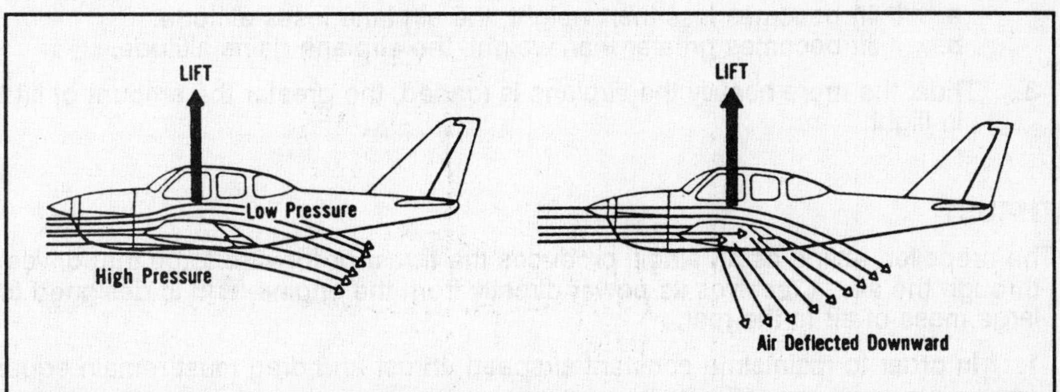


D. The amount of lift generated by the wing depends upon several factors:

1. Speed of the wing through the air
2. Angle of attack
3. Planform of the wing
4. Wing area
5. Air density

E. Lift acts upward and perpendicular to the relative wind and the lateral axis. Although lift is generated over the entire wing, an imaginary point is established which represents the resultant of all lift forces. This single point is the center of lift, sometimes referred to as the center of pressure (CP).

1. The location of the center of pressure relative to the center of gravity (weight) is very important from the standpoint of airplane stability. See Module 2.14, Airplane Stability, beginning on page 42.

## 2.7 WEIGHT

A. Weight is the force which is caused by gravity accelerating the mass of the airplane toward the Earth, and is expressed in pounds (lb.).

1. Gravity is the downward acceleration which tends to draw all bodies vertically toward the center of the Earth.

2. The airplane's center of gravity (CG) is the imaginary but determinable point on the airplane at which all weight is considered to be concentrated. It is the point of balance.

3. The center of gravity is located along the longitudinal centerline of the airplane (imaginary line from the nose to the tail) and somewhere near, but forward of, the center of lift of the wing.

   a. The location of the center of gravity depends upon the location and weight of the load (including cargo, fuel, passengers, etc.) placed in the airplane.

   b. It is determined through weight and balance calculations made by the pilot prior to flight. See Chapter 6, Weight and Balance, beginning on page 153.

      1) The exact location of the center of gravity is important during flight because of its effect on airplane stability and performance.

B. Weight has a definite relationship with lift. This relationship is simple, but important in understanding the aerodynamics of flying.

1. Lift is required to counteract the airplane's weight, which acts downward through the airplane's CG.
2. In straight-and-level, unaccelerated flight, when the lift force is equal to the weight force, the airplane is in a state of equilibrium and neither gains nor loses altitude.
    a. If lift becomes less than weight, the airplane loses altitude.
    b. If lift becomes greater than weight, the airplane gains altitude.
3. Thus, the more heavily the airplane is loaded, the greater the amount of lift that is required in flight.

## 2.8 THRUST

A. The propeller, acting as an airfoil, produces the thrust or forward force that drives the airplane through the air. It receives its power directly from the engine, and is designed to displace a large mass of air to the rear.

1. In order to maintain a constant airspeed, thrust and drag must remain equal.
2. If thrust is decreased and level flight is maintained, the airplane will slow down until thrust is again equal to drag.
3. If thrust is increased and level flight is maintained, the airplane will accelerate until thrust is again equal to drag.

## 2.9 DRAG

A. Drag is the rearward acting force resulting from the forward movement of the airplane through the air. Drag acts parallel to and in the same direction as the relative wind, as shown below. Every part of the airplane exposed to the air while the airplane is in motion produces some resistance and contributes to the total drag. Total drag may be classified into two main types: induced drag and parasite drag.

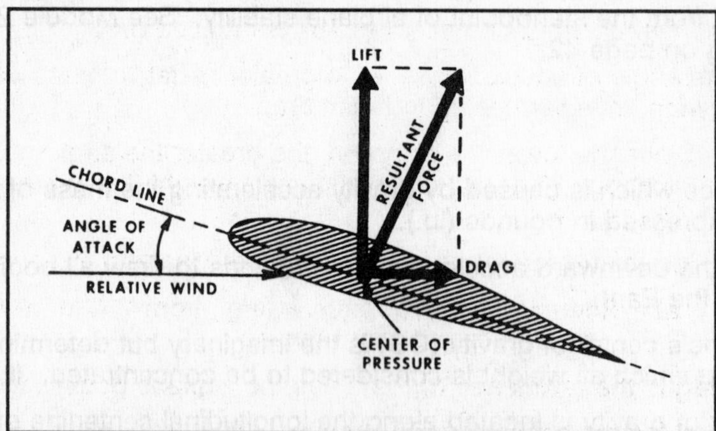


1. Induced drag is the undesirable but unavoidable by-product of lift.
    a. Whenever the wing is producing lift, we have seen that the pressure on the lower surface of the wing is greater than that of the upper surface. As a result, the air tends to flow from the high-pressure area below the wingtip upward to the low-pressure area above the wing.
        1) In the vicinity of the wingtips there is a tendency for these pressures to equalize, resulting in a lateral flow outward from the underside to the upper surface of the wing.

a) This lateral flow imparts a rotational velocity to the air at the wingtips and trails behind the wings. Thus, flow about the wingtips will be in the form of two vortices trailing behind as the wings move forward.

b) When viewed from behind the airplane, these vortices will circulate counterclockwise about the right wingtip (as shown below) and clockwise about the left wingtip.

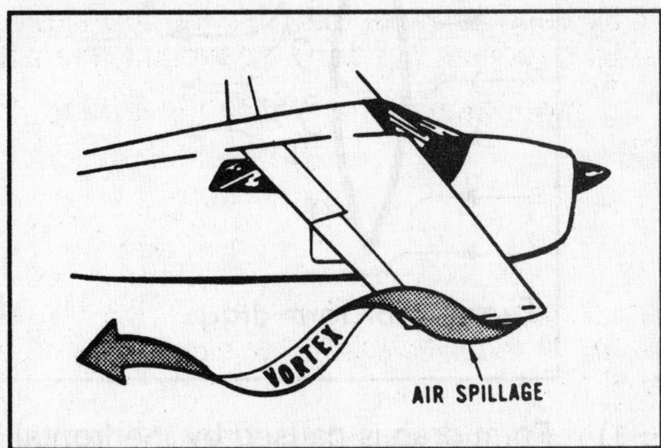


2) It can be seen that these vortices induce an upward flow of air beyond the wingtip and a downwash flow behind the wing's trailing edge.

a) This downwash has nothing in common with the downwash to produce lift. This is the source of induced drag.

b. The greater the size and strength of the vortices and consequent downwash component on the net airflow over the wing, the greater the induced drag effect becomes.

c. This downwash over the top of the wing at the tip has the same effect as bending the lift vector rearward.

1) Thus, the lift is slightly aft of perpendicular to the relative wind, creating a rearward lift component.

2) This rearward component of lift is induced drag.

d. As the angle of attack increases, a greater negative pressure is created on the top of the wing, thus increasing induced drag.

1) Since the lower the airspeed, the greater the angle of attack required to produce lift equal to the airplane's weight, the greater will be the induced drag.

2) Induced drag varies inversely as the square of the airspeed.

a) Reducing airspeed by half (e.g., from 120 kt. to 60 kt.) increases the induced drag by four times.

2. Parasite drag is the resistance of the air as the airplane passes through it.

a. Several factors affect parasite drag:

1) The more streamlined an object, the less the parasite drag

2) The more dense the air moving past the airplane, the greater the parasite drag

3) The larger the size of the object in the airstream, the greater the parasite drag

4) As speed increases, the amount of parasite drag increases as the square of the velocity. If the speed is doubled, four times as much drag is produced.

b. Parasite drag can be further classified into form drag, skin friction, and interference drag.

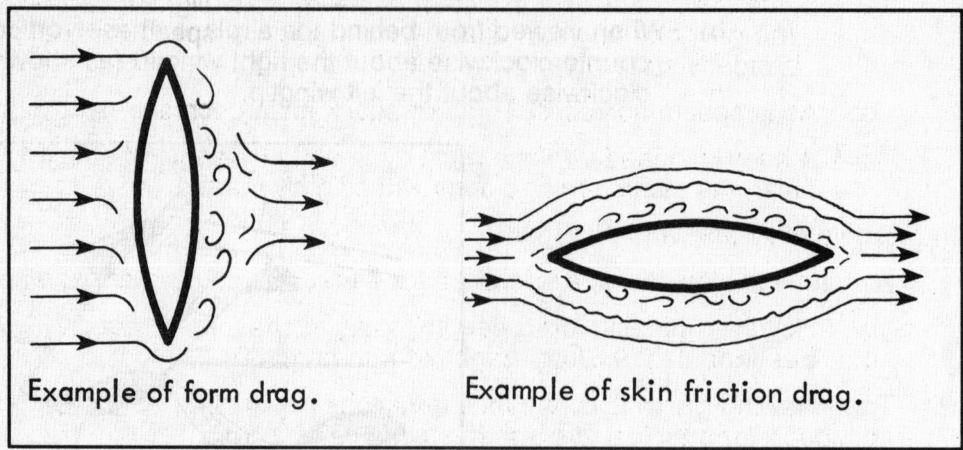
Example of form drag. Example of skin friction drag.

1) Form drag is caused by the frontal area of the airplane components being exposed to the airstream.
   a) Streamlining an object will reduce form drag.
2) Skin friction is the type of parasite drag that is most difficult to reduce. No surface is perfectly smooth; even machined surfaces, when inspected through magnification, have a ragged, uneven appearance.
   a) This rough surface will deflect the streamlines of air on the surface, causing resistance to smooth airflow.
   b) Skin friction can be minimized by employing a glossy, flat finish to surfaces, by eliminating protruding rivet heads, roughness, and other irregularities, and by keeping the airplane clean and waxed.
3) Interference drag is caused by interference of the airflow between adjacent parts of the airplane such as the intersections of wings and tail sections with the fuselage. This drag combines the effects of form and skin friction drag.
   a) Fairings are used to streamline these intersections and decrease interference drag.

## 2.10 DYNAMICS OF THE AIRPLANE IN FLIGHT

A. Lift, Angle of Attack, and Airspeed

1. The amount of lift that a given wing generates at a given altitude is directly related to its angle of attack and airspeed.
   a. As angle of attack or airspeed is increased, lift is increased.
   b. We can express this relationship in the following equation:

$$L = \alpha \times V$$

Where L is lift
$\alpha$ is angle of attack, and
V is airspeed

   1) Note that this is not a precise equation. It merely serves to illustrate the relationship between these three elements.

2. As discussed earlier, when the airplane is in steady-state, unaccelerated flight, lift is equal to weight.
   a. Since this makes lift a constant in steady-state flight, it can be seen that there is one and only one angle of attack for any given airspeed that will maintain the airplane in steady-state flight.
   b. As airspeed increases, angle of attack must decrease, and vice versa.
   c. A heavily loaded airplane must fly at a higher angle of attack for any given airspeed than the same airplane does when lightly loaded.

B. Drag, Angle of Attack, and Airspeed
1. As airspeed decreases, angle of attack increases, causing an increase in induced drag.
   a. However, parasite drag decreases as airspeed decreases.
   b. See Module 2.9, Drag, beginning on page 30.
2. The following graph illustrates the variations in parasite, induced, and total drag with airspeed for a typical airplane in steady, level flight.

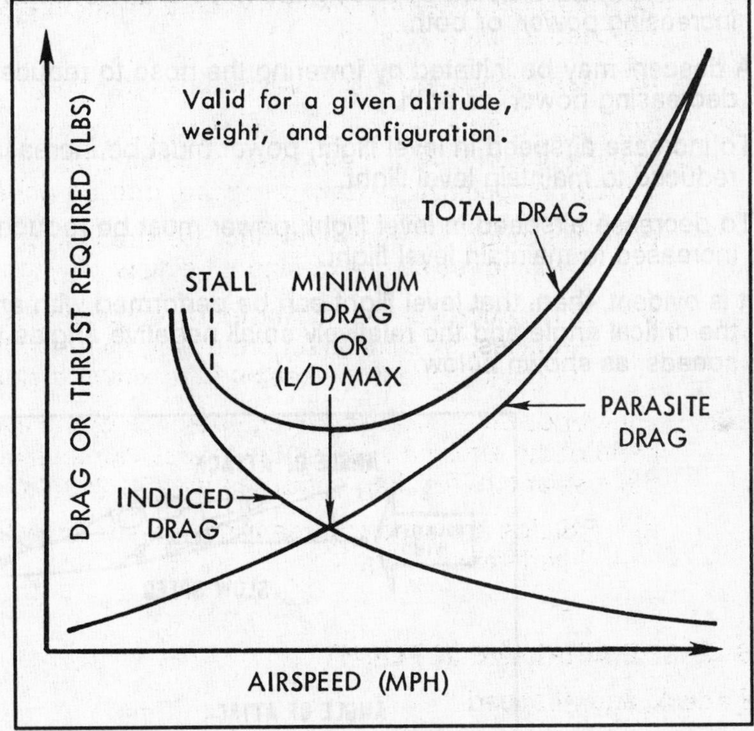


3. The amount of drag present at a given airspeed is equal to the amount of thrust required to maintain level flight at that airspeed and angle of attack.
   a. If thrust is increased beyond that required for level flight, the airplane will climb unless it is retrimmed for a lower angle of attack and a higher airspeed.
   b. If thrust is reduced, the airplane will descend.
4. Note on the Drag vs. Speed chart that the airspeed at which minimum drag occurs is the same airspeed at which the maximum lift/drag ratio ($L/D_{max}$) takes place.
   a. At this point, least thrust is required for level flight.

b. Many important items of airplane performance are obtained in flight at $L/D_{max}$. These include

1) Maximum range.

2) Maximum power-off glide range. Thus, the airspeed for $L/D_{max}$ is the airplane's best glide airspeed.

c. Flight below $L/D_{max}$ produces more drag, and requires more thrust to maintain level flight.

C. Pitch, Power, and Performance

1. Adjusting the angle of attack varies both the amounts of lift and drag being produced by the wing.

2. Adjusting the airplane's power varies the relationship of thrust to drag, allowing the airplane to change airspeed, altitude, or both.

3. Thus, the pilot can achieve a desired performance from the airplane (in terms of airspeed and altitude) through a variety of pitch and power combinations.

a. A climb may be initiated by raising the nose to increase the angle of attack, or by increasing power, or both.

b. A descent may be initiated by lowering the nose to reduce the angle of attack, or by decreasing power, or both.

c. To increase airspeed in level flight, power must be increased and angle of attack reduced to maintain level flight.

d. To decrease airspeed in level flight, power must be reduced and angle of attack increased to maintain level flight.

e. It is evident, then, that level flight can be performed with any angle of attack between the critical angle and the relatively small negative angles found sometimes at high speeds, as shown below.

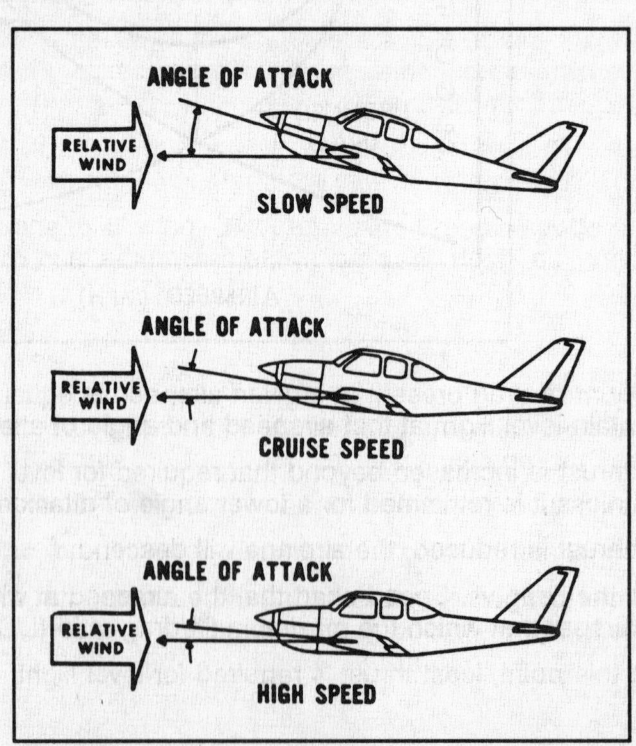

D. Effect of Air Density on Lift and Drag

1. Lift and drag vary directly with the density of the air.
    a. As air density increases, lift and drag increase.
    b. As air density decreases, lift and drag decrease.

2. Air density is affected by pressure, temperature, and humidity.
    a. At an altitude of 18,000 ft. the density of the air is one-half the density at sea level (given standard conditions). If an airplane is to maintain the same lift at high altitudes, the amount of air flowing over the wing must be the same as at lower altitudes. Thus, the speed of the air over the wings (airspeed) must be increased at high altitudes.
        1) This is why an airplane requires a longer takeoff distance to become airborne at higher altitudes than with similar conditions at lower altitudes.
    b. Because air expands when heated, warm air is less dense than cool air.
        1) When other conditions remain the same, an airplane will require a longer takeoff run on a hot day than on a cool day.
    c. Because water vapor weighs less than an equal amount of dry air, moist air (high relative humidity) is less dense than dry air (low relative humidity).
        1) Therefore, when other conditions remain the same, the airplane will require a longer takeoff run on a humid day than on a dry day.
        2) The condition is compounded on a hot, humid day because the expanded air can hold much more water vapor than on a cool day. The more moisture in the air, the less dense the air.

3. Less dense air also causes other performance losses besides the loss of lift. Engine horsepower and propeller efficiency decrease because not as many air molecules are available for combustion, resulting in a loss of power, and because propeller blades (which are airfoils) are less effective when air is less dense.
    a. Since the propeller is not pulling with the same force and efficiency as if the air were dense, it takes longer to obtain the necessary forward speed to produce the lift required for takeoff.
        1) Thus, the airplane requires a longer takeoff run.
        2) The rate of climb will also be lower for the same reasons.

4. From the above discussion it is obvious that a pilot should beware of high, hot, and humid conditions, i.e., high altitudes, hot temperatures, and high moisture content (high relative humidity).

## 2.11 GROUND EFFECT

A. It is possible to fly an airplane just clear of the surface (ground or water) at a slightly slower airspeed than that required to sustain level flight at higher altitudes.

1. Near the surface the vertical component of the airflow around the wing is restricted.
    a. This alters the wing's upwash, downwash, and wingtip vortices.

2. This interference of the ground (or water) surface with the airflow patterns about the airplane in flight is called ground effect.

B. The principal aerodynamic effects due to proximity of the ground are the changes in the aerodynamic characteristics of the wing.

1. The reduction of the wingtip vortices due to ground effect alters the spanwise lift distribution and reduces the induced angle of attack and induced drag.

2. Thus, the wing will require a lower angle of attack in ground effect to produce the same amount of lift.

   a. If the same angle of attack is maintained, an increase in lift will result.

C. Ground effect also will alter the thrust required versus velocity.

1. Since induced drag predominates at low airspeeds, the reduction of induced drag due to ground effect will cause the most significant reduction of thrust required at low airspeeds.

   a. There is no effect on parasite drag.

D. In order for ground effect to be of significant magnitude, the wing must be quite close to the ground.

1. The reduction of induced drag differs with the wing height above the ground.

   a. When the wing is at a height equal to its span, the reduction in induced drag is approximately 1.4%.

   b. When the wing is at a height equal to one-fourth its span, the reduction is approximately 23.5%.

   c. When the wing is at a height equal to one-tenth its span, the reduction is approximately 47.6%.

2. Thus, a large reduction in induced drag will take place only when the wing is very close to the ground.

   a. Because of this, ground effect is most usually recognized during the liftoff for takeoff or just prior to touchdown when landing.

E. An airplane leaving ground effect (i.e., taking off) will

1. Require an increase in angle of attack to maintain the same amount of lift.
2. Experience an increase in induced drag and thrust required.
3. Experience a decrease in stability and a slight nose-up pitch.
4. Produce a reduction in static source pressure and an increase in indicated airspeed.

F. An airplane entering ground effect (i.e., landing) will encounter the opposite phenomena.

G. Ground effect permits airplanes to lift off the ground at airspeeds lower than adequate to continue a safe climb.

1. You must make sure you have reached a safe takeoff airspeed before attempting to take off from the runway.

2. On landings, you must be aware of the airplane's tendency to float down the runway when ground effect is encountered at excessive airspeeds.

3. In your training you will learn how to use ground effect to its best advantage when departing from grass or other unpaved landing fields.

## 2.12 HOW AIRPLANES TURN

A. The lift produced by an airplane's wings is used to turn the airplane. When the wings are banked, the lift is separated into two components known as the vertical and horizontal components of lift, as shown on page 37.

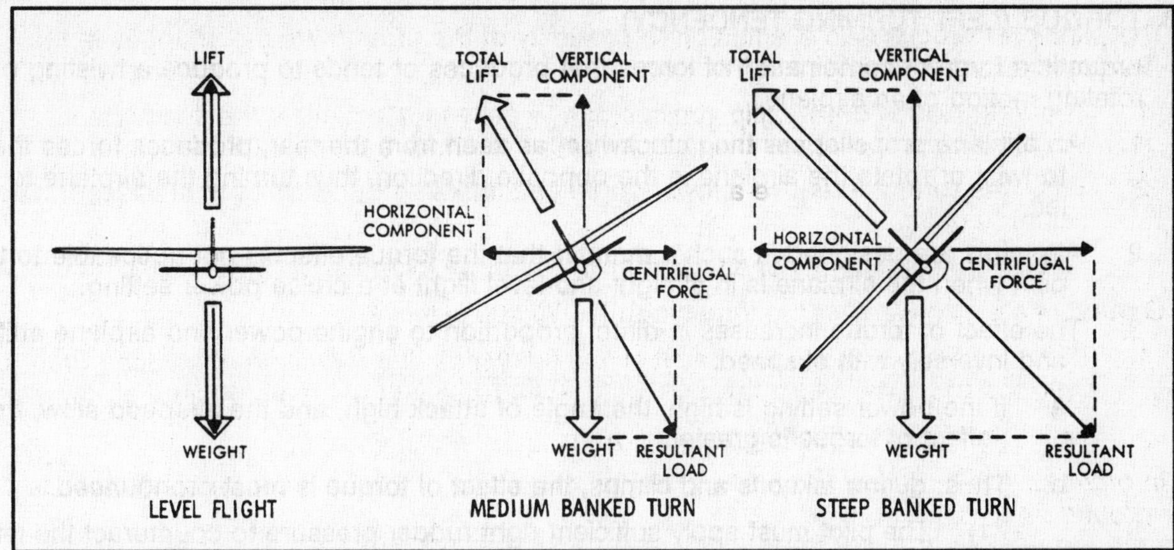


1. Until a force acts on the airplane, it tends to fly straight ahead due to inertia.
   a. Inertia describes the phenomenon that moving items continue to move in the same direction, i.e., straight flight.
2. When the airplane begins to turn, centrifugal force pulls the airplane away from the turn, i.e., tends to make it fly straight ahead.
3. The horizontal component of lift (in a bank) counteracts the centrifugal force.
   a. Therefore, the greater the bank, the sharper the turn or the greater the rate of turn because more of the total lift goes into the horizontal component.
   b. The horizontal component of lift is the force that pulls an airplane from a straight flight path to make it turn.
4. The rudder controls the yaw about the vertical axis.
   a. When applying aileron to bank the airplane, the lowered aileron (on the rising wing) produces a greater drag than the raised aileron (on the lowering wing).
      1) This increased aileron drag tends to yaw the airplane toward the rising wing (i.e., opposite the direction of turn), while the banking action is taking effect.
   b. To counteract this adverse yaw, rudder pressure must be applied simultaneously with the ailerons in the desired direction of turn. This produces a coordinated turn.
   c. For the purposes of this discussion, an airplane is in coordinated flight when it goes straight ahead through the relative wind, i.e., not sideways (about its vertical axis).
      1) In other words, the airplane is always turning at a rate appropriate to its angle of bank.

B. In a bank, the total lift consists of both horizontal lift (counteracting centrifugal force) and vertical lift (counteracting weight and gravity).
   1. Therefore, given the same amount of total lift, there is less vertical lift in a bank than in straight-and-level flight.
   2. Thus, to maintain altitude in a turn, you must
      a. Increase back pressure on the control yoke (for a higher angle of attack to produce more lift), and/or
      b. Increase power.

C. The turn is stopped by decreasing the bank of the airplane to zero, i.e., rolling the wings to level.

## 2.13 TORQUE (LEFT TURNING TENDENCY)

A. Torque is a force or combination of forces that produces or tends to produce a twisting or rotating motion of an airplane.

1. An airplane propeller spinning clockwise, as seen from the rear, produces forces that tend to twist or rotate the airplane in the opposite direction, thus turning the airplane to the left.
2. Airplanes are designed in such a manner that the torque effect is not noticeable to the pilot when the airplane is in straight-and-level flight at a cruise power setting.
3. The effect of torque increases in direct proportion to engine power and airplane attitude, and inversely with airspeed.
    a. If the power setting is high, the angle of attack high, and the airspeed slow, the effect of torque is greater.
    b. Thus, during takeoffs and climbs, the effect of torque is most pronounced.
        1) The pilot must apply sufficient right rudder pressure to counteract the left-turning tendency and maintain a straight takeoff path.
4. Torque is made up of four elements which cause or produce a twisting or rotating motion around at least one of the airplane's three axes. These four elements are
    a. Torque reaction from engine and propeller.
    b. Corkscrewing effect of the slipstream.
    c. Gyroscopic action of the propeller.
    d. Asymmetrical loading of the propeller (P factor).

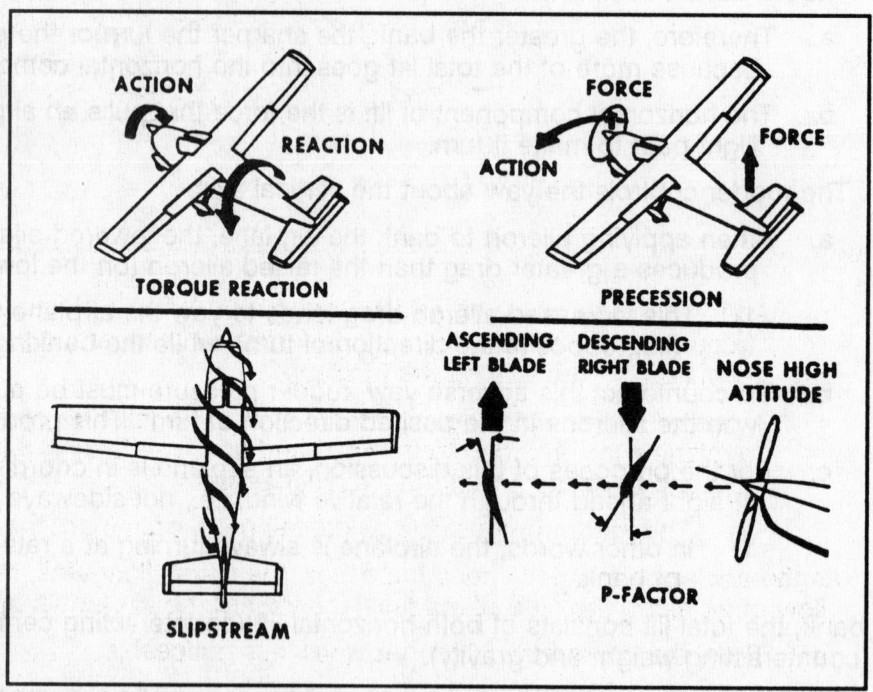


B. Torque Reaction. This is based on Newton's Third Law of Motion, which states that for every action there is an equal and opposite reaction.

1. An airplane's propeller rotates in a clockwise direction (as seen from the rear). This produces a force that tends to roll the entire airplane counterclockwise (i.e., left) about its longitudinal axis.

2. This can be understood by visualizing a rubber-band-powered model airplane.
   a. Wind the rubber band in a manner that it will unwind and rotate the propeller in a clockwise direction.
   b. If the fuselage is released while the propeller is held, the fuselage will rotate in a counterclockwise direction (as viewed from the rear).
   c. This effect of torque reaction is the same in a real propeller-driven airplane, except that instead of the propeller being held by a hand, its rotation is resisted by air.
3. Torque reaction is stronger when power is significantly advanced while the airplane is flying at a very slow airspeed.

C. Corkscrew Effect. This is based on the reaction of the air to a rotating propeller blade.
   1. The high-speed rotation of an airplane's propeller gives a corkscrew or spiraling rotation to the slipstream.
      a. At high propeller speeds and low forward speeds (e.g., takeoffs, slow flight), this spiraling rotation is very compact and exerts a strong sideward force on the airplane's vertical stabilizer, as shown below.

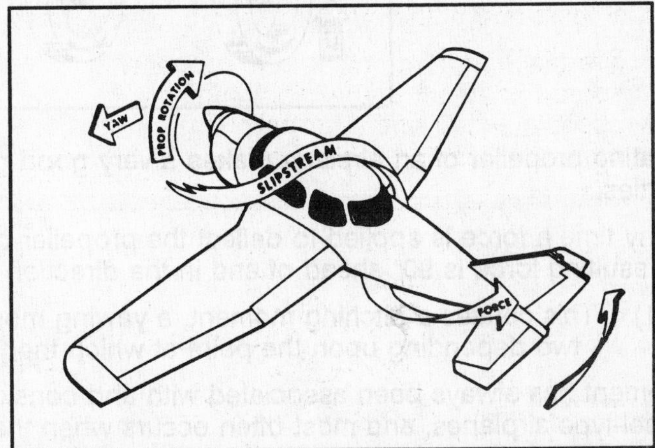


      b. As the airplane propeller rotates through the air in a clockwise direction (as viewed from the rear), the propeller blade forces air rearward in a spiraling clockwise direction of flow around the fuselage.
      c. A portion of this spiraling slipstream strikes the left side of the vertical stabilizer. The airplane's tail is forced to the right and the nose is forced to the left, causing the airplane to rotate around the vertical axis.
         1) The more compact the spiral, the more prominent the force
   2. As the airplane's forward speed increases, the spiral elongates, resulting in a straighter flow of air along the side of the fuselage toward the airplane's tail.
      a. Thus, the corkscrew effect becomes less noticeable.
   3. The corkscrew flow of the slipstream also causes a rolling moment around the longitudinal axis.
      a. This rolling moment is to the right, while the rolling moment caused by torque reaction is to the left.
         1) These forces vary greatly and it is up to the pilot to apply proper corrective action by use of the flight controls at all times.

D. Gyroscopic Action. This is based on one of the gyroscopic properties which apply to any object spinning in space, even a rotating airplane propeller.

1. Before the gyroscopic effects of the propeller can be understood, it is necessary to understand the basic principle of a gyroscope.
   a. All practical applications of the gyroscope are based upon two fundamental properties of gyroscopic action.
      1) Rigidity in space, and
      2) Precession, the one in which we are interested for this discussion.
   b. Precession is the resultant action, or deflection of a spinning rotor when a deflecting force is applied to its rim.
      1) As can be seen in the figure below, when a force is applied the resulting force takes effect 90° ahead of and in the direction of rotation.

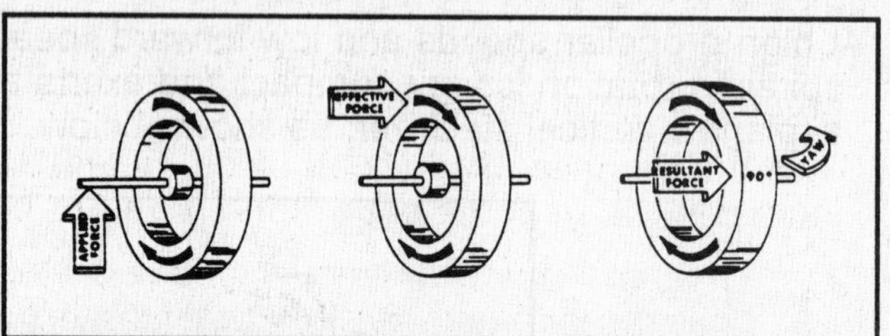


2. The rotating propeller of an airplane makes a very good gyroscope and thus has similar properties.
   a. Any time a force is applied to deflect the propeller out of its plane of rotation, the resulting force is 90° ahead of and in the direction of application.
      1) This causes a pitching moment, a yawing moment, or a combination of the two depending upon the point at which the force was applied.
3. This element has always been associated with and considered more prominent in tailwheel-type airplanes, and most often occurs when the tail is being raised during the takeoff roll as shown below.

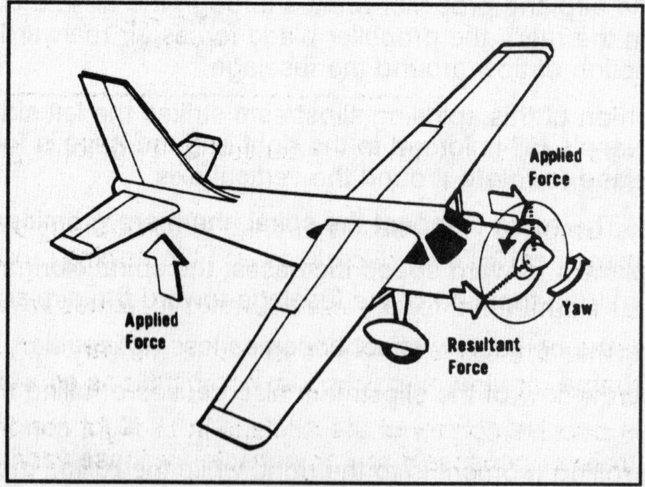


   a. This change in pitch attitude has the same effect as applying a force to the top of the propeller's plane of rotation.
   b. The resultant force acting 90° ahead causes a yawing moment to the left around the vertical axis.

c. The magnitude of this moment depends on several variables, one of which is the abruptness with which the tail is raised (i.e., the amount of force applied).

4. As a result of gyroscopic action, any yawing around the vertical axis results in a pitching moment, and any pitching around the lateral axis results in a yawing moment.

   a. To correct for the effect of gyroscopic action, it is necessary for the pilot to properly use elevator and rudder to prevent unwanted pitching and yawing.

E. Asymmetric Propeller Loading (P-Factor). The effects of P-factor or asymmetric propeller loading usually occur when the airplane is flown at a high angle of attack.

1. Asymmetrical loading of the propeller simply means that the load on the upward-moving propeller blade is different from the load on the downward-moving propeller blade.

2. When an airplane is flying at a high angle of attack (i.e., the propeller axis inclined upward), the bite (or load) of the downward-moving propeller blade is greater than the bite (load) of the upward-moving blade.

   a. This is due to the downward-moving blade meeting the oncoming relative wind at a greater angle of attack and velocity than the upward-moving blade.

   b. Since the propeller blade is an airfoil, increased angle of attack and velocity means increased lift, or in the case of the propeller blade, more thrust.

      1) Thus, the downward-moving blade on the right side (as viewed from the rear) has more thrust than the upward-moving blade, causing the airplane to yaw to the left.

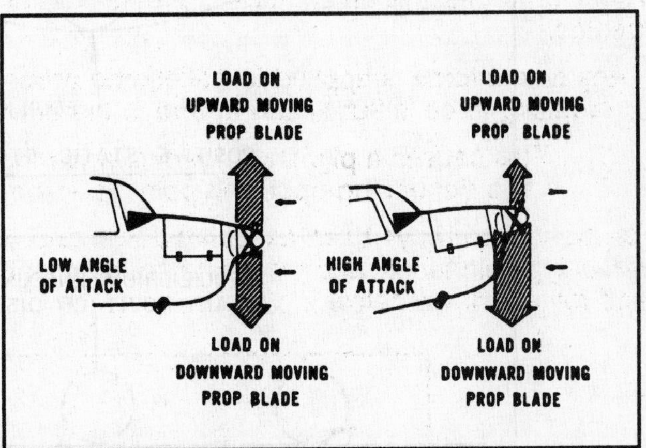


3. At low speeds the yawing tendency caused by P-factor is greater because the airplane is at a high angle of attack.

   a. As the airspeed is increased and the airplane's angle of attack is reduced, the asymmetrical loading decreases and the turning tendency is decreased.

F. Each of these four elements of torque effects varies in values with changes in flight situations.

1. The relationship of these values to each other will vary with different airplanes depending on the airframe, engine, and propeller combinations as well as other design features.

2. To maintain positive control of the airplane in all flight conditions, the pilot must apply the flight controls as necessary to compensate for these varying values.

G. It should be noted at this point that, although the rudder should never be used to turn the airplane, it is used to prevent the above-mentioned unwanted turning tendencies.

1. Aileron should never be used to counteract unwanted yaw.

## 2.14 AIRPLANE STABILITY

A. Stability is the inherent ability of a body, after its equilibrium (i.e., steady flight) is disturbed, to return to its original position. In other words, a stable airplane will tend to return to the original condition of flight if disturbed by a force such as turbulent air.

1. This means that a stable airplane is easy to fly.
2. It does not mean that a pilot can depend entirely on stability to return the airplane to the original condition. Even in the most stable airplanes, some conditions will require the use of airplane controls to return the airplane to the desired attitude. Less effort is needed to control the airplane, however, because of the inherent stability.
3. The two types of stability are static and dynamic. Within each of these are categories called positive, neutral, and negative stability.
    a. Since stability is desired around all three axes of an airplane, it can be classified as longitudinal, lateral, or vertical.

B. Static stability is the *initial* tendency that the airplane displays after its equilibrium is disturbed.

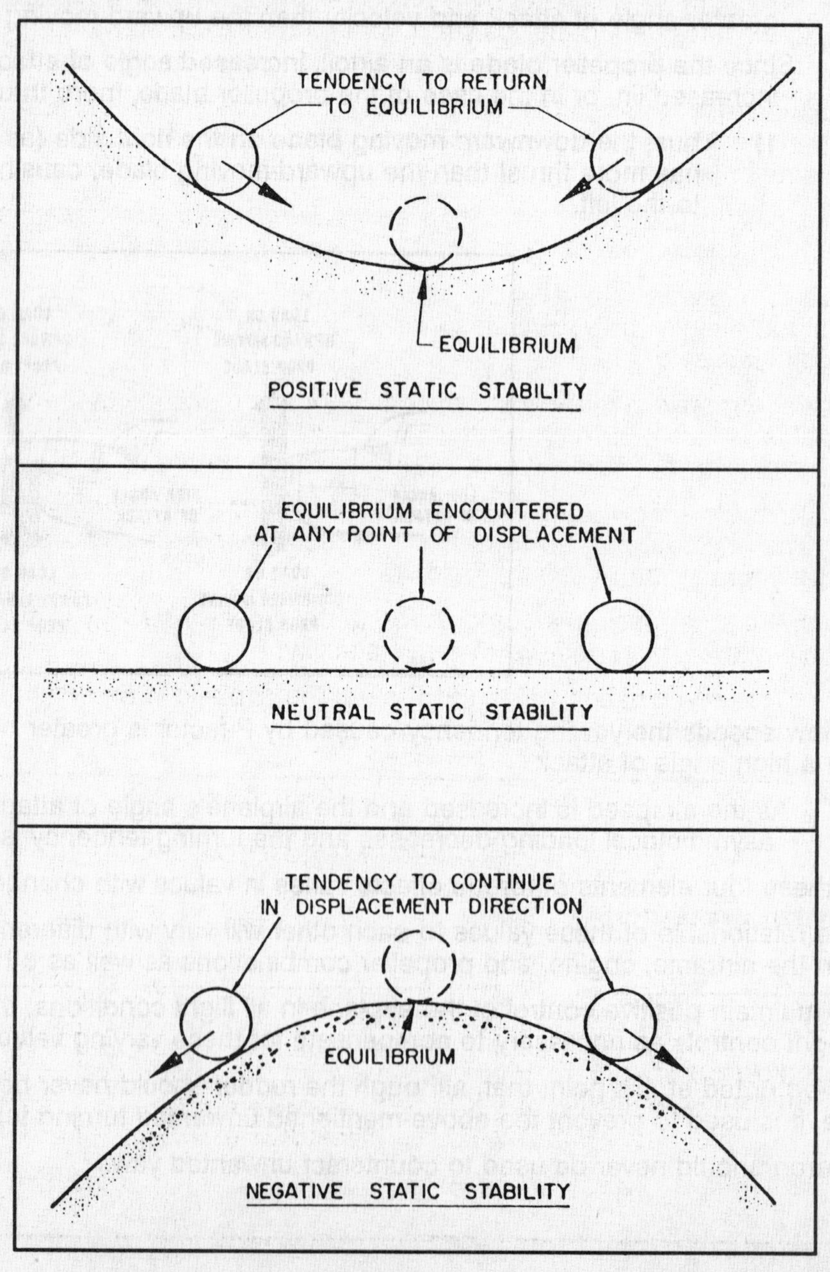

1. Positive static stability is the initial tendency of the airplane to return to the original attitude, or equilibrium, after being disturbed.
   a. This can be illustrated by a ball inside a bowl. If the ball is displaced from its normal resting place at the bottom of the bowl (i.e., its equilibrium), it will eventually return to its original position, as shown in the top figure of the illustration on the opposite page.
2. Neutral static stability is the initial tendency of the airplane to remain in a new condition (attitude) after its equilibrium has been disturbed.
   a. This can be illustrated by a ball on a flat, level surface. If the ball is displaced, it will come to rest at some new, neutral position and show no tendency to return to its original position, as shown in the middle figure of the illustration.
3. Negative static stability is the initial tendency of the airplane to continue away from the original equilibrium (attitude) after being disturbed, as shown in the bottom figure of the illustration.
   a. This can be illustrated by a ball on the top of an inverted bowl. Even the slightest displacement of the ball from its equilibrium will activate greater forces which will cause the ball to move in the direction of the applied force.
4. Positive static stability is the most desirable characteristic, because the airplane will initially attempt to move to its original trimmed attitude, as shown in the top figure of the illustration.

C. Dynamic stability is the *overall* tendency that the airplane displays after its equilibrium is disturbed. It is determined by its oscillation tendency after the initial displacement.
1. Positive dynamic stability is the overall tendency of the airplane to return to its original attitude directly, or through a series of decreasing oscillations (see the left figure in the illustration below).
2. Neutral dynamic stability is the overall tendency of the airplane to attempt to return to its original attitude, but the oscillations do not increase or decrease in magnitude as time passes (see the middle figure in the illustration below).
3. Negative dynamic stability is the overall tendency of the airplane to attempt to return to its original attitude, but the oscillations increase in magnitude as time progresses (see the right figure in the illustration below).
4. Thus, the most desirable combination of the types of stability is a combination of positive static stability with positive dynamic stability.
   a. This combination will tend to return the airplane to its original attitude (or equilibrium).

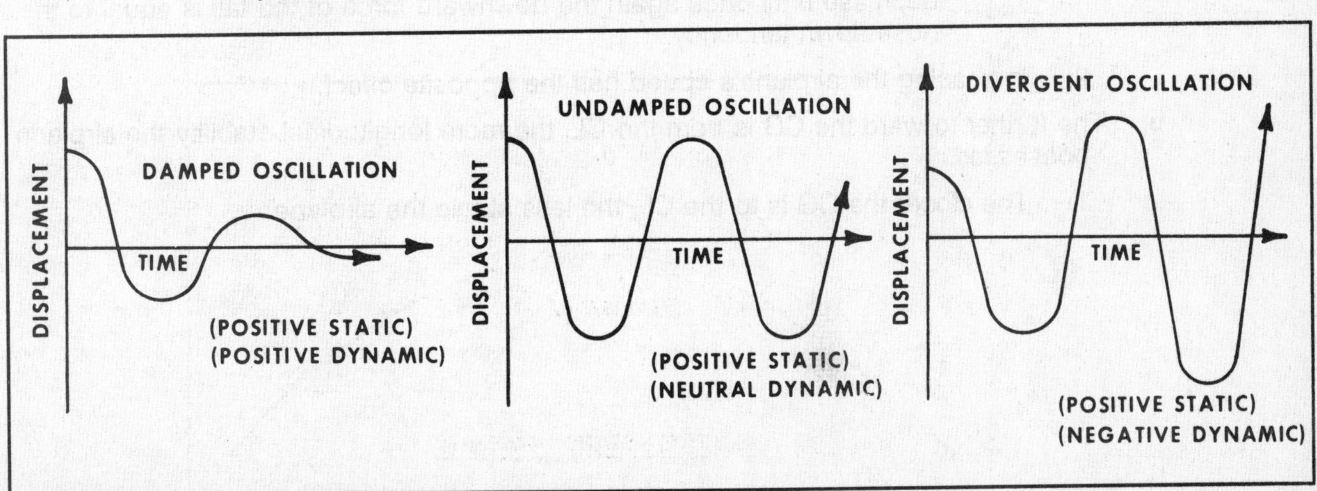

D. Longitudinal Stability about the Lateral Axis. Longitudinal stability is important to the pilot because it determines to a great extent the pitch characteristics of the airplane, particularly as this relates to the stall characteristics.

1. It would be unsafe and uncomfortable for the pilot if an airplane continually displayed a tendency to either stall or dive when the pilot's attention was diverted for some reason.
2. The location of the center of gravity (CG) with respect to the center of lift (CL) determines to a great extent the static longitudinal stability of the airplane.
   a. Positive -- if center of lift is behind the center of gravity (see left figure below)
   b. Negative -- if center of lift is in front of the center of gravity (see right figure below)
   c. Neutral -- if center of lift is at the center of gravity

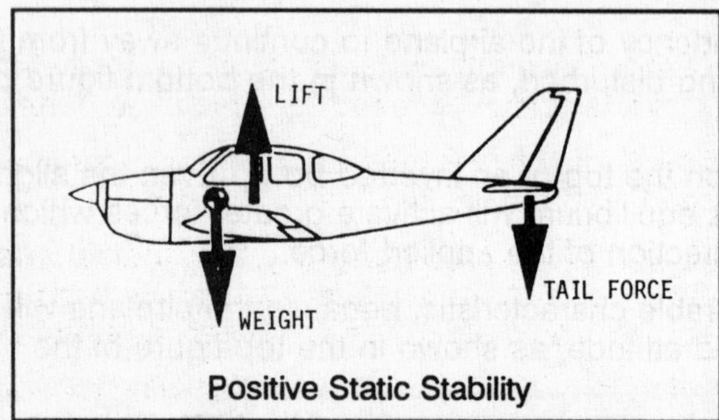

Positive Static Stability

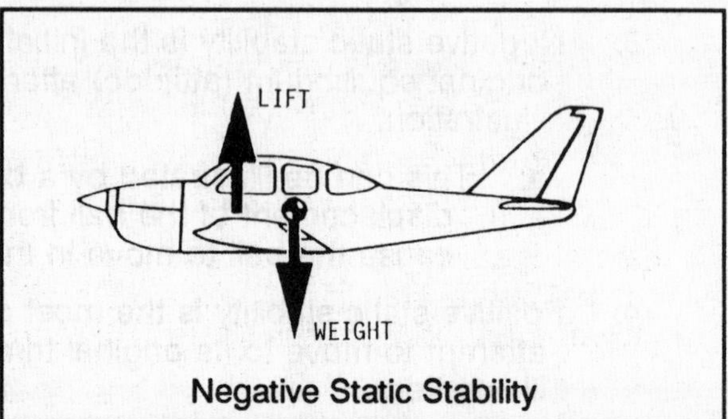

Negative Static Stability

3. Most airplanes are designed to have their CG located slightly forward of the CL, to create a nose-down tendency so the airplane will have a natural tendency to pitch downward away from a stalling condition.
   a. The nose-down tendency is offset by the air flowing downward behind the trailing edge of the wing striking the upper surface of the horizontal stabilizer (except on T-tails).
      1) If the airplane's speed decreases, the speed of the airflow over the wing is decreased. As a result, the downwash is reduced, causing a decrease in the downward force on the horizontal stabilizer, thus causing the airplane's nose to pitch down.
         a) As the airplane's speed increases in the nose-low attitude, the downward force on the horizontal stabilizer increases, causing the tail to be pushed downward, and the nose rises to a climbing attitude.
         b) If the airplane has positive dynamic stability, these oscillations will decrease until once again the downward force of the tail is equal to the nose-down tendency.
      2) Increasing the airplane's speed has the opposite effect.
   b. The further forward the CG is from the CL, the more longitudinal stability the airplane possesses.
      1) The closer the CG is to the CL, the less stable the airplane.

c. Many airplanes have the line of thrust located lower than the CG. The propeller's thrust provides a nose-up pitching force to help overcome the inherent nose heaviness.

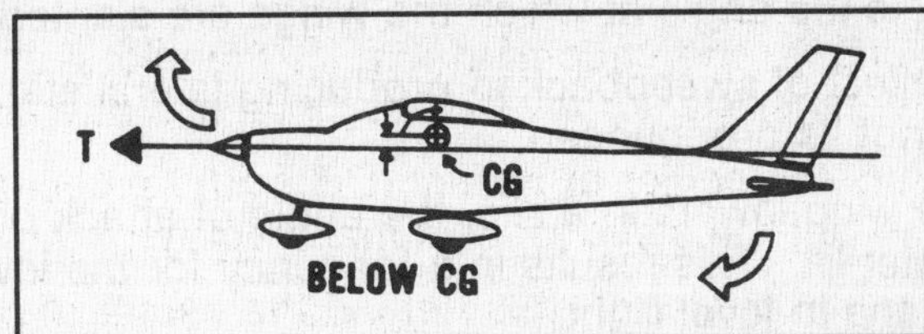


4. A common misconception about longitudinal stability is that an airplane is stable in respect to the horizon.
   a. There is only one speed for each degree of angle of attack, and eventually the airplane will stabilize at the angle of attack and airspeed for which it is trimmed.
   b. Thus, an airplane which is longitudinally stable will tend to return to its trimmed angle of attack after being disturbed from equilibrium.

E. Lateral Stability about the Longitudinal Axis. Stability about the airplane's longitudinal axis is called lateral stability. This helps to stabilize the lateral or rolling effect when one wing gets lower than the opposite wing. There are four main design factors that influence lateral stability.

1. The most common procedure for producing lateral stability is known as wing *dihedral*. The wings on either side of the airplane join the fuselage to form a slight V or angle called dihedral, and this is measured by the angle made by each wing above a line parallel to the lateral axis, as shown below.

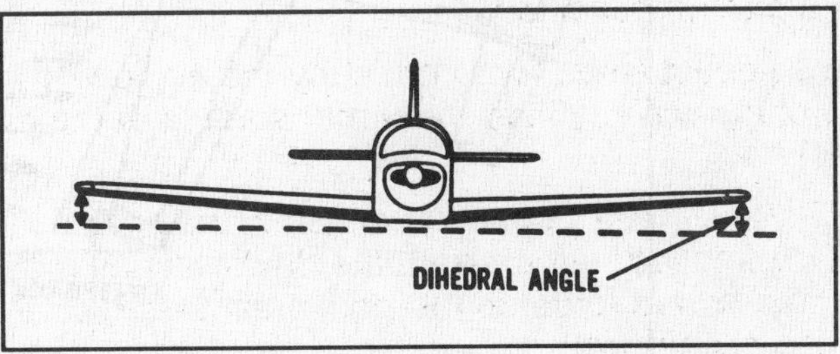


   a. If a momentary gust of wind forces one wing of the airplane to rise and the other to lower, the airplane will roll into a bank.
      1) When an airplane is banked without turning, it tends to sideslip or slide downward toward the lowered wing.
      2) Since the wings have dihedral, the air strikes the low wing at much greater angle of attack than the high wing.
      3) This increases lift on the low wing more than the high wing, and tends to restore the wings to a level attitude, as shown below.

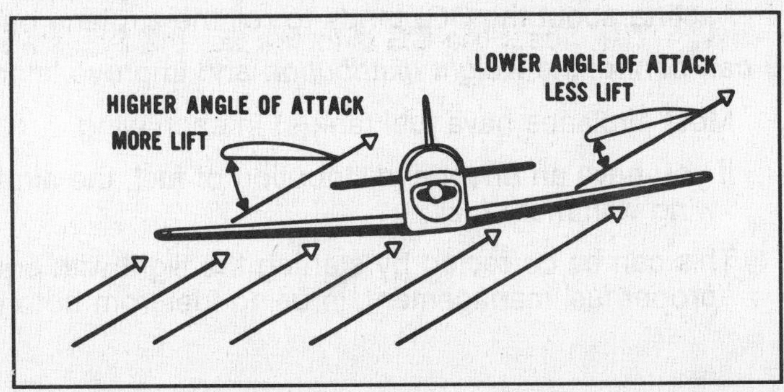

b. The effect of dihedral is to produce a rolling moment tending to return the airplane to a laterally balanced flight condition (i.e., wings level) when a sideslip occurs.

2. *Sweepback* is the angle at which the wings are slanted rearward from the root to the tip.

   a. The effect of sweepback in producing lateral stability is similar to that of the dihedral, but not as pronounced.

   b. If one wing lowers in a slip, the angle of attack on the low wing increases, producing greater lift. This results in a tendency for the lower wing to rise and return the airplane to level flight.

   c. Sweepback augments dihedral to achieve lateral stability.

   d. Another reason for sweepback is to place the center of lift farther rearward, which affects longitudinal stability more than it does lateral stability.

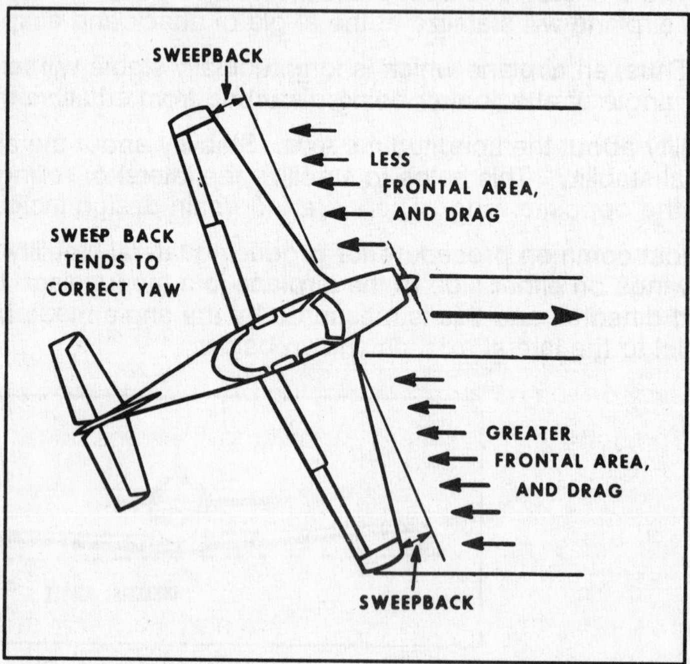


3. During flight, the side area of the airplane's fuselage and vertical stabilizer react to the airflow in much the same manner as the keel of a ship.

   a. This *keel effect* is the steadying influence on the airplane laterally about the longitudinal axis.

   b. Such laterally stable airplanes are constructed so that the greater portion of the keel area is above and behind the center of gravity, as shown on page 48.

   c. Thus, when the airplane slips to one side, the combination of the airplane's weight and the pressure of the airflow against the upper portion of the keel area (both acting about the CG) tends to roll the airplane back to wings-level flight.

4. You can control the *weight distribution* and improve lateral stability.

   a. Most airplanes have fuel tank(s) in each wing.

   b. If you have an unequal distribution of fuel, the airplane will tend to roll toward the wing with more fuel.

   c. This can be corrected by starting the flight with equal fuel in each wing and, through proper fuel management, in using fuel from both wings in an equal amount.

5. Lateral Stability or Instability in Turns
   a. Because of lateral stability, most airplanes will tend to recover from shallow banks automatically.
   b. As the bank is increased to a medium banked turn, the wing on the outside of the turn travels faster than the wing on the inside of the turn. The increased speed increases the lift on the outside wing which nearly cancels the stabilizing effect of lateral stability.
      1) Thus, during a medium banked turn, an airplane tends to hold its bank constant and requires less control input on the part of the pilot.
   c. During a steep banked turn, the increased lift on the outside wing becomes so great that it overcomes the airplane's lateral stability.
      1) Thus, the pilot must apply slight aileron pressure opposite the turn to prevent overbanking.
   d. Because rates of turn at any given bank angle vary with airspeed, the bank angle at which the airplane becomes laterally unstable also varies with airspeed.
      1) For example, a 30° banked turn is usually a stable, medium bank at 100 kt., but may be an unstable, steep bank at 50 kt.

F. Directional Stability about the Vertical Axis (Yaw). Directional stability is displayed around the vertical axis and depends to a great extent on the quality of lateral stability. If the longitudinal axis of an airplane tends to follow and parallel the flight path of the airplane through the air, whether in straight flight or curved flight, that airplane is considered to be directionally stable.
   1. Directional stability is accomplished by the vertical stabilizer or fin to the rear of the center of gravity on the upper portion of the tail section (see figure on page 48).
      a. The surface of this fin acts similar to a weathervane. It causes the airplane to turn into the relative wind.
      b. If the airplane is yawed out of its flight path during straight flight or turns, either by pilot action or turbulence, the relative wind exerts a force on one side of the vertical stabilizer and returns the airplane to its original direction of flight.
   2. Wing sweepback also aids in directional stability. If the airplane is rotated about the vertical axis, the airplane is forced sideways into the relative wind.
      a. Sweepback causes the leading wing to present more frontal area to the relative wind than the trailing wing.
      b. This increased frontal area creates more drag, which tends to force the airplane to return to its original direction of flight.
   3. The combined effects of the vertical stabilizer (fin) and sweepback can be compared with feathers of an arrow. An arrow cannot travel through the air sideways at any appreciable rate of speed.

4. Keel effect depends upon the action of the relative wind on the side area of the airplane fuselage. In a slight slip the fuselage provides a broad area upon which the relative wind will strike, forcing the fuselage to parallel the relative wind. This aids in producing vertical or yaw stability.

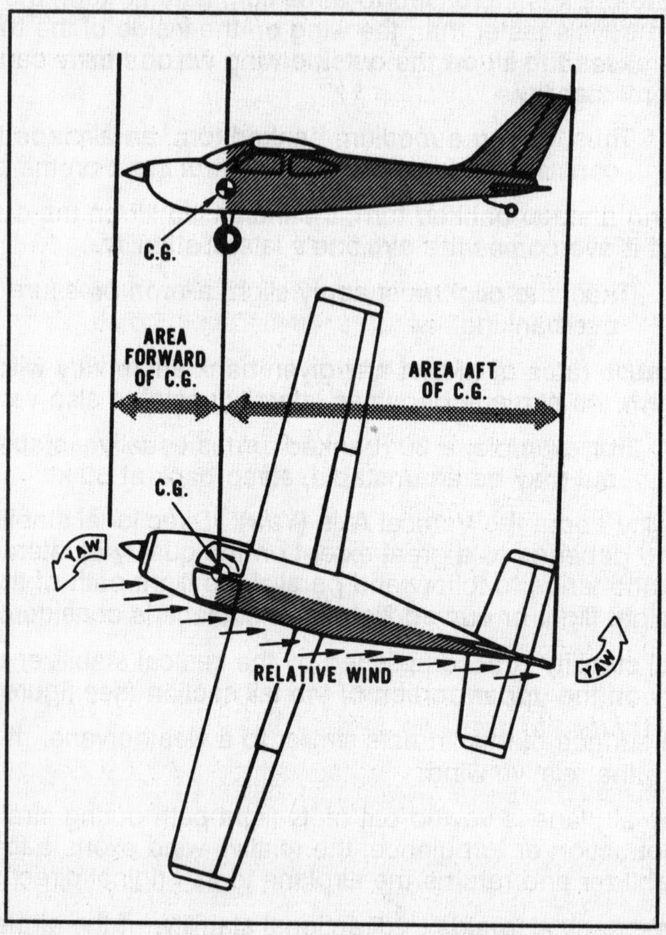


G. Effects of Lateral and Directional Stability. While most airplanes are designed to be stable, there are normally some undesirable effects. The two most common are Dutch Roll and spiral instability.

1. *Dutch Roll* is a combination rolling/yawing oscillation caused by wind gusts in turbulent air.

   a. When equilibrium is disturbed, the rolling motion precedes the yawing motion, and the rolling motion is more noticeable than the yawing motion.

   b. When the airplane rolls back toward level flight in response to dihedral effect, it rolls back too far and sideslips the other way.

      1) Thus, each oscillation overshoots the wings-level attitude because of the strong dihedral effect.

      2) If the Dutch Roll is not decreased by the directional stability, it is considered objectionable.

   c. To counteract the Dutch Roll tendency, the airplane may be designed to increase directional stability and decrease lateral stability.

      1) While suppressing the Dutch Roll tendency, this tends to cause spiral instability.

2. *Spiral instability* exists when the directional stability of the airplane is very strong compared to the lateral stability.
   a. When equilibrium is disturbed and a sideslip is introduced, the strong directional stability tends to yaw the nose back into alignment with the relative wind while the comparatively weak dihedral lags in restoring the lateral balance.
      1) Due to this yaw, the wing on the outside travels at a faster rate than the inside wing, thus increasing lift.
         a) This produces an overbanking tendency which, if not corrected by the pilot, will result in the bank angle becoming steeper and steeper.
      2) At the same time, the strong directional stability which yaws the airplane into the relative wind is actually forcing the nose to a lower pitch attitude.
      3) Thus, a slow downward spiral starts which, if not counteracted by the pilot, will gradually increase into a steep spiral dive.
   b. Normally, the rate of divergence in the spiral motion is so gradual that the pilot can control the tendency without any difficulty.
      1) Thus, if this rate of divergence is low, spiral instability is considered less objectionable than Dutch Roll.

## 2.15 LOADS AND LOAD FACTORS

A. Any force applied to deflect an airplane from a straight line produces a stress on its structure. The amount of this force is called load factor.
   1. Load factor is the ratio of the total load supported by the airplane's wings to the actual weight of the airplane and its contents:

$$\text{Load Factor} = \frac{\text{Total load supported by the wings}}{\text{Total weight of the airplane}}$$

      a. EXAMPLE: An airplane has a gross weight of 2,000 lb. During flight it is subjected to aerodynamic forces which increase the total load that the wing must support to 4,000 lb. The load factor is thus 2.0 (4,000 ÷ 2,000). The airplane wing is producing lift equal to twice the gross weight of the airplane.
   2. Another way of expressing load factor is the ratio of a given load to the pull of gravity or "G." If the weight of the airplane is equal to 1 G, and if a load of three times the actual weight of the airplane were imposed upon the wing due to curved flight, the load factor of 3 is expressed as 3 G's.
   3. In unaccelerated flight, the airplane is said to have a load factor of 1, i.e., the total lift that the wings are producing is equal to the gross weight of the airplane.
      a. If the angle of attack of the wings is increased while airspeed remains constant, e.g., in a pull-up from a dive, the wings produce more lift and thus a higher load factor.
   4. A positive load occurs when back pressure is applied to the elevator, causing centrifugal force to act in the same direction as weight.
      a. A negative load occurs when forward pressure is applied to the elevator control, causing centrifugal force to act in a direction opposite to that of weight.

B. Load Factors and Airplane Design. To be certified by the FAA, the structural strength (maximum allowable load factor) of airplanes must conform with prescribed standards set forth by Federal Aviation Regulations. Airplanes are classified as to strength and operational use by means of the category system. Most general aviation trainer-type airplanes are classified in one or more of the following categories.

1. The normal category has a maximum limit load factor of 3.8 positive G's and 1.52 negative G's.
   a. The limit load factor is the highest (both positive and negative) load factor which can be expected in normal operations under various situations. This load factor can be sustained without causing permanent deformation or structural damage to the airplane.
   b. Permissible maneuvers include:
      1) Any maneuver incidental to normal flying.
      2) Stalls.
      3) Lazy eights, chandelles, and steep turns in which the angle of bank does not exceed 60°.
2. The utility category has a maximum limit load factor of 4.4 positive G's and 1.76 negative G's.
   a. Permissible maneuvers include:
      1) All operations in the normal category.
      2) Spins (if approved for that airplane).
      3) Lazy eights, chandelles, and steep turns in which the angle of bank is more than 60°.
3. The acrobatic category has a maximum limit load factor of 6.0 positive G's and 3.0 negative G's.
   a. There are no restrictions except those shown to be necessary as a result of required flight tests.
4. This system indicates what operations can be performed in a given airplane without exceeding the load limit. Pilots are cautioned to operate the airplane within the load limit for which the airplane is designed so as to enhance safety and still benefit from the intended use of the airplane.
5. It should be noted that an aircraft's structure is designed to support a certain total load.
   a. It is vital that maximum gross weight limits as well as load factor limits be strictly observed.

C. Effect of Turns on Load Factor. A turn is made by banking the airplane so that horizontal lift from the wings pulls the airplane from its straight flight path. In a constant altitude coordinated turn, the resultant load is the result of two forces -- gravity and centrifugal force, as shown below.

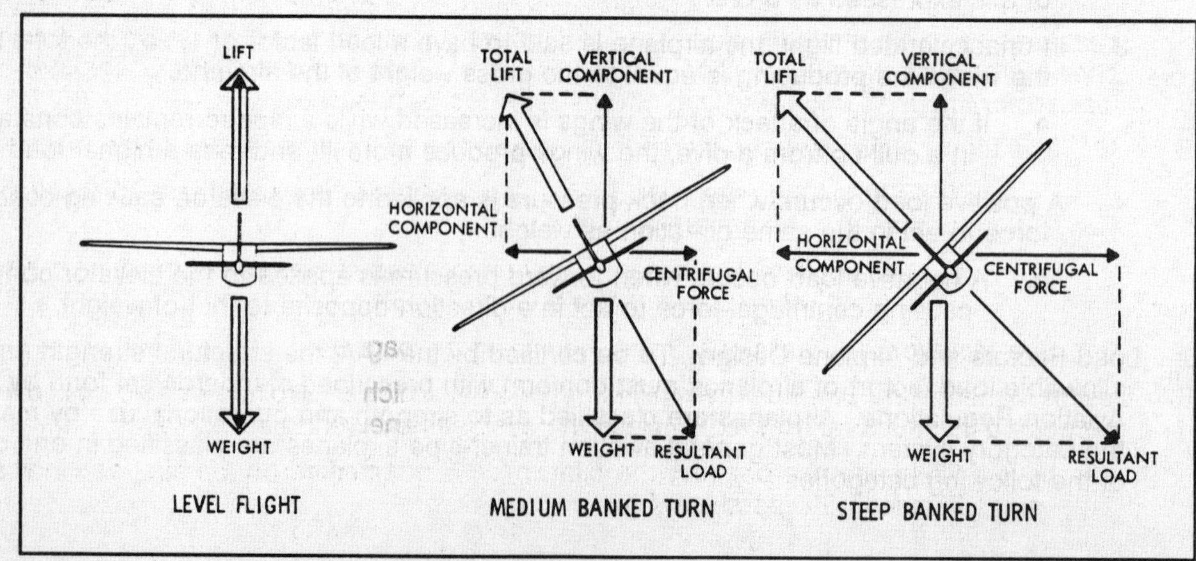

1. In any airplane, if a constant altitude is maintained during the turn, the load factor for a given degree of bank is the same.
   a. Regardless of airspeed and rate of turn, the total lift, and therefore the two components of lift shown on the opposite page remain the same.
   b. Because of this, there is no change in centrifugal force for any given bank, and thus, the load factor remains constant.
2. The load factor increases at a rapid rate after the angle of bank reaches 50°, as shown in the figure below. The wing must produce lift equal to this load factor if altitude is to be maintained.
   a. At an angle of bank of slightly more than 80° the load factor exceeds 6.0, which is the limit load factor of an acrobatic airplane.
   b. The approximate maximum bank for conventional light airplanes is 60° which produces a load factor of 2.0.

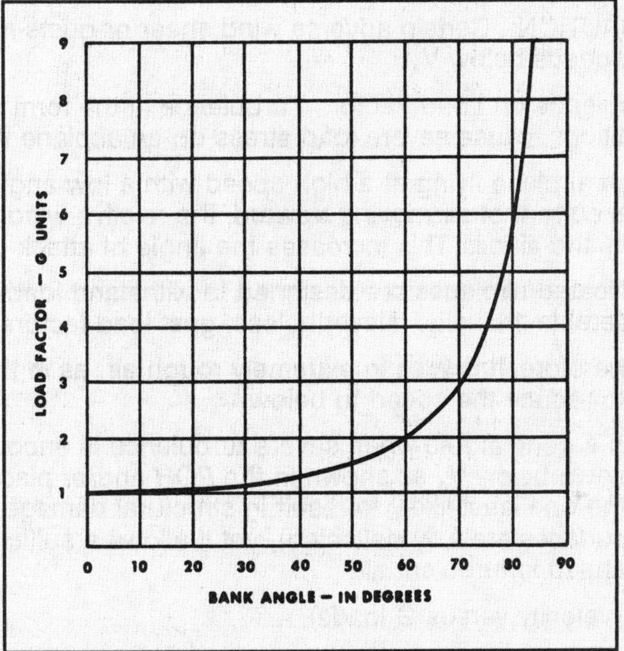


D. Effect of Load Factor on Stalling Speed. Any airplane, within the limits of its structure and the strength of the pilot, can be stalled at any airspeed. At a given airspeed, the load factor increases as angle of attack increases, and the wing stalls because the angle of attack has been increased beyond the critical angle. Therefore, there is a direct relationship between the load factor imposed upon the wing and its stalling characteristics.
   1. The airplane's stall speed increases in proportion to the square root of the load factor.
      a. EXAMPLE: Using the chart above, the load factor produced in a 75° banked, level turn is 4.0. The square root of 4 is 2.
         1) An airplane that has a normal unaccelerated stall speed of 45 kt. will stall at 90 kt. when subjected to a load of 4 G's.
   2. See Module 2.16, Stalls and Spins, beginning on page 54.
E. Design Maneuvering Speed. The maximum speed at which an airplane can be stalled without exceeding its structural (or load) limits is the design maneuvering speed ($V_A$).
   1. $V_A$ is a vital reference point for the pilot which is not marked on the airspeed indicator, since it varies with gross weight.

2. $V_A$ can be found in the *Pilot's Operating Handbook* (*POH*) for each airplane and/or on a placard within the cockpit.
   a. Older general aviation airplanes may not have a published $V_A$ in their *POH*. In this case, a rule of thumb for determining the maneuvering speed is approximately 1.7 times the normal stalling speed.
      1) Thus, an airplane which normally stalls at 35 kt. should never be stalled when the airspeed is above 60 kt. (35 kt. x 1.7 = 59.5 kt.).
   b. If the *POH* specifies more than one $V_A$, you will notice that it decreases with weight.
      1) A lighter airplane is subject to more rapid acceleration from turbulence and gusts than a heavier airplane.
3. When operating below $V_A$, a damaging positive flight load cannot (theoretically) be produced. The airplane should stall before the load becomes excessive. Any combination of flight control usage, including full deflection of the controls or gust loads created by turbulence, should not create an excessive air load if the airplane is operated below $V_A$.
   a. CAUTION: Certain adverse wind shear or gusts may cause excessive loads even at speeds below $V_A$.

F. Effect of Turbulence on Load Factor. Turbulence in the form of vertical air currents can, under certain conditions, cause severe load stress on an airplane wing.
1. When an airplane flying at a high speed with a low angle of attack suddenly encounters a vertical current of air moving upward, the relative wind changes to an upward direction as it meets the airfoil. This increases the angle of attack of the wing.
2. All certificated airplanes are designed to withstand loads imposed by turbulence of considerable intensity. Nevertheless, gust load factors increase with increasing airspeed.
   a. Therefore, it is wise in extremely rough air, as in thunderstorm or frontal conditions, to reduce the speed to below $V_A$.
   b. As a general rule when severe turbulence is encountered, the airplane should be flown below $V_A$ as shown in the *POH* and/or placard in the airplane. This speed is the one least likely to result in structural damage to the airplane (even if the control surfaces are fully deflected), yet it allows a sufficient margin of safety above stalling speed in turbulent air.

G. V-G diagram (velocity versus G loads).
1. The V-G diagram shows the flight operating strength of an airplane.
2. In the diagram on the opposite page, load factor is on the vertical axis with airspeed on the horizontal axis.
3. The lines of maximum lift capability (dashed lines) are the first items of importance on the V-G diagram.
   a. The subject airplane in the diagram on the opposite page is capable of developing no more than one positive G at 64 mph, which is the wings-level stall speed of the airplane.
   b. The maximum load factor increases dramatically with airspeed. The maximum positive lift capability of this airplane is 2 G's at 96 mph, 3 G's at 116 mph, 3.8 G's at 126 mph, etc.
      1) These are the coordinates of points on the curved line up to point C.
   c. Any load factor above this dashed line is unavailable aerodynamically. That is, the subject airplane cannot fly above the line of maximum lift capability (it will stall).

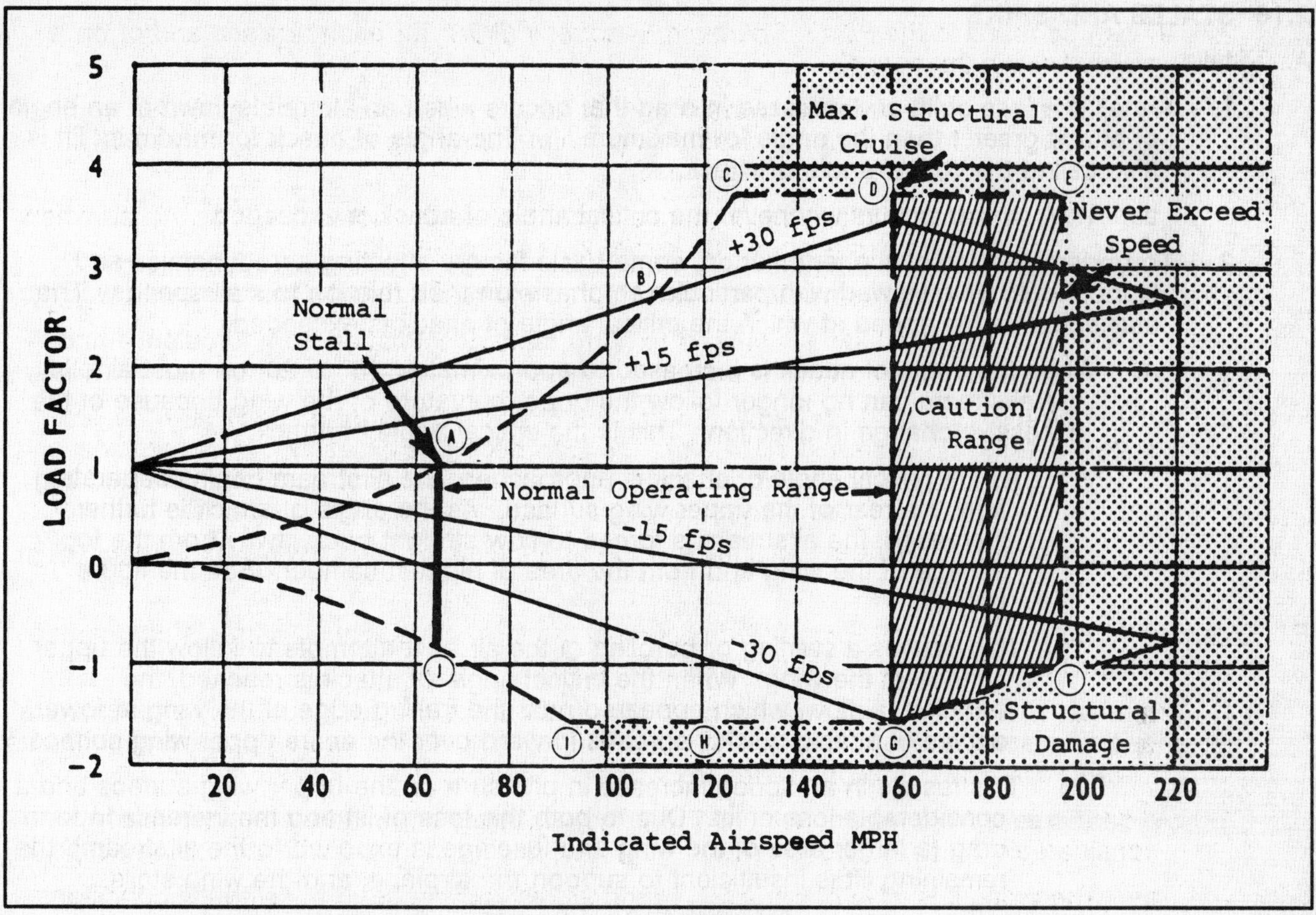


4. Point C is the intersection of the positive limit load factor (line CDE) and the line of maximum positive lift capability (dashed line up to point C).
   a. The airspeed at this point is the minimum airspeed at which the limit load can be developed aerodynamically.
   b. Any airspeed greater than point C provides a positive lift capability sufficient to damage the airplane.
      1) Any airspeed less than point C does **not** provide positive lift capability sufficient to cause damage from excessive flight loads.
   c. The usual term given to the speed at point C is the design maneuvering speed ($V_A$).
5. The limit airspeed $V_{NE}$ is a design reference point for the airplane. The subject airplane is limited to 196 mph (line EF).
   a. If flight is attempted beyond the limit airspeed, structural damage or structural failure may result from a variety of phenomena.
6. Thus, the airplane in flight is limited to a regime of airspeeds and G's which do not exceed
   a. The limit (or red line) speed (line EF).
   b. Normal stall speed (line AJ).
   c. The positive and negative limit load factor (lines CDE and IHG).
   d. The maximum lift capability (dashed lines up to C, down to I).
7. A caution range is indicated between points D, E, F, and G. Within this range certain factors must be considered to maintain flight in the envelope.
   a. Line DG represents the maximum structural cruising speed ($V_{NO}$).

## 2.16 STALLS AND SPINS

A. Stalls

1. A stall is a loss of lift and increase in drag that occurs when an aircraft is flown at an angle of attack greater than the angle for maximum lift. The angle of attack for maximum lift is also called the critical angle of attack.
   a. Thus, a stall occurs whenever the critical angle of attack is exceeded.
2. To understand the stall phenomenon, some basic factors affecting aerodynamics and flight should be reviewed with particular emphasis on their relation to stall speeds. The stall speed is the speed at which the critical angle of attack is exceeded.
   a. When the angle of attack is increased to approximately 18° to 20° on most airfoils, the airstream can no longer follow the upper curvature of the wing because of the excessive change in direction. This is the critical angle of attack.
      1) As the critical angle of attack is approached, the airstream begins separating from the rear of the upper wing surface. As the angle of attack is further increased, the airstream is forced to flow straight back, away from the top surface of the wing and from the area of highest camber. See the figure below.
      2) This causes a swirling or burbling of the air as it attempts to follow the upper surface of the wing. When the critical angle of attack is reached, the turbulent airflow, which appeared near the trailing edge of the wing at lower angles of attack, quickly spreads forward over the entire upper wing surface.
      3) This results in a sudden increase in pressure on the upper wing surface and a considerable loss of lift. Due to both this loss of lift and the increase in form drag (a larger area of the wing and fuselage is exposed to the airstream), the remaining lift is insufficient to support the airplane, and the wing stalls.
      4) To recover from a stall, the angle of attack must be decreased so that the airstream can once again flow smoothly over the wing surface.
         a) Remember that the angle of attack is the angle between the chord line and the relative wind, not between the chord line and the horizon.
         b) An airplane can be stalled in any attitude of flight with respect to the horizon and at any airspeed, if the angle of attack is increased up to and beyond the critical angle of attack.

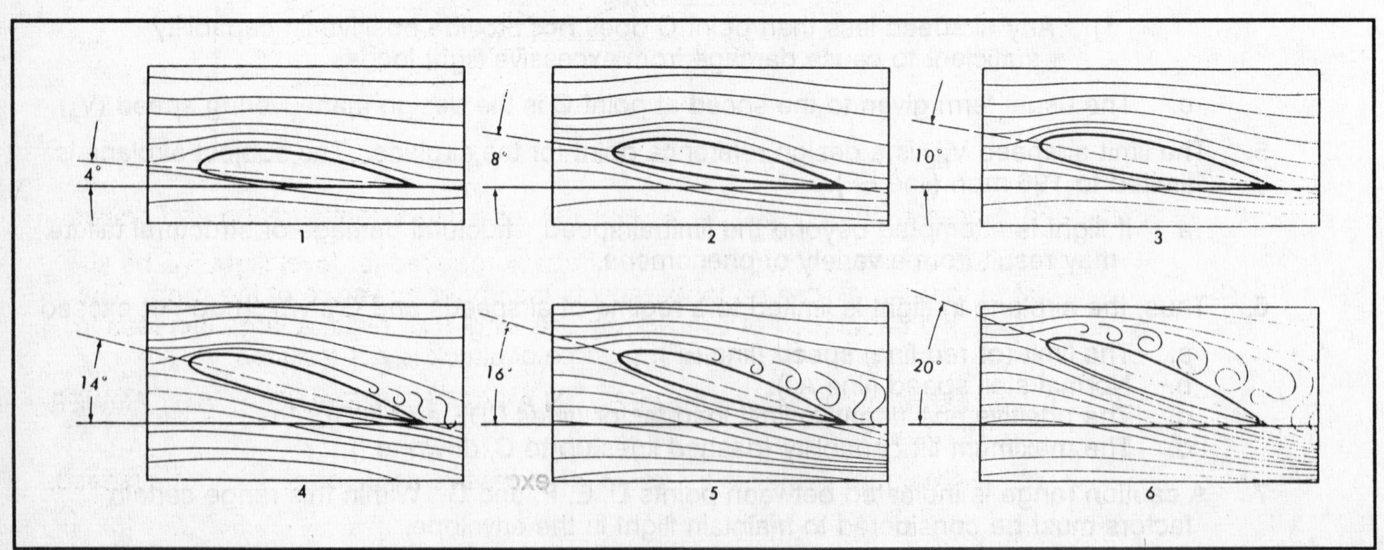

b. Most airplanes are designed so that the wings will stall progressively outward from the wing roots to the wingtips.

1) The wings are designed with washout, i.e., the wingtips have less angle of incidence than the wing roots. The *angle of incidence* is the angle between the chord line of the wing and the longitudinal axis of the airplane.

2) Thus, during flight, the tips of such wings have a smaller angle of attack than the wing roots.

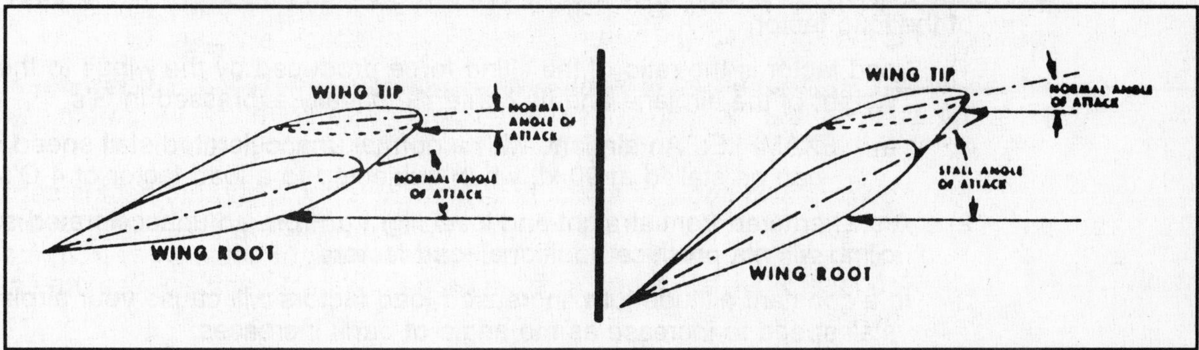


3) A stall is caused by exceeding the critical angle of attack. Since the wing roots of an airplane will exceed the critical angle before the wingtips, the roots will stall first. The wings are designed in this manner so that control of the ailerons (which are located toward the tips of the wings) will be available at high angles of attack and give the airplane more stable stalling characteristics.

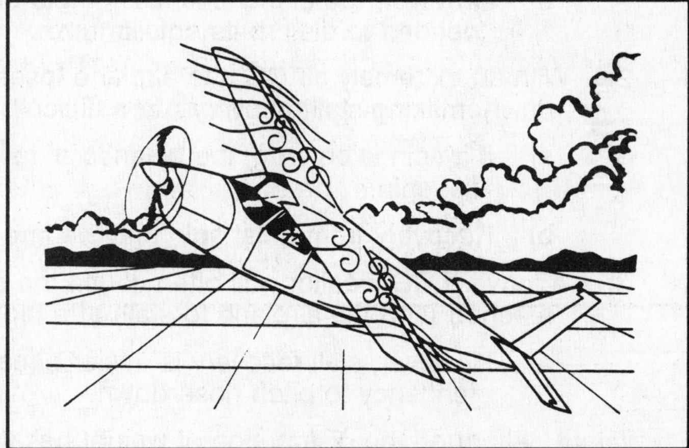

c. Airspeed is controlled primarily by the elevator for a given configuration and power.

1) If the speed is too slow, the angle of attack required for level flight will be so large that the air can no longer follow the upper curvature of the wing. The result is a separation of airflow from the wing, loss of lift, a large increase in drag, and eventually a stall if the angle of attack is not reduced.

2) A stall can occur AT ANY AIRSPEED, IN ANY ATTITUDE, AND AT ANY POWER SETTING.

a) Remember, a stall is the result of excessive angle of attack, not airspeed.

d. Configuration. Flaps, landing gear (if retractable), and other configuring devices can affect your airplane's stall speed. Flap extension will generally increase the lifting ability of the wings, thus reducing the stall speed.

1) The effect can be seen by markings on the airspeed indicator, where the lower airspeed limit of the white arc ($V_{S0}$, power-off stall speed with gear and flaps in the landing configuration) is less than the lower airspeed limit of the green arc ($V_{S1}$, power-off stall speed with the flaps and gear up).

e. Load Factor. Your airplane's stall speed increases in proportion to the square root of the load factor.

1) Load factor is the ratio of the lifting force produced by the wings to the actual weight of the airplane and its contents, usually expressed in G's.

a) EXAMPLE: An airplane with a normal unaccelerated stall speed of 45 kt. can be stalled at 90 kt. when subjected to a load factor of 4 G's.

2) A stall entered from straight-and-level flight or from an unaccelerated straight climb will not produce additional load factors.

3) In a constant altitude turn, increased load factors will cause your airplane's stall speed to increase as the angle of bank increases.

f. Center of Gravity. Because the CG location affects both angle of attack and stability, it has a significant effect on stall speed and ease of recovery.

1) As the CG is moved aft, the airplane flies at a lower angle of attack at a given airspeed.

a) Thus, the critical angle of attack will be exceeded (causing the airplane to stall) at a lower airspeed.

b) However, the airplane is less stable because less elevator force is needed to disturb its equilibrium.

2) With an extremely aft CG, the airplane loses its natural tendency to pitch nose down, making stall recovery more difficult.

a) If a spin is entered, the balance of forces on the airplane may result in a flat spin.

b) Recovery from a flat spin may be impossible.

3) A forward CG location will often cause the critical angle of attack to be reached (and the airplane to stall) at a higher airspeed.

a) However, stall recovery is easier because the airplane has a greater tendency to pitch nose down.

g. Weight. Although the distribution of weight has the most direct effect on stability, increased gross weight can also have an effect on an airplane's flight characteristics, regardless of the CG location.

1) The increased weight requires a higher angle of attack at a given airspeed to produce additional lift to support the weight.

2) Thus, the critical angle of attack will be exceeded (causing the airplane to stall) at a higher airspeed.

h. Snow, Ice, or Frost on the Wings. Even a small accumulation of snow, ice, or frost on your airplane can cause an increase in the stall speed.

1) Such accumulation changes the shape of the wing, disrupting the smooth airflow over the surface and, thus, increasing drag and decreasing lift.

i. Turbulence can cause your airplane to stall at a significantly higher airspeed than in stable conditions.

1) A vertical gust or wind shear can cause a sudden change in the relative wind and result in an abrupt increase in angle of attack.

a) Even though a gust may not be maintained long enough for a stall to develop, the airplane may stall while you attempt to control the flight path, especially during an approach in gusty conditions.

2) When flying in moderate to severe turbulence or strong crosswinds, a higher than normal approach speed should be maintained.

a) In cruise flight maintain an airspeed well above the indicated stall speed and below $V_A$ (maneuvering speed).

3. Distractions

a. Improper airspeed management resulting in stalls is most likely to occur when the pilot is distracted by one or more other tasks.

1) Pilots at all skill levels must be aware of the increased risk of entering into an inadvertent stall/spin while performing tasks that are secondary to controlling the airplane.

b. Some distractions include:

1) Locating a checklist,
2) Attempting a restart after an engine failure,
3) Flying a traffic pattern on a windy day,
4) Reading a chart,
5) Making fuel and/or distance calculations, or
6) Attempting to retrieve items from the floor, back seat, or glove compartment.
7) Attempting to avoid obstruction

4. Stall Recognition

a. There are several ways to recognize that a stall is impending before it actually occurs. When one or more of these indicators is noted, initiation of a recovery should be instinctive.

1) Vision is useful in detecting a stall condition by noting the attitude of the airplane and the airspeed approaching stall speed. This sense can be fully relied on only when the stall is the result of an intentional unusual attitude of the airplane.

2) Hearing is also helpful in sensing a stall condition, since the tone level and intensity of sounds incidental to flight decrease as the airspeed decreases.

3) Kinesthesia, or the mind's sensing of changes in direction of speed of motion, is probably the most important and the best indicator to the trained and experienced pilot. If this sensitivity is properly developed, it will warn of a decrease in speed or the beginning of a settling or "mushing" of the airplane.

4) The feeling of control pressures is also very important. As speed is reduced, the "live" resistance to pressures on the controls becomes progressively less.

a) The airplane controls become less and less effective as one approaches the critical angle of attack.

b) In a complete stall, all controls can be moved with almost no resistance and with little immediate effect on the airplane.

5) Many airplanes are equipped with stall warning devices (e.g., a horn) to alert the pilot when the airflow over the wing(s) approaches a point that will not allow lift to be sustained.

b. It is vital that you maintain positive control of the airplane at all times in the following ways.

1) Know your airplane.

a) Have an intimate familiarity with the pitch attitudes, power settings, and flap configurations appropriate to various phases of flight.

b) Be aware of the sights and sounds of even the slightest changes of pitch, bank, and yaw.

2) Fly the airplane in trim. A trimmed airplane can (and should) be flown hands-off so that it remains stable while distractions are being handled.

B. Spins

1. A spin is an aggravated stall that results in what is termed autorotation, in which the airplane follows a corkscrew path in a downward direction.

a. If one wing is allowed to drop at the beginning of a stall, the nose will begin to yaw in the direction of the lowered wing.

1) Unless rudder is applied to keep the nose from yawing, the airplane begins to slip toward the lowered wing.

2) This causes the airplane to weathervane into the relative wind, i.e., toward the lowered wing, thus continuing the yaw.

b. At the same time, the airplane continues to roll toward the lowered wing.

1) The lowered wing has an increasingly greater angle of attack, due to the upward motion of the relative wind against its surfaces.

a) It is, then, well beyond the critical angle of attack, and suffers an extreme loss of lift and an increase in drag.

2) The rising wing, since the relative wind is striking it at a smaller angle, has a smaller angle of attack than the opposite wing.

a) The rising wing, in effect, becomes less stalled, and thus develops some lift, so that the airplane continues to roll.

3) This autorotation, combined with the effects of centrifugal force and the different amounts of drag on the two wings, becomes a spin and the airplane descends, rolling and yawing until recovery is effected.

c. Remember that, in order to spin, an airplane's wings must first both be stalled, then one wing becomes less stalled than the other.

2. A spin may be broken down into three phases.

a. The incipient phase is the transient period between a stall and a fully developed spin, when a final balancing of aerodynamic and inertial forces has not yet occurred.

b. The steady state phase is that portion of the spin in which it is fully developed, and the aerodynamic forces are in balance.

c. The recovery phase begins when controls are applied to stop the spin and ends when level flight is attained.

3. In the absence of specific recovery techniques in your airplane's *POH*, the following technique is suggested for spin recovery.
   a. Close the throttle.
      1) Power aggravates the spin characteristics and causes an abnormal loss of altitude in the recovery.
   b. Apply opposite rudder to slow the rotation.
   c. Apply positive forward elevator movement to break the stall.
      1) In some airplanes, opposite rudder and forward elevator may need to be held for some time before the spinning stops.
   d. Neutralize the rudder as the spin rotation stops.
      1) Otherwise excessive yaw can occur in the other direction, placing great strain on the airframe, and potentially resulting in a secondary spin.
   e. Return to level flight.
      1) Avoid excessive elevator back pressure which could result in a secondary stall.
4. It cannot be sufficiently stressed that the intentional spinning of an airplane for which spins are not specifically approved is prohibited and extremely dangerous.
   a. To be certified for spins in the Normal and Utility categories, an airplane must be recoverable from an incipient spin, not a fully developed spin (i.e., beyond one turn).
   b. The pilot of an airplane placarded against spins should assume that the airplane may become uncontrollable in a spin.
5. Continued practice in stalls will help you develop a more instinctive and prompt reaction in recognizing an approaching spin.
   a. It is essential to learn to apply immediate corrective action any time it is apparent that the airplane is nearing spin conditions.

# CHAPTER THREE
# AIRPLANE PERFORMANCE



Performance means the ability of an airplane to accomplish certain things that make it useful for certain purposes. For example, the ability of the airplane to land and take off in a very short distance is important to the pilot who operates in and out of confined fields. The ability to carry heavy loads, fly at high altitudes at fast speeds, or travel long distances is essential performance for operators of airlines and executive-type airplanes. The charts and tables used to determine an airplane's performance are found in Section 5, Performance, of that airplane's *Pilot's Operating Handbook (POH)*.

This chapter begins with discussion of the various factors that affect airplane performance. It concludes with examples of various airplane performance graphs, charts, and tables with explanations on how to use them. Note that weight and balance, which also affect performance, are covered in Chapter 6, Weight and Balance, beginning on page 153.

## 3.1 DETERMINANTS OF AIRPLANE PERFORMANCE

A. Air density is perhaps the single most important factor affecting airplane performance. The general rule is as air density decreases, so does airplane performance.

1. Temperature, altitude, barometric pressure, and humidity all affect air density. The density of the air DECREASES
   a. As air temperature INCREASES.
   b. As altitude INCREASES.
   c. As barometric pressure DECREASES.
   d. As humidity INCREASES.
2. The engine produces power in proportion to the weight or density of the air.
   a. As air density decreases, the power output of the engine decreases.
      1) This is true of all engines not equipped with a supercharger or turbocharger.
3. The propeller produces thrust in proportion to the mass of air being accelerated through the rotating blades.
   a. As air density decreases, propeller efficiency decreases.
4. The wings produce lift as a result of the air passing over and under them.
   a. As air density decreases, the lift efficiency of the wing decreases.

B. Conditions Which Affect an Airplane's Takeoff Performance

1. As air density decreases, the takeoff run increases.
   a. If an airplane of given weight and configuration is operated at a higher density altitude, the airplane will still require the same amount of lift to become airborne.
      1) Thus, the airplane will take off at the same indicated airspeed at all density altitudes.
      2) Due to the reduced air density, the true airspeed will be greater.
2. A headwind will shorten the takeoff run and increase the angle of climb.
3. A tailwind will increase the takeoff run and decrease the angle of climb.
   a. Taking off with a tailwind decreases performance significantly.
4. A runway which is muddy, wet, soft, rough, or covered with snow or tall grass has a retarding force and increases the takeoff distance.
5. On takeoff, an upslope runway provides a retarding force which impedes acceleration, resulting in a longer ground run.
   a. Downhill operations will usually shorten the distance.

C. Conditions Which Affect an Airplane's Cruise Performance

1. As air density decreases (e.g., an increase in altitude), available engine power decreases.
   a. However, because drag also decreases, less thrust is required to maintain a given airspeed.
   b. Thus, fuel consumption decreases as altitude increases.
2. A headwind will decrease groundspeed and consequently increase the total amount of fuel consumed for that flight.
   a. A tailwind will increase the groundspeed and conserve fuel.

D. Conditions Which Affect an Airplane's Landing Performance

1. As air density decreases, required landing distance increases.
   a. However, indicated airspeed for landing is the same for an airplane at all altitudes.
2. A headwind will require a steeper approach angle and shorten the landing roll.
3. A tailwind will require a shallower approach angle and increase the landing roll.
   a. Landing with a tailwind decreases performance significantly.
4. A runway which is muddy, wet, soft, rough, or covered with snow or tall grass may decrease the landing roll.
   a. However, ice or snow covering the surface will affect braking action and increase the landing roll considerably.
5. Landing uphill usually results in a shorter landing roll.
   a. Downhill operations will usually increase the landing roll.

## 3.2 STANDARD ATMOSPHERE

A. The standard atmosphere is a hypothetical atmosphere based on certain average conditions worldwide. These include

1. A sea-level surface temperature of 15°C (59°F).

2. A sea-level surface pressure of 29.92 in. Hg (1013.2 mb).
   a. Hg is the abbreviation for mercury.
   b. Mb is the abbreviation for millibars.
3. Relative humidity of 0%.
4. A standard temperature lapse rate (i.e., a decrease in temperature as altitude increases) of approximately 2°C per 1,000 ft.
5. A standard pressure lapse rate (i.e., a decrease in pressure as altitude increases) of approximately 1" Hg per 1,000 ft.
6. A standard decrease in density as altitude increases.

B. This standard atmosphere provides a basis from which to determine air density and thus to evaluate airplane performance in actual atmospheric conditions.
   1. The performance charts prepared by airplane manufacturers are based on a standard atmosphere and analytically expanded for various parameters (e.g., weight, altitude, temperature, etc.). They appear in the airplane's *POH*.

## 3.3 PRESSURE ALTITUDE

A. In the standard atmosphere, sea-level surface pressure is 29.92 in. Hg (1013.2 mb).
   1. Pressure falls at a fixed rate upward through this hypothetical atmosphere.
   2. Thus, in the standard atmosphere, any given pressure can be found at only one specific altitude.

B. Pressure altitude is the altitude in the standard atmosphere where the pressure is the same as where you are in the actual atmosphere.

C. Pressure altitude can be determined by either of two methods:
   1. By setting the barometric scale of the altimeter to 29.92 and reading the indicated altitude, or
   2. By applying a correction factor to the elevation according to the reported altimeter setting as shown in the right side of the figure on page 65.

## 3.4 DENSITY ALTITUDE

A. Density altitude is a measurement of the density of the air.
   1. Simply put, it is the altitude in the standard atmosphere where air density is the same as where you are in the actual atmosphere.
      a. As air density decreases, density altitude is said to increase.
   2. Density altitude is used in determining an airplane's performance capabilities.

B. Because of the inescapable influence density altitude has on an airplane and engine performance, it is important for every pilot to understand its effects. Air density is affected by pressure, temperature, and humidity.
   1. The density of air is directly proportional to pressure.
      a. Since air is a gas, it can be compressed or expanded.
         1) When air is compressed (i.e., increase in pressure), a greater amount of air occupies a given volume. Thus, the density of air is increased.
         2) When pressure is decreased on a given volume of air, the air expands and occupies a greater space, thus the density of air is decreased.

2. The density of air varies inversely with temperature.
   a. As the temperature of the air increases, the air expands, occupying more volume.
      1) Thus, a given volume holds less air, and air density is decreased.
   b. As air temperature decreases, the air contracts, and density is increased.
3. Humidity is the amount of water vapor in the air and is not generally considered a major factor in density altitude computation because the effect of humidity is related more to engine power than to aerodynamic efficiency.
   a. Water vapor is lighter than air, thus moist air is lighter (i.e., less dense) than dry air.
      1) Warm, moist air is less dense (i.e., has a higher density altitude) than cold, dry air.
   b. Humidity affects engine power because the water vapor uses airspace that is available for vaporized fuel.
      1) As humidity increases, less air enters the cylinders and causes a slight increase in density altitude.
   c. Aircraft performance charts do not account for variations in humidity.
      1) If high humidity does exist, it is wise to add 10% to your computed takeoff distance and anticipate a reduced climb rate.
4. In the atmosphere, both temperature and pressure decrease with altitude, and have conflicting effects on density. However, the fairly rapid drop in pressure as altitude is increased usually has a dominating effect over the decrease in temperature.
   a. Thus, we can expect the air density to decrease with altitude.

C. At power settings of less than 75%, or at density altitudes above 5,000 ft., it is essential that normally aspirated engines be leaned for maximum power on takeoff, unless equipped with an automatic altitude mixture control.
1. The excessively rich mixture adds another detriment to overall performance.
2. Turbocharged engines need not be leaned for takeoff in high density altitude conditions because they are capable of producing manifold pressure equal to or higher than sea level pressure.
3. At airports of higher elevations, such as those in the western U.S., high temperatures sometimes have such an effect on density altitude that safe operations may be impossible.
   a. Even at lower elevations with excessively high temperature or humidity, airplane performance can become marginal, and it may be necessary to reduce the airplane's weight for safe operations.

D. Density altitude is determined by finding the pressure altitude (indicated altitude when the airplane's altimeter is set to 29.92) and adjusting for the temperature.
1. This adjustment is made using a density altitude chart or your flight computer.
2. The flight computer calculation is shown in Chapter 12, Flight Computers.

E. Density Altitude Chart
1. Adjust the airport elevation to pressure altitude based upon the actual altimeter setting in relation to the standard altimeter setting of 29.92.
   a. On the next chart, the correction in feet is provided for different altimeter settings.
2. Plot the intersection of the actual air temperature (listed on the horizontal axis of the chart) with the pressure altitude (indicated by the diagonal lines).
3. Move straight across to the vertical column. This is the density altitude.

4. EXAMPLE: Outside air temperature 90°F
Altimeter setting 30.20" Hg
Airport elevation 4,725 ft.

   a. Note that the altimeter setting of 30.20 requires a –257-ft. correction factor.
   b. Subtract 257 ft. from field elevation of 4,725 ft. to obtain pressure altitude of 4,468 ft.
   c. Locate 90°F on the bottom axis of the chart and move up vertically to intersect the diagonal pressure altitude line of 4,468 ft.
   d. Move horizontally to the left axis of the chart to obtain the density altitude of 7,400 ft.

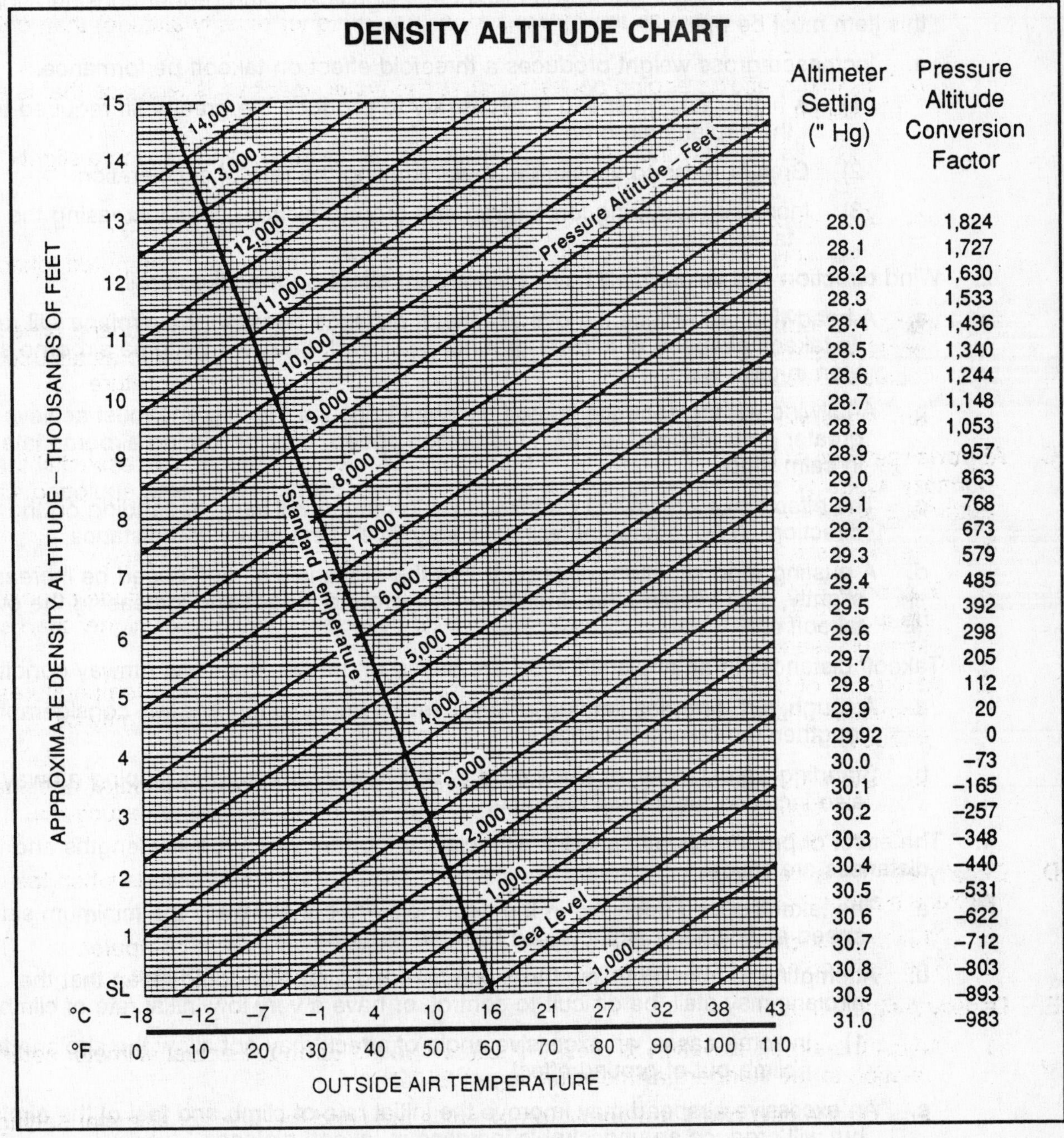


| Altimeter Setting (" Hg) | Pressure Altitude Conversion Factor |
|---|---|
| 28.0 | 1,824 |
| 28.1 | 1,727 |
| 28.2 | 1,630 |
| 28.3 | 1,533 |
| 28.4 | 1,436 |
| 28.5 | 1,340 |
| 28.6 | 1,244 |
| 28.7 | 1,148 |
| 28.8 | 1,053 |
| 28.9 | 957 |
| 29.0 | 863 |
| 29.1 | 768 |
| 29.2 | 673 |
| 29.3 | 579 |
| 29.4 | 485 |
| 29.5 | 392 |
| 29.6 | 298 |
| 29.7 | 205 |
| 29.8 | 112 |
| 29.9 | 20 |
| 29.92 | 0 |
| 30.0 | –73 |
| 30.1 | –165 |
| 30.2 | –257 |
| 30.3 | –348 |
| 30.4 | –440 |
| 30.5 | –531 |
| 30.6 | –622 |
| 30.7 | –712 |
| 30.8 | –803 |
| 30.9 | –893 |
| 31.0 | –983 |

5. Some performance charts may only require pressure altitude and temperature, thus you will not use a density altitude chart.

## 3.5 TAKEOFF PERFORMANCE

A. The minimum takeoff distance is of primary interest in the operation of any airplane because it defines the runway requirements.

1. The minimum takeoff distance is obtained by taking off at the minimum safe speed that allows sufficient margin above stall and provides satisfactory control and initial rate of climb. This speed is found in the airplane's *POH*.

B. To obtain minimum takeoff distance, the forces which act on the airplane must provide the maximum acceleration during the takeoff roll. Any item that alters the takeoff speed or acceleration rate during the takeoff roll will affect the takeoff distance.

1. The effect of gross weight on takeoff distance is significant, and proper consideration of this item must be made.
   a. Increased gross weight produces a threefold effect on takeoff performance.
      1) A higher takeoff speed is necessary to produce the greater lift required to get the airplane airborne.
      2) Greater mass to accelerate, thus reducing the rate of acceleration.
      3) Increased retarding force (drag and ground friction), thus increasing the takeoff distance.
2. Wind direction and velocity will have a significant effect on the takeoff roll.
   a. A headwind will reduce the overall takeoff distance because the airplane will reach its takeoff airspeed at a lower groundspeed and, thus, will become airborne sooner than in calm wind.
   b. A tailwind will increase the takeoff distance because the airplane must achieve a greater groundspeed to attain the takeoff speed, thus becoming airborne later than in calm wind.
   c. The effects of a crosswind on takeoff performance will vary, depending on the wind direction. A 90° crosswind will have very little effect on takeoff distance.
   d. A gusting wind situation will require that the airplane's takeoff speed be increased slightly, thus keeping the airplane on the ground longer and increasing the overall takeoff roll.
3. Takeoff distances in an airplane's *POH* are based on paved, dry, level runway conditions.
   a. A rough, dirt, or grass landing strip will retard acceleration and will considerably lengthen the takeoff distance.
   b. Standing water, snow, or slush on a paved runway or an uphill-sloping runway will also increase the takeoff distance.
4. The effect of proper takeoff speed is especially important when runway lengths and takeoff distances are critical.
   a. The takeoff speed specified in the airplane's *POH* is generally the minimum safe speed at which the airplane can become airborne.
   b. Attempting to take off below the recommended airspeed could mean that the airplane may stall, be difficult to control, or have a very low initial rate of climb.
      1) In some cases, an excessive angle of attack may not allow the airplane to climb out of ground effect.
   c. An excessive airspeed may improve the initial rate of climb and feel of the airplane, but will produce an undesirable increase in takeoff distance.

5. An increase in density altitude has the following effects on takeoff performance.
   a. Decreased thrust and reduced accelerating force
      1) Non-turbocharged engines have less available power.
      2) Propeller efficiency is decreased.
   b. Greater takeoff speed
      1) A higher true airspeed is required to provide sufficient lift for takeoff;
      2) But *indicated* airspeed will remain the same regardless of density altitude.
   c. Accurate determination of pressure altitude (not field elevation) and temperature is essential for predicting takeoff performance.
6. The most critical conditions of takeoff performance are the result of some combination of high gross weight, altitude, temperature, and unfavorable wind.

C. Takeoff performance data can normally be found in Section 5, Performance, in the airplane's *POH*. These may be presented in either a graph or a chart.

1. Takeoff performance graphs are either presented in terms of density altitude (as in the following example) or in terms of pressure altitude and temperature.
   a. First, compute the density altitude.
   b. Second, find the density altitude on the left-hand side of the graph. Move horizontally to the right until you intersect the ground run line or the 50-ft. barrier line as appropriate.
   c. From either point of intersection, drop vertically to the bottom of the graph to determine the takeoff distance in feet for your airplane.
   d. EXAMPLE: At 1,000-ft. density altitude the ground run would be just over 750 ft. and it would require just over 1,750 ft. to clear a 50-ft. obstacle with flaps at 25° and a paved, level, and dry runway.

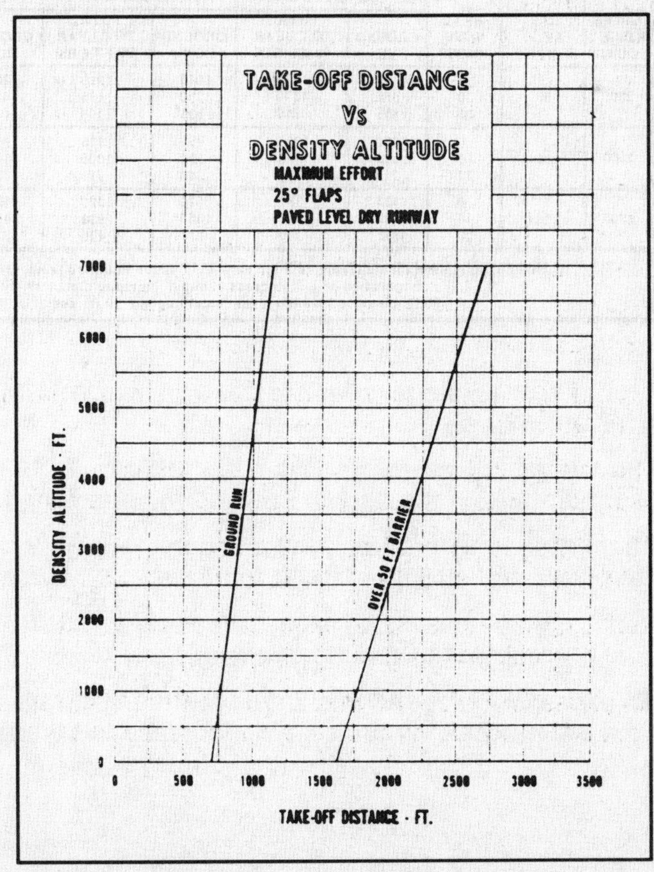

2. Takeoff performance charts can often incorporate more variables, including headwind, gross weight, altitude, and temperature.
   a. Takeoff performance is affected by the airplane's gross weight. The chart below gives the data for gross weight of 1,700, 2,000, and 2,300 lb. If you are carrying a gross weight between these figures, you must interpolate.
   b. Headwind alternatives are 0, 10, and 20 kt. If actual headwind is between these figures, you must interpolate.
   c. The altitudes given are sea level, 2,500, 5,000, and 7,500 ft. MSL. You must interpolate for altitudes between these numbers.
   d. Separate distances are given for the ground run and to clear a 50-ft. obstacle.
   e. The notes to the chart indicate that you must
      1) Increase the distance 10% for each 25°F above standard temperature at any altitude. Temperatures given on the chart are standard.
      2) Increase distance (for either a ground run or to clear an obstacle) by 7% of the "50-ft. obstacle" distance if using a dry grass runway rather than a paved runway.
   f. EXAMPLE: If your gross weight is 2,150 lb. with no headwind at 5,000 ft. and 41°F, your ground run on a paved runway with no flaps would be 1,080 ft. This is halfway between the 905 ft. at 2,000 lb. and 1,255 ft. at 2,300 lb.
      1) If the temperature were 66°F, you would have to add 10%, or 108 ft. Thus, your total ground run would be 1,188 ft.

## TAKE-OFF DATA

**TAKE-OFF DISTANCE FROM HARD SURFACE RUNWAY WITH FLAPS UP**

| GROSS WEIGHT POUNDS | IAS AT 50' MPH | HEAD WIND KNOTS | AT SEA LEVEL & 59° | | AT 2500 FT. & 50°F | | AT 5000 FT. & 41°F | | AT 7500 FT. & 32°F | |
|---|---|---|---|---|---|---|---|---|---|---|
| | | | GROUND RUN | TOTAL TO CLEAR 50 FT OBS | GROUND RUN | TOTAL TO CLEAR 50 FT OBS | GROUND RUN | TOTAL TO CLEAR 50 FT OBS | GROUND RUN | TOTAL TO CLEAR 50 FT OBS |
| 2300 | 68 | 0 | 865 | 1525 | 1040 | 1910 | 1255 | 2480 | 1565 | 3855 |
| | | 10 | 615 | 1170 | 750 | 1485 | 920 | 1955 | 1160 | 3110 |
| | | 20 | 405 | 850 | 505 | 1100 | 630 | 1480 | 810 | 2425 |
| 2000 | 63 | 0 | 630 | 1095 | 755 | 1325 | 905 | 1625 | 1120 | 2155 |
| | | 10 | 435 | 820 | 530 | 1005 | 645 | 1250 | 810 | 1685 |
| | | 20 | 275 | 580 | 340 | 720 | 425 | 910 | 595 | 1255 |
| 1700 | 58 | 0 | 435 | 780 | 520 | 920 | 625 | 1095 | 765 | 1370 |
| | | 10 | 290 | 570 | 355 | 680 | 430 | 820 | 535 | 1040 |
| | | 20 | 175 | 385 | 215 | 470 | 270 | 575 | 345 | 745 |

NOTES: 1. Increase distance 10% for each 25°F above standard temperature for particular altitude.
2. For operation on a dry, grass runway, increase distances (both "ground run" and "total to clear 50 ft. obstacle") by 7% of the "total to clear 50 ft. obstacle" figure.

## 3.6 CLIMB PERFORMANCE

A. Climb performance depends upon the airplane's reserve power or thrust. Reserve power is the available power over and above that required to maintain level flight at a given airspeed.

1. If an airplane has an engine which produces 200 total available horsepower (HP) and the airplane requires only 130 HP at a certain level flight airspeed, the power available for climb is 70 HP.

B. Two airspeeds important to climb performance are the *best angle-of-climb speed* ($V_X$), and the *best rate-of-climb speed* ($V_Y$)

1. $V_X$ provides the greatest gain in altitude for distance traveled over the ground and is used to clear obstacles immediately after takeoff on short-length runways.
2. $V_Y$ provides the greatest gain in altitude over a period of time and is used during a normal takeoff or after clearing all obstacles during departure when $V_X$ was used.
3. These airspeeds are found in the airplane's *POH*.

C. The climb performance of an airplane is affected by certain variables. Climb performance would be most critical with high gross weight, at high altitude, in obstructed takeoff areas, or during malfunction of an engine.

1. The conditions of the airplane's maximum climb angle or maximum climb rate occur at specific speeds, and variations in speed will produce variations in climb performance.
2. Weight has a very pronounced effect on airplane performance.
   a. If weight is added to the airplane, it must fly at a higher angle of attack to maintain a given altitude and speed.
      1) This increases the induced drag of the wings, as well as the parasite drag of the airplane.
         a) Additional power is needed to overcome increased drag, which means that less reserve power is available for climbing.
   b. Generally, an increase in weight will reduce the maximum rate of climb and the airplane must be operated at a higher climb speed to achieve the smaller maximum climb rate.
3. An increase in altitude will also increase the power required and decrease the power available. Thus, altitude greatly affects climb performance.
   a. The speeds for maximum rate of climb and maximum angle of climb vary with altitude.
      1) As altitude increases, the speed for maximum angle of climb also increases.
      2) As altitude increases, the speed for maximum rate of climb decreases.
      3) As altitude is increased, these various speeds finally converge at the absolute ceiling of the airplane.
   b. At the absolute ceiling, there is no excess of power and only one speed will allow steady level flight. Thus, the rate of climb is zero.
   c. The service ceiling is the altitude at which the airplane is unable to climb at a rate of 100 feet per minute (fpm).

D. Climb performance charts are found in the airplane's *POH*.
   1. This chart provides information at various gross weights, altitudes, and temperatures. It states the indicated airspeed, the rate of climb (fpm), and gallons of fuel used.
   2. In the example chart below, the gross weights of 1,700, 2,000, or 2,300 lb. are given on the left. Interpolate as necessary.
   3. Altitudes of sea level, 5,000, 10,000, or 15,000 ft. are given. Interpolate as necessary.
   4. The notes give important information. In the example chart, Note 3 says to decrease rate of climb by 20 fpm for each 10°F above the standard temperatures.
   5. EXAMPLE: With a gross weight of 2,000 lb. and pressure altitude of 5,000 ft. with a temperature of 61°F, the rate of climb would be 570 fpm. Note that the 610-fpm rate of climb must be reduced by 40 fpm since the temperature of 61°F is 20°F above the standard temperature of 41°F.

**MAXIMUM RATE-OF-CLIMB DATA**

| | AT SEA LEVEL & 59°F | | | AT 5000 FT. & 41°F | | | AT 10,000 FT. & 23°F | | | AT 15,000 FT. & 5°F | | |
|---|---|---|---|---|---|---|---|---|---|---|---|---|
| GROSS WEIGHT POUNDS | IAS MPH | RATE OF CLIMB FT/MIN | GAL. OF FUEL USED | IAS MPH | RATE OF CLIMB FT/MIN | FROM S.L. FUEL USED | IAS MPH | RATE OF CLIMB FT/MIN | FROM S.L. FUEL USED | IAS MPH | RATE OF CLIMB FT/MIN | FROM S.L. FUEL USED |
| 2300 | 82 | 645 | 1.0 | 81 | 435 | 2.6 | 79 | 230 | 4.8 | 78 | 22 | 11.5 |
| 2000 | 79 | 840 | 1.0 | 79 | 610 | 2.2 | 76 | 380 | 3.6 | 75 | 155 | 6.3 |
| 1700 | 77 | 1085 | 1.0 | 76 | 825 | 1.9 | 73 | 570 | 2.9 | 72 | 315 | 4.4 |

NOTES: 1. Flaps up, full throttle, mixture leaned for smooth operation above 3000 ft.
2. Fuel used includes warm up and take-off allowance.
3. For hot weather, decrease rate of climb 20 ft./min. for each 10°F above standard day temperature for particular altitude.

## 3.7 CRUISE AND RANGE PERFORMANCE

A. The ability of an airplane to convert fuel energy into flying distance is one of the most important items of airplane performance. This may be expressed in either range or endurance.
   1. If maximum range (i.e., flying distance) is desired, the flight condition must provide a maximum of speed versus fuel flow.
   2. If maximum endurance (i.e., flying time) is desired, the flight condition must provide a minimum of fuel flow.

B. Cruise and range performance charts are found in the airplane's *POH*. These charts are normally based upon density altitude, the engine RPM setting, and fuel capacity.
   1. Charts in the *POH* will usually provide the following information:
      a. The percentage of brake horsepower (% of power)
      b. True airspeed
      c. Range in miles
      d. Endurance in time (hours)
   2. Example of one type of cruise performance chart (see opposite page).
      a. Given the first two columns (altitude and RPM), the last five columns are the result.
      b. EXAMPLE: Given an altitude of 6,500 ft. and 2,500 RPM, you are using 66% power, will achieve a true airspeed of 126 mph, use 7.5 GPH, have an endurance of 4.7 hr., and have a range of 587 SM assuming no wind, standard conditions, etc.

1) As in all performance charts, you must read the conditions and notes that apply (e.g., Note 4 refers to nonstandard temperature conditions).

**CRUISE & RANGE PERFORMANCE**

GROSS WEIGHT-2200 LBS.
STANDARD CONDITIONS
ZERO WIND
LEAN MIXTURE

| ALTITUDE | RPM | PERCENT POWER | TRUE AIR SPEED—MPH | GALLONS / HOUR | ENDURANCE HOURS | RANGE MILES |
|---|---|---|---|---|---|---|
| | 2600 | 81 | 136 | 9.3 | 3.9 | 524 |
| | 2500 | 73 | 129 | 8.3 | 4.3 | 555 |
| 2500 | 2400 | 65 | 122 | 7.5 | 4.8 | 586 |
| | 2300 | 58 | 115 | 6.6 | 5.4 | 617 |
| | 2200 | 52 | 108 | 6.0 | 6.0 | 645 |
| | 2600 | 77 | 135 | 8.8 | 4.0 | 539 |
| | 2500 | 69 | 129 | 7.9 | 4.5 | 572 |
| 4500 | 2400 | 62 | 121 | 7.1 | 5.0 | 601 |
| | 2300 | 56 | 113 | 6.4 | 5.5 | 628 |
| | 2200 | 51 | 106 | 5.7 | 6.1 | 646 |
| | 2700 | 81 | 140 | 9.3 | 3.8 | 530 |
| | 2600 | 73 | 134 | 8.3 | 4.2 | 559 |
| 6500 | 2500 | 66 | 126 | 7.5 | 4.7 | 587 |
| | 2400 | 60 | 119 | 6.8 | 5.2 | 611 |
| | 2300 | 54 | 112 | 6.1 | 5.7 | 632 |
| | 2700 | 77 | 139 | 8.8 | 4.0 | 547 |
| | 2600 | 70 | 132 | 7.9 | 4.4 | 575 |
| 8500 | 2500 | 63 | 125 | 7.2 | 4.9 | 598 |
| | 2400 | 57 | 118 | 6.5 | 5.3 | 620 |
| | 2300 | 52 | 109 | 5.9 | 5.8 | 635 |
| | 2700 | 73 | 138 | 8.3 | 4.2 | 569 |
| | 2600 | 66 | 130 | 7.6 | 4.6 | 590 |
| 10500 | 2500 | 60 | 122 | 6.9 | 5.0 | 610 |
| | 2400 | 55 | 115 | 6.3 | 5.4 | 625 |
| | 2300 | 50 | 106 | 5.7 | 5.9 | 631 |

NOTES:

1. Range and endurance data include allowance for take-off and climb.
2. Fuel consumption is for level flight with mixture leaned. See Section III for proper leaning technique. Continuous operations at powers above 75% should be with full rich mixture.
3. Speed performance is without wheel fairings. Add 2 MPH for wheel fairings.
4. For temperatures other than standard, add or subtract 1%power for each 10° F. below or above standard temperature respectively.

## 3.8 GLIDE PERFORMANCE

A. Glide performance is the distance that an airplane will travel with the engine inoperative.

   1. The best glide distance is obtained by gliding at the angle of attack that provides the maximum lift-drag ratio ($L/D_{max}$). This optimal condition is determined for each airplane and the speed at which it occurs at a given gross weight is used as the recommended best glide airspeed for the airplane.

B. The effect of wind is to decrease range when gliding with a headwind component, and to increase it when gliding with a tailwind component.

   1. The endurance (time) of the glide is unaffected by wind.

C. Variations in gross weight do not affect the gliding angle, provided the proper airspeed is used for each gross weight. Airplane manufacturers generally use a representative operational condition to determine the best glide airspeed.

1. The fully loaded airplane will sink faster but at a greater forward speed, and although it will reach the ground much quicker, it will have traveled exactly the same distance as the lighter airplane.

    a. The endurance of the glide is less for a heavier airplane than a lighter one.

D. Glide performance charts can be found in some *POHs*. Note the stated conditions under which the chart values are determined and how various conditions can change these values.

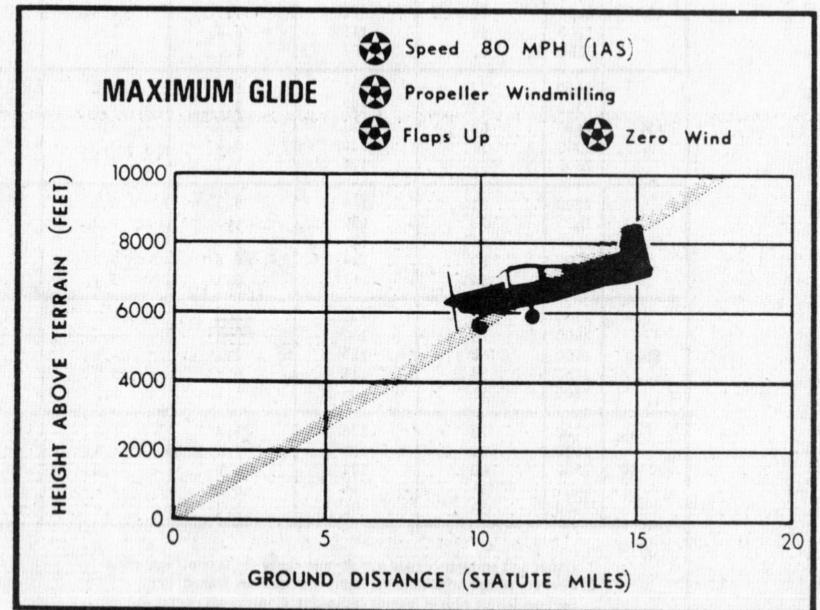


1. The chart above illustrates a glide ratio of 52,800/6,000 = 8.8 to 1.0 because the airplane will glide 10 SM from 6,000 ft. (in no wind, flaps up, etc.). In other words, when the airplane is at 6,000 ft., the airplane can glide for 10 SM (5,280 ft. in a SM times 10 SM is 52,800 ft.).

## 3.9 CROSSWIND PERFORMANCE

A. Takeoffs and landings in certain crosswind conditions are inadvisable or even dangerous. If the crosswind is strong enough that the airplane is incapable of preventing a sideways drift, a hazardous landing condition may result.

1. Always consider the takeoff or landing capabilities with respect to the reported surface wind conditions and the available landing directions.
2. The airplane's *POH* indicates the maximum crosswind component capability of the airplane.
3. Some *POHs* have a chart so the pilot can determine the crosswind component.

B. Many airplanes have an upper limit to the amount of direct crosswind in which they can land (usually about 20% of stall speed). Crosswinds of less than 90° are converted into a 90° component on graphs. Variables on crosswind component graphs are

1. Angle between wind and runway
2. Knots of total wind velocity

C. Refer to the example crosswind component graph below.

1. Note the example on the graph of a 40-kt. wind at a 30° angle.
2. Find the 30° wind angle line (A). This is the angle between the wind direction and runway direction, e.g., runway 16 and wind from 190°.
3. Find the 40-kt. wind velocity arc. Note the intersection of the wind arc and the 30° angle line (B).

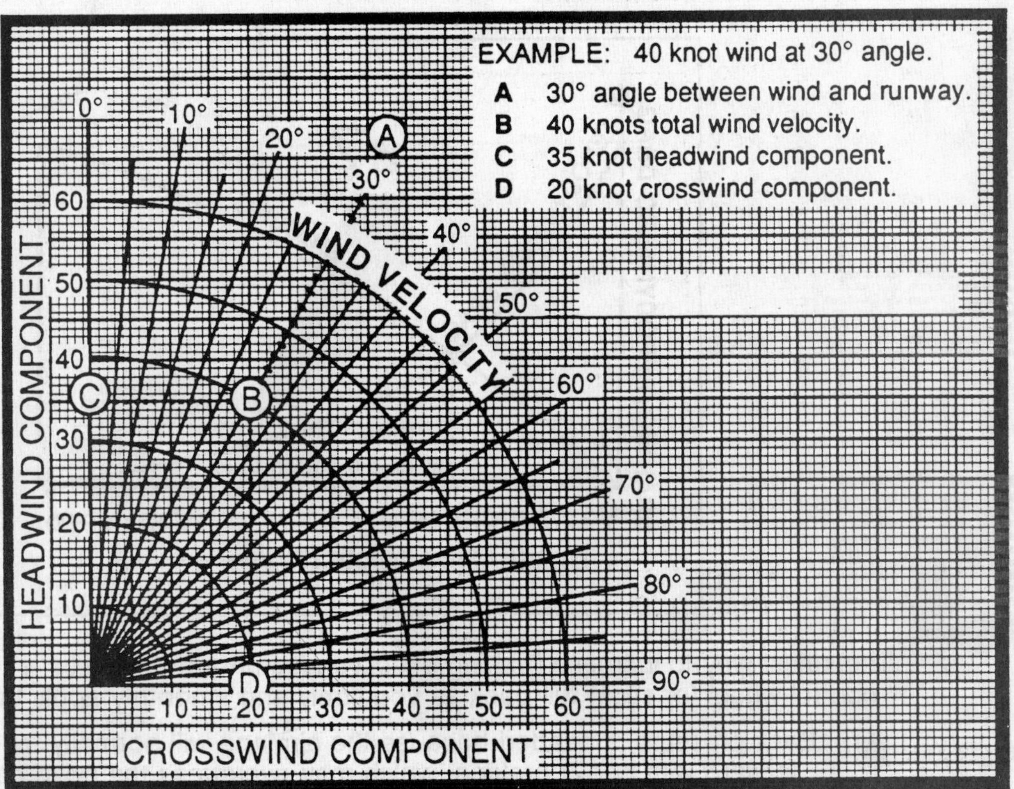


4. Drop straight down from B to determine the crosswind component of 20 kt. (D). Landing in this situation is like having a direct crosswind of 20 kt.
5. Back at B, move horizontally to the left to determine the headwind component of 35 kt. (C). Landing in this situation is like having a headwind of 35 kt.

## 3.10 LANDING PERFORMANCE

A. The minimum landing distance is obtained by landing at the minimum safe speed that allows sufficient margin above the stall speed and provides satisfactory control and capability for a go-around.

1. Generally, the landing speed is some fixed percentage of the stall speed or minimum control speed for the airplane in the landing configuration. This airspeed is found in the airplane's *POH*.
2. To obtain minimum landing distance at the specified landing speed, the forces which act on the airplane must provide maximum deceleration during the landing roll.
   a. At touchdown, the airplane is still producing lift and the application of brakes is not effective.
   b. For most airplanes, aerodynamic drag is the single biggest factor in slowing the airplane in the first 25% of its speed decay.

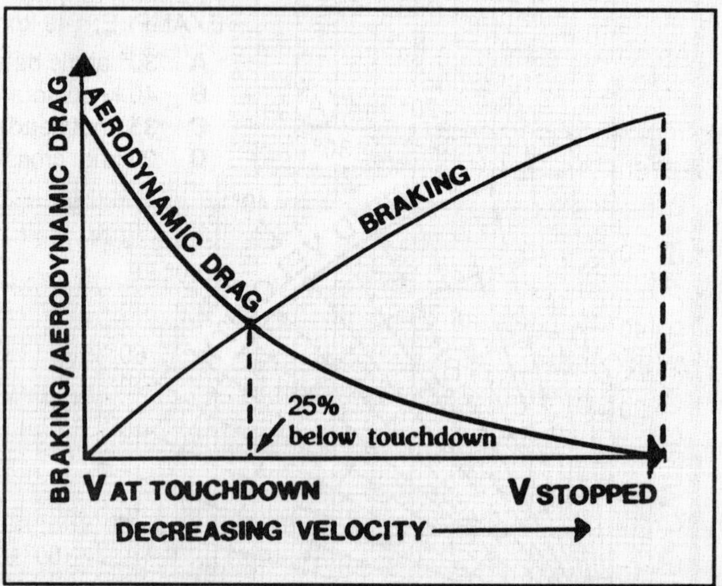


   c. The safest way to increase braking effectiveness on a dry surface is to hold the control wheel (or stick) full back as you firmly and smoothly apply brakes.
      1) Back pressure is needed because the airplane will normally tend to lean forward with heavy braking, which may overstress the nose gear.

B. In addition to proper technique, many variables affect the landing performance of an airplane. Any item which alters the landing speed or deceleration rate during the landing roll will affect the landing distance.

1. The effect of gross weight is one of the principal items determining the landing distance.
   a. An increase in gross weight will require a greater landing speed to support the airplane.
   b. This requires the brakes to absorb more energy to stop the airplane, which will increase the landing distance.

2. The effect of wind must be considered in predicting landing performance. Since the airplane will land at a particular airspeed independent of the wind, the principal effect of wind on landing distance is due to the change in groundspeed at which the airplane touches down.
   a. A headwind will reduce the landing distance because the groundspeed at touchdown is reduced.
   b. A tailwind will increase the landing distance because the groundspeed at touchdown is increased.
3. Density altitude will affect the landing performance. An increase in density altitude will increase the touchdown groundspeed but will not alter the net retarding force.
   a. The airplane at altitude will land at the same indicated airspeed, but because of the reduced density, the true airspeed (TAS) will be greater.
      1) Thus, the higher TAS increases the touchdown groundspeed, which increases the landing distance.
   b. As a rule of thumb, the increase in landing distance is approximately 3.5% for each 1,000 ft. of altitude.
4. The effect of proper landing speed is important when runway lengths and landing distances are critical.
   a. The approach speeds specified in the airplane's *POH* are normally the minimum safe speeds at which the airplane can be flown.
      1) Any attempt to approach the runway below the specified speed may mean that the airplane may stall, be difficult to control, or develop high rates of descent.
   b. A higher-than-recommended speed at landing will improve the controllability somewhat (especially in crosswinds), but will cause an increase in landing distance.
      1) The airplane may touch down farther down the runway, and require more distance to stop.
5. The runway condition and slope will also affect the landing distance.
   a. A wet, icy, or snow-covered runway (concrete or grass) will not allow good braking. This will increase the landing distance.
      1) All braking effectiveness may be lost if the airplane's tires are hydroplaning, which is caused by a thin layer of water that separates the tires from the runway.
   b. A downsloping runway will increase the landing distance, because the touchdown may be a little farther down the runway and the braking is not as effective going downhill as on a level or upsloping runway.
6. The most critical conditions of landing performance are the result of some combination of high gross weight, high density altitude, and unfavorable wind.
   a. These conditions produce the greatest landing distance and provide critical levels of energy dissipation required of the brakes.
   b. In all cases, it is necessary to make an accurate prediction of minimum landing distance to compare with the available runway.

C. Landing distance graphs or tables are found in the airplane's *POH*. Most assume a dry, paved, level runway surface. If these do not exist, some charts will have correction factors. For those that do not, note that the actual landing performance will not match the values listed in the performance chart.

1. The data on the chart are based on the listed associated conditions, i.e., power, flaps, gear, runway, weight, and approach speed.
2. You need to distinguish between distances for clearing a 50-ft. obstacle and no 50-ft. obstacle at the end of the runway.
   a. Ground roll is the term for landing distance given no 50-ft. obstacle.
3. Example landing distances chart

**NORMAL LANDING DISTANCES**

| ASSOCIATED CONDITIONS | |
|---|---|
| POWER | OFF |
| FLAPS | 35° |
| GEAR | DOWN |
| RUNWAY | PAVED,LEVEL, DRY SURFACE |
| WEIGHT | 2750 POUNDS |
| APPROACH SPEED | 85 MPH/74 KTS IAS |

NOTES:

1. GROUND ROLL IS APPROXIMATELY 45% OF TOTAL DISTANCE OVER 50 FT. OBSTACLE
2. FOR EACH 100 LBS. BELOW 2750 LBS. REDUCE TABULATED DISTANCE BY 3% AND APPROACH SPEED BY 1 MPH.

| WIND COMPONENT DOWN RUNWAY | SEA LEVEL | | 2000 FT | | 4000 FT | | 6000 FT | | 8000 FT | |
|---|---|---|---|---|---|---|---|---|---|---|
| KNOTS | OAT °F | TOTAL OVER 50 FT OBSTACLE FEET | OAT °F | TOTAL OVER 50 FT OBSTACLE FEET | OAT °F | TOTAL OVER 50 FT OBSTACLE FEET | OAT °F | TOTAL OVER 50 FT OBSTACLE FEET | OAT °F | TOTAL OVER 50 FT OBSTACLE FEET |
| | 23 | 1578 | 16 | 1651 | 9 | 1732 | 2 | 1820 | -6 | 1916 |
| | 41 | 1624 | 34 | 1701 | 27 | 1787 | 20 | 1880 | 13 | 1983 |
| 0 | 59 | 1670 | 52 | 1752 | 45 | 1842 | 38 | 1942 | 31 | 2050 |
| | 77 | 1717 | 70 | 1804 | 63 | 1899 | 56 | 2004 | 49 | 2118 |
| | 95 | 1764 | 88 | 1856 | 81 | 1956 | 74 | 2066 | 66 | 2187 |
| | 23 | 1329 | 16 | 1397 | 9 | 1472 | 2 | 1555 | -6 | 1644 |
| | 41 | 1372 | 34 | 1444 | 27 | 1524 | 20 | 1611 | 13 | 1707 |
| 15 | 59 | 1414 | 52 | 1491 | 45 | 1575 | 38 | 1668 | 31 | 1770 |
| | 77 | 1458 | 70 | 1540 | 63 | 1626 | 56 | 1727 | 49 | 1833 |
| | 95 | 1502 | 88 | 1588 | 81 | 1682 | 74 | 1784 | 66 | 1898 |
| | 23 | 1079 | 16 | 1142 | 9 | 1212 | 2 | 1289 | 6 | 1372 |
| | 41 | 1119 | 34 | 1186 | 27 | 1260 | 20 | 1341 | 13 | 1430 |
| 30 | 59 | 1158 | 52 | 1230 | 45 | 1308 | 38 | 1395 | 31 | 1489 |
| | 77 | 1199 | 70 | 1275 | 63 | 1357 | 56 | 1449 | 49 | 1548 |
| | 95 | 1240 | 88 | 1320 | 81 | 1407 | 74 | 1502 | 66 | 1608 |

   a. Headwind alternatives are 0, 15, and 30 kt. If the actual headwind is between these figures, you must interpolate.
   b. The altitudes given are sea level, 2,000, 4,000, 6,000, and 8,000 ft. MSL. If your altitude is between these figures, you must interpolate.
   c. For each headwind and altitude, five outside air temperatures are given. You must interpolate if the current temperature is between these figures.
   d. Ground roll is approximately 45% of the total distance over a 50-ft. obstacle (see Note 1 on the Normal Landing Distances chart).
   e. EXAMPLE: Given a weight of 2,750 lb., a 15-kt. headwind at 2,000 ft., and 52°F, the landing distance over a 50-ft. obstacle would be 1,491 ft. Ground roll would be 671 ft. (45% x 1,491 ft.).

# CHAPTER FOUR
# AIRPLANE INSTRUMENTS, ENGINES, AND SYSTEMS



Chapter 2, Introduction to Airplanes and Aerodynamics, explained the basic airframe and flight control surfaces. This chapter explains the airplane's systems in further detail.

## 4.1 PITOT-STATIC SYSTEM

A. The pitot-static system provides the source of air pressure for operation of the

1. Altimeter.
2. Vertical speed indicator.
3. Airspeed indicator.

B. The two major parts of the pitot-static system are

1. The impact pressure chamber and lines,
2. The static pressure chamber and lines.

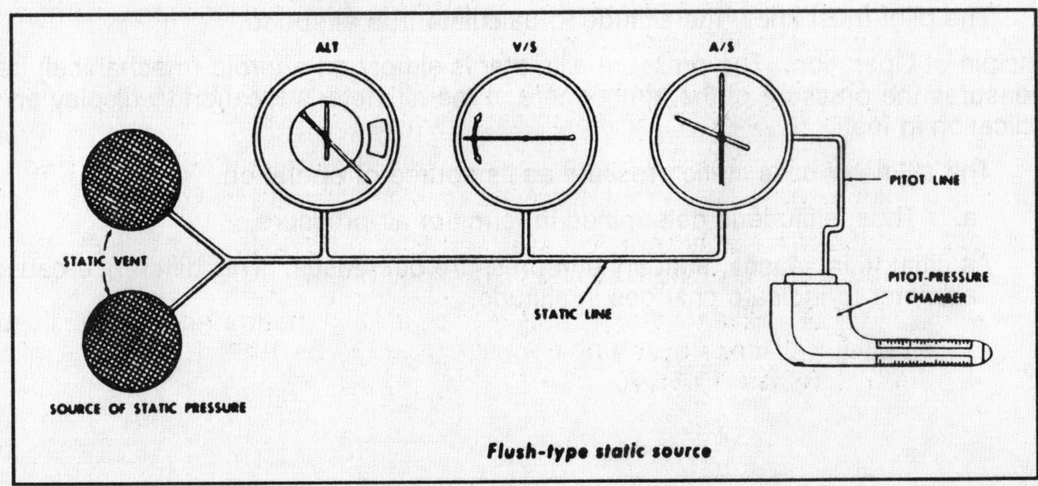

*Flush-type static source*

C. The impact air pressure (air striking the airplane because of its forward motion) is taken from a pitot tube. It is mounted either on the leading edge of the wing or on the nose and is aligned to the relative wind.

   1. The pitot tube provides impact air pressure only to the airspeed indicator.

D. The static pressure (pressure of the still air) is usually taken from the static line attached to a vent or vents mounted flush with the side of the fuselage.

   1. In some older airplanes, the static source is found on the pitot tube.
   2. The static pressure lines provide static air pressure to the altimeter, vertical speed indicator, and airspeed indicator.

E. An alternate source for static pressure is provided in most airplanes in the event the static ports become clogged. This source usually is vented to the inside of the cockpit.

   1. Because of the venturi effect of the flow of air around the cockpit, this alternate static pressure is usually lower than the pressure provided by the normal static air source.
      a. Since the air flowing around the cockpit is accelerated, there is a lower pressure around the cockpit (similar to air flowing over a wing). The air pressure in the cockpit is then lower as well.
   2. Because of this lower pressure, the following differences in the instrument indications usually occur when the alternate static source is used:
      a. The altimeter may indicate a higher-than-actual altitude.
      b. The vertical speed indicator will initially indicate a climb while in level flight, then return to a level indication.
      c. The airspeed indicator will indicate a greater-than-actual airspeed.

## 4.2 ALTIMETER

A. The altimeter (ALT) measures the height of the airplane above a given level. Since it is the only instrument that gives altitude information, the altimeter is one of the most important instruments in the airplane. Knowing the aircraft's altitude is vitally important to the pilot for several reasons:

   1. The pilot must be sure that the airplane is flying high enough to clear terrain or obstructions along the intended route.
   2. To reduce the possibility of a midair collision, the pilot must maintain altitudes in accordance with air traffic rules.
   3. Altitudes are often selected to take advantage of favorable winds and weather conditions.
   4. The pilot must know the altitude to calculate true airspeed.

B. Principle of Operation. The pressure altimeter is simply an aneroid (mechanical) barometer that measures the pressure of the atmosphere at the altimeter's location to display an altitude indication in feet.

   1. The altimeter uses static pressure as its source of operation.
      a. Thus, altitude is determined in terms of air pressure.
   2. As altitude increases, atmospheric pressure decreases. This difference causes the altimeter to indicate changes in altitude.

3. The presentation of altitude varies considerably among different types of altimeters. Some may have only one pointer (or hand), but most have three pointers.
   a. Movement of the aneroid element is transmitted through a gear train to the three pointers which sweep the calibrated dial to indicate the altitude.
      1) The shortest pointer (which is under the intermediate pointer and cannot be seen in the figure below) indicates altitude in tens of thousands of feet.
      2) The intermediate pointer indicates altitude in thousands of feet.
      3) The longest pointer indicates altitude in hundreds of feet. Note that the altimeter shown is subdivided into 20-ft. increments.
   b. The altimeter below indicates an altitude of 100 ft.

4. This indicated altitude is correct only if the International Standard Atmosphere (ISA) conditions exist: a surface temperature of 15°C (59°F) at sea level, a surface pressure of 29.92 in. of mercury (Hg) at sea level, and a lapse rate (decrease of temperature with altitude) of approximately 2°C per 1,000 ft.
   a. Since actual atmospheric pressure continually changes, a means is provided to adjust the altimeter to compensate for these pressure changes.
      1) This is accomplished through a system by which the altimeter setting is set to a barometric scale located on the face of the altimeter.
   b. In the altimeter shown above, the altimeter setting knob is located on the lower-left corner of the instrument and the barometric scale is located between the numerals 2 and 3.
      1) The altimeter above is set to 30.34 (in. of Hg).

C. Effect of Nonstandard Pressure and Temperature

1. If no means were provided for adjusting altimeters to nonstandard pressure, flight could be hazardous.

   a. EXAMPLE: If a flight is made from a HIGH pressure area to a LOW pressure area without adjusting the altimeter, the actual altitude of the airplane will be LOWER than the indicated altitude. When flying from a LOW to a HIGH pressure area without adjusting the altimeter, the actual altitude of the airplane will be HIGHER than the indicated altitude.

   b. These errors can be corrected by setting the altimeter for changes in pressure.

2. Variations from standard air temperature also affect the altimeter. On a warm day, the expanded air is lighter in weight per unit volume than on a cold day. Consequently, the pressure levels are raised.

   a. EXAMPLE: The pressure level at which the altimeter indicates 10,000 ft. will be HIGHER on a warm day than under standard conditions. On a cold day the reverse is true and the 10,000-ft. pressure level will be LOWER.

3. The adjustment made by the pilot to compensate for nonstandard pressures does NOT compensate for nonstandard temperatures.

   a. If terrain or obstacle clearance is a factor in selecting a cruising altitude, particularly at higher altitudes, remember to anticipate that COLDER-THAN-STANDARD TEMPERATURE will place the aircraft LOWER than the altimeter indicates. Therefore, a higher indicated altitude should be used to provide adequate terrain clearance.

4. Memory Aid: From high to low (temperature or pressure) look out below.

D. Setting the Altimeter. To adjust the altimeter for variation in atmospheric pressure, the pressure scale in the altimeter setting window (calibrated in inches of Hg) is adjusted to correspond with the given altimeter setting.

1. Flight Service Stations (FSSs) reporting the altimeter setting take a measurement of their local atmospheric pressure hourly and correct it to sea level pressure. These altimeter settings are applicable only in the vicinity of the reporting station. Therefore, it is necessary to readjust the altimeter setting as the flight progresses.

2. FAA regulations (91.121) concerning altimeter settings:

   a. The cruising altitude of an airplane below 18,000 ft. MSL shall be maintained by reference to an altimeter that is set to the current reported altimeter setting of a station located along the route of flight and within 100 NM of the airplane.

      1) If there is no such station, the current reported altimeter setting of an appropriate available station shall be used.

      2) In an airplane having no radio, the altimeter shall be set to the elevation of the departure airport or an appropriate altimeter setting available before departure.

   b. At or above 18,000 ft. MSL, the altimeter must be set to 29.92.

3. Over high mountainous terrain, certain atmospheric conditions can cause the altimeter to indicate an altitude of 1,000 ft., or more, HIGHER than the actual altitude.

   a. For this reason a generous margin of altitude should be allowed.

   b. In addition, allow for possible downdrafts which are particularly prevalent (and extremely dangerous) if high winds are encountered.

E. Types of Altitude

1. Absolute Altitude -- the vertical distance of an airplane above the terrain. It is expressed as a number of feet AGL (above ground level).
2. True Altitude -- the vertical distance of the aircraft above sea level -- the actual altitude. It is expressed as a number of feet above MSL (mean sea level).
    a. Airport, terrain, and obstacle elevations found on aeronautical charts are given as true altitudes.
3. Indicated Altitude -- the altitude read directly from the altimeter after it is set to the current altimeter setting.
4. Pressure Altitude -- the altitude indicated when the altimeter setting window is adjusted to 29.92.
    a. Pressure altitude is used in computations to determine density altitude, true altitude, true airspeed, etc.
5. Density Altitude -- This is pressure altitude corrected for nonstandard temperature variations.
    a. When the temperature is standard, pressure altitude and density altitude are the same.
    b. If the temperature is above standard, density altitude will be higher than pressure altitude. If the temperature is below standard, density altitude will be lower than pressure altitude.
    c. This is important because density altitude directly affects the airplane's performance as discussed in Chapter 3, Airplane Performance, beginning on page 61.

## 4.3 VERTICAL SPEED INDICATOR

A. The vertical speed indicator (VSI) indicates whether the airplane is climbing, descending, or in level flight. The rate of climb or descent is indicated in feet per minute (fpm). If properly calibrated, the indicator will register zero in level flight.

B. Principle of Operation. Although the vertical speed indicator operates solely from static pressure, it is a differential pressure instrument.

1. The case of the instrument is airtight except for a restricted passage (also known as a calibrated leak) to the static line of the pitot-static system. The sealed case contains a diaphragm with connecting linkage and gearing to the indicator pointer. The diaphragm also receives air from the static line but this is not a restricted passage.
2. When the airplane is on the ground or in level flight, the pressures inside the diaphragm and the instrument case remain the same and the pointer indicates zero.
3. When the airplane climbs or descends, the pressure inside the diaphragm changes immediately. But the restricted passage causes the pressure of the rest of the case to remain higher or lower for a short time. This differential pressure causes the diaphragm to contract or expand. The movement of the diaphragm is indicated on the instrument needle as a climb or descent.

## 4.4 AIRSPEED INDICATOR

A. The airspeed indicator (ASI) indicates the speed at which the airplane is moving through the air mass in which it is flying.

1. Airspeed must not be confused with groundspeed, which is the speed at which the airplane is moving across the ground.
2. The airspeed indicator is a very important instrument because there are maximum and minimum airspeed limitations for the airplane.
    a. FAA regulations and air traffic control use indicated airspeed values on speed limitations.

B. Principle of Operation. The airspeed indicator (ASI) is a sensitive, differential pressure instrument which measures the difference between (1) pitot (impact) pressure and (2) static pressure (the atmospheric pressure at the airplane's flight level).

1. The instrument is contained within a sealed case in which is mounted a diaphragm.
    a. The impact pressure line is connected to one side of the diaphragm.
    b. The other side is vented to the static source.
2. As the airplane moves, impact pressure becomes greater than static pressure, causing the diaphragm to expand.
    a. Expansion or contraction of the diaphragm moves the indicator needle by means of gears and levers.
3. The airspeed dial may be calibrated in miles per hour (mph), knots (kt.), or both.

C. The three kinds of airspeed useful for pilots:

1. Indicated Airspeed (IAS) -- the direct instrument reading obtained from the airspeed indicator, uncorrected for variations in air density or installation and instrument errors.
2. Calibrated Airspeed (CAS) -- indicated airspeed corrected for installation and instrument errors.
    a. Although manufacturers attempt to keep airspeed errors to a minimum, it is not possible to eliminate them along the entire airspeed operating range.
        1) Installation (position) error is caused by the static port(s) sensing erroneous static pressure. The slipstream flow causes disturbances at the static port(s) preventing true static pressure measurement.
        2) Also, at varying angles of attack, the pitot tube does not always point directly into the relative wind, which causes erroneous impact pressure measurement.

b. At certain airspeeds and with certain flap settings, the installation and instrument error may be several knots. This error is generally greatest at low airspeeds.

c. In the cruising and higher airspeed ranges, IAS and CAS are approximately the same.

d. To determine CAS, read the IAS and then correct it by using an airspeed calibration chart or table found in the airplane's *POH*.

1) EXAMPLE: The airspeed calibration table for a Cessna 152 is shown below.

**AIRSPEED CALIBRATION**

CONDITIONS:
Power required for level flight or maximum rated RPM dive.

| | | | | | | | | | | | |
|---|---|---|---|---|---|---|---|---|---|---|---|
| FLAPS UP | | | | | | | | | | | |
| KIAS | 40 | 50 | 60 | 70 | 80 | 90 | 100 | 110 | 120 | 130 | 140 |
| KCAS | 46 | 53 | 60 | 69 | 78 | 88 | 97 | 107 | 117 | 127 | 136 |
| FLAPS 10° | | | | | | | | | | | |
| KIAS | 40 | 50 | 60 | 70 | 80 | 85 | --- | --- | --- | --- | --- |
| KCAS | 44 | 52 | 61 | 70 | 80 | 84 | --- | --- | --- | --- | --- |
| FLAPS 30° | | | | | | | | | | | |
| KIAS | 40 | 50 | 60 | 70 | 80 | 85 | --- | --- | --- | --- | --- |
| KCAS | 43 | 51 | 61 | 71 | 82 | 87 | --- | --- | --- | --- | --- |

3. True Airspeed (TAS) -- calibrated airspeed corrected for density altitude. TAS is the true speed of an airplane through the air.

a. Because air density decreases with an increase in altitude, the airplane must be flown faster at higher altitudes to cause the same pressure difference between the pitot impact and static pressures.

1) Therefore, for a given TAS, IAS decreases as altitude increases.
2) For a given IAS, TAS increases with an altitude increase.

b. A pilot can calculate TAS by using the flight computer. The CAS is corrected for temperature and pressure variation on the airspeed correction scale. This method is explained in Chapter 12, Flight Computers, beginning on page 317.

1) Some airspeed indicators (called true airspeed indicators) have this function built in. With an adjusting knob, pressure altitude is set opposite outside air temperature in the window at the top of the instrument, as in the next illustration.

a) The TAS is then read under the needle. On the airspeed indicator shown below, the IAS is 153 kt. or 176 mph and the TAS is approximately 202 mph.

c. The following rule of thumb may be used to approximate TAS. Add to IAS 2% for each 1,000 ft. of altitude.

1) EXAMPLE: Given IAS is 140 kt. and altitude is 6,000 ft., find TAS.

Solution:

2% x 6 = 12% (.12)
140 x .12 = 16.8
140 + 16.8 = 156.8 kt. (TAS)

D. Most airplanes use a standard color code on airspeed indicators to highlight vital airspeed ranges.

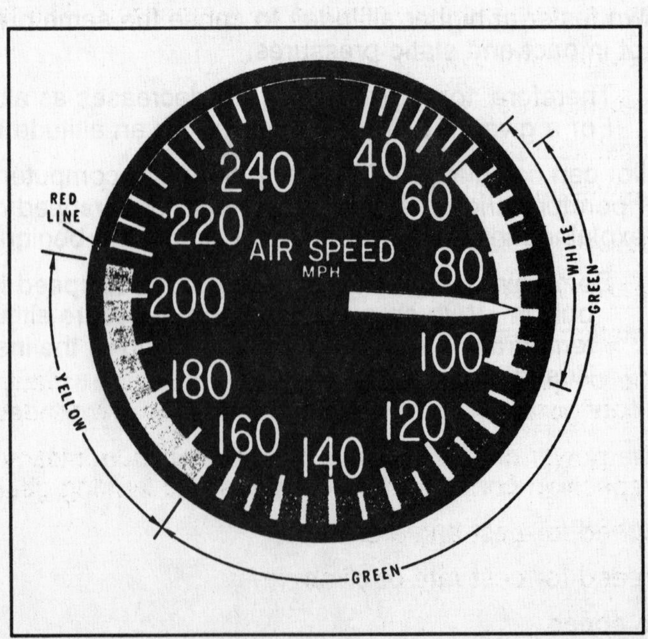

1. Flap operating range (the white arc).
2. Power-off stalling speed with the wing flaps and landing gear in the landing position (the lower limit of the white arc).
3. Maximum flaps extended speed (the upper limit of the white arc). This is the highest airspeed at which the pilot should extend full flaps. Extending the flaps at higher airspeeds could result in severe strain or structural failure.
4. Normal operating range (the green arc).
5. Power-off stalling speed with the wing flaps and landing gear retracted (the lower limit of the green arc).
6. Maximum structural cruising speed (the upper limit of the green arc). This is the maximum speed for normal operation.
7. Caution range (the yellow arc). The pilot should avoid this area unless in smooth air.
8. Never-exceed speed (the red line). This is the maximum speed at which the airplane can be operated safely. This speed should never be exceeded intentionally.

E. Other Airspeed Limitations. Some other important airspeed limitations are not marked on the face of the airspeed indicator. These speeds are generally found on placards in view of the pilot and/or in the airplane's *POH*.

1. Design maneuvering speed ($V_A$) is the maximum speed at which full, abrupt deflection of the controls may be made without overstressing the airplane.
   a. Your airplane should be flown at or below this airspeed when rough air or severe turbulence is expected.
2. Landing gear operating speed ($V_{LO}$) is the maximum speed for extending or retracting the landing gear.
3. Best glide airspeed is the airspeed that provides the best lift/drag ratio angle of attack in a power-off glide. It will allow the pilot to glide the farthest.
4. Best angle of climb speed ($V_X$) is important when a short field takeoff is required to clear an obstacle. It will allow the pilot to gain the most altitude in a given distance.
5. Best rate of climb speed ($V_Y$) is the airspeed that will give the pilot the most altitude in a given period of time.

F. The following are abbreviations for performance speeds. These definitions, as well as the specific speeds for your airplane, need to be memorized. The letter V means velocity.

$V_A$ -- design maneuvering speed

$V_{FE}$ -- maximum flap extended speed

$V_{LE}$ -- maximum landing gear extended speed

$V_{LO}$ -- maximum landing gear operating speed

$V_{NE}$ -- never-exceed speed

$V_{NO}$ -- maximum structural cruising speed

$V_R$ -- rotation speed

$V_{S0}$ -- the power-off stalling speed or the minimum steady flight speed in the landing configuration (i.e., flaps and landing gear extended)

$V_{S1}$ -- the power-off stalling speed or the minimum steady flight speed obtained in a specified configuration (i.e., flaps and landing gear retracted)

$V_X$ -- speed for best angle of climb

$V_Y$ -- speed for best rate of climb

Best glide speed

## 4.5 GYROSCOPIC FLIGHT INSTRUMENTS

A. Several flight instruments contain gyroscopes which are used for their operation. These instruments are the turn indicator, heading indicator, and attitude indicator.

1. Gyroscopic instruments are operated either by a vacuum or an electrical system. In most light airplanes, the vacuum system powers the heading and attitude indicators and the electrical system powers the turn indicator.

B. Vacuum System. The vacuum or suction system spins the gyro by drawing a stream of air against the rotor vanes to spin the rotor at high speeds. This is essentially the same way a water wheel or turbine operates. Normally, a vacuum pump is used to provide the vacuum required to spin the rotors.

1. A typical vacuum system (illustrated below) consists of an engine-driven vacuum pump, an air/oil separator, a vacuum regulator, a relief valve, an air filter, and tubing and manifolds necessary to complete the connections. A suction gauge on the airplane's instrument panel indicates the amount of vacuum in the system.

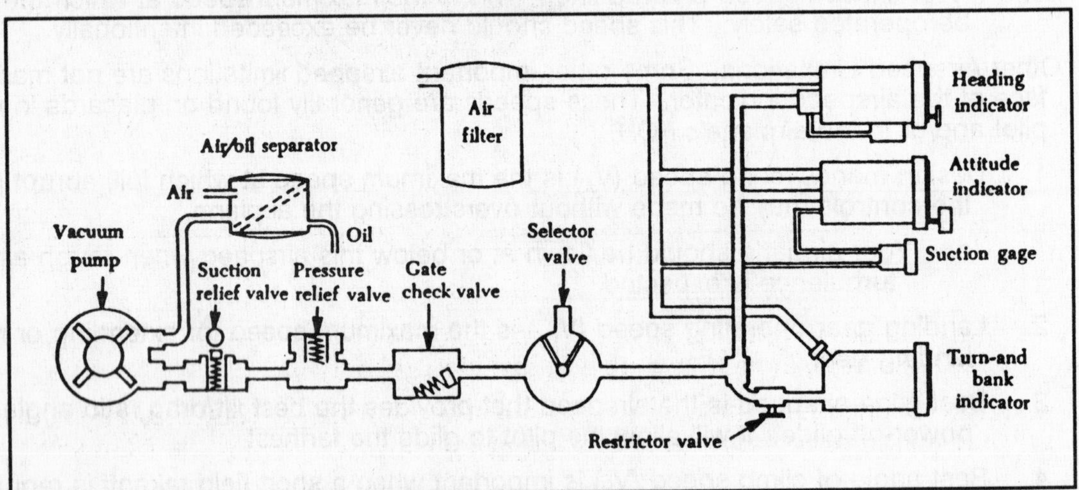


C. Gyroscopic Principles. Any spinning object exhibits gyroscopic properties. A wheel designed and mounted to utilize these properties is called a gyroscope. The two fundamental properties of gyroscopic action are illustrated below and on the following page: rigidity in space and precession.

1. Rigidity in space can best be explained by applying Newton's First Law of Motion, which states: "A body at rest will remain at rest; or if in motion in a straight line, it will continue in a straight line unless acted upon by an outside force."

   a. An example of this law is the rotor of a universally (freely) mounted gyro. When the wheel is spinning, it exhibits the ability to remain in its original plane of rotation regardless of how the base is moved.

   b. The attitude indicator and the heading indicator use the gyroscopic property of rigidity for their operation. Therefore, their rotors must be universally mounted.

2. Precession is the deflection of a spinning wheel when a deflective force is applied to its rim. The deflection is 90° ahead in the direction of rotation and in the direction of the applied force, as illustrated on page 87.

   a. The rate at which the wheel precesses is directly proportional to the deflective force.
   b. The turn indicator uses the gyroscopic property of precession for its operation.

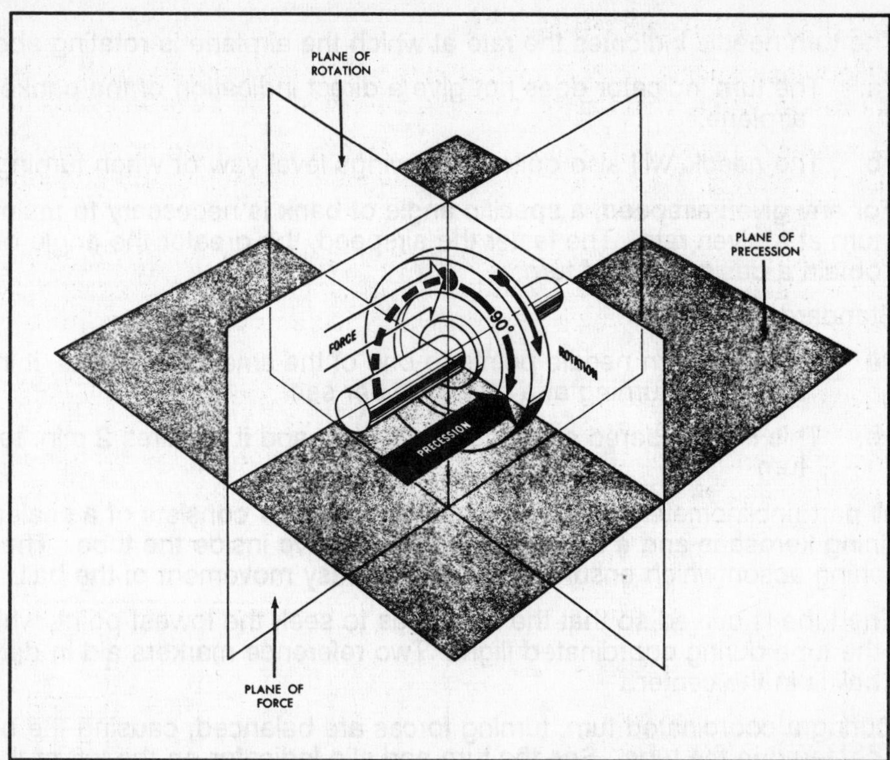


3. Two important design characteristics of an instrument gyro are
   a. Great weight or high density for size.
   b. Rotation at high speeds with low friction bearings.
4. The mountings of the gyro wheels are called "gimbals." They may be circular rings, rectangular frames, or a part of the instrument case itself (as in flight instruments).

## 4.6 TURN AND SLIP INDICATOR

A. The turn and slip indicator (T&SI) is a type of turn indicator used in some airplanes to indicate rate and quality of turn and to serve as an emergency source of bank information if the attitude indicator fails.
   1. It is illustrated on page 88.
   2. The T&SI is actually a combination of two instruments: the turn needle and the ball (or inclinometer).
      a. The turn needle is gyro-operated to show rate of turn.
      b. The ball in the inclinometer reacts to gravity and/or centrifugal force to indicate the need for directional trim (which is provided by the pilot's use of the rudder).

B. The turn needle is operated by a gyro (usually driven by electricity). Semirigid mounting of the gyro permits it to rotate freely about the lateral and longitudinal axes of the airplane but restricts its rotation about the vertical axis.
   1. When the airplane is turned, or rotated around the vertical axis, a deflective force is set up causing the gyro to precess (i.e., to tilt). The amount of this tilting is transmitted to the turn needle through linkage.
   2. As the rate of turn increases, the precession of the gyro increases, resulting in an indicated increased rate of turn.
   3. A spring assembly attached to the gyro keeps the turn needle upright when a deflective force is not applied.

4. The turn needle indicates the rate at which the airplane is rotating about its vertical axis.
    a. The turn indicator does not give a direct indication of the banked attitude of the airplane.
    b. The needle will also deflect in a wings level yaw or when turning while taxiing.
5. For any given airspeed, a specific angle of bank is necessary to maintain a coordinated turn at a given rate. The faster the airspeed, the greater the angle of bank required to obtain a desired rate of turn.
6. Standard rate turn
    a. When the turn needle points to one of the small side marks, it indicates that the airplane is turning at a rate of 3° per sec.
    b. This is considered a standard rate turn, and it requires 2 min. to complete 360° of turn.

C. The ball part (inclinometer) of the turn and slip indicator consists of a sealed, curved glass tube containing kerosene and a ball which is free to move inside the tube. The fluid provides a dampening action which ensures smooth and easy movement of the ball.
1. The tube is curved so that the ball tends to seek the lowest point, which is the center of the tube during coordinated flight. Two reference markers aid in determining when the ball is in the center.
2. During a coordinated turn, turning forces are balanced, causing the ball to remain centered in the tube. See the turn and slip indicator on the left of the diagram below.
3. If turning forces are unbalanced, i.e., improper rudder is used, the ball moves away from the center of the tube in the direction of the excessive force.
    a. In a skid, the rate of turn is too great for the angle of bank, and excessive centrifugal force moves the ball to the outside of the turn. See the middle turn and slip indicator in the diagram below.
        1) To achieve coordinated flight from a skid, the pilot should increase the bank angle, reduce the rate of turn by reducing the rudder force to center the ball, or a combination of both.

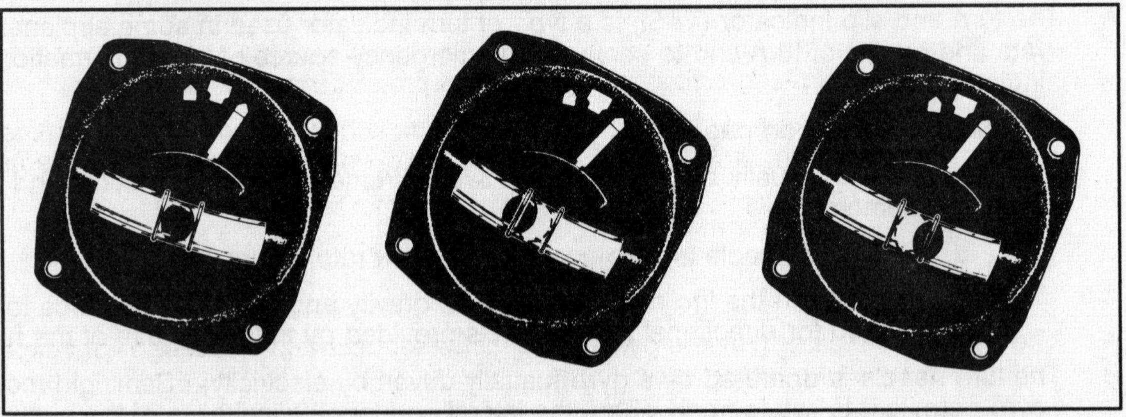

    b. In a slip, the rate of turn is too slow for the angle of bank, and the lack of centrifugal force moves the ball to the inside of the turn. See the turn and slip indicator on the right of the diagram above.
        1) To achieve coordinated flight from a slip, the pilot should decrease the bank angle, increase the rate of turn by applying rudder pressure to center the ball, or a combination of both.
    c. Remember: In slips you have used too little rudder (or opposite rudder). In skids you have used too much rudder.

4. The ball then is a visual aid to determine coordinated use of the aileron and rudder control. During a turn it indicates the quality of the turn, i.e., whether the airplane has the correct rate of turn for the angle of bank.

## 4.7 TURN COORDINATOR

A. The turn coordinator (TC) is another type of turn indicator that is used extensively. It replaces the turn needle of the turn and slip indicator with a miniature airplane to show the movement of the airplane about both the longitudinal axis and vertical axis (recall that the T&SI indicated movement around the vertical axis, not the longitudinal axis).

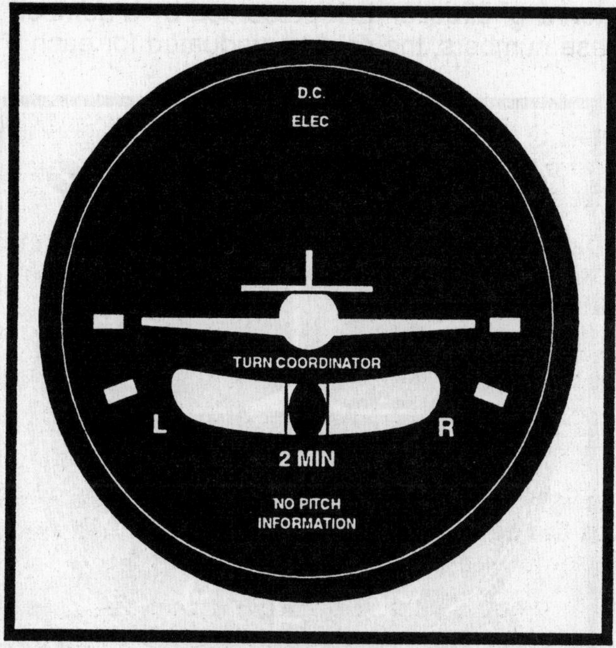


1. This design realigns the gyro so that it precesses in reaction to movement about both the yaw and roll axes, thus showing rate of roll as well as rate of turn.
2. Your view of the miniature airplane is from the tail, so when you roll to the right, the miniature airplane also banks to the right proportionally to the roll rate.
3. When the roll rate is zero (i.e., when the bank is held constant), the instrument indicates the rate of turn. It will also tilt in a wings level yaw or when turning while taxiing.

B. The ball in the TC works in the same manner as in the T&SI.

## 4.8 HEADING INDICATOR

A. The heading indicator (HI) is a gyroscopic instrument commonly used in light airplanes as the primary source of heading information.

1. Errors in the magnetic compass are numerous. This makes straight flight and precision turns to headings difficult, particularly in turbulent air.
2. The heading indicator is not affected by the forces that make the magnetic compass difficult to interpret.
3. In most light airplanes, the HI is powered by the vacuum system.

B. Operation of the heading indicator depends upon the gyroscopic principle of rigidity in space.

1. The rotor turns in a vertical plane. Fixed to the rotor is a compass card.
2. Since the rotor remains rigid in space, the points on the card hold the same position in space relative to the vertical plane.
3. Once the HI is operating (i.e., minutes after the airplane engine is started), the compass card must be set to the heading shown on the magnetic compass.
4. As both the instrument case and the airplane revolve around the vertical axis, the card provides clear and accurate heading information.
    a. The compass card has letters for cardinal headings (N, E, S, W).
    b. Each 30° interval of direction is represented by a number.
    c. Between these numbers, the card is graduated for each 5°.

C. Because of precession, caused chiefly by bearing friction or improper vacuum pressure, the heading indicator may creep or drift from a heading to which it is set.

1. Among other factors, the amount of drift depends largely upon the condition of the instrument. If the bearings are worn, dirty, or improperly lubricated, drift may be excessive.
2. The HI should be compared to the magnetic compass every 15 min. for accuracy.
    a. This can only be done accurately when the airplane is in straight, level, and unaccelerated flight.

D. The bank and pitch limits of the heading indicator vary with the particular design and make of instrument.

1. Some heading indicators found in light airplanes have limits of approximately 55° of pitch and 55° of bank.
    a. When either of these attitude limits is exceeded, the precessional force causes the instrument to tumble or spill, which causes the heading card to spin rapidly, and the instrument no longer gives the correct indication until reset.
    b. After spilling, it may be reset with the adjustment knob at the edge of the instrument.
2. Other heading indicators are designed not to tumble.

## 4.9 ATTITUDE INDICATOR

A. The attitude indicator (AI), with its miniature aircraft and horizon bar, depicts the attitude of the airplane.

1. The relationship of the miniature airplane to the horizon bar is the same as the relationship of the real airplane to the actual horizon.
2. The instrument gives an instantaneous indication of even the smallest changes in attitude.
3. In most light airplanes, the AI is powered by the vacuum system.

B. The gyro in the attitude indicator is mounted on a horizontal plane and depends upon rigidity in space for its operation. The horizon bar is fixed to the gyro. It remains in a horizontal plane as the airplane is pitched or banked about its lateral or longitudinal axis. The dial (banking scale) indicates the bank angle.

C. An adjustment knob is provided with which the pilot may move the miniature airplane up or down to align it with the horizon bar to suit the pilot's line of vision. Normally, it is adjusted so that the wings overlap the horizon bar during straight-and-level cruising flight.

D. The attitude indicator is highly reliable and the most realistic flight instrument on the instrument panel. Its indications are very close approximations of the actual attitude of the airplane.

## 4.10 MAGNETIC COMPASS

A. The magnetic compass (the only direction-seeking instrument in the airplane) is used primarily to set the heading indicator prior to flight, and to verify its continued accuracy during flight. It contains two steel magnetized needles fastened to a float around the edge of which is mounted a compass card.

1. The needles are parallel, with their north-seeking end pointed in the same direction.
2. One segment at a time of the floating compass card shows through the face of the instrument.
   a. The compass card has letters for cardinal headings (N, E, S, W).
   b. Each 30° interval of direction is represented by a number, the last zero of which is omitted. For example, 30° would appear as a 3 and 300° would appear as 30.
   c. Between these numbers, the card is graduated for each 5°.

3. The float assembly, consisting of the magnetized needles, compass card, and float, is mounted on a pedestal and sealed in a chamber filled with white kerosene.
    a. This fluid decreases oscillations and lubricates the pivot point on the pedestal, and due to buoyancy, part of the weight of the card is taken off the pivot that supports the card.
    b. The pedestal is the mount for the float assembly. The float assembly is balanced on the pivot, which allows free rotation of the card and allows it to tilt at an angle up to 18°.
4. At the rear of the compass bowl, a diaphragm is installed to allow for any expansion or contraction of the liquid, thus preventing the formation of bubbles or possible bursting of the case.
5. A glass face is on one side of the compass, and mounted behind the glass is a lubber (reference) line by which compass indications are read.

## 4.11 COMPASS ERRORS

A. In order to use the magnetic compass effectively, a pilot must understand some basic properties of magnetism, their effect on the instrument, and the errors they produce.
    1. A magnet is a piece of metal that has the property of attracting another metal.
        a. The force of attraction is greatest at the poles (or points near each end of the magnet) and the least attraction is in the area halfway between the two poles.

2. Lines of force flow from each end of these poles in all directions, bending around and flowing toward the other poles to form a magnetic field.

   a. Such a magnetic field surrounds the Earth, with the lines of force oriented approximately to the north and south magnetic poles.

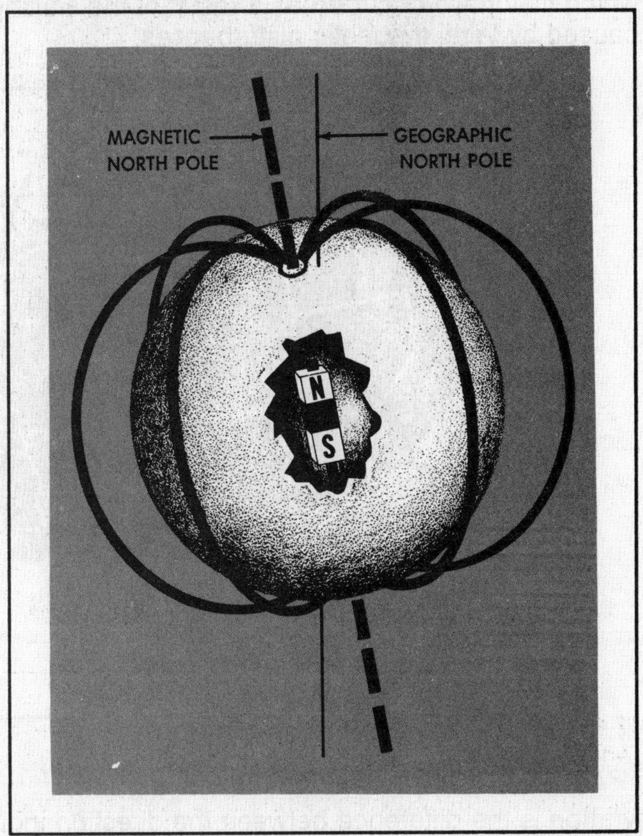


3. Compass errors include

   a. Magnetic variation,
   b. Compass deviation,
   c. Magnetic dip,
   d. Compass card oscillation.

B. **Magnetic variation** is the angular difference between true and magnetic north.

1. Although the magnetic field of the Earth lies roughly north and south, the Earth's magnetic poles do not coincide with its geographic poles, which are used in the construction of aeronautical charts.

   a. At most places on the Earth's surface, the needles of a magnetic compass will not point to True North. They point to Magnetic North.

   b. Furthermore, local magnetic fields from mineral deposits and other conditions may distort the Earth's magnetic field and cause an additional error with reference to True North.

2. Lines of equal magnetic variations are called isogonic lines, and are plotted in degrees of east and west variation on aeronautical charts.
   a. A line connecting points of zero degree variation is called the agonic line.
   b. These lines are replotted periodically on aeronautical charts to correct any change which may have occurred as a result of the shifting of the poles, or any changes caused by local magnetic disturbances.

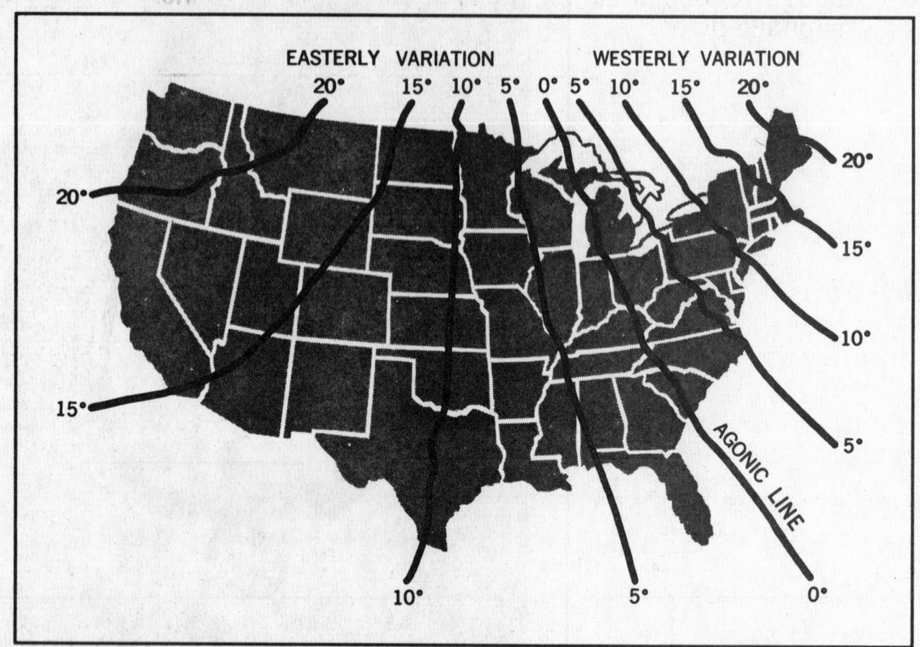


3. Magnetic variation will be discussed further in Chapter 12, Flight Computers, on page 317.

C. **Compass deviation** is the difference between the direction indicated by a magnetic compass not installed in an airplane and one installed in an airplane.
   1. The compass needles are affected not only by the Earth's magnetic field, but also by magnetic fields generated when an airplane's electrical equipment is operated and by metal components in the airplane.
      a. These magnetic disturbances within the airplane (deviation) may deflect the needles slightly from alignment with Magnetic North.
   2. If an airplane changes heading, the compass's direction-sensitive, magnetized needles may continue to point in about the same direction while the airplane turns. As the airplane turns, metallic and electrical equipment in the airplane change their position relative to the steel needles. As this happens, their influence on the compass needle changes and compass deviation changes.
      a. Thus, deviation depends in part on the heading of the airplane, and also on the electrical components in use.
   3. To reduce compass deviation error, each compass is checked and compensated periodically by adjustment.
      a. The errors remaining after "swinging" the compass are recorded on a compass correction card mounted in the airplane near the magnetic compass.
      b. To fly compass headings, the pilot refers to the compass correction card for corrected headings to steer.

4. **Compass deviation** will be discussed further in Chapter 12, Flight Computers, on page 317.

D. **Magnetic dip** is the tendency of the compass needles to point down as well as to the magnetic pole. The resultant error is known as dip error, greatest at the poles and zero at the magnetic equator.

1. Note in the figure below how lines of force in the Earth's magnetic field are parallel to the Earth's surface at the magnetic equator, and curve increasingly downward closer to the magnetic poles.

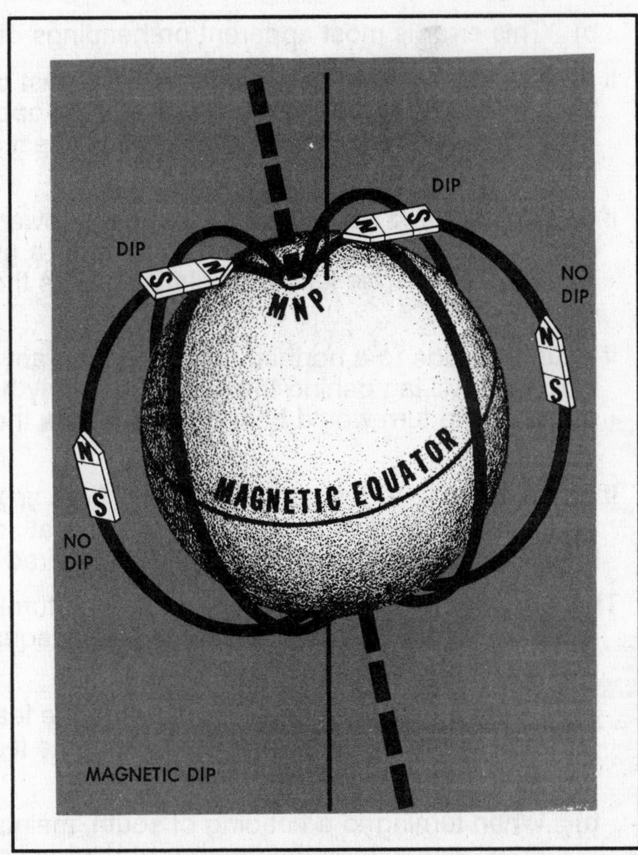


a. A magnetic needle will tend to assume the same direction and position as the line of force. Thus, the needle will be parallel with the Earth's surface at the magnetic equator, but will point increasingly downward as it is moved closer to the magnetic pole.

2. Since the compass card is designed to respond only to the horizontal plane of the Earth's magnetic field, it turns freely only in the horizontal plane. Any movement of the card from the horizontal results in dip errors.

3. Discussion of these magnetic dip errors is limited to the Northern Hemisphere; the errors are reversed in the Southern Hemisphere.
   a. Northerly and southerly turning error is the most pronounced of the dip errors.
      1) Due to the mounting of the magnetic compass, when the airplane is banked, the card is also banked as a result of centrifugal force.
         a) While the card is in the banked attitude, the vertical component of the Earth's magnetic field causes the north-seeking ends of the compass to dip to the low side of the turn, giving an erroneous turn indication.
         b) This error is most apparent on headings of north and south.
      2) If an airplane on a northerly heading turns east or west, the initial indication of the compass lags or indicates a turn in the opposite direction. This lag diminishes as the turn progresses toward east or west where there is no turning error.
      3) If an airplane on a southerly heading turns toward the east or west, the initial indication of the compass needle will show a greater amount of turn than is actually made. This lead also diminishes as the turn progresses toward east or west.
      4) If a turn is made to a northerly heading from any direction, the compass indication will lag behind the turn at northerly headings. Therefore, the rollout of the turn would be indicated before the desired heading is actually reached.
      5) If a turn is made to a southerly heading from any direction, the compass indication will lead or be ahead of the turn at southerly headings. Therefore, the rollout would be indicated after the desired heading is actually passed.
      6) The amount of lead or lag to be used when turning to northerly or southerly headings varies with, and is approximately equal to, the latitude of the locality over which the turn is being made.
         a) When turning to a heading of north, the lead for roll-out must include the number of degrees of latitude, plus the lead normally used in recovery from turns.
         b) When turning to a heading of south, maintain the turn until the compass passes south by the number of degrees of latitude, minus the normal roll-out lead.
      7) When on an easterly or westerly heading, no error is apparent while entering a turn to the north or south. The errors in 4) and 5) above become evident only after you are well into the turn.
   b. Acceleration error is also due to the dip of the Earth's magnetic field.
      1) Due to the pendulous-type mounting, the aft end of the compass card is tilted upward when accelerating, and downward when decelerating during changes of airspeed.
         a) This deflection of the compass card from the horizontal results in an error which is most apparent on headings of east and west only.
      2) When accelerating on either an east or west heading, the error will cause the compass to indicate a turn toward north.
      3) When decelerating on either an east or west heading, the error will cause the compass to indicate a turn toward south.
      4) Memory aid: ANDS means **A**cceleration -- **N**orth/**D**eceleration -- **S**outh.

E. **Compass card oscillation** error results from erratic movement of the compass card, which may be caused by turbulence or rough control technique.

1. During oscillation, the compass is affected by all the factors previously discussed.

## 4.12 AIRPLANE ENGINES

A. Since the engine develops the power to give the airplane its forward motion, thus enabling it to fly, the pilot should have a basic knowledge of how an engine works and how to control its power.

1. Knowledge of a few general principles of engine operation will help the pilot obtain increased dependability and efficiency from the engine and, in many instances, this knowledge will help in avoiding engine failure.

2. The airplane's *POH* should be consulted for specific operation and limitations of an airplane's engine.

B. The engine is commonly referred to as the powerplant.

1. Not only does the engine provide power to propel the airplane, but it powers the units which furnish electrical, hydraulic, and pneumatic energy for operation of electric motors, pumps, controls, lights, radios, instruments, retractable landing gear, and flaps.

a. In many cases the engine also provides heat for crewmembers' and passengers' comfort and for deicing equipment.

2. In view of these varied functions, it is properly referred to as an engine or powerplant rather than as a motor.

C. Most light training-type airplane engines are internal combustion of the reciprocating type, which operate on the same principle as automobile engines.

1. Internal combustion is the process by which a mixture of fuel and air is burned in a chamber from which the power can be taken directly.

2. In a reciprocating engine, pressures from burning and expanding gases cause a piston to move up and down in an enclosed cylinder.

a. This reciprocating motion of the piston is transferred through a connecting rod into rotary motion of a crankshaft that is attached directly or geared to a propeller.

D. Reciprocating engines can be further classified as to the manner in which the fuel is introduced into the cylinder.

1. In training-type airplanes the usual method is by carburetion, a process of atomizing, vaporizing, and mixing fuel with air in a unit called a carburetor, before the mixture enters the engine's cylinders.

a. The mixture of fuel and air is then drawn into each of the cylinders by the moving pistons, or is forced under pressure into the cylinders by a turbocharger or supercharger.

2. The other method of supplying the combustible fuel is by fuel injection, whereby the fuel is injected under pressure by a pump directly into the cylinders (or just prior to the cylinders in some systems) where it vaporizes and mixes with air.

3. These will be discussed in more detail in Module 4.17, Induction System, beginning on page 103.

E. The propeller, which uses the engine power to produce thrust, is discussed in Module 4.18, Propellers, beginning on page 109.

F. The basic parts of a reciprocating engine are the crankcase, cylinders, pistons, connecting rods, valves, spark plugs, and crankshaft, as shown below.

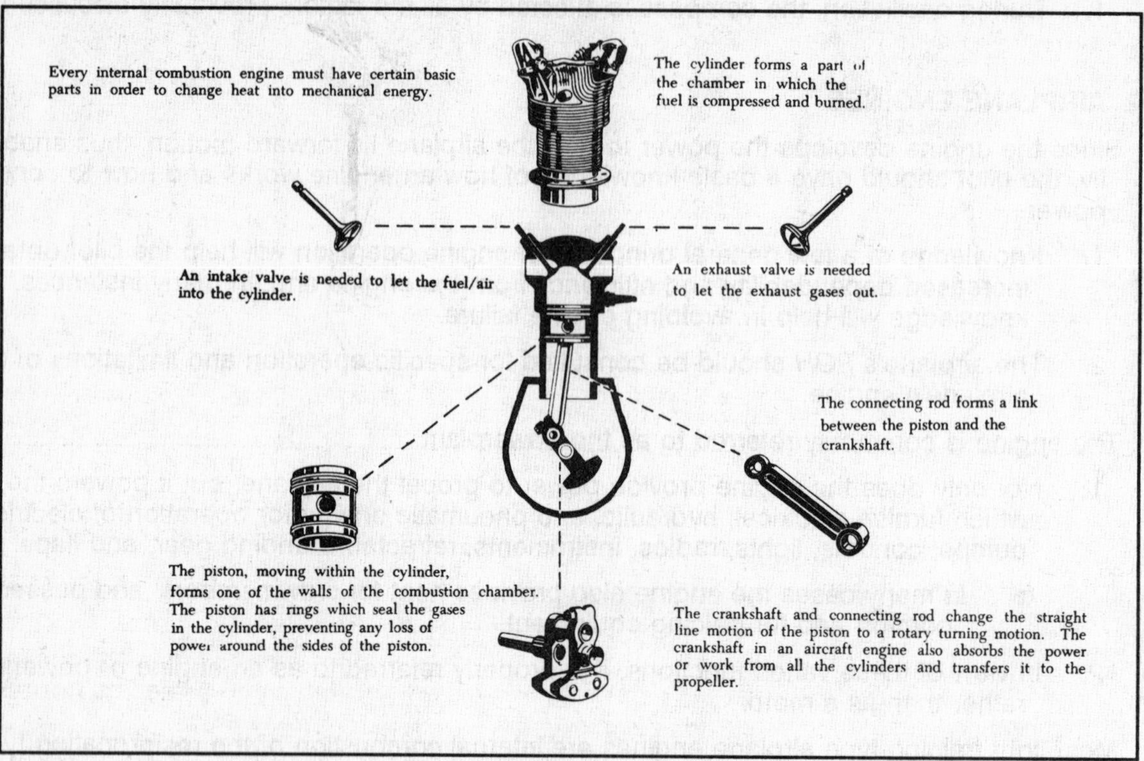


1. In the head or top of each cylinder are two valves and two spark plugs.
   a. One of these valves opens and closes a passage leading from the carburetor (or induction manifold) and is called the intake valve.
   b. The other opens and closes a passage leading to the outside (or exhaust manifold) and is called the exhaust valve.
2. Inside each cylinder is a movable piston which is attached to a crankshaft by means of a connecting rod.
   a. When the rapidly expanding gases (resulting from the heat of combustion of the fuel/air mixture ignited by spark plugs) push the piston down within the cylinder, it causes the crankshaft to rotate.
   b. At the same time, pistons in the other cylinders and attached to the same crankshaft are moved within their individual cylinders by the rotation of the crankshaft and go through exactly the same sequence or cycle.

## 4.13 HOW AN ENGINE OPERATES

A. The series of operations or events through which each cylinder of a reciprocating engine must pass in order to operate continuously and deliver power is called an engine cycle.
1. For the engine to complete one cycle, the piston must complete four strokes. This requires two revolutions of the crankshaft.
   a. The four strokes are the intake, compression, power, and exhaust.
2. Ignition of the fuel/air mixture at the end of the compression stroke adds a fifth event; thus, it is known as the four-stroke, five-event cycle.

B. The following describes one cycle of engine operation.

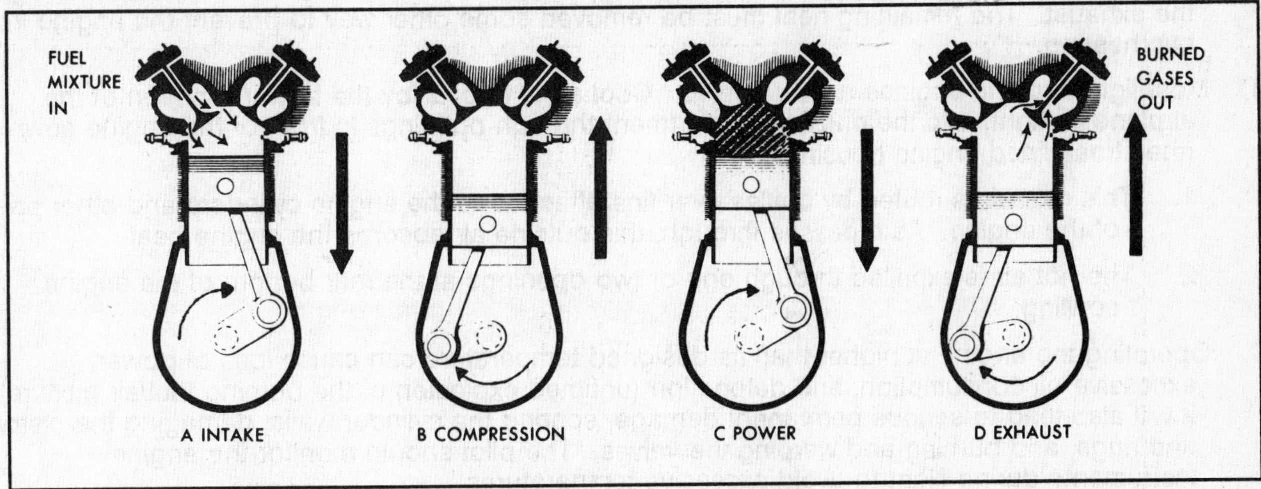


1. During the intake stroke (Diagram A) the piston moves downward, the exhaust valve is closed, and the intake valve is open, drawing the fuel/air mixture into the cylinder.
   a. When the piston approaches the lower limit of its downward stroke, the intake valve closes and traps the fuel/air mixture within the cylinder.
2. During the compression stroke (Diagram B) the piston moves upward. The fuel/air mixture is highly compressed between the piston and the cylinder head when the uppermost position (top dead center) is reached.
3. Ignition of the fuel/air mixture takes place slightly before the piston reaches top dead center of the compression stroke.
   a. An electric spark passes across the electrodes of each spark plug in the cylinder and ignites the mixture.
4. During the power stroke (Diagram C) the gaseous mixture, expanding as it burns, forces the piston downward and causes it to deliver mechanical energy to the crankshaft.
   a. As the mixture burns, temperature and pressure within the cylinder rise rapidly.
   b. Both valves are closed at the beginning of this stroke.
5. During the exhaust stroke (Diagram D) the energy delivered to the crankshaft during the power stroke causes the crankshaft to rotate on its bearings and thus move the piston upward again.
   a. The exhaust valve, which opened during the latter part of the power stroke, allows the burned gases to be ejected from the cylinder.
   b. The cycle is then ready to begin again.

C. Airplane engines normally have four or more cylinders. Each individual cylinder has its own four-stroke cycle, but all cylinders do not pass through the sequence of events simultaneously.

1. While one cylinder is operating on the power stroke, others are passing through the compression, exhaust, or intake strokes.
   a. This is accurately timed to occur in the correct sequence and at the right instant.
2. This arrangement provides a steady flow of power.

D. In order to start the engine initially, the crankshaft must be rotated by an outside power source until the ignition and power events take place.

1. This rotation is generally accomplished by an electric motor (i.e., a starter) which is geared to the crankshaft.

## 4.14 COOLING SYSTEM

A. The burning fuel within the cylinders produces intense heat, most of which is expelled through the exhaust. The remaining heat must be removed some other way to prevent the engine from overheating.

B. Most light airplane engines are air cooled. Cool air is forced (by the forward motion of the airplane in flight) into the engine compartment through openings in front of the engine cowl (the streamlined engine housing).

   1. This ram air is routed by baffles over fins attached to the engine cylinders and other parts of the engine. As it passes through, this outside air absorbs the engine heat.

   2. The hot air is expelled through one or two openings at the rear bottom of the engine cowling.

C. Operating the engine at higher than its designed temperature can cause loss of power, excessive oil consumption, and detonation (untimed explosion of the burning fuel/air mixture). It will also lead to serious permanent damage, scoring the cylinder walls, damaging the pistons and rings, and burning and warping the valves. The pilot should monitor the engine instruments during flight to avoid excessive temperatures.

   1. Oil pressure gauge -- indicates that the oil pump is working correctly to circulate the engine oil to all moving parts. Engine oil is very important both as a lubricant and for dissipating engine temperature.

   2. Oil temperature gauge -- indicates the temperature of the oil. This gauge gives only an indirect and delayed indication of rising engine temperatures. However, it should be used to determine engine temperature if this is the only means available.

   3. Cylinder head temperature gauge -- an additional instrument in many airplanes which indicates a direct and immediate engine temperature change.

   4. Each of these instruments is usually color-coded with a green arc to indicate the normal operating range.

      a. A red line indicates maximum or minimum allowable temperature or pressure.

      b. Caution ranges may be indicated by a yellow arc, which may be below and/or above the green arc.

D. To avoid or reduce excessive cylinder head temperatures a pilot can open the cowl flaps (if available), increase airspeed, enrich the mixture, or reduce power.

   1. Cowl flaps are hinged covers which fit over the opening(s) through which the hot air is expelled. By adjusting the cowl flap opening, the pilot can regulate the amount of airflow over the engine and thus the engine temperature during flight.

      a. Restricting the flow of expelled hot air (closing the cowl flaps) will increase engine temperature.

      b. If the engine temperature is high, the cowl flaps can be opened to permit a greater flow of air through the system, thereby decreasing the engine temperature.

      c. The cowl flaps are usually opened during low airspeed and high power operations such as takeoffs and climbs.

      d. During higher speed and lower power operations such as cruising flight and descents, the cowl flaps are usually closed.

   2. In airplanes not equipped with cowl flaps, the engine temperature can be controlled under normal operating conditions by changing the airspeed or the power output of the engine.

      a. High engine temperatures can be decreased by increasing airspeed and/or reducing power.

   3. A richer fuel to air mixture also helps an engine run cooler.

## 4.15 IGNITION SYSTEM

A. The function of the ignition system is to provide an electrical spark to ignite the fuel/air mixture in the cylinders.

B. The ignition system of the engine is completely separate from the airplane's electrical system.

  1. The magneto-type ignition system is used on most reciprocating airplane engines.

C. Magnetos are engine-driven self-contained units that generate and supply electrical current. However, before they can produce current, the magnetos must be actuated by the engine crankshaft.

  1. During engine start, the airplane's battery supplies power to the starter which rotates the crankshaft, thus allowing the magnetos to produce the sparks for the ignition of the fuel in each cylinder.

  2. After the engine starts, the starter system is disengaged, and the battery no longer contributes to the actual operation of the engine.

D. Airplane engines are equipped with a dual magneto ignition system.

  1. Each cylinder has two spark plugs. One magneto supplies the current to one set of plugs; the second magneto supplies the current to the other set of plugs.

  2. The ignition switch thus has four positions: OFF, LEFT, RIGHT, and BOTH.

    a. With the switch in the L or R position, only one magneto is supplying current and only one set of spark plugs is firing.

    b. With the switch in the BOTH position, both magnetos are supplying current and both sets of spark plugs are firing.

  3. The main advantages of the dual system are

    a. Increased safety. If one magneto system fails, the engine may be operated on the other system until landing.

    b. Improved engine performance. The dual system allows for more complete and even combustion of the mixture, because the fuel mixture will be ignited on each side of the combustion chamber and burn toward the center.

E. It is important to leave the ignition switch on BOTH for flight and turn it completely OFF after shutting down the engine.

  1. The entire purpose of the dual system is defeated when the switch is left on L or R, and the engine's performance is greatly affected.

  2. Even with the electrical master switch OFF, if the ignition switch is on either BOTH or L or R magnetos, the engine could fire if the propeller is moved from outside the airplane.

    a. Also if the magneto switch ground wire is disconnected, the magneto is ON even when the ignition switch is in the OFF position.

## 4.16 FUEL SYSTEM

A. The fuel system stores fuel and transfers it to the airplane engine. Fuel systems are classified according to the way the fuel is moved to the engine from the fuel tanks: the "gravity feed" and the "fuel pump" systems.

  1. The gravity feed system, usually found on high-wing carburetor airplanes, uses the force of gravity to transfer the fuel from the tanks to the engine. Since the fuel tanks are generally installed in the wings, they are above the carburetor and the fuel is gravity-fed through the system and into the carburetor.

2. The fuel pump system must be used in low-wing airplanes and airplanes with fuel-injected engines. Such a system generally has two fuel pumps.
   a. The primary fuel pump is engine-driven (mechanical). It provides sufficient fuel pressure to the engine after start for all normal operations.
   b. The auxiliary fuel pump (boost pump) is electrically driven, and manually controlled by the pilot. It is used for engine start, for added safety during takeoff and landing, and for emergency situations in which the primary fuel pump has failed.
   c. A fuel pressure gauge, which indicates the pressure in the fuel lines, is provided with a fuel pump system. The normal operating pressure can be found in the airplane's *POH* or on the gauge by color coding.

B. Most airplanes are designed to use space in the wings to mount fuel tanks. All tanks have filler openings covered by a cap.
   1. Also included are lines connecting to the engine, a fuel gauge, strainers, and vents which permit air to replace the fuel consumed during flight.
   2. Fuel overflow vents are provided to discharge fuel if it expands because of high temperatures.
   3. Tanks have drain plugs or valves (sumps) at the bottom from which water and other sediment can be drained.

C. Fuel lines transfer the fuel from the tanks to the engine.
   1. Fuel lines pass through a selector assembly located in the cockpit.
      a. The fuel selector assembly may be a simple on/off valve or a more complex arrangement which permits the pilot to select individual tanks or use all tanks at the same time.
   2. Many airplanes are equipped with fuel strainers, called sumps, located between the fuel selector and the carburetor.
      a. Similar to the fuel tank drains, these are placed at low points in the fuel lines.
      b. The sumps filter the fuel and trapped water and sediment into a drainable container.
   3. A manual fuel primer in some airplanes helps to start the engine, particularly in cold weather.
      a. Activating the primer draws fuel from the tanks and vaporizes it directly into one or two of the cylinders through small fuel lines.
      b. When an engine is cold, it does not generate sufficient heat to vaporize the fuel. The primer helps start the engine and keep it running until sufficient engine heat is generated.

D. The proper fuel for an engine will burn smoothly from the spark plug outward, exerting a smooth pressure downward on the piston.
   1. Using low-grade fuel or too lean a mixture can cause detonation.
   2. Detonation or knock is a sudden explosion or shock to a small area of the piston top, similar to striking it with a hammer.
      a. Detonation produces extreme heat which often progresses into preignition, causing severe structural stresses on engine parts.
   3. Anti-knock qualities of aviation fuels are designated by grades, such as 80/87, 100LL, 100/130, 108/135, and 115/145 (the latter are generally no longer available). The higher the grade, the more compression the fuel can stand without detonating. The more compression the fuel can stand without detonation, the more power can be developed from it. The first of the two numbers in a fuel designation indicates the lean-mixture rating (as during cruise), and the second the rich-mixture rating (as during takeoff and climb).

4. No engine manufacturer recommends using a fuel with a lower octane/grade rating than that specified for the engine. When a pilot is faced with a shortage of the correct type of fuel, always use whatever alternate fuel grade is specified by the manufacturer or the next higher grade. Availability of different fuel grades at servicing facilities will be largely dependent on the classes of aircraft using the particular airport. The engine manufacturers have made information available concerning satisfactory alternate grade fuels for those which have been discontinued.

5. DO NOT USE AUTOMOTIVE FUEL unless an appropriate supplemental type certificate (STC) has been obtained for an engine, approving it for auto gas use.

6. Fuel Color

   a. Most fuel pumps or trucks are plainly marked indicating the type and grade of fuel. However, a pilot may determine whether (s)he is receiving the proper grade by the color of the fuel itself.

   b. Dyes are added by the refinery for ready identification of the various grades of aviation gasoline:

| GRADE | COLOR |
|---|---|
| 80/87 | Red |
| 100LL (low lead) | Blue |
| 100/130 | Green |

E. During refueling, the flow of fuel through the hose and nozzle creates a fire hazard. This is due to static electricity. Following some simple procedures can minimize the hazard.

1. A ground wire should be attached to the aircraft before the cap is removed from the tank.
2. The refueling nozzle should be grounded to the aircraft before and during refueling.
3. The fuel truck should be also grounded to the aircraft and the ground.

## 4.17 INDUCTION SYSTEM

A. In reciprocating aircraft engines, the induction system completes the process of taking in outside air, mixing it with fuel, and delivering this mixture to the cylinders.

1. The system includes the air scoops and ducts, the carburetor or fuel injector, the intake manifold, and (if installed) the turbo or superchargers.

2. Two types of induction systems are commonly used in reciprocating engines.

   a. The carburetor system mixes the fuel and air in the carburetor before this mixture enters the intake manifold.

   b. In a fuel injection system, the fuel is fed into injection pumps, which force it under high pressure directly into (or just prior to) the cylinders where it mixes with air.

3. All airplane engines incorporate a throttle and mixture control device that is operated by the pilot in the cockpit.

   a. The throttle controls the amount of fuel/air mixture that goes into the engine. Generally, the more fuel/air mixture, the more power is developed by the engine.

      1) The throttle is opened (i.e., more fuel/air mixture) by a forward movement of the control and closed (i.e., less fuel/air mixture) by a rearward movement of the control.

2) Engine power can be determined by the following instruments.

a) The tachometer indicates the speed at which the engine crankshaft is rotating. The dial is calibrated in revolutions per minute (RPM).

i) In an airplane equipped with a fixed-pitch propeller, RPM is controlled by the throttle control.

ii) In an airplane equipped with a constant-speed propeller, RPM is controlled by the propeller control.

b) The manifold pressure (MP) gauge is installed in airplanes with a turbocharger and/or a constant-speed propeller.

i) This gauge indirectly indicates the power output of the engine by measuring the pressure of the air in the fuel/air induction manifold.

- The higher the MP, the greater the power being developed by the engine

ii) The dial is calibrated in inches of mercury (in. Hg).

3) Smooth, gentle throttle movements are necessary to prevent overly rapid cooling and heating of various engine parts.

a) Also, crankshaft counterbalances can be upset by rapid changes in throttle settings.

b. The mixture control adjusts the fuel/air ratio to compensate for varying air densities as the airplane changes altitude.

1) Engines are designed to operate with maximum power at a set fuel/air ratio (e.g., 12:1). Because an airplane is constantly operating at varying altitudes that imply varying air densities, fuel flow must be varied to maintain the ratio of fuel to air that will produce optimal power.

a) If the fuel/air mixture is too rich, there is too much fuel in terms of the weight of the air.

i) Excessive fuel consumption, rough engine operation, and appreciable loss of power will occur.

ii) Also, a cooling effect causes below normal temperatures in the cylinders, which results in spark plug fouling.

b) Conversely, operating with an excessively lean mixture (i.e., too little fuel in terms of the weight of the air) will result in rough engine operation, detonation, overheating, and a loss of power.

2) Carburetors are normally calibrated at sea-level pressure to meter the correct amount of fuel with the mixture control in a "full rich" position. Recall that, as altitude increases, air density decreases.

a) As altitude increases, the weight of air decreases, even though the volume of air entering the carburetor remains the same.

i) To compensate the mixture must be leaned (i.e., reduce the amount of fuel) to maintain the proper fuel/air ratio.

b) An exhaust gas temperature (EGT) gauge, in an airplane so equipped, provides the most accurate means for determining the proper mixture, since this temperature varies with the ratio of fuel to air entering the cylinders.

c) A fuel injected engine usually has a fuel flow indicator on the instrument panel. The mixture control is moved to set the manufacturer's recommended fuel flow.

d) In engines equipped with no instruments to help in leaning, a simplistic method is to lean the mixture until engine roughness develops, then enrich the mixture slightly until the engine runs smoothly again.

B. Carburetor System

1. The outside air enters the air intake in the front part of the engine cowling, and passes through an air filter.
   a. An alternate air source, located within the engine cowling, is available in the event the external air filter is obstructed by ice or other matter.
   b. This source is selected by applying carburetor heat, which introduces heated, unfiltered air into the carburetor.
2. The air flows into the carburetor through the venturi (a narrow throat in the carburetor), which accelerates the air.
   a. The increased speed of the air flow is accompanied by a decrease in pressure (Bernoulli's Principle), which draws the fuel from the main discharge nozzle into the airstream where it is mixed with the flowing air.
   b. The fuel/air mixture is then drawn through the intake manifold and into the combustion chambers where it is ignited.
3. The "float-type carburetor" acquires its name from a float which rests on fuel within the float chamber. A needle attached to the float opens and closes an opening in the fuel lines.
   a. This meters the correct amount of fuel into the carburetor, depending upon the position of the float, which is controlled by the level of fuel in the float chamber.

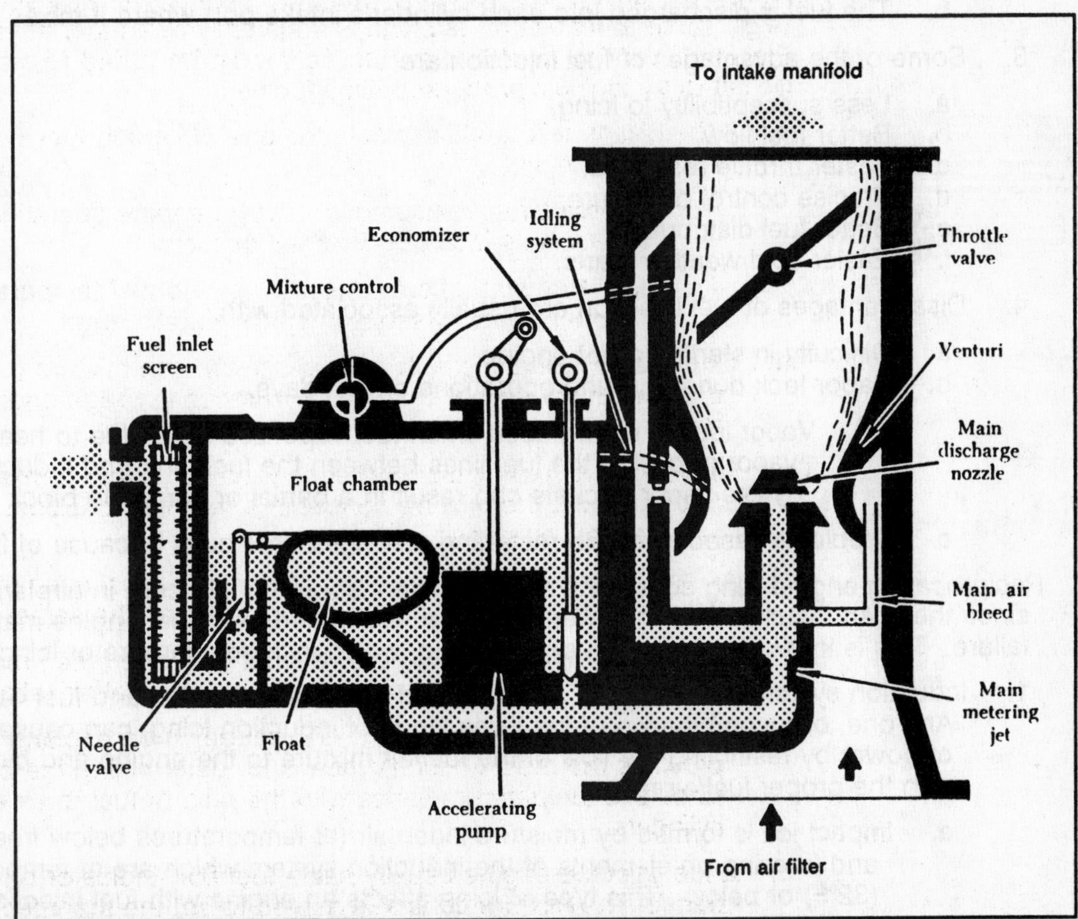

4. The throttle control varies the airflow by means of the throttle valve in the throat of the carburetor.

   a. The accelerating pump is also connected to the throttle linkage.

      1) This allows an extra amount of fuel to flow into the carburetor as the throttle is opened.

      2) If the throttle is opened quickly, the airflow initially increases at a rate greater than the fuel flow (i.e., lean mixture). The accelerator pump prevents this from occurring.

5. The idling system provides sufficient fuel to mix with the air to keep the engine idling at low RPM.

6. The economizer is connected to the mixture control linkage. Moving the mixture control back moves a small needle in the carburetor which restricts the fuel flow through the main metering jet.

C. Fuel Injection System

1. The air intake for the fuel injection system is similar to that used in the carburetor system.

   a. In many designs, the alternate air source is actuated automatically when the external air filter becomes obstructed.

      1) The pilot may also manually activate the alternate air source.

   b. The air passes to the cylinders where it is mixed with the fuel.

2. An engine-driven fuel pump provides pressurized fuel to the fuel injectors.

   a. A specific amount of fuel is injected, based on mixture and throttle control settings.
   b. The fuel is discharged into each cylinder's intake port where it mixes with the air.

3. Some of the advantages of fuel injection are

   a. Less susceptibility to icing,
   b. Better fuel flow,
   c. Faster throttle response,
   d. Precise control of mixture,
   e. Better fuel distribution,
   f. Easier cold weather starts.

4. Disadvantages of fuel injection are usually associated with

   a. Difficulty in starting a hot engine.
   b. Vapor lock during ground operations on hot days.

      1) Vapor lock is a term used when fuel vaporizes (e.g., due to heat) and forms a vapor pocket in the fuel lines between the fuel tank and induction system. These vapor pockets can result in a partial or complete block of the fuel flow.

   c. Problems associated with restarting an engine that quits because of fuel starvation.

D. Reciprocating engine icing conditions are a constant source of concern in airplane operations since they can result in loss of power and, if not eliminated, eventual engine malfunction or failure. This is known as induction system icing, which includes carburetor icing.

1. Induction system icing may be characterized as impact, throttle, and fuel vaporization ice. Any one, or a combination of the three kinds of induction icing, can cause a serious loss of power by restricting the flow of the fuel/air mixture to the engine and by interference with the proper fuel/air ratio.

   a. Impact ice is formed by moisture-laden air (at temperatures below freezing) striking and freezing on elements of the induction system which are at temperatures of 0°C (32°F) or below. This type of icing affects an engine with fuel injection, as well as those with a carburetor.

1) Under these conditions, ice may build up on such components as the air scoops, heat or alternate air valves, intake screens, and protrusions in the carburetor.

2) Impact icing can be expected to build most rapidly when the ambient air temperature is about –4°C (25°F), when the supercooled moisture in the air is still in a semiliquid state.

b. Throttle ice is usually formed at or near a partially closed throttle, typical of an off-idle or cruise power setting.

1) This occurs when water vapor in the air condenses and freezes because of the cooling restriction caused by the carburetor venturi and the throttle butterfly valve.

2) This icing normally affects the carburetor-type engine, but may also affect the fuel-injected engine.

c. Fuel vaporization icing normally occurs in conjunction with throttle icing and is commonly called carburetor icing since it occurs predominately in float-type carburetors. It is not a problem in fuel injection systems because fuel is vaporized by other means.

1) The vaporization of fuel, combined with the decreasing air pressure as it flows through the carburetor, causes a sudden cooling of the mixture.

2) The temperature of the air passing through the carburetor may drop as much as 15°C (27°F) within a fraction of a second. Water vapor in the air is squeezed out by this cooling.

a) If the temperature in the carburetor reaches 0°C (32°F) or below, the moisture will be deposited as frost or ice inside the carburetor passages.

b) Even a slight accumulation of ice will reduce power and may lead to complete engine failure, particularly when the throttle is partially or fully closed.

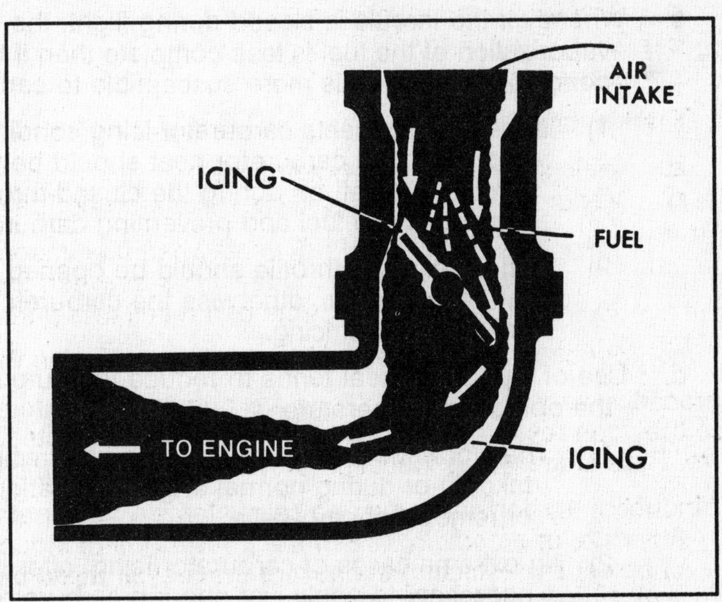


2. Conditions Conducive to Carburetor Icing. On dry days, or when the temperature is well below freezing, there is generally not enough moisture in the air to cause trouble. But if the temperature is between –7°C (20°F) and 21°C (70°F), with visible moisture or high humidity, the pilot should be constantly on the alert for carburetor ice.

3. Indications of Carburetor Icing. For airplanes with fixed-pitch propellers, the first indication of carburetor icing is a loss of RPM. For airplanes with controllable pitch (constant-speed) propellers, the first indication is usually a drop in manifold pressure.
   a. In both cases, a roughness in engine operation may develop later.
   b. There will be no reduction in RPM in airplanes with constant-speed propellers, since propeller pitch is automatically adjusted to compensate for the loss of power, thus maintaining constant RPM. See Module 4.18, Propellers, on page 109.
4. Use of Carburetor Heat. The carburetor heater is an anti-icing device that preheats the air before it reaches the carburetor. It can be used to melt any ice or snow entering the intake, to melt ice that forms in the carburetor passages (provided the accumulation is not too great), and to keep the fuel mixture above the freezing temperature to prevent formation of carburetor ice.
   a. When conditions are conducive to carburetor icing during flight, periodic checks should be made to detect its presence. If detected, FULL carburetor heat should be applied immediately, and remain in the "on" position until the pilot is certain that all the ice has been removed. If ice is present, applying partial heat or leaving heat on for an insufficient time might aggravate the condition.
   b. When carburetor heat is first applied there will be a drop in RPM in airplanes equipped with fixed-pitch propellers. There will be a drop in manifold pressure in airplanes equipped with controllable-pitch propellers.
      1) If there is no carburetor ice present, there will be no further change in RPM or manifold pressure until the carburetor heat is turned off. Then the RPM or manifold pressure will return to the original reading before heat was applied.
      2) If carburetor ice is present, there will normally be a rise in RPM or manifold pressure after the initial drop (often accompanied by intermittent engine roughness). This is due to the ingestion of the water from the melted ice. When the carburetor heat is turned off, the RPM or manifold pressure will rise to a setting greater than that before application of the heat. The engine should also run more smoothly after the ice melts.
   c. Whenever the throttle is closed during flight, the engine cools rapidly and vaporization of the fuel is less complete than if the engine is warm. In this condition the engine is more susceptible to carburetor icing.
      1) If the pilot suspects carburetor-icing conditions and anticipates closed-throttle operation, the carburetor heat should be turned to "full-on" before closing the throttle, and left on during the closed-throttle operation. The heat will aid in vaporizing the fuel and preventing carburetor ice.
      2) Periodically, the throttle should be opened smoothly for a few seconds to keep the engine warm, otherwise the carburetor heater may not provide enough heat to prevent icing.
   d. Use of carburetor heat tends to reduce the output of the engine and also to increase the operating temperature.
      1) Therefore, the heat should not be used when full power is required (as during takeoff) or during normal engine operation except to check for the presence or removal of carburetor ice.
      2) In extreme cases of carburetor icing, after the ice has been removed it may be necessary to apply just enough carburetor heat to prevent further ice formation. However, this must be done with caution.
      3) If carburetor ice still forms, apply FULL heat to remove it. **NOTE:** Partial use of the carburetor heat may raise the temperature of the induction air into the range that is likely for the formation of ice, thus increasing the risk of icing.

e. Check the engine manufacturer's recommendations for the correct use of carburetor heat.

5. Carburetor Air Temperature Gauge. Some airplanes are equipped with this gauge useful in detecting potential icing conditions.

   a. Usually, the face of the gauge is calibrated in degrees Celsius. A yellow arc indicates the carburetor air temperatures at which icing may occur. This yellow arc ranges between –15°C and +5°C.

   b. If the air temperature and moisture content of the air are such that carburetor icing is improbable, the engine can be operated with the indicator in the yellow range with no adverse effects.

   c. However, if the atmospheric conditions are conducive to carburetor icing, the indicator must be kept outside the yellow arc by application of carburetor heat.

6. Outside Air Temperature Gauge (OAT). Most airplanes are equipped with this gauge calibrated in degrees both Celsius and Fahrenheit. It is useful for obtaining the outside or ambient air temperature for calculating true airspeed and also in detecting potential icing conditions.

## 4.18 PROPELLERS

A. A propeller is a rotating airfoil. It is thus subject to induced drag, stalls, and other aerodynamic principles that apply to any airfoil. The propeller provides the necessary thrust to move the airplane through the air.

1. The airplane propeller consists of two or more blades and a central hub to which the blades are attached. Each blade of an airplane propeller is essentially a rotating wing which produce forces that create the thrust to move the airplane through the air.

2. The power needed to rotate the propeller blades is furnished by the engine. The engine rotates the airfoils of the blades through the air at high speeds, and the propeller transforms the rotary power of the engine into forward thrust.

3. A cross section of a typical propeller blade is shown below. This section or blade element is an airfoil comparable to a cross section of an airplane wing.

   a. One surface of the blade is cambered or curved, similar to the upper surface of an airplane wing, while the other surface is flat like the bottom surface of a wing.

   b. As with a wing, the leading edge is the thick edge of the blade that meets the air as the propeller rotates.

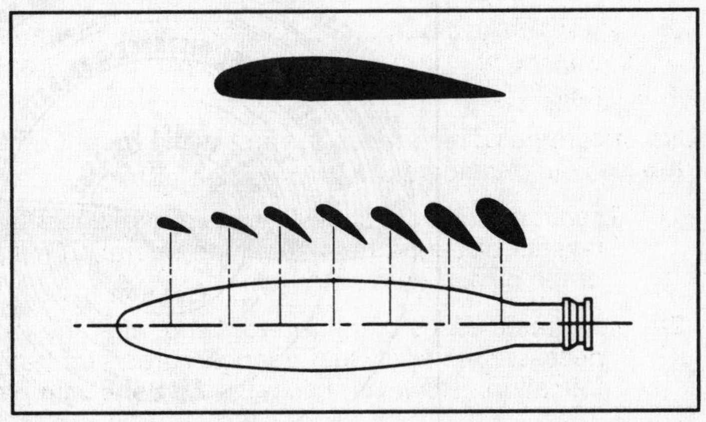

4. To understand the action of a propeller, consider first its motion, which is both rotational and forward. As shown in the figure below, each section of a propeller blade moves downward and forward.

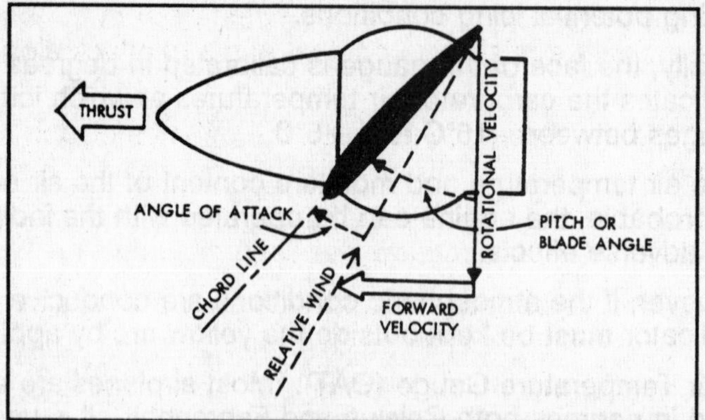


a. The angle at which the air (relative wind) strikes the propeller blade is its angle of attack.

1) The air deflection produced by this angle causes the dynamic pressure at the back side of the propeller blade to be greater than atmospheric, thus creating thrust.

2) The shape of the blade also creates thrust, because it is cambered like the airfoil shape of a wing.

a) As the air flows past the propeller, the pressure on one side is less than that on the other.

b) As in a wing, this produces a reaction force in the direction of the lesser pressure.

i) The area of decreased pressure is in front of the propeller, and the force (thrust) is in a forward direction.

b. Aerodynamically, thrust is the result of the propeller shape and the angle of attack of the blade.

5. A propeller is twisted because the outer parts of the propeller blades, like all things that turn about a central point, travel faster than the portions near the hub (see below).

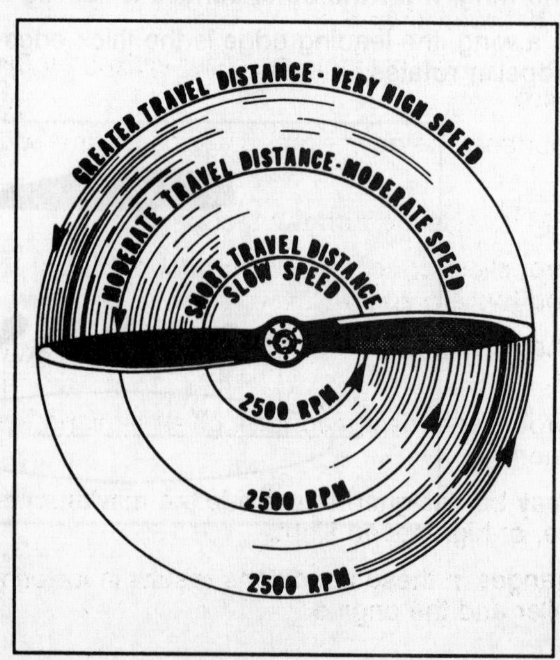

a. If the blades had the same geometric pitch throughout their lengths, at cruise speed the portions near the hub could have negative angles of attack while the propeller tips would be stalled.

b. Twisting, or variations in the geometric pitch of the blades, permits the propeller to operate with a relatively constant angle of attack along its length when in cruising flight.

6. Propeller slip is the difference between the geometric pitch of the propeller and its effective pitch.

a. Geometric pitch is the theoretical distance a propeller would advance in one revolution if it were rotated in a solid medium.

1) Effective pitch is the actual distance a propeller moves forward through the air in one revolution.

b. Geometric or theoretical pitch is based on no slippage, but actual or effective pitch includes propeller slippage in the air.

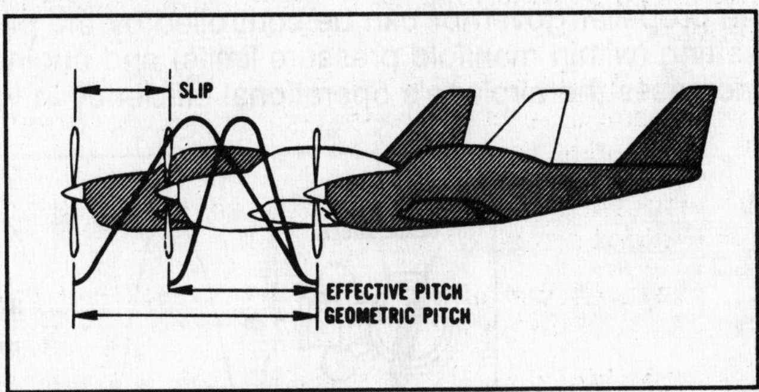


7. Propeller efficiency depends on the amount of slippage.

a. Since the efficiency of any machine is the ratio of the useful power output to the actual power output, propeller efficiency is the ratio of thrust horsepower to brake horsepower (i.e., the horsepower the engine is delivering to the crankshaft).

b. Propeller efficiency varies from 50% to 87%, depending on propeller slippage.

c. A propeller is most efficient, i.e., has the least amount of slippage, at angles of attack between 1° and 4°.

B. Fixed-pitch propeller. The pitch of this propeller is fixed by the manufacturer. It cannot be changed by the pilot.

1. The throttle controls the power output of the engine, which has a direct relationship to RPM.

a. The RPM is registered on the tachometer.

2. Fixed-pitch propellers are designed for best efficiency (i.e., ideal angle of attack) at one rotational and forward speed.

a. Any other combination of RPM and airspeed results in a less efficient angle of attack.

b. Each propeller is designed for a given airplane, engine combination, and flight condition.

3. A propeller may be designed to provide the maximum propeller efficiency for either takeoff, climb, cruise, or high-speed flight.

a. Any changes in these conditions results in lowering the efficiency of both the propeller and the engine.

C. Controllable-pitch propellers. The pitch on these propellers can be changed in flight by the pilot. These propellers vary from a simple two-position propeller to the constant-speed propeller, which allows any pitch angle between a minimum and maximum pitch setting. The following discussion refers to the constant-speed propeller.

1. An airplane equipped with a controllable-pitch propeller has two controls:
    a. The throttle controls the power output of the engine (registered on the manifold pressure gauge).
        1) The manifold pressure (MP) gauge is a simple barometer that measures the air pressure in the engine intake manifold in inches of mercury.
    b. The propeller control regulates the engine RPM and in turn the propeller RPM.
        1) The RPM is registered on the tachometer.
2. Constant-speed propeller systems consist of a governor unit which controls the pitch angle of the blades so the engine's speed (RPM) remains constant. The governor regulates the flow of oil into and out of the propeller hub to control the blade angle.
    a. The propeller governor can be controlled by the pilot, so that any desired angle setting (within manifold pressure limits) and engine RPM can be obtained. This increases the airplane's operational efficiency in various flight conditions.

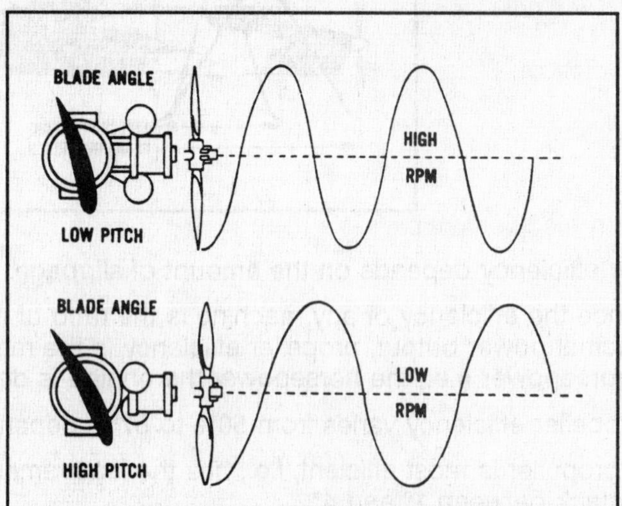


    b. Once the pilot has set the propeller to a given RPM, the propeller governor will automatically change the pitch to counteract any tendency for the engine to vary from this RPM.
        1) If MP or engine power is increased, the propeller governor automatically increases the pitch of the blade (i.e., more propeller drag) to maintain RPM.
3. A controllable-pitch propeller permits the pilot to select the blade angle that will result in the most efficient performance for a particular flight condition.
    a. A low-pitch, high-RPM setting reduces propeller drag and allows maximum power for takeoff.
    b. After airspeed is attained during cruising flight, the propeller pitch is changed to a higher angle or increased pitch. The blade takes a larger bite of air at a lower power setting, thus increasing the efficiency of the propeller.
    c. This process is similar to the automatic shifting of gears from low to high in an automobile.

4. Any given RPM has a maximum MP that should not be exceeded.
   a. If MP is excessive for a given RPM, pressure within the cylinders could be exceeded, thus placing undue stress on them.
   b. If repeated too frequently, such stress could weaken the cylinder components and eventually cause engine failure.
   c. Avoid high MP settings with low RPM.

## 4.19 ELECTRICAL SYSTEM

A. Electrical energy is required to operate the starter, navigation and communication radios, lights, and other airplane equipment.
   1. Most light airplanes are equipped with a 12-volt battery and a 14-volt direct-current electrical system.
   2. Some airplanes are equipped with a 24-volt battery and a 28-volt direct-current system to provide an electrical reserve capacity for more electrical equipment, including additional electrical energy for starting.

B. A basic airplane electrical system consists of the following components:
   1. Alternator or generator
   2. Battery
   3. Master switch or battery switch
   4. Bus bar, fuses, and circuit breakers
   5. Voltage regulator
   6. Ammeter
   7. Starting motor
   8. Associated electrical wiring
   9. Accessories

C. Engine-driven generators or alternators supply electric current to the electrical system and also maintain a sufficient electrical charge in the battery (which is used primarily for starting).
   1. Electrical energy stored in a battery provides a source of electricity for starting the engine and a limited supply of electricity for use if the alternator or generator fails.
   2. The main disadvantage of a generator is that it may not produce a sufficient amount of electrical current at low engine RPM to operate the entire electrical system. Therefore, during operations at low engine RPM the electrical needs must be drawn from the battery, which may quickly be depleted.
   3. Most airplanes are equipped with an alternator. It produces a sufficient amount of electrical current at low engine RPM by first producing alternating current which is converted to direct current.
      a. Another advantage is that the electrical output of an alternator is more constant throughout the ranges of engine speed.
      b. Alternators are also lighter in weight, less expensive to maintain, and less prone to overloading during conditions of heavy electrical loads.

D. Some airplanes are equipped with receptacles to which ground power units (GPUs) can be connected to provide electrical energy for starting.
   1. These are very useful, especially during cold weather starting.
   2. Do NOT start an engine using a GPU when the battery is dead. Electrical energy will be forced into the dead battery, causing the battery to overheat and possibly explode, resulting in damage to the airplane.

E. A master switch is installed to turn the electrical system on or off. Turning the master switch on provides electrical energy to all the electrical equipment circuits except the ignition system (which receives electricity from the magnetos).

1. In addition, an alternator switch permits the pilot to exclude the alternator from the electrical system in the event of alternator failure. With the alternator switch off, the entire electrical load is placed on the battery.

   a. In such case, all nonessential electrical equipment should be turned off to conserve the energy stored in the battery.

F. Although additional electrical equipment may be found in some airplanes, the following equipment commonly uses the electrical system:

1. Starter motor
2. Interior and exterior lighting
3. Flaps
4. Radio equipment
5. Turn indicator
6. Fuel gauges
7. Stall warning system
8. Pitot heat
9. Clock

G. A bus bar is used as a terminal in the airplane electrical system to connect the main electrical system to the equipment that uses the electricity. This simplifies the wiring system and provides a common point from which to distribute voltage throughout the system.

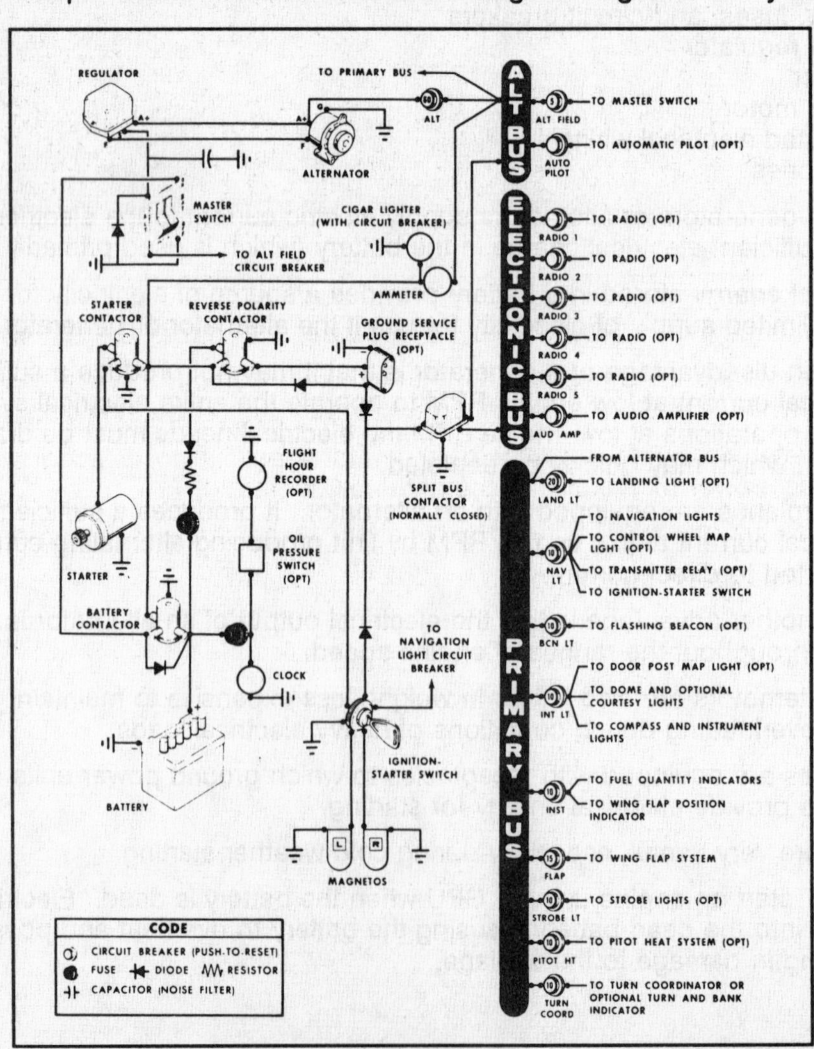

H. Fuses or circuit breakers protect the circuits and equipment from electrical overload.

1. Spare fuses of the proper amperage limit should be carried in the airplane at all times to replace defective or blown fuses.
2. Circuit breakers have the same function as a fuse but can be manually reset (rather than replaced) if an overload condition occurs in the electrical system.
   a. They are usually manually reset by pushing them in when they "pop out."
   b. If a circuit breaker pops out a second time after being reset, there is probably a short in that circuit. Accordingly, you should not continue to push the circuit breaker in. Fire may result.
3. Placards at the fuse or circuit breaker location identify the circuit by name and the amperage limit of the circuit.

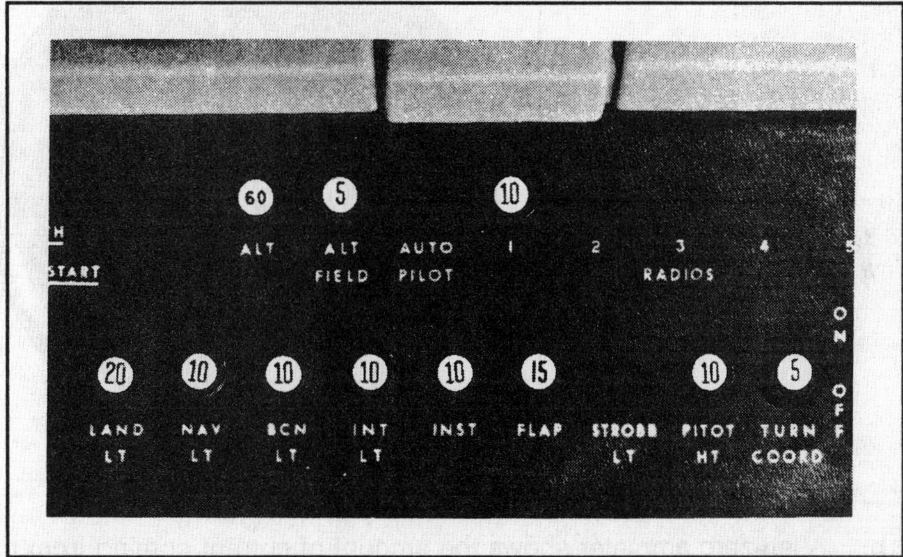


I. An ammeter is an instrument used to monitor the performance of the airplane electrical system.

1. Not all airplanes are equipped with an ammeter. Some are simply equipped with a light which, when lit, indicates a discharge in the system as a generator/alternator malfunction.
2. An ammeter shows if the generator/alternator is producing an adequate supply of electrical power by measuring the amperes of electricity.
   a. This instrument also indicates whether the battery is receiving an electrical charge.
3. See the illustration on page 116.

4. Ammeters are of either the center-zero or the left-zero type.
   a. A center-zero ammeter shows charge to or discharge from the battery.
      1) If the needle indicates a positive value, it means that the battery is being charged.
      2) If the needle indicates a negative value, it means that the battery is being discharged. This may occur during starting. At any other time, a negative value indicates an overload on the system or a defective alternator or generator.

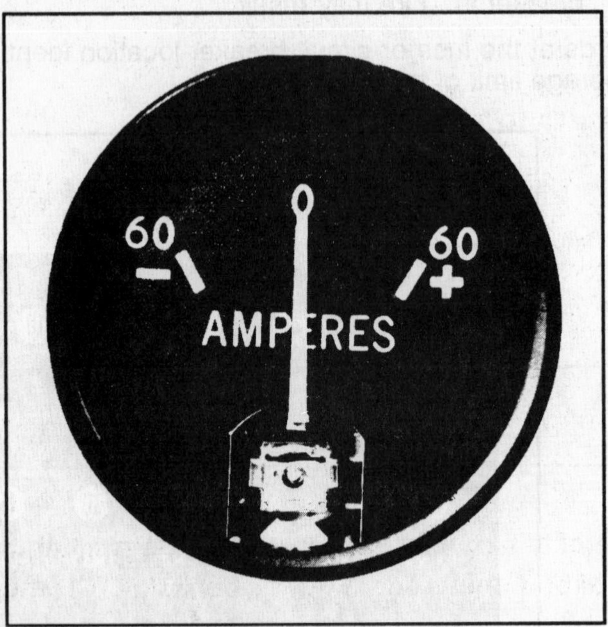


   b. A left-zero ammeter shows the amount of current coming from the alternator/generator.
      1) If the needle indicates zero and electrical equipment is being used, it means the generator/alternator has failed and current is being drawn from the battery.
   c. After power is drawn from the battery for starting, the needle will indicate a noticeable positive charge value for a short time. Then it should stabilize to a lower positive charge value.

# CHAPTER FIVE
# AIRPORTS AND AIR TRAFFIC CONTROL



The purpose of this chapter is to describe airports in terms of the facilities you will use as a pilot. Relatedly, airport operations, air traffic control (ATC), and radio communication procedures are discussed.

## 5.1 RUNWAY AND TAXIWAY MARKINGS

A. The FAA has established standard airport and runway markings. Since most airports are marked in this manner, it is important for you to know and understand these markings.

1. Markings for runways on airports and STOLports (Short Take Off and Landing) are white.
2. Markings for taxiways, closed areas, hazardous areas, and holding positions (even if they are on a runway) are yellow.

B. The following runway and taxiway standard markings relate to paved surfaces. At some smaller airports these markings may be slightly different.

1. Runway Numbers -- Runway numbers and letters are determined from the approach direction. The runway number is the whole number nearest one-tenth the magnetic direction of the runway. Letters differentiate between left (L), right (R), or center (C) parallel runways, if applicable.
   1) For two parallel runways "L" "R."
   2) For three parallel runways "L" "C" "R."
2. Runway markings are determined by the type of operations that runway is designed to handle (i.e., VFR or IFR traffic). You should know all types of markings as you may operate on any of these runway types.

a. Visual Runway Marking -- used for operations under visual flight rules (VFR):

1) Centerline marking. The runway centerline is a white dashed line.

2) Designation marking (i.e., runway number)

3) Threshold marking on runways used, or intended to be used, by international commercial air transport (see illustrations below and on page 119)

   a) The threshold is the designated beginning of the runway that is available and suitable for the landing of aircraft.

   b) The threshold marker is a set of four hash marks on either side of the centerline.

4) Fixed distance marking on runways 4,000 ft. or longer used by jet aircraft

   a) The first fixed distance marker is a single heavy hash mark on either side of the centerline. This is located 1,000 ft. from the threshold.

   b) Additional distance markers may be used every 500 ft. up to 3,000 ft. from the threshold or midpoint of the runway.

5) Holding position markings for taxiway/runway intersections (see the top diagram on page 121)

   a) These markings consist of four yellow lines, two solid and two dashed, extending across the width of the taxiway.

   b) The solid lines are always on the side where the aircraft is to hold.

6) Holding position markings at runway/runway intersections when runways are normally used for "land, hold short operations" or taxiing

   a) A sign with a white inscription on a red background is installed adjacent to these holding position markings.

   b) A land, hold short operation is one in which ATC instructions are "Cleared to land runway X, hold short of runway Y." The pilot must either exit runway X prior to runway Y or stop on runway X prior to runway Y.

b. Nonprecision Instrument Runway Marking -- Used on runways served by an instrument approach. Includes all of the visual runway markings below except it will always have the threshold marking.

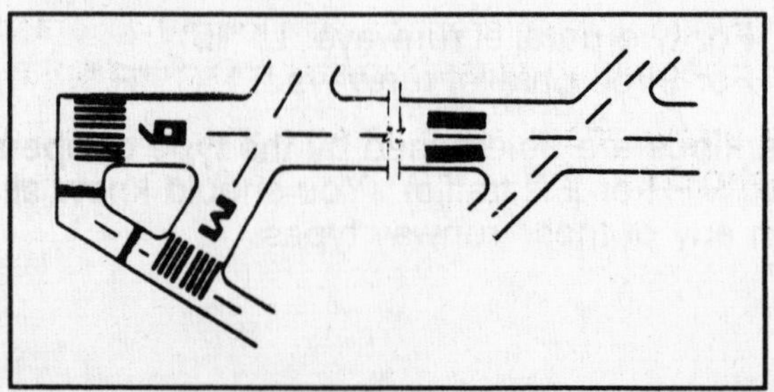

c. Precision Instrument Runway Marking -- Used on runways served by an instrument approach and on runways having special operating requirements. Includes all of the visual and nonprecision instrument markings except it will always have fixed distance markers, plus:

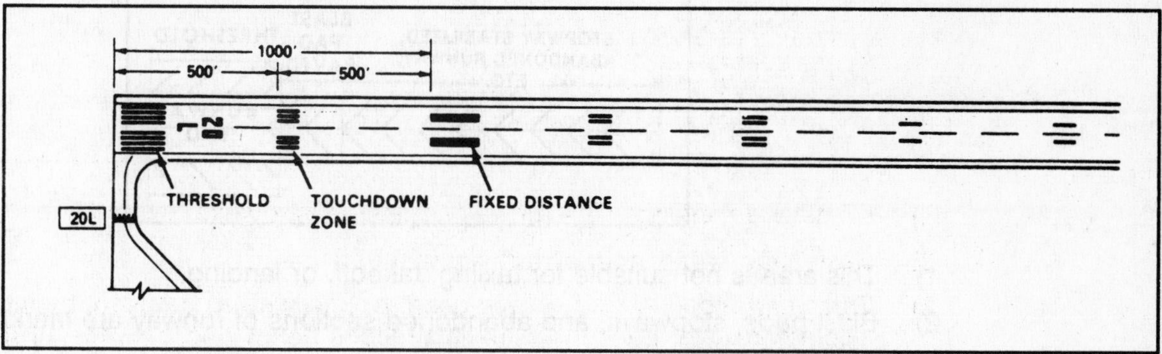


1) Touchdown zone marker.

a) The touchdown zone marker is a set of three hash marks on either side of the centerline.

b) This marker is located 500 ft. from the threshold.

2) Side stripes -- A single, white line on each side of the runway.

3. Additional Runway Markings

a. Displaced Threshold -- A threshold that is not at the beginning of the paved runway.

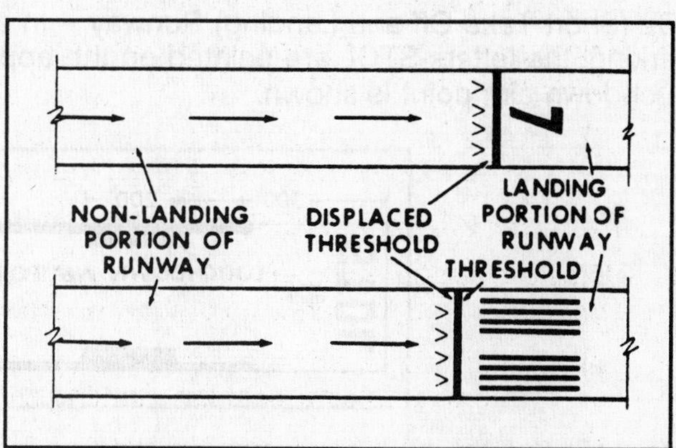


1) The paved area before the displaced runway threshold (marked by arrows) is available for taxiing, the takeoff of aircraft, and a landing rollout from the opposite direction, but not for landing in the direction of the runway in question.

2) A 10-ft. white threshold bar is located across the width of the runway at the displaced threshold.

3) White arrows are located along the centerline in the area between the beginning of the runway and the displaced threshold.

b. White arrow heads are located across the width of the runway just prior to the threshold bar.

c. Paved Areas beyond the Runway End -- Any paved area beyond the runway end that is not intended to be used is marked with yellow chevrons across the width of the pavement.

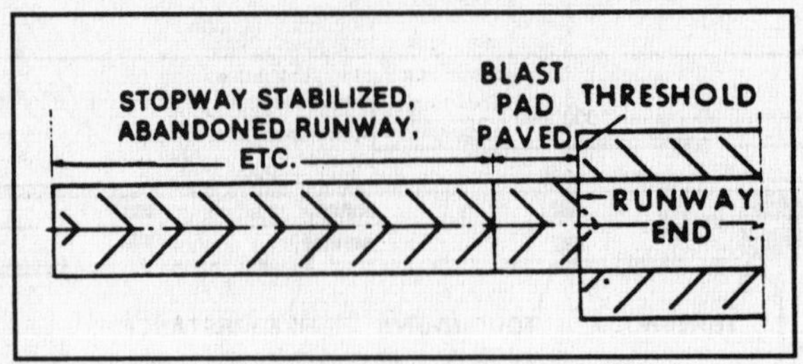


1) This area is not suitable for taxiing, takeoff, or landing.

2) Blast pads, stopways, and abandoned sections of runway are marked in this manner.

d. Closed Runway -- A runway surface which may appear usable but which, due to the nature of its structure or other reasons, has become unusable. It is marked with an X.

e. STOL (Short Take Off and Landing) Runway -- In addition to normal runway number marking, the letters STOL are painted on the approach end of the runway and a touchdown aim point is shown.

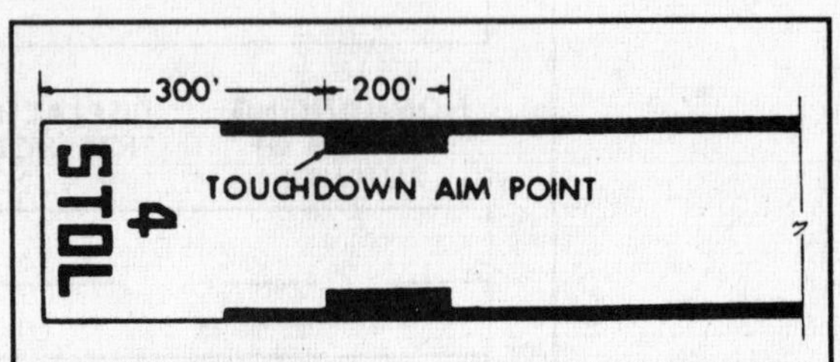


4. Taxiway Markings

a. The taxiway centerline is marked with a continuous yellow line.

b. When the taxiway edge is marked, two continuous yellow lines spaced 6 in. apart are used.

c. Holding position markings for ILS critical areas consist of two yellow solid lines spaced 2 ft. apart connected by pairs of solid lines spaced 10 ft. apart extended across the width of the taxiway as shown in the next figure.

1) A sign with an inscription "ILS" in white on a red background is installed adjacent to these holding position markings.

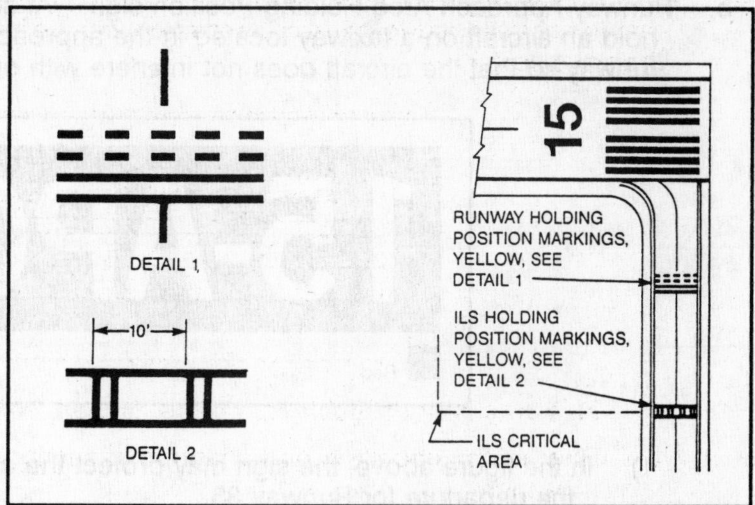


d. Holding position markings for taxiway/taxiway intersections consist of one dashed line extending across the width of the taxiway as shown below. They are installed on taxiways where ATC normally holds aircraft short of a taxiway intersection.

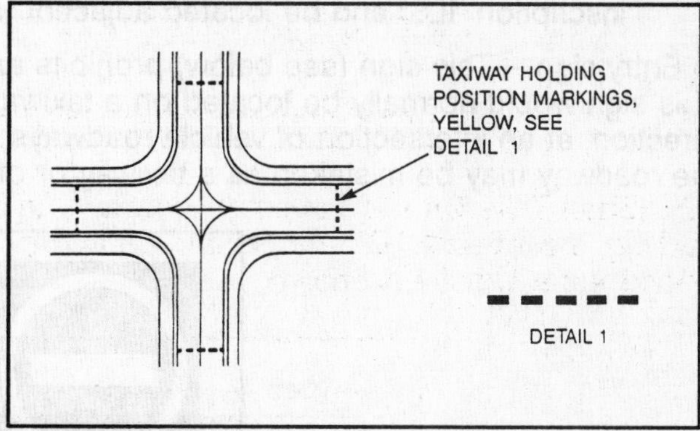


C. Airport signs are used on runways and taxiways to provide information. There are six types of signs installed on airports.

1. Mandatory instruction signs have white characters on a red background.

   a. Runway Holding Position sign is located at the holding position on taxiways that intersect a runway or on runways that intersect other runways.

1) The runway numbers on the sign are arranged to correspond to the respective runway threshold.

   a) EXAMPLE: In the figure above, "15-33" indicates that the threshold for Runway 15 is to the left and the threshold for Runway 33 is to the right.

b. Runway Approach Area Holding Position sign -- At some airports, it is necessary to hold an aircraft on a taxiway located in the approach or departure area for a runway so that the aircraft does not interfere with operations on that runway.

1) In the figure above, the sign may protect the approach to Runway 15 and/or the departure for Runway 33.

c. ILS Critical Area Holding Position sign -- At some airports, when the instrument landing system (ILS) is being used, it is necessary to hold an aircraft on a taxiway at a location other than the marked runway holding position.

1) In these situations the holding position sign for these operations will have the inscription "ILS" and be located adjacent to ILS holding position marking.

d. No Entry sign -- This sign (see below) prohibits an aircraft from entering an area. This sign would normally be located on a taxiway intended to be used in only one direction, at an intersection of vehicle roadways with runways or taxiways, or where the roadway may be mistaken as a taxiway or other aircraft movement area.

2. Location signs are used to identify either a taxiway or a runway on which the aircraft is located. Other location signs provide a visual clue to pilots to assist them in determining when they have exited an area.

a. Taxiway Location sign -- This sign has yellow characters on a black background and a yellow border as shown below.

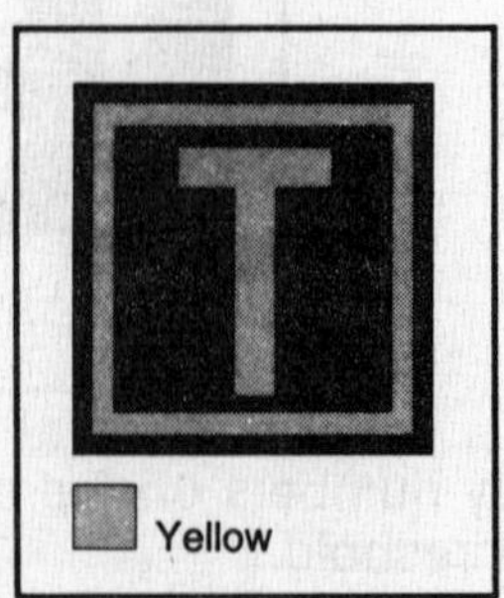

1) These signs are installed along taxiways either by themselves or in conjunction with direction signs or runway holding position signs.

b. Runway Location sign -- This sign is similar to the taxiway location sign except it will indicate on which runway the aircraft is located.

c. Runway Boundary sign -- This sign has a yellow background with a black inscription with a graphic depicting the pavement holding position marking, as shown below.

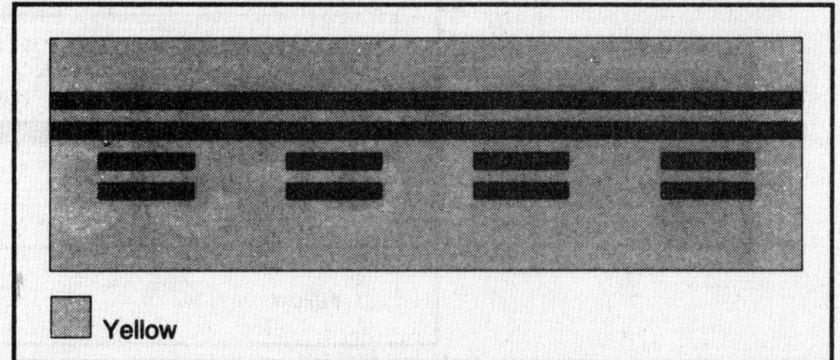


1) This sign, which faces the runway and is visible to the pilot exiting the runway, is located adjacent to the holding position marking on the pavement.

2) This sign is intended to provide pilots with another visual clue which they can use as a guide in deciding when they are "clear of the runway."

d. ILS Critical Area Boundary sign -- This sign has a graphic depicting the ILS pavement holding position marking.

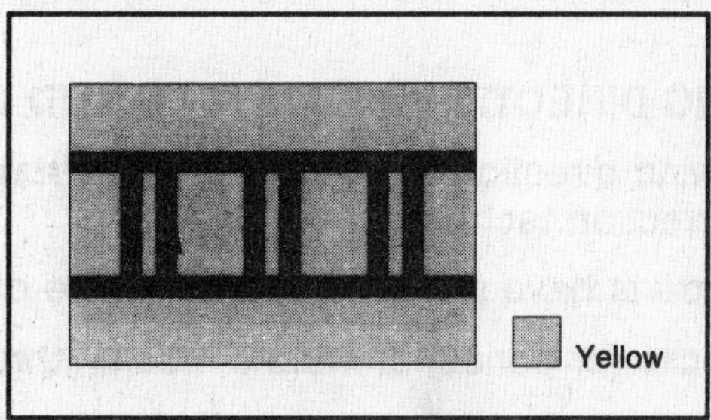


1) This sign is located adjacent to the pavement marking and is intended to assist the pilot in deciding when they are "clear of the ILS critical area."

3. Direction signs have black characters on a yellow background. The inscription identifies the designation(s) of the intersecting taxiway(s) leading out of the intersection that a pilot would normally be expected to turn onto or hold short of. Each designation is accompanied by an arrow indicating the direction of the turn.

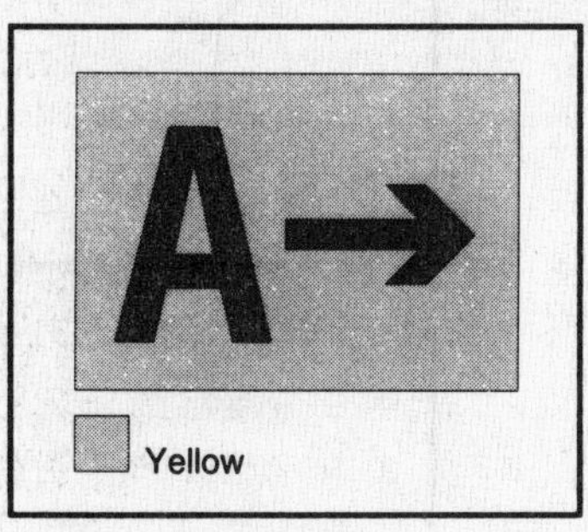

4. Destination signs also have black characters on a yellow background indicating a destination on the airport. These signs always have an arrow showing the direction of the taxiing route to that destination.
   a. Destinations commonly shown include runways, aprons (i.e., ramp), terminals, military areas (shown below), civil aviation areas, cargo areas, international areas, and fixed based operators (FBOs).

5. Information signs have black characters on a yellow background. They are used to provide the pilot with information on such things as areas that cannot be seen from the control tower, applicable radio frequencies, and noise abatement procedures.
6. Runway distance remaining signs are located along one or both side(s) of the runway. These signs have white numbers on a black background.
   a. The number on the sign indicates the distance (in thousands of feet) of runway remaining.

## 5.2 WIND AND LANDING DIRECTION INDICATORS AND SEGMENTED CIRCLES

A. You need to know wind direction to select the active runway at uncontrolled airports and to plan your crosswind correction technique.
   1. Virtually all airports have a wind indicator of one of the following types:
      a. Wind socks (or cones) are fabric "socks" through which wind blows.
         1) The toe of the sock points in the direction the wind is GOING (land in the opposite direction).
         2) The vertical angle out from the pole indicates the strength of the wind.
            a) A limp sock means no wind.
            b) A horizontal sock means strong wind.

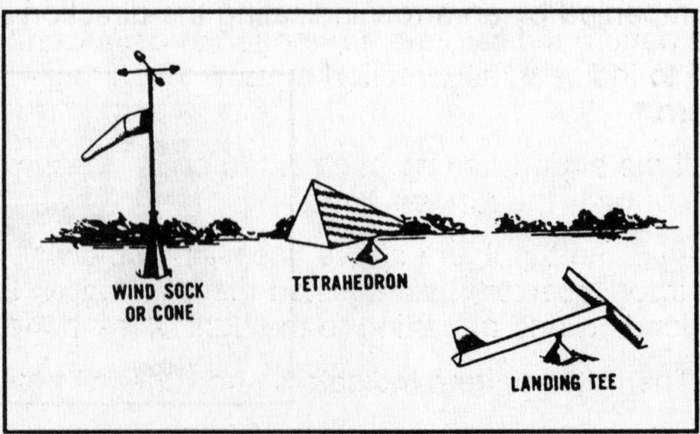

b. Wind (landing) tees have the stem (bottom) of the "T" pointing in the direction the wind is GOING (land in the opposite direction). Think of the wind tee as a small airplane with the wings represented by the crossbar (top) of the "T." It is landing into the wind.

1) Indicates the direction of the wind,
2) But NOT the wind velocity.

c. Tetrahedrons point to the direction from which the wind is COMING (land in that direction).

1) Indicates the direction of the wind,
2) But NOT the wind velocity.

2. Some airports have a landing direction indicator (tetrahedron) that is manually set by the airport operator to show the direction of landings and takeoffs.

a. Think of the tetrahedron as a delta-wing jet fighter. It is landing into the wind.
b. Pilots are cautioned against using the tetrahedron as a wind indicator.

3. Where wind or landing direction indicators do not exist, observe the flow of traffic or use natural indicators.

a. Smoke from ground fires, power plants, etc., shows wind direction.
b. The lee side (direction wind is coming from) of lakes and ponds tends to be smooth.

B. The segmented circle system provides traffic pattern information at airports without operating control towers. It consists of the

1. Segmented circle -- located in a position affording maximum visibility to pilots in the air and on the ground. A wind and/or landing direction indicator is usually in the center.

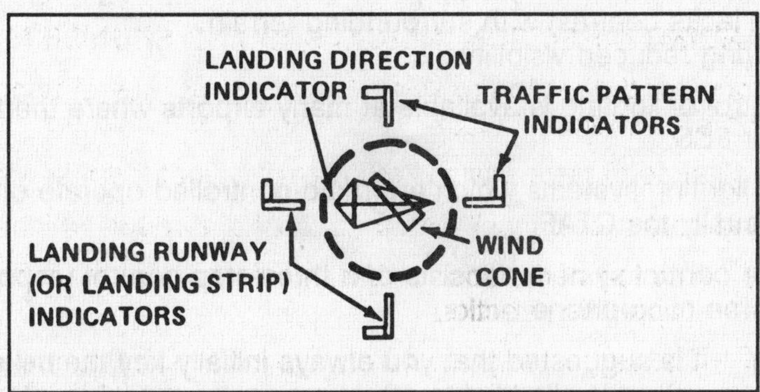


2. Landing strip (runway) indicators are installed in pairs as shown in the segmented circle above and are used to show the alignment of landing strips (i.e., landing runway).

3. Traffic pattern indicators are arranged in pairs with the landing strip indicators and are used to indicate the direction of turns when there is a variation from the normal left traffic pattern.

a. If the airport has no segmented circle, traffic pattern indicators may be installed on or near the runway ends.

4. EXAMPLE: In the figure above, the wind is blowing from the bottom right of the page, and the airport operator has adjusted the tetrahedron to show the horizontal runway to be in use, landing and departing to the right of the page.

a. The traffic pattern indicators show the left traffic pattern is to be used on this runway.

## 5.3 AIRPORT LIGHTING

A. Runway Lights

1. Edge lights are white and can be low, medium, or high intensity (the latter two can be controlled by control tower personnel).
   a. Runway edge lights help you identify runways as you approach the airport and also help you align your airplane on final approach.
   b. Designated instrument runways have the last 2,000 ft. lighted in aviation yellow (from the opposite approach these lights are white).
2. In-runway lights are found in some precision approach (designed for IFR traffic) runways.
   a. Centerline lights at 50-ft. intervals.
   b. Touchdown zone lights, marking the first 3,000 ft. of the runway.
   c. Centerline lighting systems have the last 3,000 to 1,000 ft. alternate red and white lights with the last 1,000 ft. all red (from the opposite approach these lights are white).
3. Runway threshold lights and runway end lights are straight lines of lights across each end of the runway.
   a. The threshold (beginning of runway) lights are green.
   b. The runway end lights are usually red.
4. Runway end identifier lights (REIL) are available at some airports. They are a pair of synchronized flashing white lights near the threshold of the runway. They help identify the beginning of the runway
   a. If it is surrounded by a preponderance of other lighting.
   b. If it lacks contrast with surrounding terrain.
   c. During reduced visibility.
5. Pilot control of lighting is available at many airports where there is no operating control tower or FSS.
   a. All lighting systems which are radio-controlled operate on the same frequency, usually the CTAF.
   b. The control system consists of a three-step control responsive to seven, five, and/or three microphone clicks.
      1) It is suggested that you always initially key the mike seven times to assure that all controlled lights are at maximum available intensity.
      2) You may lower the intensity (if applicable) by keying five or three times.
   c. Due to the close proximity of airports using the same frequency, radio-controlled lighting receivers may be set at a low sensitivity requiring the airplane to be relatively close.
      1) The lights will usually be activated for 15 min.
   d. The *Airport/Facility Directory* contains descriptions of pilot-controlled lighting at all available airports and their frequencies.

B. Taxiway lights are available at some airports.

1. They are blue and outline the usable limits of the taxiways.
2. Taxiway centerline lights are used during low visibility conditions. They emit a green light.

C. Airport Rotating Beacons

1. Primary purpose is to identify the location of airports at night.
2. Usually 12-30 flashes per min.
3. White and green alternating flashes indicate a lighted land airport for civil use.
4. Two whites and a green indicate a military airport.
5. A flashing amber light near the center of an airport's segmented circle or on top of a building means that a right-hand traffic pattern is in effect.
6. Operation of the green and white rotating beacon in a control zone during the day indicates that the weather is not VFR, i.e.,
   a. Less than 3 mi. visibility, and/or
   b. Ceiling less than 1,000 ft.
   c. However, there is no regulatory requirement for daylight operation of the rotating beacon.

D. Approach light systems (ALS) are designed for IFR transition to the runway lights, i.e., to help pilots coming through clouds on final approach to find the runway.

1. Approach light systems are a configuration of signal lights starting at the landing threshold and extending into the approach area (before you get to the runway).
   a. Some systems include sequenced flashing lights which appear to the pilot as a ball of light traveling toward the runway at high speed twice a second.

E. Obstructions are marked and lighted to warn pilots of their presence during daytime and night-time conditions. They may be marked/lighted in any of the following combinations:

1. Aviation red obstruction lights -- flashing aviation red beacons and steady aviation red lights at night. Aviation orange and white paint is used for daytime marking.
2. High-intensity white obstruction lights -- flashing high intensity white lights during daytime with reduced intensity for twilight and nighttime operation. With this type of system, the red obstruction lights and aviation orange and white paint may be omitted.
3. Dual lighting -- a combination of flashing aviation red beacons and steady aviation red lights at night and flashing high-intensity white lights in daylight. Aviation orange and white paint may be omitted.

## 5.4 VISUAL APPROACH SLOPE INDICATOR (VASI)

A. The VASI provides a color-coded visual glide path using a system of lights positioned alongside the runway, near the designated touchdown point. Its visual glide path safely clears all obstructions in the final approach area.

1. Once the principles and color code of the lighting system are understood, you simply note the colors and adjust your airplane's rate of descent to stay on the visual glide slope.
2. The VASI is especially effective during approaches over water or featureless terrain where other sources of visual reference are lacking or misleading, and at night.
3. It provides optimal descent guidance for landing and minimizes the possibility of undershooting or overshooting the designated touchdown area.

4. When you make an approach to land on a runway at a controlled airport that has an operating visual slope indicator, you are required to remain at or above the glide slope until it is necessary for a safe landing (FAR 91.129).
   a. This does not prohibit you from making normal bracketing maneuvers above or below the glide slope for the purpose of remaining on the glide slope.

B. Basically, the VASI system uses color differentiation between red and white.
   1. Each light unit projects a beam of light having a white segment in the upper part of the beam and a red segment in the lower part of the beam.
   2. When on the proper glide path, you will, in effect, overshoot the downwind (near) bars and undershoot the upwind (far) bars. Thus, the downwind bars will be seen as white and the upwind bars as red.
   3. From a position below the glide path you will see all the light bars as red. From above the glide path all the light bars will appear white.
   4. Passing through the glide path from a low position, you will see a transition in color from red to white. This will occur if you maintain or gain altitude.

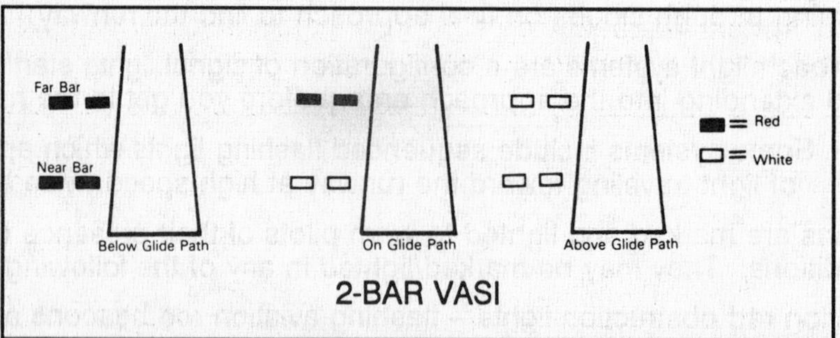


   5. Passing through the glide path from a high position, you will see a transition in color from white to red. This will occur if you begin above the VASI glide path and your rate of descent is too great (i.e., exceeds the VASI glide path).

C. Three-bar VASI installations provide two visual glide paths as shown below.
   1. The lower glide path is provided by the near and middle bars and is normally set at a 3° incline. The upper glide path, provided by the middle and far bars, is normally 1/4° higher. This higher glide path is intended for use only by high cockpit aircraft to provide a sufficient threshold-crossing height.
   2. When using a three-bar VASI it is not necessary to use all three bars. The near and middle bars constitute a two-bar VASI for using the lower glide path. Also, the middle and far bars constitute a two-bar VASI for using the upper glide path.
   3. The upper glide path is used by large aircraft, the lower by light, general aviation aircraft.

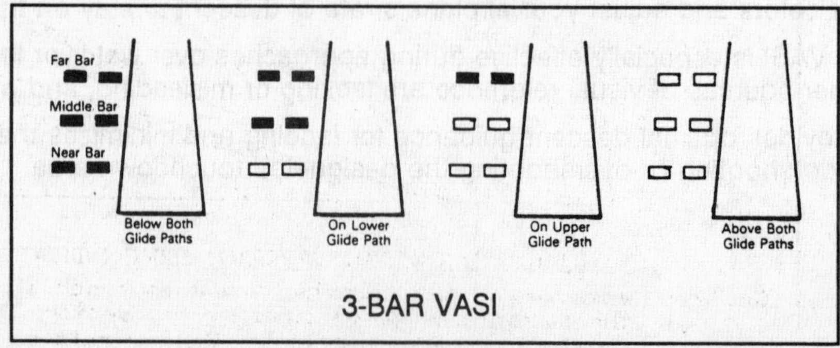

D. The Precision Approach Path Indicator (PAPI) uses lights similar to the VASI but in a single row of either two or four lights.

1. The row of light units is normally installed on the left side of the runway.
2. The glide path indications are depicted below.

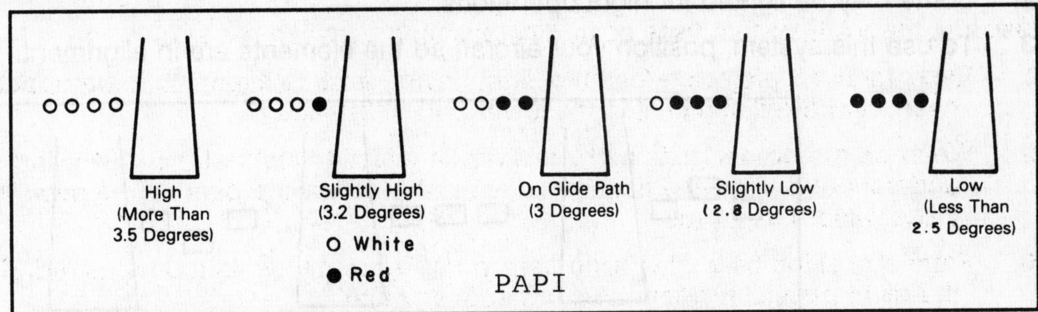


E. The Tri-color Approach Slope Indicator normally consists of a single light unit, projecting a three-color visual approach path into the final approach area of the runway.

1. In this system, the below glide path indication is red, the above glide path indication is amber, and the on-path indication is green.

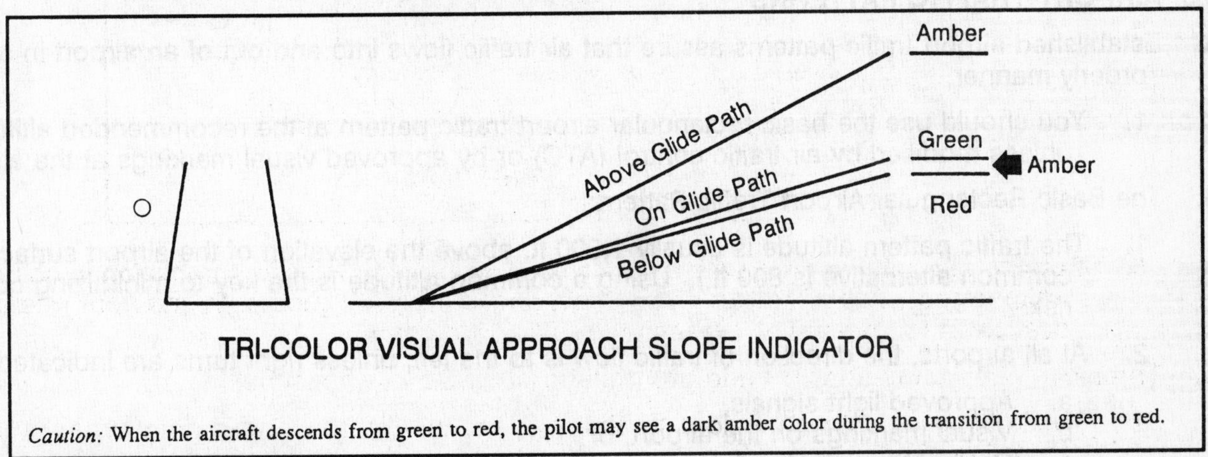


TRI-COLOR VISUAL APPROACH SLOPE INDICATOR

*Caution:* When the aircraft descends from green to red, the pilot may see a dark amber color during the transition from green to red.

F. Pulsating Visual Approach Slope Indicators normally consist of a single light unit projecting a two-color visual approach path.

1. Below the glide slope you see a pulsating red light.
2. Above the glide slope you see a pulsating white light.
3. On the glide slope you see a steady white light.

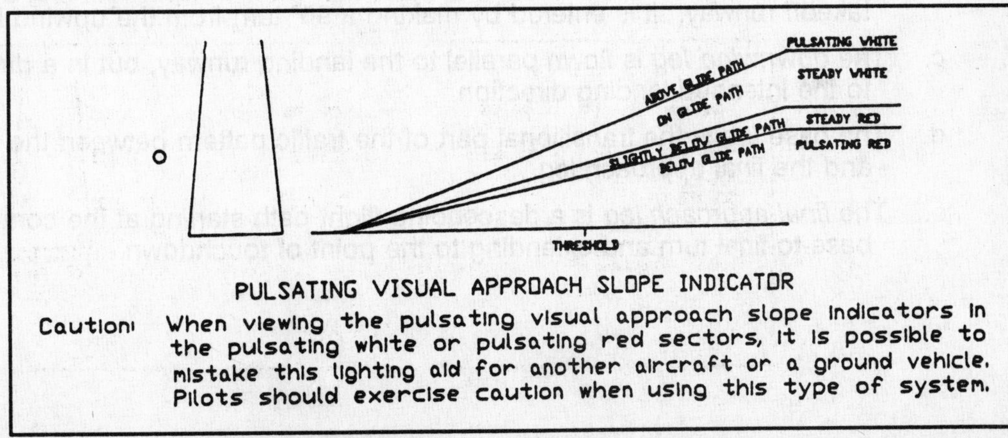


PULSATING VISUAL APPROACH SLOPE INDICATOR

Caution: When viewing the pulsating visual approach slope indicators in the pulsating white or pulsating red sectors, it is possible to mistake this lighting aid for another aircraft or a ground vehicle. Pilots should exercise caution when using this type of system.

G. Alignment of Elements System is not a lighting aid, but is included here because it is used as a visual glide slope indicator.

1. It is a low cost system consisting of painted plywood panels, normally black and white or fluorescent orange.
2. Some may be lighted for night operations.
3. To use this system, position your aircraft so the elements are in alignment.

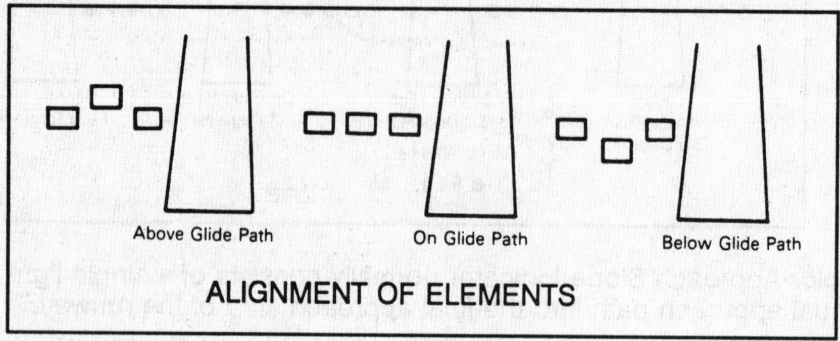


ALIGNMENT OF ELEMENTS

## 5.5 AIRPORT TRAFFIC PATTERNS

A. Established airport traffic patterns assure that air traffic flows into and out of an airport in an orderly manner.

1. You should use the basic rectangular airport traffic pattern at the recommended altitude unless modified by air traffic control (ATC) or by approved visual markings at the airport.

B. The Basic Rectangular Airport Traffic Pattern:

1. The traffic pattern altitude is usually 1,000 ft. above the elevation of the airport surface (a common alternative is 800 ft.). Using a common altitude is the key to minimizing collision risk.
2. At all airports, the direction of traffic flow is to the left, unless right turns are indicated by
   a. Approved light signals,
   b. Visual markings on the airport, or
   c. Control tower instructions.
3. The basic rectangular traffic pattern consists of five "legs" positioned in relation to the runway in use as illustrated on page 131.
   a. The *upwind leg* of the traffic pattern is a straight course aligned with, and leading from, the takeoff runway.
   b. The *crosswind leg* is horizontally perpendicular to the extended centerline of the takeoff runway. It is entered by making a 90° turn from the upwind leg.
   c. The *downwind leg* is flown parallel to the landing runway, but in a direction opposite to the intended landing direction.
   d. The *base leg* is the transitional part of the traffic pattern between the downwind leg and the final approach leg.
   e. The *final approach leg* is a descending flight path starting at the completion of the base-to-final turn and extending to the point of touchdown.

4. The Traffic Pattern

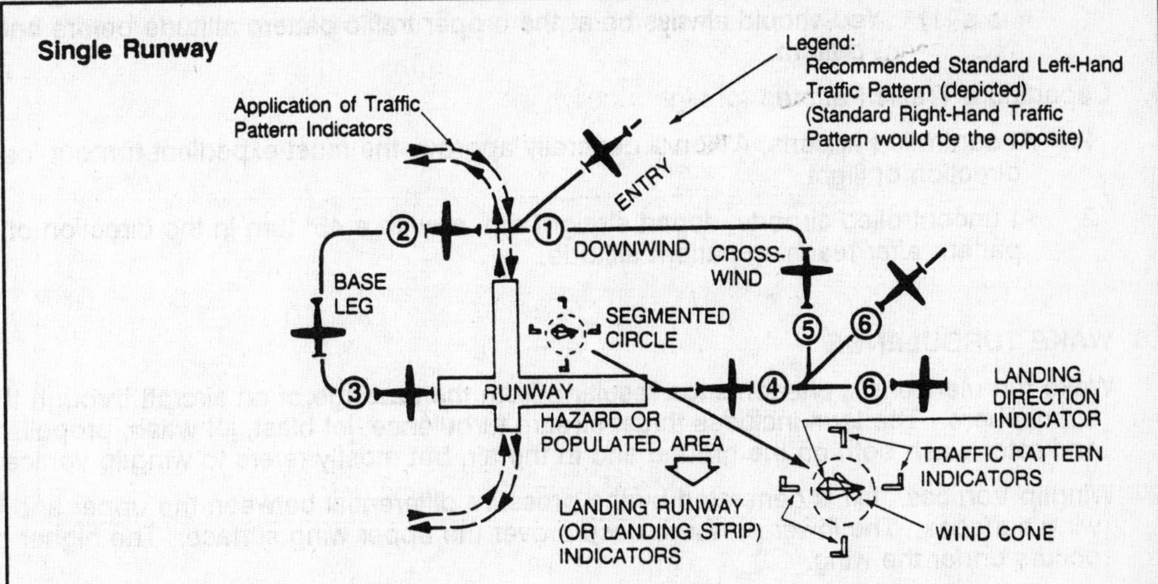


Key:

1. Enter pattern in level flight, abeam the midpoint of the runway, at pattern altitude.
2. Maintain pattern altitude until abeam approach end of the landing runway, or downwind leg.
3. Complete turn to final at least ¼ mi. from the runway.
4. Continue straight ahead until beyond departure end of runway.
5. If remaining in traffic pattern, commence turn to crosswind leg beyond the departure end of the runway, within 300 ft. of pattern altitude. Some pilots use 500 ft. AGL or similar rule of thumb.
6. If departing the traffic pattern, continue straight out, or exit with a 45° left turn beyond the departure end of the runway, after reaching pattern altitude.

C. Entering a Traffic Pattern

1. At a controlled airport (i.e., with an operating control tower), the controller will direct when and where you should enter the traffic pattern.
   a. Once in the pattern, the controller may request that you perform some maneuvers for better traffic spacing, including
      1) Shortening or extending the downwind leg,
      2) Increasing or decreasing your speed, or
      3) A 360° turn or S-turns to provide spacing ahead of you.
2. To enter the traffic pattern at an airport without a control tower, inbound pilots are expected to observe other aircraft already in the pattern and to conform to the traffic pattern in use.
   a. If no other aircraft are in the pattern, traffic and wind indicators on the ground must be checked to determine which runway and traffic pattern direction should be used.
      1) Overfly the airport at least 500 to 1,000 ft. above the traffic pattern altitude.
      2) After the proper traffic pattern direction has been determined, you should proceed to a point well clear of the pattern before descending to the pattern altitude.

b. When approaching an airport for landing, you should enter the traffic pattern at a 45° angle to the downwind leg at the midpoint of the runway.

1) You should always be at the proper traffic pattern altitude before entering the pattern.

D. Departing a Traffic Pattern

1. At controlled airports, ATC will generally approve the most expedient turnout for the direction of flight.

2. At uncontrolled airports, depart straight out, or with a 45° turn in the direction of the traffic pattern after reaching pattern altitude.

## 5.6 WAKE TURBULENCE

A. Wake turbulence is a phenomenon resulting from the passage of an aircraft through the atmosphere. The term includes thrust stream turbulence, jet blast, jet wash, propeller wash, and rotor wash both on the ground and in the air, but mostly refers to wingtip vortices.

B. Wingtip Vortices. Lift is generated by the pressure differential between the upper and lower wing surfaces. The lower pressure occurs over the upper wing surface. The higher pressure occurs under the wing.

1. This pressure differential triggers a roll-up of the airflow behind the wing.

a. It results in swirling air masses trailing downstream of the wingtips.

2. After the roll-up is completed, the wake consists of two counter rotating cylindrical vortices.

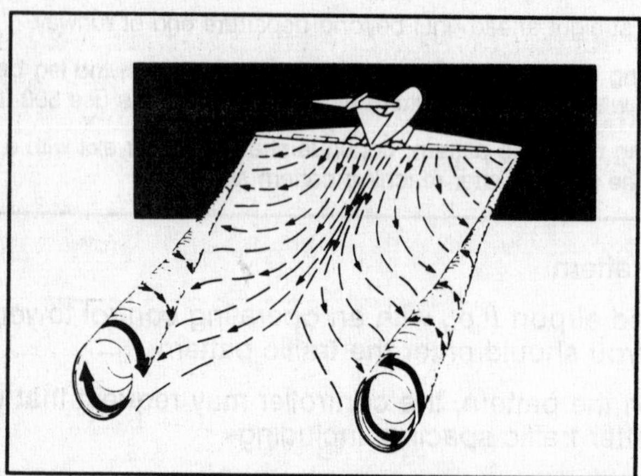

C. The strength of an airplane's wingtip vortices are governed by the weight, speed, and wing shape of the generating aircraft.

1. The angle of attack of the wingtip directly affects the strength of its vortex.

a. As weight increases, angle of attack increases.

b. A wing in the clean configuration (flaps retracted) has a greater angle of attack at the wingtip than when flaps are extended.

c. As airspeed decreases, angle of attack increases.

2. Thus, the greatest vortex strength occurs when the generating aircraft is HEAVY, CLEAN, and SLOW, e.g., during landing and especially during takeoff.

3. Wake turbulence presents a hazard to any aircraft that is significantly lighter than the generating aircraft.
    a. An airplane encountering such wake turbulence could incur major structural damage while in flight.
    b. The usual hazard is associated with induced rolling which can exceed the rolling capability of the encountering aircraft.
        1) That is, your airplane may be uncontrollable in the wake turbulence of a large transport airplane.

D. Trailing vortices have certain behavioral characteristics which can help you visualize the wake location and avoid them:
1. Vortices are generated from the moment the airplane rotates for takeoff (i.e., nosewheel off the ground), since trailing vortices are a by-product of wing lift.

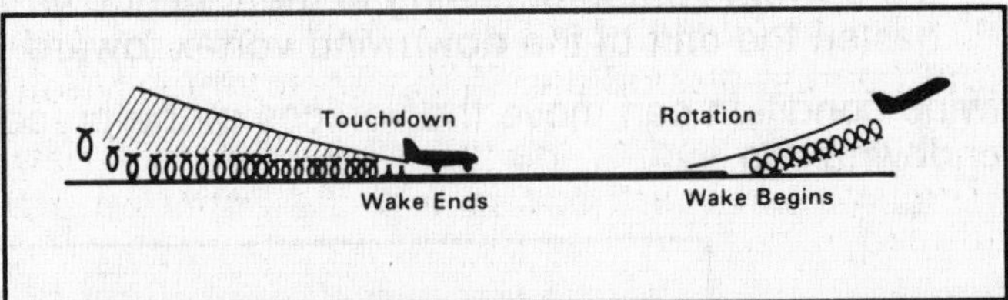


2. The vortex circulation is outward, upward, and around the wingtips. Each vortex is about two wingspans in width and one wingspan in depth.
    a. The vortices remain spaced about a wingspan apart, drifting with the wind, at altitudes greater than a wingspan from the ground.
    b. If you encounter persistent vortex turbulence, a slight change of altitude and lateral position (preferably upwind) will provide a flight path clear of the turbulence.
3. Vortices from large aircraft sink at a rate of about 400 to 500 fpm and level off at a distance about 900 ft. below the flight path of the generating aircraft.
    a. You should fly at or above the large aircraft's flight path, altering course as necessary to avoid the area behind and below the generating aircraft.

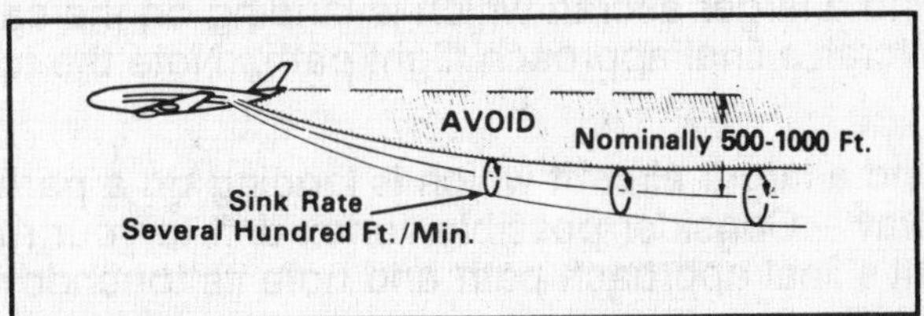


4. When the vortices of large aircraft sink close to the ground (within 100 to 200 ft.), they tend to move laterally over the ground at a speed of about 2 or 3 kt.

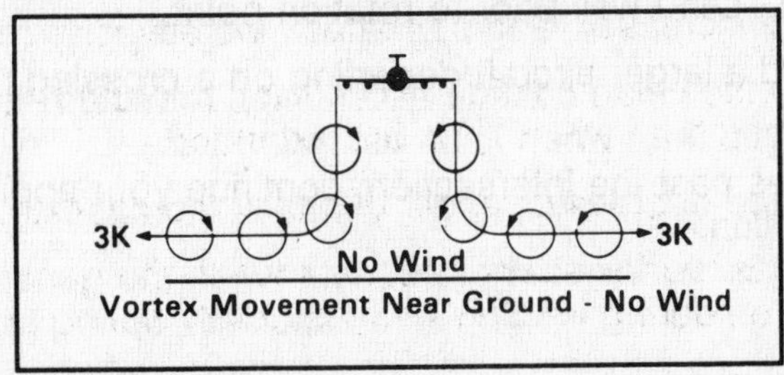

Vortex Movement Near Ground - No Wind

a. A crosswind will decrease the lateral movement of the upwind vortex and increase the movement of the downwind vortex.

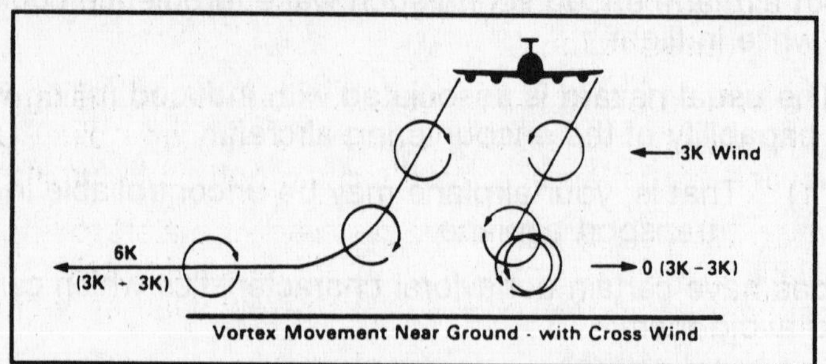


1) Thus, a light wind with a cross runway component of 1 to 5 kt. could result in the upwind vortex remaining in the touchdown zone for a period of time and hasten the drift of the downwind vortex toward another runway.

b. A tailwind condition can move the vortices of the preceding aircraft forward into the touchdown zone.

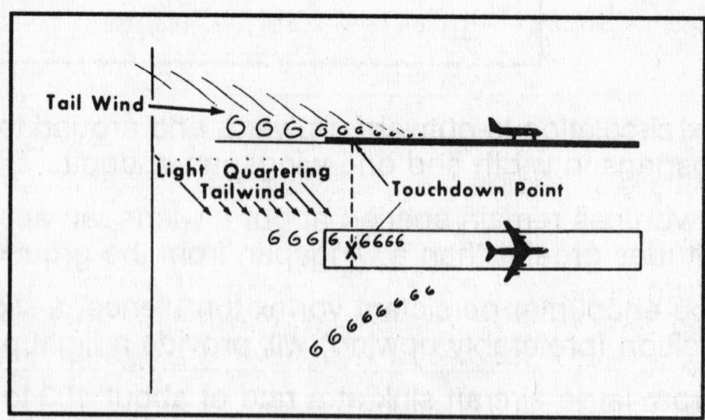


1) A light quartering tailwind requires the maximum caution.

E. The following vortex avoidance procedures are recommended:

1. Landing behind a larger aircraft which is landing on the same runway -- Stay at or above the larger aircraft's final approach flight path. Note the touchdown point and land beyond it.
2. Landing behind a larger aircraft which is landing on a parallel runway closer than 2,500 ft. to your runway -- Consider possible vortex drift to your runway. Stay at or above the larger aircraft's final approach path and note its touchdown point.
3. Landing behind a larger aircraft which is landing on a crossing runway -- Cross above the larger aircraft's flight path.
4. Landing behind a larger aircraft departing on the same runway -- Note the larger aircraft's rotation point. Land well prior to rotation point.
5. Landing behind a larger aircraft departing on a crossing runway -- Note the larger aircraft's rotation point.

   a. If it rotates past the intersection, continue your approach and land prior to the intersection.

b. If the larger aircraft rotates prior to the intersection, avoid flight below the larger aircraft's flight path.

1) Abandon the approach unless your landing is assured well before reaching the intersection.

6. Departing behind a larger aircraft taking off -- Note the larger aircraft's rotation point. You should rotate prior to the larger aircraft's rotation point. Continue to climb above and stay upwind of the larger aircraft's climb path until turning clear of its wake.
7. Intersection takeoffs on the same runway -- Be alert to adjacent larger aircraft operations, particularly upwind of your runway. If intersection takeoff clearance is received, avoid a subsequent heading which will cross below a larger aircraft's path.
8. Departing or landing after a larger aircraft has executed a low approach, missed approach, or touch-and-go landing -- Because vortices settle and move laterally near the ground, the vortex hazard may exist along the runway and in your flight path.

   a. You should ensure that an interval of at least 2 min. has elapsed before your takeoff or landing.

9. En route VFR -- Avoid flight below and behind a larger aircraft's path. If you observe a larger aircraft above and on the same track as your airplane (meeting or overtaking), adjust your position laterally, preferably upwind.

## 5.7 RADIO COMMUNICATIONS AND PHRASEOLOGY

A. Airplane communication radios greatly facilitate flying. Pilots use radios to

1. Obtain air traffic control (ATC) clearances.

   a. Ground control
   b. Tower control, e.g., takeoffs and landings
   c. Approach and departure control (in the vicinity of the airport)
   d. En route control from ATC center

2. Obtain weather briefings, file flight plans, etc., with Flight Service Stations (FSS).
3. Communicate with FBOs and each other on UNICOM and MULTICOM frequencies.

B. Airplane communication radios operate on frequencies between 118.000 MHz and 135.975 MHz.

1. Channels exist every .05 MHz, e.g., 120.80, 120.85, 120.90, 120.95, etc.

   a. Thus, 360 channels exist between 118.0 and 135.95.

2. Most new communication radios have 720 channels by having a channel every .025 MHz.
3. Virtually all FAA frequencies are in multiples of .05 MHz.

C. Radio communications are a critical link in the ATC system. The link can be a strong bond between you and the controller or it can be broken with surprising speed and disastrous results.

1. The single most important thought in pilot-controller communications is understanding.

   a. Good phraseology enhances safety and is a mark of a professional pilot.
   b. Jargon, chatter, and "CB" slang have no place in ATC communications.

D. Phonetic Alphabet

1. You should use the phonetic alphabet when identifying your airplane during initial contact with air traffic control facilities.
2. Additionally, use the phonetic equivalents for single letters and for spelling out groups of letters or difficult words during adverse communication conditions.

3. Work through the following listing of alphabetic phonetic equivalents, saying each out loud to learn it.

   a. Note that the Morse code is also provided. Although it is not used as frequently as it once was, occasionally you may need it for identification, e.g., at a VOR without voice facilities. You need not learn the Morse code, just keep it handy.

| | | | | | | | |
|---|---|---|---|---|---|---|---|
| A | .- | Alpha | (AL-FAH) | T | - | Tango | (TANG-GO) |
| B | -... | Bravo | (BRAH-VOH) | U | ..- | Uniform | (YOU-NEE-FORM) |
| C | -.-. | Charlie | (CHAR-LEE) or (SHAR-LEE) | V | ...- | Victor | (VIK-TAR) |
| D | -.. | Delta | (DELL-TAH) | W | .-- | Whiskey | (WISS-KEY) |
| E | . | Echo | (ECK-OH) | X | -..- | Xray | (ECKS-RAY) |
| F | ..-. | Foxtrot | (FOKS-TROT) | Y | -.-- | Yankee | (YANG-KEY) |
| G | --. | Golf | (GOLF) | Z | --.. | Zulu | (ZOO-LOO) |
| H | .... | Hotel | (HOH-TEL) | | | | |
| I | .. | India | (IN-DEE-AH) | | | | |
| J | .--- | Juliett | (JEW-LEE-ETT) | 1 | .---- | One | (WUN) |
| K | -.- | Kilo | (KEY-LOH) | 2 | ..--- | Two | (TOO) |
| L | .-.. | Lima | (LEE-MAH) | 3 | ...-- | Three | (TREE) |
| M | -- | Mike | (MIKE) | 4 | ....- | Four | (FOW-ER) |
| N | -. | November | (NO-VEM-BER) | 5 | ..... | Five | (FIVE) |
| O | --- | Oscar | (OS-CAR) | 6 | -.... | Six | (SIX) |
| P | .--. | Papa | (PAH-PAH) | 7 | --... | Seven | (SEVEN) |
| Q | --.- | Quebec | (KEH-BECK) | 8 | ---.. | Eight | (AIT) |
| R | .-. | Romeo | (ROW-ME-OH) | 9 | ----. | Nine | (NIN-ER) |
| S | ... | Sierra | (SEE-AIR-RAH) | 0 | ----- | Zero | (ZEE-RO) |

E. Figures

1. Figures indicating hundreds and thousands in round numbers, as for ceiling heights, and upper wind levels up to 9,900 are spoken in accordance with the following:

   a. EXAMPLES: 500 is "FIVE HUNDRED."
      4,500 is "FOUR THOUSAND FIVE HUNDRED."

2. Numbers above 9,900 are spoken by separating the digits preceding the word "thousand."

   a. EXAMPLES: 10,000 is "ONE ZERO THOUSAND."
      13,500 is "ONE THREE THOUSAND FIVE HUNDRED."

3. Airway numbers. Airways are routes between navigational aids, such as VORs (i.e., airways are highways in the sky).

   a. EXAMPLE: V12 is "VICTOR TWELVE."

4. All other numbers are spoken by pronouncing each digit.

   a. EXAMPLE: 10 is "ONE ZERO."

5. When a radio frequency contains a decimal point, the decimal point is spoken as "POINT."

   a. EXAMPLE: 122.1 is "ONE TWO TWO POINT ONE."

F. Altitudes and Flight Levels

1. Up to but not including 18,000 ft. MSL, state the separate digits of the thousands, plus the hundreds, if appropriate.

   a. EXAMPLES: 12,000 is "ONE TWO THOUSAND."
      12,500 is "ONE TWO THOUSAND FIVE HUNDRED."

2. At and above 18,000 ft. MSL (FL 180), state the words "flight level" followed by the separate digits of the flight level.
   a. EXAMPLE: FL 190 is "FLIGHT LEVEL ONE NINER ZERO" (19,000 ft. MSL).

G. Directions. The three digits of bearing, course, heading, and wind direction should always be magnetic. The word "TRUE" must be added when it applies.

1. EXAMPLES:
   a. (Magnetic course) 005 is "ZERO ZERO FIVE."
   b. (True course) 050 is "ZERO FIVE ZERO TRUE."
   c. (Magnetic bearing) 360 is "THREE SIX ZERO."
   d. (Magnetic heading) 100 is "ONE ZERO ZERO."
   e. (Wind direction) 220 is "TWO TWO ZERO."
2. Wind velocity (speed) is always included with wind direction, e.g., "THREE FOUR ZERO AT ONE ZERO."
   a. ATC gives winds in magnetic direction.
   b. FSS gives winds in true direction, from weather reports and forecasts.

H. Speeds

1. Say the separate digits of the speed followed by the word "knots."
   a. EXAMPLES: 250 is "TWO FIVE ZERO KNOTS."
      185 is "ONE EIGHT FIVE KNOTS."
2. The controller may omit the word "knots" when using speed adjustment procedures, e.g., "INCREASE SPEED TO ONE FIVE ZERO."

I. Time

1. The FAA uses Coordinated Universal Time for all operations.
   a. Abbreviated as UTC, Z, or Zulu.
2. To convert from Standard Time to Coordinated Universal Time:
   a. Eastern Standard Time, add 5 hr.
   b. Central Standard Time, add 6 hr.
   c. Mountain Standard Time, add 7 hr.
   d. Pacific Standard Time, add 8 hr.
3. For Daylight Time, use 4-5-6-7 instead of 5-6-7-8.
4. To convert from Zulu to local time, subtract rather than add.
5. The 24-hr. clock system is used in radio transmissions. The hour is indicated by the first two figures and the minutes by the last two figures.
   a. EXAMPLES: 0000 is "ZERO ZERO ZERO ZERO" (midnight)
      0920 is "ZERO NINER TWO ZERO" (9:20 a.m.)
      1850 is "ONE EIGHT FIVE ZERO" (6:50 p.m.)

J. Your radio broadcasts can be thought of as

1. Who you are,
2. Where you are, and
3. What you want to do.

This works in virtually all situations.

## 5.8 UNCONTROLLED AIRPORTS

A. An uncontrolled airport is an airport that does not have an operating control tower (i.e., there is no air traffic control over movements of aircraft on the ground or around the airport in the air).

1. It is essential that pilots be alert and look for other traffic and exchange information when approaching or departing an uncontrolled airport.
   a. This is of particular importance since other aircraft may not have communication capability, or in some cases, pilots may not communicate their presence or intentions.
2. To achieve the greatest degree of safety, it is essential that all radio-equipped aircraft transmit/receive on a common frequency identified for the purpose of airport advisories.
   a. The key to communicating at an uncontrolled airport is the selection of the correct frequency. The term CTAF, which stands for Common Traffic Advisory Frequency, is synonymous with this program.
      1) CTAF is a frequency designated for the purpose of carrying out airport advisory practices at an uncontrolled airport.
      2) CTAF may be a UNICOM, MULTICOM, FSS, or tower frequency.
      3) The CTAF at an airport is indicated on the sectional chart by a © next to the appropriate frequency.
   b. Pilots of inbound aircraft should monitor and communicate as appropriate on the CTAF 10 mi. from the airport.
      1) Pilots of departing aircraft should monitor and communicate on the CTAF from start-up, during taxi, and until 10 mi. from the airport unless the FARs or local procedures require otherwise.
3. There are three ways for you to communicate your intentions and obtain airport/traffic information when operating at an uncontrolled airport.
   a. Local Airport Advisory (LAA).
   b. UNICOM (an Aeronautical Advisory Station), or
   c. Make a self-announced broadcast.

B. LAA is a service provided by an FSS located at an uncontrolled airport.

1. The FSS should be contacted on the CTAF for airport advisories, including traffic and weather information.
2. Recommended LAA Phraseologies
   a. Inbound example
      1) Pilot: JONESBORO RADIO, PIPER TOMAHAWK 1617T IS 10 MILES SOUTH, AT (ALTITUDE), LANDING JONESBORO, REQUEST AIRPORT ADVISORY.
   b. Outbound example
      1) Pilot: JONESBORO RADIO, TOMAHAWK 1617T, READY TO TAXI, VFR, DEPARTING TO THE (DIRECTION), REQUEST AIRPORT ADVISORY.

C. UNICOM is a nongovernment air/ground radio communication station which may provide airport advisories at airports where there is no tower or FSS. UNICOM stations may provide pilots with weather information, wind direction, the recommended runway, or other necessary information.

1. If the UNICOM frequency is designated as the CTAF, it will be identified on aeronautical charts and the Airport/Facility Directory.
   a. UNICOM frequencies include 122.8, 122.7, 122.725, 122.975, and 123.0 MHz.
2. In communicating with a UNICOM station the following practices will help reduce frequency congestion, facilitate a better understanding of pilot intentions, help identify the location of aircraft in the traffic pattern, and enhance safety of flight.
   a. Select the correct UNICOM frequency.
   b. State the identification (i.e., airport name) of the UNICOM station you are calling at the beginning and end of each transmission.
   c. Speak slowly and distinctly.
   d. Approximately 10 mi. from the airport, report altitude, state your airplane type, airplane identification, location relative to the airport, whether landing or overflight, and request wind information and runway in use.
   e. Report on downwind, base, and final approach.
   f. Report leaving the runway.
3. Recommended UNICOM Phraseologies
   a. Inbound examples
      1) Pilot: JONESVILLE UNICOM CESSNA ONE ZERO TWO FOXTROT, 10 MILES NORTH DESCENDING THROUGH (ALTITUDE) LANDING JONESVILLE, REQUEST WIND AND RUNWAY INFORMATION JONESVILLE.
         a) Response: CESSNA CALLING JONESVILLE, WIND THREE FOUR ZERO AT SEVEN, RUNWAY THREE SIX IN USE WITH TWO AIRCRAFT IN THE PATTERN.
      2) Pilot: JONESVILLE TRAFFIC CESSNA ONE ZERO TWO FOXTROT ENTERING (DOWNWIND/BASE/FINAL) FOR RUNWAY THREE SIX (FULL STOP/ TOUCH-AND-GO) JONESVILLE.
      3) Pilot: JONESVILLE TRAFFIC CESSNA ONE ZERO TWO FOXTROT CLEAR OF RUNWAY THREE SIX JONESVILLE.
   b. Outbound examples
      1) Pilot: JONESVILLE UNICOM CESSNA ONE ZERO TWO FOXTROT (LOCATION ON AIRPORT) TAXIING TO RUNWAY THREE SIX, REQUEST WIND AND TRAFFIC INFORMATION JONESVILLE.
      2) Pilot: JONESVILLE TRAFFIC CESSNA ONE ZERO TWO FOXTROT DEPARTING RUNWAY THREE SIX. REMAINING IN THE PATTERN/ DEPARTING THE PATTERN TO THE (DIRECTION) (AS APPROPRIATE) JONESVILLE.

D. MULTICOM is a frequency (122.9 MHz) used for self-announce procedures at uncontrolled airports that are not served by an FSS or a UNICOM.

1. At such an airport, the MULTICOM frequency will be identified on charts as the CTAF.
2. Use the same phraseology as explained for UNICOM.

E. Summary of Recommended Communication Procedures

| | FACILITY AT AIRPORT | FREQUENCY USE | COMMUNICATION/BROADCAST PROCEDURES | |
|---|---|---|---|---|
| | | | OUTBOUND | INBOUND |
| 1. | UNICOM (No Tower or FSS) | Communicate with UNICOM station on published CTAF frequency (122.7, 122.8, 122.725, 122.975, or 123.0). If unable to contact UNICOM station, use self-announce procedures on CTAF. | Before taxiing and before taxiing on the runway for departure. | 10 miles out. Entering downwind, base, and final. Leaving the runway. |
| 2. | No Tower, FSS, or UNICOM | Self-announce on MULTICOM frequency 122.9. | Before taxiing and before taxiing on the runway for departure. | 10 miles out. Entering downwind, base, and final. Leaving the runway. |
| 3. | No Tower in operation, FSS open | Communicate with FSS on CTAF frequency. | Before taxiing and before taxiing on the runway for departure. | 10 miles out. Entering downwind, base, and final. Leaving the runway. |
| 4. | FSS closed (No Tower or Tower closed) | Self-announce on CTAF. | Before taxiing and before taxiing on the runway for departure. | 10 miles out. Entering downwind, base, and final. Leaving the runway. |

F. Observing and avoiding other aircraft at uncontrolled airports is of paramount importance.

1. Relatedly, being considerate to the other pilots should have high priority both in the air and on the ground.
2. Self-announce position and intentions on the appropriate frequency.
3. Make a 360° turn at the end of the runway before take-off to carefully scan for local traffic.
4. Follow local traffic pattern, noise abatement, and other procedures diligently.
5. Final approach should not be made shorter than necessary. A short final may lead to a missed approach because aircraft may taxi to runway without seeing you.
6. Finally, do not assume absence of traffic because few airplanes use an airport.

## 5.9 CONTROLLED AIRPORTS

A. A controlled airport is an airport that has an operating control tower and normally has both

1. Ground control for control of aircraft taxiing on the surface of the airport (except the runway).
2. Tower control for control of aircraft on the active runway and within the Class D airspace area (formerly an airport traffic area).

B. Many busy airports also have approach control and departure control.

1. The approach or departure controller coordinates arriving and departing traffic, usually for a busy airport with a control tower.
2. Approach and departure control coordinates traffic outside the traffic area (but often vectors you well within the airport traffic area before handing you over to the control tower).

C. Clearance delivery is a required communication at very busy and medium density airports. It is used before contacting ground control.

D. Automatic Terminal Information Service (ATIS) is a continuous airport advisory service also provided at very busy and medium density airports.

## 5.10 AUTOMATIC TERMINAL INFORMATION SERVICE (ATIS)

A. If available, the ATIS frequency is listed on the sectional chart just under the tower control frequency for the airport, e.g., ATIS 125.05. ATIS provides a continuous transmission that provides information for arriving and departing aircraft, including

1. Weather for the airport, such as clouds and visibility information.
2. Surface wind direction (magnetic) and velocity.
3. Altimeter setting.
4. Active runway and instrument approaches in use.
5. Approach and departure control frequencies.
6. Other relevant airport information, e.g., closed runways.

B. The purpose of ATIS is to relieve the ground controllers' and approach controllers' workload. They need not repeat the same information.

C. The ATIS broadcast is updated whenever any official weather is received regardless of content or changes, or when a change is made in other pertinent data such as runway change. Each new broadcast is labeled with a letter of the alphabet at the beginning of the broadcast, e.g., "this is information alpha," or "information bravo."

1. Every aircraft arriving at or departing from an airport with ATIS should monitor ATIS before contacting approach, tower, clearance delivery, or ground control to receive that airport's weather information.

2. When you contact approach, tower, clearance delivery, or ground control you should indicate you have the ATIS information by stating "with information (the letter code labeling the broadcast)."

   a. EXAMPLES:

      1) DAYTONA APPROACH, CESSNA 66421, TWO ZERO MILES NORTH, INBOUND TO DAYTONA REGIONAL WITH INFORMATION ALPHA.

      2) DAYTONA GROUND, CESSNA 66421, AT DAYTONA BEACH AVIATION, REQUEST TAXI, VFR SOUTHBOUND WITH INFORMATION BRAVO.

   b. NOTE: The phrase "HAVE NUMBERS" does not indicate receipt of the ATIS broadcast and should never be used for this purpose.

## 5.11 GROUND CONTROL

A. At a controlled airport, you will usually talk with ground control before taxiing. The ground controller coordinates the movement of aircraft on the surface of the airport. When you call ground control, you should say five things:

1. Address the ground controller, e.g., "Gainesville ground."
2. Type of airplane and the airplane's number, e.g., "Beech Skipper 66421."
3. Where you are on the airport surface, e.g., "North ramp," and at which FBO (if more than one).
4. Where you want to go and that you are ready to taxi, e.g., "Taxi VFR southbound."
5. Tell them you have ATIS (if appropriate), e.g., "with Golf" if Golf is the current ATIS designation.

B. The ground controller will respond with four items:

1. The airplane identification, e.g., "Skipper 66421."
2. Taxi to the active runway, e.g., "Taxi runway 10."
3. The wind direction and speed, e.g., "Wind 140 at 7."
4. The altimeter setting, e.g., "Altimeter 29.93." At this time you should check and reset your altimeter if necessary.

NOTE: Wind and altimeter will not be given if ATIS is available.

C. You should acknowledge the controller, e.g., "Beech Skipper 66421 taxi runway 10." ATC may use an abbreviated call sign here, e.g., "421." Continue to monitor ground control as you taxi (you will switch to the tower frequency just before you are ready to take off).

1. Safe ATC facilities and controllers generally require you to read back all clearances. This is a good practice.
2. Be careful to note if you are given a clearance other than to the active runway, e.g., "Hold short of runway 24" -- do NOT cross runway 24.
   a. You are required to read back to the controller all runway hold short instructions.
3. Whenever you need directions, ask ground control, e.g., "Ground, Beech Skipper 66421 unfamiliar with airport. Request progressives to active runway."
   a. Progressives are step-by-step routing directions.

## 5.12 TOWER CONTROL

A. The tower controller coordinates all aircraft activity on the active runway and within the Class D airspace area (formerly the airport traffic area). The Class D airspace area is the airspace generally within a 4-NM radius around the airport extending up to 2,500 ft. above the airport surface.

B. When you are ready for takeoff, tell the tower three things:

1. You will address the tower, e.g., "Gainesville tower."
2. Identify your airplane, e.g., "Beech Skipper 66421."
3. State your intention (request), e.g., "Ready to take off runway 6."

C. The tower controller may then issue a clearance for takeoff if appropriate, e.g., "Beech Skipper 66421 cleared for takeoff runway 6, left turn northbound approved." However, listen carefully to the response.

1. The controller may issue certain restrictions on your departure, such as right turn or maintain runway heading, or you may ask for your direction of flight.
2. The tower may not clear you due to traffic, e.g., "Skipper 66421, hold short, landing traffic."
3. Once you have received a clearance for takeoff, you should acknowledge, e.g., "Beech 66421 cleared for takeoff runway 6."
4. You should monitor tower control until you are out of the Class D airspace area.
5. If there is a departure control to contact, the tower will direct you to that frequency when appropriate, e.g., "Beech 66421 contact departure control 125.65, good day."
6. If you are going to a nearby practice area, and it is customary to monitor the tower, you should do so.

a. Practice areas (for student pilots and instruction) are usually designated by the FAA or local airport authorities to keep instructional activities from interfering with normal traffic.

b. Ask your flight instructor about this.

D. Tower control is also used for landing. When approaching an airport to land, you must contact the tower prior to entering the Class D airspace area.

1. Address the tower, telling them who you are, where you are, and what you want.

a. Remember, the Class D airspace area generally has a 4-NM radius and extends up to 2,500 ft. AGL.

b. It is good practice to contact tower control 10 SM out so they have time to route you to the active runway and coordinate you with the other traffic.

2. EXAMPLE: "Jacksonville Tower, Beech Skipper 66421, 10 mi. southwest, landing."

## 5.13 APPROACH CONTROL AND DEPARTURE CONTROL (FOR VFR AIRCRAFT)

A. The approach or departure controller coordinates arriving or departing traffic, usually to a busy airport with a control tower. These controllers coordinate traffic outside the traffic area.

1. Use of approach and departure control is mandatory in Class B airspace areas (formerly TCAs) and Class C airspace areas (formerly ARSAs) for all aircraft, including VFR traffic.

a. Class B airspace exists around major airports (e.g., Atlanta, Georgia).
b. Class C airspace exists around other busy airports (e.g., Jacksonville, Florida).

2. Use of approach and departure control is highly encouraged in Terminal Radar Service Areas (TRSAs), but it is not mandatory.

B. When approaching an area serviced by approach control, you should contact approach control for traffic advisories, sequencing for landing, and instructions for flying through a busy area.

C. Departure control is used for leaving busy traffic areas and required for use in leaving airports within Class B and Class C airspace areas.

1. If requested and/or mandatory, tower will switch you over to departure control when appropriate.

2. If you request departure control from the tower without prior arrangement, you will have to give your type of airplane, call sign, location, altitude, request, etc., with departure control as you did with approach control coming in.

## 5.14 CLEARANCE DELIVERY

A. A clearance delivery frequency is used at busy airports (usually one within Class B or Class C airspace areas) to issue clearances to aircraft on the ground prior to taxiing.

1. Clearance delivery frequency may be found in the *Airport/Facility Directory*. It is also generally given in the ATIS broadcast.

B. Call clearance delivery before contacting the ground controller, and tell him/her four things:

1. Your type of aircraft and identification, e.g., "Cessna 1152L."
2. You are VFR, e.g., "VFR."
3. Your destination, e.g., "Jacksonville."
4. The altitude at which you wish to fly, e.g., "At 4,500 ft."

C. The controller will respond with a clearance for you consisting of
   1. Direction to fly after departure, e.g., "Fly runway heading."
   2. An altitude to climb to, e.g., "Up to but not above 2,000 ft."
   3. A transponder code setting, e.g., "Squawk 4645."
   4. The frequency for departure control, e.g., "Departure frequency will be 125.65."

D. You should copy the clearance, then read it back to the controller.

## 5.15 EMERGENCIES

A. If your airplane is experiencing an emergency such as loss of power, if you become doubtful about any condition that could adversely affect flight safety, or you become apprehensive about your safety for any reason, use the emergency frequency, which is 121.5 MHz.
   1. When you broadcast on this frequency you will receive immediate attention at the Flight Service Stations and towers receiving 121.5.
   2. All towers, Flight Service Stations, and radar facilities monitor the emergency frequency but normally only one FAA facility at a given location monitors the frequency.
   3. If you are already on an ATC control frequency, e.g., a control tower or approach control, you should declare an emergency with them, since they are already conversant with your call sign, location, etc.

B. You should immediately state your
   1. Airplane call sign.
   2. Location and altitude.
   3. Problem.
   4. Extent of the distress, e.g., requiring no delay, priority, or emergency handling.

C. If equipped with a radar beacon transponder and if unable to establish voice communications with an air traffic control facility, set the transponder to Code 7700.

## 5.16 RADIO FAILURE PROCEDURES

A. ATC light signals are used to communicate with aircraft that have no radios or have experienced a radio communication equipment failure at a controlled airport.
   1. ATC light signals have the meaning shown in the following table:

| Light Signal | On the Ground | In the Air |
|---|---|---|
| Steady Green | Cleared for takeoff | Cleared to land |
| Flashing Green | Cleared to taxi | Return for landing *(to be followed by steady green at proper time)* |
| Steady Red | Stop | Give way to other aircraft and continue circling |
| Flashing Red | Taxi clear of landing area (runway) in use | Airport unsafe -- Do not land |
| Flashing White | Return to starting point on airport | Not applicable |
| Alternating Red and Green | General warning signal -- Exercise extreme caution | General warning signal -- Exercise extreme caution |

B. Radio Failure Procedures at Controlled Airports

1. Arriving Aircraft

   a. If you receive no response to your transmission inbound, you may have a radio failure.

   b. If you are receiving tower transmissions, but none are directed toward you, you should suspect a transmitter failure.

      1) Determine the direction and flow of traffic, enter the traffic pattern, and look for light signals.

      2) During daylight, acknowledge tower transmissions or light signals by rocking your wings. At night, acknowledge by blinking the landing or navigation lights.

      3) After landing, telephone the tower to advise them of the situation.

   c. If you are receiving no transmissions on tower or ATIS frequency, suspect a receiver failure.

      1) Transmit to the tower in the blind your position, situation, and intention to land.
      2) Determine the flow of traffic, enter the pattern, and wait for light signals.
      3) Acknowledge signals as described above and by transmitting in the blind.
      4) After landing, telephone the tower to advise them of the situation.

2. Departing Aircraft

   a. If you experience radio failure prior to leaving the parking area, make every effort to have the equipment repaired.

   b. If you are unable to have the malfunction repaired, call the tower by telephone and request authorization to depart without two-way radio communications.

      1) If tower authorization is granted, you will be given departure information and requested to monitor the tower frequency or watch for light signals, as appropriate.

      2) During daylight, acknowledge tower transmissions or light signals by promptly executing action authorized by light signals.

         a) When in the air, rock your wings.

      3) At night, acknowledge by blinking the landing or navigation lights.

   c. If your radio malfunctions after departing the parking area (ramp), watch the tower for light signals or monitor the appropriate (ground or tower) frequency. However, you should return to the ramp.

## 5.17 EMERGENCY LOCATOR TRANSMITTER (ELT)

A. Emergency Locator Transmitters (ELTs) of various types are independently powered and of incalculable value in an emergency. They have been developed as a means of locating downed aircraft and their occupants.

1. They are designed to emit a distinctive audio tone for homing purposes on the emergency frequencies 121.5 MHz and 243.0 MHz.
2. The power source is designed to be capable of providing power for continuous operation for at least 48 hr. or more at a very wide range of temperatures. It can expedite search and rescue operations as well as facilitate accident investigation.
3. The ELT is required for most general aviation and small private aircraft. The pilot and other occupants could survive a crash impact only to die of exposure before they are located. These transmitters are made by several manufacturers for civil aviation use.

B. The ELT is equipped with a gravity switch which, when armed, automatically activates the ELT upon an impact of sufficient force.

1. Once the transmitter is activated and the signal detected, search aircraft with homing equipment can locate the scene. Search aircraft use special search patterns to locate the transmitter site.

C. ELTs generally have three switch positions: "ON," "OFF," and "ARMED."

1. "On" provides continuous broadcast on 121.5 MHz and 243.0 MHz.
2. "Off" means no broadcast is possible and the gravity switch cannot be activated.
3. "Armed" means the gravity switch will be activated in a crash situation, which turns on the broadcast.
4. Normally, the ELT is in a rear area of the airplane and is always set on "armed." They are affixed as far aft as possible to avoid possible damage from crash impact.

D. Do NOT inadvertently activate the ELT in the air or on the ground.

1. Accidental or unauthorized activation will generate an emergency signal that will lead to expensive and wasteful searches.
2. A false ELT signal could also interfere with genuine emergency transmissions and hinder or prevent the timely location of crash sites.
   a. Frequent false alarms could also result in complacency and decrease the vigorous reaction that must be attached to all ELT signals.
3. Numerous cases of inadvertent activation have occurred as a result of aerobatics, hard landings, movement by ground crews, and airplane maintenance. These false alarms can be minimized by monitoring 121.5 MHz as follows:
   a. In flight when a receiver is available.
   b. Prior to engine shutdown at the end of each flight.
   c. When the ELT is handled during installation or maintenance.
   d. When maintenance is being performed in the vicinity of the ELT.
   e. When the airplane is moved by a ground crew.
4. If an ELT signal is heard, turn off your ELT to determine whether it is transmitting. If it has been activated, maintenance might be required before the unit is returned to the "armed" position.

E. Pilots are encouraged to monitor 121.5 MHz while in flight to assist in identifying possible emergency ELT transmissions. On receiving a signal, the pilot should report the following information to the nearest air traffic facility or Flight Service Station (FSS):
   1. Position at the time the signal was first heard and last heard.
   2. Position at maximum signal strength.
   3. Flight altitude and frequency (i.e., 121.5 MHz or 243.0 MHz).
   4. If possible, position should be given relative to a navigation aid.

F. ELTs should be tested in accordance with the manufacturer's instructions, preferably in a shielded or screened room to prevent the broadcast of signals which could trigger a false alert.
   1. When this cannot be done, airplane operational testing is authorized on 121.5 MHz and 243.0 MHz as follows:
      a. Tests should be conducted only during the first 5 min. after any hour.
         1) If tests must be made any other time, it must be coordinated with the nearest FAA Control Tower or FSS.
      b. Tests should be no longer than three audible sweeps.
      c. If the antenna is removable, a dummy load should be substituted during test procedures.
      d. Airborne tests are not authorized.

G. ELT batteries must be replaced or recharged (if rechargeable)
   1. If the battery has been used for more than 1 cumulative hour.
   2. When 50% of the battery's useful life has expired.

## 5.18 ATC RADAR

A. Radar is a method in which radio waves are transmitted into the air and received when they have been reflected by an object in the path of the beam. This is known as primary radar.
   1. Range is determined by measuring the time it takes (at the speed of light) for the radio wave to go out to the object and return to the receiving antenna.
   2. Direction is determined by the position of the rotating antenna when the reflected portion of the radio wave is received.

B. The characteristics of radio waves are such that they normally travel in a continuous straight line unless they are affected by the following:
   1. The bending of the radio wave caused by abnormal phenomena such as temperature inversions
      a. This may cause extraneous blips to appear on the radarscope if the radio wave has been bent toward the ground or may decrease the detection range if the wave is bent upward.
   2. Radar energy that strikes dense objects (e.g., precipitation, ground obstacles, mountains, etc.) will be reflected and displayed on the radarscope, blocking out aircraft at the same range and greatly weakening or completely eliminating the display of targets at a greater range.
      a. Secondary radar and the electronic elimination of stationary and slow moving targets by a method called moving target indicator (MTI) is effectively used to combat ground clutter and some weather phenomena.
   3. Relatively low altitude aircraft will not be seen if they are screened by mountains or are below the radar beam due to the earth's curvature. Remember, radar is line-of-sight.

C. The Air Traffic Control Radar Beacon System (ATCRBS), also known as secondary radar, consists of three major components.

1. Interrogator -- A ground-based radar beacon transmitter-receiver which scans at the same time as primary radar and transmits discrete radio signals requesting all transponders on the mode being used to reply.

   a. The replies received from the transponders are displayed on the radarscope along with primary radar targets (aircraft with no transponder).

2. Transponder -- This airborne (i.e., installed on your airplane) radar beacon transmitter-receiver automatically receives the signals from the interrogator and selectively replies with a specific pulse group (code) only to those interrogations received on the mode to which it is set.

   a. These replies are independent of, and much stronger than, a primary radar return.

3. Radarscope -- This is used to display returns from both the primary and secondary radar systems. These returns, called targets, are what the controller refers to in the control and separation of traffic.

   a. A video mapping unit generates an actual map on the radarscope, which may depict data such as airports, navigation aids, obstructions, prominent geographic features, etc.

## 5.19 TRANSPONDER OPERATION

A. Since most airplanes you will fly will be equipped with a transponder you should understand the proper operating procedures. The figure below illustrates a typical transponder.

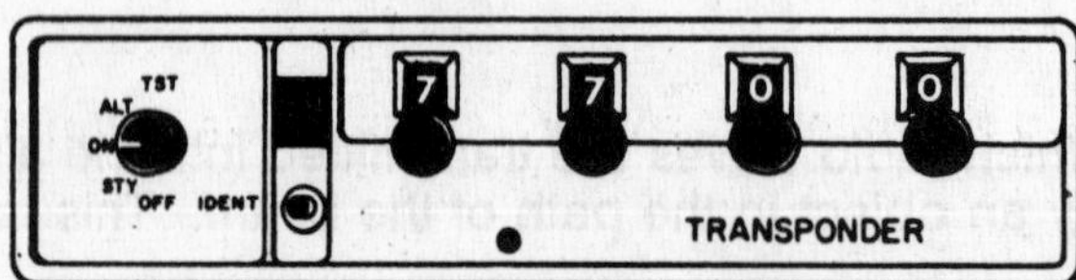


1. The function switch controls the application of power and selects the operating mode. It has four positions.

   a. OFF -- turns the transponder off.

   b. STY (Standby) -- turns the transponder on for equipment warm-up. The transponder does not reply to interrogations in this position.

   c. ON -- turns the transponder on and allows the transponder to reply to Mode A (no altitude reporting) interrogations.

   d. ALT -- turns the transponder on and allows the transponder to transmit either Mode A or Mode C (altitude reporting) replies as requested by the interrogating signal.

2. The reply/monitor light flashes to indicate when the transponder is replying to interrogations. This light will glow steadily during initial warm-up, when the IDENT signal is transmitted, and to show proper operation during self-test operation.
3. The IDENT (ID) switch, when depressed, selects a special identifier signal that is sent with the transponder reply to an interrogation signal. This allows the controller to confirm an aircraft identity or to identify an aircraft.
    a. The IDENT signal should only be used at the request of a controller.
4. The dimmer (DIM) control allows the pilot to control the intensity level of the reply light.
5. The self-test (TST) switch causes the transponder to generate a self-interrogating signal to provide a check of the transponder operation.
6. Code selector knobs (4) allow you to set the proper four-digit transponder code.
7. Code selector windows (4) display the selected code. In each window any number between zero and seven can be selected, allowing a total of 4,096 possible codes.

B. Mode C (Automatic Altitude Reporting)

1. This system converts your airplane's altitude in 100-ft. increments to coded digital information, which is transmitted in the reply to the interrogating radar facility.
2. If your airplane is Mode C equipped, you must set your transponder to reply Mode C (i.e., set function switch to ALT), unless ATC requests otherwise.
    a. If ATC requests that you "STOP ALTITUDE SQUAWK," you should set the function switch from ALT to ON.
3. An instruction by ATC: "STOP ALTITUDE SQUAWK, ALTITUDE DIFFERS (number of feet) FEET," may be an indication that your transponder is transmitting incorrect altitude information or that you have an incorrect altimeter setting.
    a. The encoding altimeter equipment of the Mode C function is preset to a setting of 29.92. Computers at the radar facility correct for current altimeter settings and display indicated altitudes on the radarscope.
    b. Although an incorrect altimeter setting has no effect on the Mode C altitude information transmitted by the transponder, it will cause you to fly at a different altitude.
    c. When a controller indicates that an altitude readout is invalid, you should check to verify that your airplane's altimeter is set correctly.
    d. FAR 91.411 requires that the automatic pressure altitude reporting system be inspected every 24 months.
4. Mode C is required for the following operations:
    a. When flying at or above 10,000 ft. MSL, except that airspace below 2,500 ft. AGL
    b. Within 30 NM of a Class B airspace primary airport
        1) Special FAR (SFAR) No. 62 to Part 91 permits aircraft operations to and from certain smaller airports that lie within 30 NM of a Class B airspace primary airport without Mode C. See SFAR No. 62 or the *Airman's Information Manual* (*AIM*) for details. This SFAR is effective until December 30, 1993.
    c. Within and above a Class C airspace area
    d. Flying into, within, or across the U.S. ADIZ (Air Defense Identification Zone)

C. All VFR pilots should set their transponders to code 1200, unless otherwise instructed by ATC.

1. Transponders should be turned to the ON or ALT (if Mode C equipped) position as late as practicable prior to takeoff and to the SBY position as soon as practicable after clearing the active runway.
2. Transponders are required to be inspected and tested every 24 calendar months (FAR 91.413).
3. Certain special codes have been set aside for emergency use.
   a. 7500 is the code for hijacking.
   b. 7600 is the code for lost radio communications.
   c. 7700 is the code for an emergency.
   d. 7777 is the code used for military interceptor operations.
4. When making code changes, you should avoid the selection of codes 7500, 7600, or 7700. These codes will cause alarms to be activated at the radar facility.
   a. EXAMPLE: When switching from code 2700 to 7200, switch first to 2200 then to 7200, NOT to 7700 and then 7200.

D. Controllers will use the following phraseology when referring to the operation of the transponder.

1. SQUAWK (number) -- Operate transponder on designated code (number).
2. IDENT -- Engage the IDENT feature of the transponder.
3. SQUAWK (number) and IDENT -- Select the specified code and then engage the IDENT feature of transponder.
4. SQUAWK STANDBY -- Switch function switch to SBY.
5. SQUAWK ALTITUDE -- Switch function selector to ALT to activate Mode C.
6. STOP ALTITUDE SQUAWK -- Switch function selector from ALT to ON.
7. STOP SQUAWK -- Turn transponder off (i.e., OFF position).
8. SQUAWK MAYDAY -- Select code 7700.
9. SQUAWK VFR -- Operate transponder on code 1200.

## 5.20 RADAR SERVICES TO VFR AIRCRAFT

A. ATC radar facilities provide a variety of services to participating VFR aircraft on a workload-permitting basis.

1. To participate, you must be able to communicate with ATC, be within radar coverage, and be radar identified by the controller.
2. Among the services provided are
   a. VFR flight following,
   b. Terminal radar programs, and
   c. Radar assistance to lost aircraft.

B. VFR Flight Following

1. To obtain flight following, you should contact ATC on the appropriate frequency after leaving the traffic area of your departure airport.
   a. Use the departure frequency listed for the airport in the A/FD.
   b. Inform ATC that you are requesting VFR flight following, and announce your departure point and destination.

c. The controller will assign you a transponder code, and ask your aircraft type and cruising altitude.

2. When you are using flight following, ATC will advise you of any traffic that may be in a position to warrant your attention.

   a. Radar traffic information given to you will include the following:

      1) The traffic's position relative to yours in terms of the 12 hr. clock, or distance and direction with respect to a fix

         a) EXAMPLES:

            i) "TRAFFIC at 1 O'CLOCK" would be about 30° right of your airplane's nose.

            ii) "TRAFFIC 8 miles (NM) SOUTH OF AIRPORT SOUTHEAST BOUND"

      2) Distance from you in NM

      3) Direction in which the target is heading

      4) Type of aircraft and altitude, if known

   b. The controller can only observe your airplane's track (course) on the radarscope, thus the traffic advisories are based on this, and you should take into account your wind correction angle to maintain track.

      1) When given a traffic advisory of traffic at 1 o'clock, you should look from the nose of your airplane to the right wing for the traffic.

      2) Once you have the traffic in sight, you should report this to the controller and maintain visual contact until it is no longer a factor in your flight.

         a) If you do not see the traffic, you should report "NEGATIVE TRAFFIC" to the controller.

3. When receiving this service, you must monitor the assigned frequency at all times. This is to preclude the controller's concern for radio failure or emergency assistance to aircraft under his/her control.

   a. This service does not include vectors (i.e., headings provided by ATC) away from conflicting traffic unless requested by the pilot.

   b. You should inform the controller when changing altitude.

   c. When advisory service is no longer desired, advise the controller before changing frequency and then change your transponder code to 1200.

   d. When you are outside the controller's airspace, the controller will advise you that radar service is terminated and instruct you to squawk VFR.

C. Terminal Radar Programs

1. Many larger airports have radar facilities which can provide radar advisories, sequencing, and, in some cases, separation from other participating aircraft.

   a. Many of these airports are identified as Terminal Radar Service Areas (TRSAs), Class C airspace areas, and Class B airspace areas on the sectional chart.

      1) Other airports that have radar facilities are so indicated in the *A/FD*.

   b. Pilot participation in this program is urged whenever available.

      1) Participation is mandatory when operating in a Class B or Class C airspace area.

2. When arriving, you should contact approach control on the published frequency and state your position, altitude, destination, and that you have received the ATIS (if available).
   a. The proper frequency may be found on the sectional chart or in the *A/FD*.
   b. Approach control will specify when to contact the tower.
3. When departing, you should inform ATC of your destination and/or route of flight and proposed cruising altitude.
   a. ATC will normally advise participating VFR aircraft when leaving the geographical limits of the controller's radar. Radar service is not terminated unless specifically stated by the controller.
4. While operating in Class B airspace, Class C airspace, or a TRSA, you
   a. Must maintain an altitude when assigned by ATC unless the altitude assignment is to maintain at or below a specified altitude.
   b. Should coordinate with ATC prior to any altitude change when not assigned an altitude.

D. Radar Assistance to Lost Aircraft
1. If you become lost, ATC can provide you with radar assistance and vectors to your desired destination.
   a. You must be within radar coverage to use this service.
2. To find the proper frequency for ATC in your area, it may be necessary to contact the nearest control tower or FSS.
   a. Inform ATC that you are lost, and state your last known position and your destination.
   b. By assigning you a transponder code and observing you on radar, the controller will be able to tell you your position and suggest a heading to your destination.
3. An emergency situation can easily be avoided by asking for help as soon as you are in doubt as to your exact position.
   a. Taking advantage of flight following when available keeps you operating within the ATC system and allows you always to keep a controller "at your fingertips."

E. You must clearly understand that these programs in no way relieve you of your primary responsibility of flying the airplane legally and safely.
1. It is still your task
   a. To see and avoid other traffic,
   b. To adjust your operations and flight path as necessary to avoid wake turbulence,
   c. To maintain appropriate terrain and obstruction clearance, and
   d. To maintain basic VFR visibility and distance from clouds.
2. If ATC assigns a route, heading, and/or altitude that will make you compromise your responsibilities to the above areas, you must contact the controller to advise him/her and obtain a revised clearance or instructions.

# CHAPTER SIX
# WEIGHT AND BALANCE



The weight and balance of the airplane must be reviewed prior to each flight, particularly cross-country flights. You are concerned not only with the weight of the airplane but also the location of its center of gravity (CG). You should not attempt a flight until you are satisfied with the weight and balance condition.

## 6.1 OVERVIEW

A. Effects of Weight on Flight Performance

1. Increased weight reduces the flight performance of your airplane in almost every respect. The most important performance deficiencies of the overloaded airplane are

   a. Higher takeoff speed required.
   b. Longer takeoff run required.
   c. Reduced rate and angle of climb.
   d. Shorter range.
   e. Reduced cruising speed.
   f. Reduced maneuverability.
   g. Higher stalling speed.
   h. Higher landing speed required.
   i. Longer landing roll required.

B. Effects of Weight on Airplane Structure

1. An airplane is certified to be able to withstand certain loads placed on its structure.

   a. As long as gross weight and load factor limits are observed, the total load on the airplane will remain within limits.

   b. If the maximum gross weight is exceeded, load factors well within the load factor limits can cause structural damage.

2. Structural failures from overloading may be dramatic and catastrophic, but more often they affect structural components gradually in a way which is difficult to detect.

   a. The results of habitual overloading tend to be cumulative, and may result in structural failure later during completely normal operations.

   b. Overloading can also accelerate metal fatigue.

C. Effects of Balance on Flight Performance

1. The CG location affects the total load placed on the wings in flight.

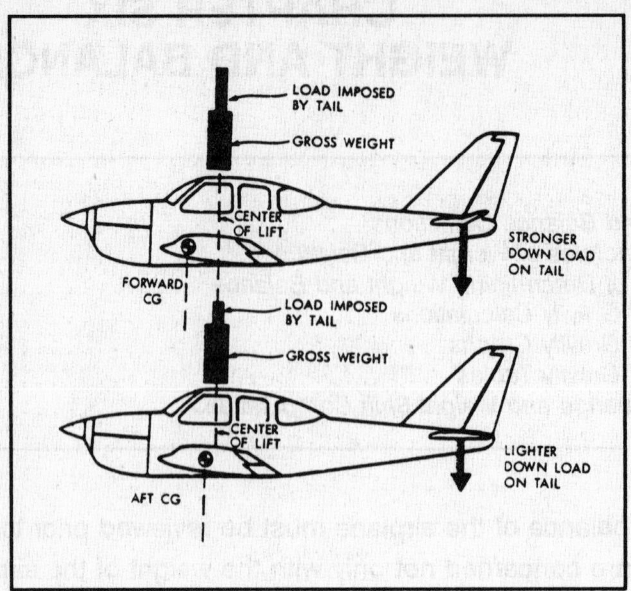


2. With a forward CG, a greater downward force on the tail is required to maintain level cruising flight.
   a. This adds to the total lift required from the wing.
   b. Thus, the wing flies at a higher angle of attack, which results in more drag and a higher stall speed.
3. With an aft CG, less downward force on the tail is required, resulting in less lift required by the wing.
   a. Thus, the wing flies at a lower angle of attack with less drag and a higher cruise speed.

D. Effect of Balance on Stability

1. In general, an airplane becomes less stable and controllable as the CG moves aft.
   a. The elevator has a shorter arm (i.e., distance) from the CG and requires greater deflection to produce the same result.
   b. Recovery from a stall is more difficult because the airplane's tendency to pitch down is reduced.
   c. If the CG is moved beyond the aft limit, stall and spin recovery may become impossible.
2. As the CG moves forward, the airplane becomes more nose-heavy.
   a. If the CG is moved beyond the forward limit, the elevator may no longer be able to hold the nose up, particularly at low airspeeds, e.g., takeoff, landing, and power-off glides.

## 6.2 WEIGHT AND BALANCE DEFINITIONS

A. **Arm (moment arm)** -- the horizontal distance in inches from the reference datum line to the center of gravity of any item. The distance is considered positive (+) if measured aft of the datum and negative (–) if measured forward of the datum.

B. **Basic empty weight** -- the combined weight of the airframe, engines, and all operating equipment that has a fixed location and is permanently installed in the airplane. It includes optional and special equipment, fixed ballast, hydraulic fluid, unusable (residual) fuel, and undrainable (residual) oil. Most airplane manufacturers include all oil in the empty weight.

C. **Center of gravity (CG)** -- the point about which an airplane would balance if it were possible to suspend it at that point. It is the mass center of the airplane, or the theoretical point at which the entire weight of the airplane is assumed to be concentrated.

D. **Center of gravity limits** -- the specified forward and aft points within which the CG must be located during flight for safe control and maneuverability. These limits are indicated on pertinent airplane specifications (i.e., weight and balance records).

E. **Center of gravity range** -- the distance between the forward and aft CG limits as indicated on pertinent airplane specifications.

F. **Datum (reference datum)** -- an imaginary vertical plane or line from which all measurements of arm are taken. The datum is established by the manufacturer. All moment arms and the location of CG range are measured from this point.

G. **Fuel load** -- the usable part of the fuel load of the airplane. It includes only usable fuel, not fuel required to fill the lines or that which remains trapped in the tank sumps, i.e., residual fuel.

H. **Gross weight** -- the loaded weight of the airplane. It includes the empty weight of the airplane, all fuel and oil, and all persons and baggage.

I. **Maximum landing weight** -- the maximum gross weight at which the airplane may normally be landed.

J. **Maximum ramp weight** -- the maximum weight approved for ground maneuvers. It includes the weight of start, taxi, and runup fuel.

K. **Maximum takeoff weight** -- the maximum allowable weight at the start of the takeoff run. Some airplanes are approved for loading to a greater ramp weight to allow for fuel burnoff during ground operation.

L. **Moment** -- the product of the weight of an item multiplied by its arm. Moments are expressed in pound-inches (lb.-in.) or in.-lb.

M. **Moment index (or index)** -- a moment divided by a constant such as 100, 1000, or 10,000. This simplifies weight and balance computations for airplanes when heavy items and long arms result in large, unmanageable numbers.

N. **Standard weights** -- established for numerous items involved in weight and balance computations.

1. Gasoline is 6 lb./U.S. gal.
2. Oil is 7.5 lb./U.S. gal.

O. **Useful load** -- the weight of the pilot, copilot, passengers, baggage, usable fuel, and drainable oil (if not included in the empty weight). It is the empty weight subtracted from the maximum allowable gross weight.

## 6.3 BASIC PRINCIPLES OF WEIGHT AND BALANCE

A. Total weight is the weight of the empty airplane plus the weight of everything loaded on it.

1. The point at which the airplane will balance is the center of gravity (CG). It is the imaginary point at which all the weight is concentrated.
2. To provide the necessary balance between longitudinal stability and elevator control, the CG is usually located slightly forward of the center of lift.

B. The safe zone within which the CG must fall is called the CG range.

1. The extremities of the range are called the forward and aft CG limits.
2. These limits are usually specified in inches, along the longitudinal axis of the airplane, measured from the datum.
3. The datum is an arbitrary point, established by airplane designers. It will probably vary in location between different airplanes.

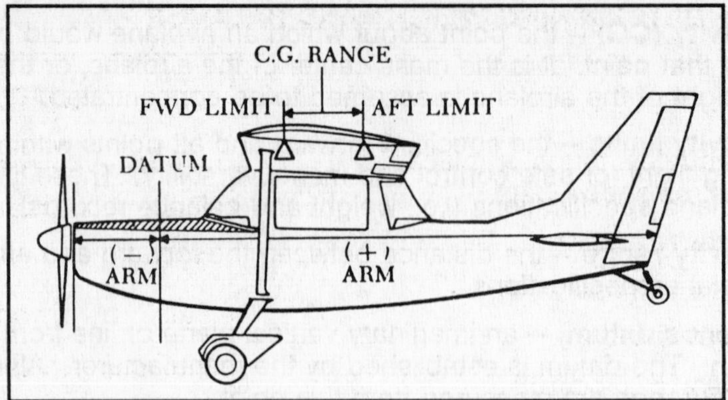


C. The distance from the datum line to any component part of the airplane, or any object loaded on the airplane, is called an arm.

1. When the object or component is located aft of the datum it is measured in positive (+) inches. If located forward of the datum it is measured in negative (–) inches.

2. Recall that the moment is the weight of an object multiplied by its arm (distance from the datum). The moment is a measurement of the gravitational force which causes a tendency of the weight to rotate about a point or axis. It is expressed in lb.-in. or in.-lb.

D. EXAMPLE: In the diagram at the right, assume that a weight of 50 lb. is placed on the board at a point 100 in. from the datum (fulcrum). The downward force of the weight at that spot can be determined by multiplying 50 lb. by 100 in., which produces a moment of 5,000 lb.-in. (50 x 100).

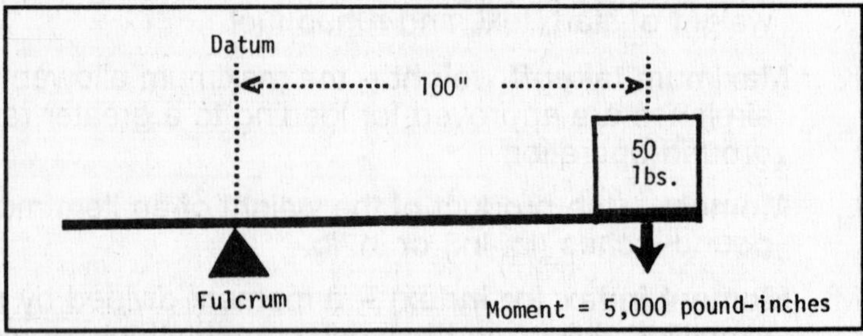


1. To establish a balance, a total of 5,000 lb.-in. must be applied to the other end of the board. Any combination of weight and distance which, when multiplied, produces 5,000 lb.-in. moment to the left of the datum will balance the board.

2. If a 100-lb. weight is placed at a point 25 in. to the left of the datum, and a second 50-lb. weight is placed at a point 50 in. to the left of the datum, the sum of the product of these two weights and their distances will total a moment of 5,000 lb.-in., which will balance the board.

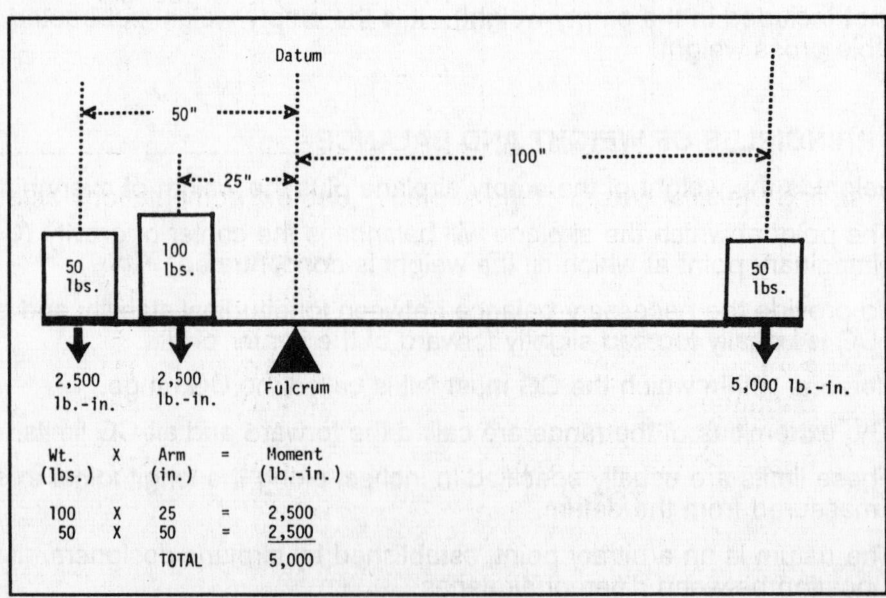


| Wt. (lbs.) | X | Arm (in.) | = | Moment (lb.-in.) |
|---|---|---|---|---|
| 100 | X | 25 | = | 2,500 |
| 50 | X | 50 | = | 2,500 |
| | | TOTAL | | 5,000 |

## 6.4 METHODS OF DETERMINING WEIGHT AND BALANCE

A. By center of gravity calculations
   1. See below
B. By loading schedules, found on placards in the airplane, as shown here
C. By center of gravity graphs
   1. See pages 158 and 160
D. By center of gravity tables
   1. See pages 162 and 163

**LOADING SCHEDULE**

| Fuel | Passengers | Baggage |
|---|---|---|
| Full | 2 rear | 100 lb. |
| 39 gal. | 1 front and 2 rear | None |
| Full | 1 front and 1 rear | Full |

Includes pilot and full oil

## 6.5 CENTER OF GRAVITY CALCULATIONS

A. The center of gravity (CG) is determined by dividing the total moments by the total weight.
   1. A moment is the weight of an individual item multiplied by its arm.
   2. The arm is the number of inches that the item is forward (–) or aft (+) of the datum.
B. Determine the CG location of the airplane shown below. Note the oil is **not** included in the empty weight of this airplane.

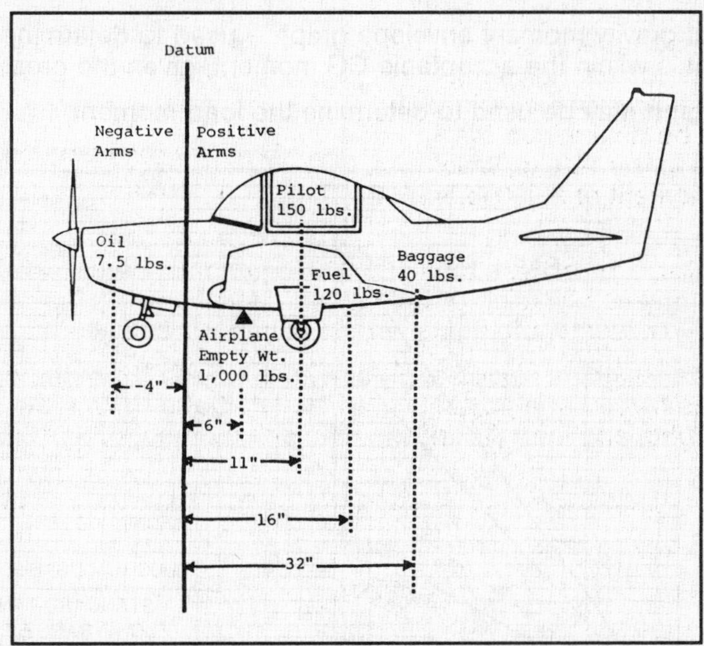


   1. First, find the total weight of the airplane. See the computations below.

| Item | Weight (lb.) | Arm (in.) | Moment (lb.-in.) |
|---|---|---|---|
| Airplane empty weight .......... | 1,000.0 | 6 | 6,000.0 |
| Pilot ........................ | 150.0 | 11 | 1,650.0 |
| Baggage ...................... | 40.0 | 32 | 1,280.0 |
| Oil -- 4 qt. (7.5 lb./gal.) .......... | 7.5 | –4 | –30.0 |
| Fuel -- 20 gal. (6 lb./gal.) ........ | 120.0 | 16 | 1,920.0 |
| TOTAL ........... | 1,317.5 | | 10,820.0 |

a. Presumably the total weight of 1,317.5 lb. is within the maximum weight limit. However, even if an airplane is certified for a specified maximum gross takeoff weight, it will not necessarily take off safely with this load under all conditions.
   1) Conditions which affect takeoff and climb performance are high elevations, high temperatures, and high humidity (high density altitudes).
   2) Other factors to consider prior to takeoff are runway length, surface, and slope; surface wind; and obstacles.
   3) These factors may require a reduction in weight prior to flight.

2. Second, compute the total moments (see the computations on page 157).
3. Last, compute the CG and check to see that it is within the limitations contained in the airplane operating manual.

$$CG = \frac{\text{Total Moments (lb.-in.)}}{\text{Total Weight (lb.)}} = \frac{10{,}820.0}{1{,}317.5} = 8.21 \text{ in. aft of datum}$$

## 6.6 CENTER OF GRAVITY GRAPHS

A. Graphs are frequently used to compute center of gravity.
   1. Loading graph -- used to compute the moment of individual items.
   2. Center of gravity moment envelope graph -- used to determine whether the airplane's moment is within the acceptable CG moment, given the gross weight of the airplane.

B. The loading graph may be used to determine the load moment.

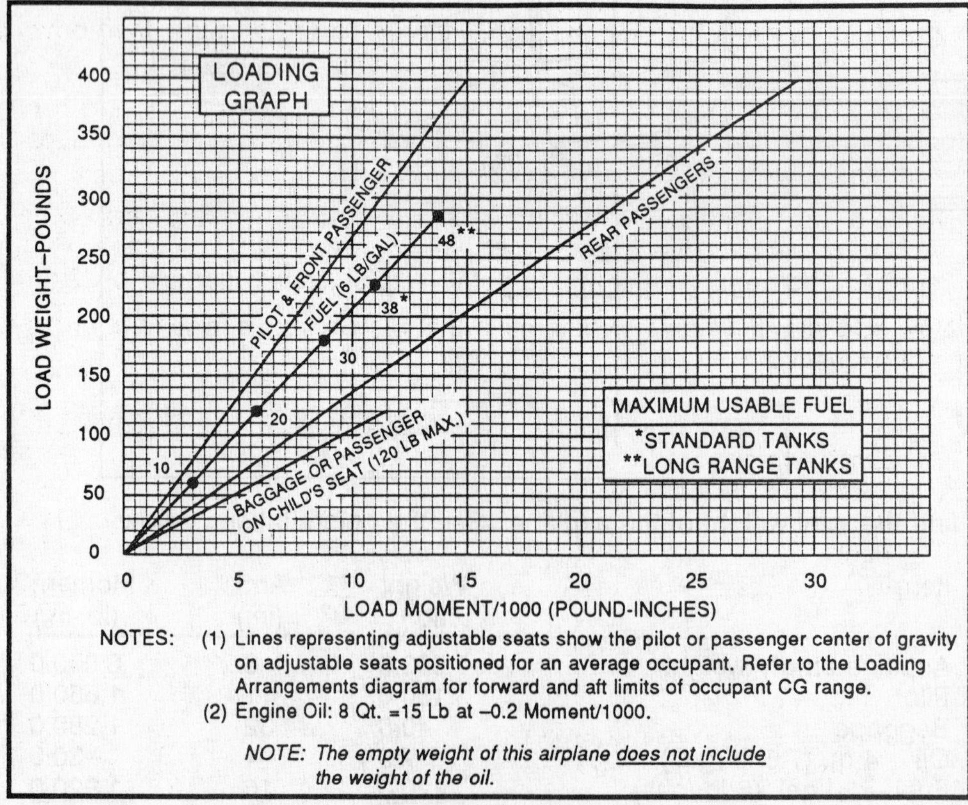

NOTES: (1) Lines representing adjustable seats show the pilot or passenger center of gravity on adjustable seats positioned for an average occupant. Refer to the Loading Arrangements diagram for forward and aft limits of occupant CG range.
(2) Engine Oil: 8 Qt. =15 Lb at –0.2 Moment/1000.

*NOTE: The empty weight of this airplane does not include the weight of the oil.*

1. On most graphs, the load weight in pounds is listed on the vertical axis. Diagonal lines represent various items such as fuel, baggage, pilot and front seat passengers, and back seat passengers.
   a. Move horizontally to the right across the chart from the amount of weight to intersect the line which represents the particular item.
   b. From the point of intersection of the weight with the appropriate diagonal line, drop straight down to the bottom of the chart to the moments displayed on the horizontal axis.
2. Then total the weights and moments for all items being loaded.
3. Note that each moment shown on the graph is actually a moment index, or moment/1,000. This reduces the moments to smaller, more manageable numbers.
4. EXAMPLE: Determine the load (total) moment/1,000 in the following situation.

| | Weight (lb.) | Moment/1,000 (lb.-in.) |
|---|---|---|
| Empty weight | 1,364 | 51.7 |
| Pilot & front seat passenger | 400 | ? |
| Baggage | 120 | ? |
| Usable fuel (38 gal.) | 228 | ? |
| Oil (8 qt.) | 15 | –0.2 |

   a. Compute the moment of the pilot and front seat passenger by referring to the loading graph and locate 400 on the weight scale. Move horizontally across the graph to intersect the diagonal line representing the pilot and front passenger, and then to the bottom scale which indicates a moment of approximately 15.0.
   b. Locate 120 on the weight scale for the baggage. Move horizontally across the graph to intersect the diagonal line that represents baggage, then down vertically to the bottom which indicates a moment of approximately 11.5.
   c. Locate 228 on the weight scale for the usable fuel. Move horizontally across the graph to intersect the diagonal line representing fuel, then down vertically to the bottom scale which indicates a moment of 11.0.
   d. Notice a –0.2 moment for the engine oil (see note 2 on the illustration on page 158). Add all moments except this negative moment and obtain a total of 89.2. Then subtract the negative moment to obtain a total aircraft moment of 89.0.
   e. Now add all the weights to determine that the airplane's maximum gross weight is not exceeded.

| | Weight (lb.) | Moment/1,000 (lb.-in.) |
|---|---|---|
| Empty weight | 1,364 | 51.7 |
| Pilot & passengers | 400 | 15.0 |
| Baggage | 120 | 11.5 |
| Fuel | 228 | 11.0 |
| Oil | 15 | –0.2 |
| | 2,127 | 89.0 |

C. The center of gravity moment envelope chart is a graph showing CG moment limits for various gross weights. Acceptable limits are established as an area on the graph. This area is called the envelope. Weight is on the vertical axis and moments on the horizontal axis.

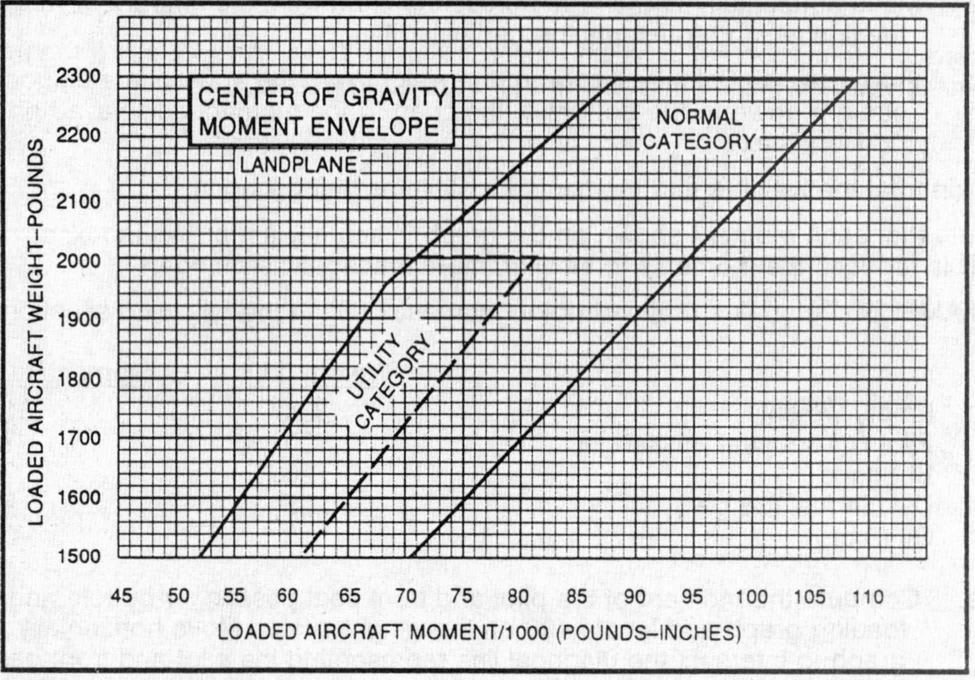


1. Identify the center of gravity point on the center of gravity moment envelope graph by plotting the total loaded aircraft weight across to the right.
2. Plot the total moment upward from the bottom.
3. The intersection will be within the CG moment envelope if the airplane has been loaded within limits.
4. EXAMPLE: Using the data from page 159, locate the weight of 2,127 lb. on the vertical axis and then move across the chart to the moment line of 89.0. The point of intersection will indicate that the aircraft is within both CG (i.e., normal category) and gross weight (i.e., less than 2,300 lb.) limits.

## 6.7 CENTER OF GRAVITY TABLES

A. Another approach to determining weight and CG limits is to use
   1. Tables of moments (see the figure on page 162).
   2. Tables of moment limits at various weights (see the figure on page 163).

B. First, determine total moment from the moment tables. Then check to see if the total moment is within maximum and minimum limits on the moment limit table.

C. EXAMPLE: Determine whether the airplane's weight and balance is within limits given the following data and using the figures on pages 162 and 163.

| | |
|---|---|
| Front seat occupants | 340 lb. |
| Rear seat occupants | 160 lb. |
| Fuel (main tanks) | 44 gal. |
| Baggage | 55 lb. |

   1. As in most weight and balance problems, you should begin by setting up a schedule as below. Note that the empty weight (page 162) is given as 2,015 lb. with a moment/100 of 1,554 lb.-in. Also note that empty weight includes the oil.

| | Weight (lb.) | Moment/100 (lb.-in.) |
|---|---|---|
| Empty weight (w/oil) | 2,015 | 1,554 |
| Front seat | 340 | 289 |
| Rear seat | 160 | 194 |
| Fuel (44 gal.) | 264 | 198 |
| Baggage | 55 | 77 |
| | 2,834 | 2,312 |

   2. Next, compute the individual moments.
      a. The front seat occupants' moment for 340 lb. can be calculated by adding the moments for 200 lb. (170 lb.-in.) and 140 lb. (119 lb.-in.). Thus the moment/100 for 340 lb. is 289 lb.-in.
      b. The rear seat occupants' moment/100 for 160 lb. is 194 lb.-in., which is read directly from the table.
      c. Determine the weight and moment/100 for 44 gal. of fuel in the main wing tanks. The weight is 264 lb. with a moment/100 of 198 lb.-in.
      d. The baggage moment/100 for 55 lb. can be calculated by interpolating between 50 lb. and 60 lb. The moment/100 for 50 lb. is 70 lb.-in. and the moment/100 for 60 lb. is 84 lb.-in. Thus, the moment/100 for 55 lb. is 77 lb.-in. [(70 + 84) ÷ 2 = 77].
   3. Next add the total weight and total moments.
   4. The last step is to go to the Moment Limits vs. Weight Chart (see page 163).
      a. Locate the weight of 2,834 lb. (between 2,830 and 2,840 lb. on chart).
      b. Note the moment/100 of 2,312 lb.-in. is within the limits of 2,287 and 2,405 at 2,830 lb.

# USEFUL LOAD WEIGHTS AND MOMENTS

## OCCUPANTS

| FRONT SEATS ARM 85 | | REAR SEATS ARM 121 | |
|---|---|---|---|
| Weight | Moment/100 | Weight | Moment/100 |
| 120 | 102 | 120 | 145 |
| 130 | 110 | 130 | 157 |
| 140 | 119 | 140 | 169 |
| 150 | 128 | 150 | 182 |
| 160 | 136 | 160 | 194 |
| 170 | 144 | 170 | 206 |
| 180 | 153 | 180 | 218 |
| 190 | 162 | 190 | 230 |
| 200 | 170 | 200 | 242 |

## USABLE FUEL

### MAIN WING TANKS ARM 75

| Gallons | Weight | Moment/100 |
|---|---|---|
| 5 | 30 | 22 |
| 10 | 60 | 45 |
| 15 | 90 | 68 |
| 20 | 120 | 90 |
| 25 | 150 | 112 |
| 30 | 180 | 135 |
| 35 | 210 | 158 |
| 40 | 240 | 180 |
| 44 | 264 | 198 |

### AUXILIARY WING TANKS ARM 94

| Gallons | Weight | Moment/100 |
|---|---|---|
| 5 | 30 | 28 |
| 10 | 60 | 56 |
| 15 | 90 | 85 |
| 19 | 114 | 107 |

## BAGGAGE OR 5TH SEAT OCCUPANT ARM 140

| Weight | Moment/100 |
|---|---|
| 10 | 14 |
| 20 | 28 |
| 30 | 42 |
| 40 | 56 |
| 50 | 70 |
| 60 | 84 |
| 70 | 98 |
| 80 | 112 |
| 90 | 126 |
| 100 | 140 |
| 110 | 154 |
| 120 | 168 |
| 130 | 182 |
| 140 | 196 |
| 150 | 210 |
| 160 | 224 |
| 170 | 238 |
| 180 | 252 |
| 190 | 266 |
| 200 | 280 |
| 210 | 294 |
| 220 | 308 |
| 230 | 322 |
| 240 | 336 |
| 250 | 350 |
| 260 | 364 |
| 270 | 378 |

## *OIL

| Quarts | Weight | Moment/100 |
|---|---|---|
| 10 | 19 | 5 |

*Included in basic Empty Weight

**Empty Weight ~ 2015**

**MOM / 100 ~ 1554**

**MOMENT LIMITS vs WEIGHT**

Moment limits are based on the following weight and center of gravity limit data (landing gear down).

| WEIGHT CONDITION | FORWARD CG LIMIT | AFT CG LIMIT |
|---|---|---|
| 2950 lb (takeoff or landing) | 82.1 | 84.7 |
| 2525 lb | 77.5 | 85.7 |
| 2475 lb or less | 77.0 | 85.7 |

## MOMENT LIMITS vs WEIGHT (Continued)

| Weight | Minimum Moment 100 | Maximum Moment 100 |
|---|---|---|
| 2100 | 1617 | 1800 |
| 2110 | 1625 | 1808 |
| 2120 | 1632 | 1817 |
| 2130 | 1640 | 1825 |
| 2140 | 1648 | 1834 |
| 2150 | 1656 | 1843 |
| 2160 | 1663 | 1851 |
| 2170 | 1671 | 1860 |
| 2180 | 1679 | 1868 |
| 2190 | 1686 | 1877 |
| 2200 | 1694 | 1885 |
| 2210 | 1702 | 1894 |
| 2220 | 1709 | 1903 |
| 2230 | 1717 | 1911 |
| 2240 | 1725 | 1920 |
| 2250 | 1733 | 1928 |
| 2260 | 1740 | 1937 |
| 2270 | 1748 | 1945 |
| 2280 | 1756 | 1954 |
| 2290 | 1763 | 1963 |
| 2300 | 1771 | 1971 |
| 2310 | 1779 | 1980 |
| 2320 | 1786 | 1988 |
| 2330 | 1794 | 1997 |
| 2340 | 1802 | 2005 |
| 2350 | 1810 | 2014 |
| 2360 | 1817 | 2023 |
| 2370 | 1825 | 2031 |
| 2380 | 1833 | 2040 |
| 2390 | 1840 | 2048 |
| 2400 | 1848 | 2057 |
| 2410 | 1856 | 2065 |
| 2420 | 1863 | 2074 |
| 2430 | 1871 | 2083 |
| 2440 | 1879 | 2091 |
| 2450 | 1887 | 2100 |
| 2460 | 1894 | 2108 |
| 2470 | 1902 | 2117 |
| 2480 | 1911 | 2125 |
| 2490 | 1921 | 2134 |
| 2500 | 1932 | 2143 |
| 2510 | 1942 | 2151 |
| 2520 | 1953 | 2160 |
| 2530 | 1963 | 2168 |
| 2540 | 1974 | 2176 |
| 2550 | 1984 | 2184 |
| 2560 | 1995 | 2192 |
| 2570 | 2005 | 2200 |
| 2580 | 2016 | 2208 |
| 2590 | 2026 | 2216 |

| Weight | Minimum Moment 100 | Maximum Moment 100 |
|---|---|---|
| 2600 | 2037 | 2224 |
| 2610 | 2048 | 2232 |
| 2620 | 2058 | 2239 |
| 2630 | 2069 | 2247 |
| 2640 | 2080 | 2255 |
| 2650 | 2090 | 2263 |
| 2660 | 2101 | 2271 |
| 2670 | 2112 | 2279 |
| 2680 | 2123 | 2287 |
| 2690 | 2133 | 2295 |
| 2700 | 2144 | 2303 |
| 2710 | 2155 | 2311 |
| 2720 | 2166 | 2319 |
| 2730 | 2177 | 2326 |
| 2740 | 2188 | 2334 |
| 2750 | 2199 | 2342 |
| 2760 | 2210 | 2350 |
| 2770 | 2221 | 2358 |
| 2780 | 2232 | 2366 |
| 2790 | 2243 | 2374 |
| 2800 | 2254 | 2381 |
| 2810 | 2265 | 2389 |
| 2820 | 2276 | 2397 |
| 2830 | 2287 | 2405 |
| 2840 | 2298 | 2413 |
| 2850 | 2309 | 2421 |
| 2860 | 2320 | 2428 |
| 2870 | 2332 | 2436 |
| 2880 | 2343 | 2444 |
| 2890 | 2354 | 2452 |
| 2900 | 2365 | 2460 |
| 2910 | 2377 | 2468 |
| 2920 | 2388 | 2475 |
| 2930 | 2399 | 2483 |
| 2940 | 2411 | 2491 |
| 2950 | 2422 | 2499 |

## 6.8 WEIGHT CHANGE AND WEIGHT SHIFT COMPUTATIONS

A. The FAA provides two formulas for weight change and one formula for weight shift. They are not reproduced here because the following weight change and weight shift formula is much simpler and intuitively appealing. It is adapted from a class handout developed by Dr. Melville R. Byington at Embry-Riddle Aeronautical University (used with permission).

B. **Basic Theory** -- The issue is **If the CG started out there, and certain changes occurred, where is it now?** It can be answered directly using a SINGLE, UNIVERSAL, UNCOMPLICATED FORMULA.

1. At **any** time, the CG is simply the sum of all moments divided by the sum of all weights.

$$CG = \frac{\Sigma M}{\Sigma W}$$

2. Since CG was known at some previous (#1) loading condition (with moment = $M_1$ and weight = $W_1$), it is logical that this become the point of departure. Due to weight addition, removal, or shift, the moment has changed by some amount, $\Delta M$. The total weight has also changed, **if** and only if, weight has been added or removed. Therefore, the current CG is merely the current total moment divided by the current total weight. In equation format,

$$CG = \text{Current Moment/Current Weight becomes } CG = \frac{M_1 \pm \Delta M}{W_1 \pm \Delta W}$$

3. This UNIVERSAL FORMULA will accommodate ANY WEIGHT CHANGE AND/OR CG SHIFT PROBLEM! Before proceeding, certain conventions deserve review:
   a. Any weight added causes a + moment change (Weight removed is –).
   b. Weight **shifted** rearward causes a + moment change (Forward is –).
   c. A weight **shift** changes only the moment ($\Delta W = 0$).

C. EXAMPLES:

1. An airplane takes off at 6,230 lb. with a CG location at station 79.0. What is the location of the CG after 50 gal. (300 lb.) of fuel has been consumed from station 87.0?

$$CG = \frac{M_1 \pm \Delta M}{W_1 \pm \Delta W} = \frac{6{,}230\ (79) - 300\ (87)}{6{,}230 - 300} = 78.6\ in.$$

2. An airplane takes off at 3,000 lb. with CG at station 60. Since takeoff 25 gal. (150 lb.) of fuel has been consumed. Fuel cell CG is station 65. After takeoff, a 200-lb. passenger moved from station 50 to station 90. Find the resulting CG.

$$CG = \frac{M_1 \pm \Delta M}{W_1 \pm \Delta W} = \frac{3{,}000\ (60) - 150\ (65) + 200\ (90 - 50)}{3{,}000 - 150} = 62.54\ in.$$

3. Gross weight of an airplane is 10,000 lb. 500 lb. of cargo is shifted 50 in. How far does the CG shift? (Note original CG and direction of shift is unspecified. Since datum is undefined, why not define it, temporarily, as the initial CG location, even though it is unknown? This causes $M_1$ to become zero! Incidentally, the **direction** of CG shift corresponds precisely to the **direction** of the weight shift.)

$$CG = \frac{M_1 \pm \Delta M}{W_1 \pm \Delta W} = \frac{500 \times 50}{10{,}000} = 2.5\ in.$$

# CHAPTER SEVEN
# AVIATION WEATHER



Almost all activity, but especially flying, is affected by the weather. Weather becomes very important to pilots as they attempt to fly long distances. Long trips (several hundred miles or more) almost always require transition from at least one weather system to another. Even during local flying, the weather can change and require you to land or at least to take special precautions. The most difficult aspect of weather is that it is always changing.

The outline in this book contains a brief introduction to weather concepts, along with a user-friendly guide to the most widely used weather reports and forecasts. For a complete and detailed explanation of the topics in this chapter, see Gleim's *Aviation Weather*, which combines the FAA's *Aviation Weather* (AC 00-6A) and *Aviation Weather Services* (AC 00-45C) into one easy-to-understand book.

As with some of the earlier chapters, this chapter cannot be read or studied in a single sitting. You should work through one or two modules each day.

## 7.1 THE EARTH'S ATMOSPHERE

A. Composition. Air is a mixture of several gases.

1. Dry air consists of 78% nitrogen and 21% oxygen. The other 1% consists of other gases including argon, carbon dioxide, neon, and helium.
2. In the atmosphere, however, air is never completely dry. It may contain as much as 5% water vapor. This proportion of water vapor (humidity) decreases the other gases proportionately.

B. Vertical structure. The Earth's atmosphere is divided into four layers.

1. Troposphere -- from the Earth's surface up to about 20,000 ft. at the poles and about 65,000 ft. at the equator.
   a. Temperature usually decreases as altitude increases.
   b. Most weather and virtually all flight occur in the troposphere.
2. Stratosphere -- the layer above the troposphere. Only special aircraft can fly in the stratosphere.
   a. The tropopause is a very thin layer marking the boundary between the troposphere and the stratosphere.
3. Mesosphere -- the layer above the stratosphere. Only rockets, spaceships, and the like can reach the mesosphere and thermosphere.
   a. Ionosphere and exosphere are terms used in some classifications for the regions above the stratosphere.
4. Thermosphere -- the layer above the mesosphere. It contains the last remnants of the atmosphere before space.

C. International Standard Atmosphere (ISA). This is a standard reference used by engineers, meteorologists and pilots. The "standard" is obtained from the average of conditions throughout the atmosphere for all latitudes, seasons, and altitudes.

1. Standard sea-level temperature has been established at 15°C (59°F).
2. Standard sea-level pressure is 29.92 in. Hg (1013.2 mb).
   a. Hg is the abbreviation for mercury.
   b. Mb is the abbreviation for millibar.
3. In the standard atmosphere, temperature and pressure change at fixed rates with changes in altitude.
   a. Pressure decreases about 1 in. per 1,000-ft. increase in altitude.
   b. Temperature decreases 2.0°C (3.5°F) per 1,000 ft. in altitude (this is known as the standard lapse rate).
4. These changes are important because changes in temperature and in pressure affect the altimeter readings in your airplane.
   a. The standard lapse rate is used to calibrate the pressure altimeter and to calculate airplane performance data.

D. Air Pressure and Density

1. Air is matter and has weight, and since it is a gas, it is compressible.
   a. The more it is compressed, the denser it becomes.
2. Air pressure at a given location is the result of the weight of the air above that location.
   a. Thus, the higher the altitude, the lower the pressure.

3. Air density is the weight of the air, i.e., the amount of air molecules in a given area.
   a. As altitude increases, pressure decreases, causing the air to become less compressed and less dense.
   b. As temperature increases, the air molecules become more active and move apart, resulting in fewer molecules per area and less density.
   c. As humidity increases, lighter water molecules replace air molecules, resulting in lighter (less dense) air.
4. As air becomes less dense, there is a negative physiological effect on humans.
   a. The rate at which the lungs absorb oxygen is partially a function of the pressure of the oxygen in the air.
   b. Since the atmosphere consists of about 20% oxygen, the oxygen pressure is 20% of the total air pressure at any given altitude.
      1) On the Earth's surface, our bodies are accustomed to an oxygen partial pressure of about 3 psi.
      2) Since this pressure becomes less as we increase our altitude, the rate of oxygen absorption into the body is lower.
   c. See Module 14.2, Hypoxia, beginning on page 357.

## 7.2 TEMPERATURE

A. Temperature is a measure of hot or cold. It is a critical factor in
   1. The formation of weather systems
   2. Airplane performance

B. Temperature scales. Celsius (C) and Fahrenheit (F) are the two common temperature scales.
   1. Celsius -- used for temperatures above the surface. It is becoming the world standard for surface temperatures as well. It is based on the freezing point of 0°C and boiling point of 100°C of water at sea level.
      a. It is used to report temperatures aloft in the Winds and Temperatures Aloft Forecasts.
   2. Fahrenheit -- based on the freezing point of 32°F and boiling point of 212°F of water at sea level.
      a. It is used to report surface temperatures in the Surface Aviation Observation reports.
   3. The difference between freezing and boiling is 100°C or 180°F. Thus, the ratio between °C and °F is 100/180 or 5/9. Since 0°F is 32 Fahrenheit degrees colder than 0°C, you must apply this difference when comparing temperatures on the two scales.
      a. You can convert from one scale to the other using one of the following formulae:
         1) $C = 5/9 \times (F - 32)$.
         2) $F = (9/5 \times C) + 32$.
      b. EXAMPLES:
         1) 72°F is 22.2°C [$5/9 \times (72 - 32)$].
         2) 10°C is 50°F [$(9/5 \times 10) + 32$].
      c. You can also use your flight computer for the conversion. See Chapter 12, Flight Computers, on page 317.

C. Heat is a form of energy. When a substance contains heat, it exhibits the property we measure as temperature, which is the degree of a substance's warmth or coldness.

1. A specific amount of heat added to or removed from a substance will raise or lower its temperature a definite amount. Each substance has a unique temperature change per specific change in heat.

   a. EXAMPLE: If a land surface and a water surface have the same temperature and an equal amount of heat is added, the land surface becomes hotter than the water surface. Conversely, with equal heat loss, the land becomes colder than the water.

2. Every physical process of weather is either accompanied by, or is the result of, heat exchanges.

D. Temperature variations. Five main types of temperature variations affect weather.

1. Diurnal variation. This is the change in temperature from day to night and night to day brought about by the rotation of the Earth.

2. Seasonal variation. In addition to its daily rotation, the Earth revolves around the sun. Since the Earth's axis is tilted with respect to its orbit, the angle at which a particular spot or region receives solar radiation varies throughout the year. This accounts for the temperature variations of the four seasons.

3. Variation with latitude. The sun is nearly overhead in the equatorial regions. Since the Earth is spherical, the sun's rays reach the higher latitudes at an angle. For this reason, the equatorial regions receive the most radiant energy and are the warmest.

4. Variations with topography. Temperature is also affected by terrain. Since land heats and cools at a faster rate than water, air temperatures over land vary more widely than those over large bodies of water, which tend to have more minimal temperature changes. Wet soil, swamps, and thick vegetation also help to control temperature fluctuations.

   a. Air temperature over land can vary as much as 50°F between the daily high and low over rocky or sandy deserts.

   b. Air temperature over water, near a shoreline, or over a swamp or marsh, may only vary about 10°F during the same time period.

5. Temperature variation with altitude. The amount of temperature decrease with increases in altitude is defined as the lapse rate.

   a. The standard lapse rate in the troposphere is 2°C per 1,000 ft.

   b. An increase in temperature with an increase in altitude is called an inversion, because the lapse rate is inverted.

      1) An inversion may occur when the ground cools faster than the air over it. Air in contact with the ground becomes cold, while only a few hundred feet up the temperature has changed very little. Thus, there is a temperature increase with height.

      2) Inversions may occur at any altitude.

## 7.3 ATMOSPHERIC PRESSURE

A. Atmospheric pressure is the force per unit area exerted by the weight of the atmosphere.

1. Atmospheric pressure is measured with a barometer. There are two types of barometers:

   a. Mercurial barometer -- an evacuated (vacuum) glass tube with the open end submerged in a dish of mercury which is open to the atmosphere. Atmospheric pressure forces mercury up into the vacuum of the glass tube. The height of the column of mercury is a measure of the atmospheric pressure.

b. Aneroid barometer -- consists of a partially evacuated flexible metal cell connected to a registering mechanism. As the atmospheric pressure changes, the metal cell expands or contracts which drives a needle along a scale which is calibrated in pressure units.

2. Pressure units. Pressure is expressed in several ways.

a. "Inches of mercury" or "millibars" are terms commonly used with barometers.

b. The term millibar precisely expresses pressure as a force per unit area.

c. The millibar is rapidly becoming a universal pressure unit, but altimeters are still set in inches of mercury, e.g., 29.95.

B. Pressure Analyses. Sea level pressures are plotted on the surface analysis chart. Then lines are drawn to connect all points of equal pressure. These lines of equal pressure are called "isobars." The surface weather map is an isobaric analysis showing identifiable, organized pressure patterns. Surface weather maps are illustrated and discussed in Module 7.23, Surface Analysis Chart, beginning on page 206. There are five pressure patterns or systems:

1. Low -- a center of pressure surrounded on all sides by higher pressure.

2. High -- a center of pressure surrounded on all sides by lower pressure.

3. Trough -- an elongated area of low pressure.

4. Ridge -- an elongated area of high pressure.

5. Col -- the neutral area between two highs and two lows. It is also the intersection of a trough and a ridge.

C. Pressure Variation

1. Pressure varies from standard with changes in altitude and temperature of the air. Other factors also affect pressure but their effects are negligible.

a. Altitude. At higher altitudes, the weight of the air above decreases.

1) This decrease in pressure from air above results in a lower atmospheric pressure.

2) Within the lower few thousand feet of the troposphere (i.e., near the Earth's surface), pressure decreases at a rate of roughly 1 in. per 1,000 ft. of altitude. As one goes higher, this rate of decrease slows.

b. Temperature. Like most substances, air expands as it becomes warmer and shrinks as it cools.

1) When air is warm and expands, there is less pressure because the same amount of air exists in a larger area.

2) When air is cooled it contracts. The pressure is greater than that of the warm air because the same amount of air takes up a smaller area.

2. Sea level pressure. Since pressure varies with altitude, we cannot readily compare pressures between airports or weather stations at different altitudes. The pressures need to be adjusted to a common level.

a. This common level is mean sea level (MSL).

b. EXAMPLE: Given a pressure at 5,000 ft. of 25.15 in. Hg, the sea level pressure is 25.15 in. plus approximately 5 in. (1 in. per 1,000 ft.) = 30.15 in. Hg.

c. Altimeter settings in local weather reports are the local pressure adjusted to MSL.

## 7.4 ALTIMETRY

A. The altimeter in an airplane is essentially an aneroid barometer with its scale calibrated in height.

B. Altitude (height) is categorized into five types:

1. True altitude -- actual altitude above mean sea level.
2. Indicated altitude -- the altitude above mean sea level indicated on the altimeter when it is set to the current local altimeter setting.
3. Corrected (approximately true) altitude -- the indicated altitude corrected for the temperature (when different from the temperature at the reporting station). The computation is made on your flight computer. See Module 12.7, Corrected (Approximately True) Altitude, beginning on page 325.
4. Pressure altitude -- the altitude in the standard atmosphere where the pressure is the same as where you are. It is the indicated altitude on an altimeter when set to standard sea level pressure (29.92 in. Hg).
   a. At 18,000 ft. MSL and above, all altimeters are set to 29.92. That is, pressure altitude is used.
   b. Determining pressure altitude is also an intermediate step in computing density altitude.
5. Density altitude -- the altitude in the standard atmosphere where the air density is the same as where you are. It is pressure altitude corrected for nonstandard temperature.
   a. Density altitude is computed to evaluate the performance capabilities of airplanes.
   b. Density altitude is computed in the following manner.
      1) Determine pressure altitude by setting the altimeter to 29.92.
      2) Then convert the pressure altitude to density altitude by correcting for the temperature on your flight computer. See Module 12.6, True Airspeed and Density Altitude, beginning on page 324.

## 7.5 WIND

A. Convection

1. When two surfaces are heated unequally, the surfaces heat the air lying over them unequally.
   a. The warmer air expands and becomes lighter or less dense than the cool air.
   b. The denser, cool air is drawn to the ground by its greater weight, lifting or forcing the warm air upward.
   c. The rising air spreads and cools, eventually descending to complete the convection circulation.
2. The horizontal air flow in a convective current is wind.
3. Convection on both large and small scales accounts for systems ranging from hemispheric circulations down to local eddies.

B. Pressure Gradient Force

1. Pressure differences must create a force in order to drive the wind. This force is called the pressure gradient force.
   a. The force is from higher pressure to lower pressure and is perpendicular to isobars (i.e., lines of equal pressure shown on a weather chart).
      1) The closer the spacing of isobars, the stronger the pressure gradient. The stronger the pressure gradient, the stronger the wind.

2. Due to uneven heating of the Earth, surface pressure is low in warm equatorial regions and high in cold polar regions.
   a. A pressure gradient develops from the poles to the Equator.
   b. If the Earth did not rotate, this would be the only force acting on the wind, and circulation would consist of two giant hemispheric convective currents.
      1) Cold air would sink at the poles and blow straight to the Equator where it would be warmed and forced upward, and high-level winds would blow directly to the poles.
   c. Because the Earth does rotate, this simple circulation is greatly distorted.

C. Coriolis Force
1. Coriolis force is a deflective force resulting from the Earth's rotation.
   a. The force deflects air to the right in the Northern Hemisphere and to the left in the Southern Hemisphere.
   b. This force is at a right angle (90°) to wind direction and directly proportional to wind speed.
      1) Thus, as wind speed increases, Coriolis force increases.
2. Coriolis force varies with latitude from zero at the Equator to a maximum at the poles.
3. When a pressure gradient force is first established, wind begins to blow from higher to lower pressure directly across the isobars.
   a. However, the instant air begins moving, Coriolis force deflects it to the right until it is deflected a full 90° and is now parallel to the isobars.

D. General Circulation
1. As air is forced upward at the Equator and begins its high-level trek northward, the Coriolis force turns to the right, and becomes westerly in direction at about 30°N latitude.
   a. As air over the pole begins its low-level journey southward toward the Equator, it likewise is deflected to the right, and becomes easterly in direction at about 60°N latitude.
   b. Air tends to "pile up" between 30° and 60° latitude in both hemispheres.
      1) The added weight of the air increases the pressure into semipermanent high-pressure belts.
2. The building of these high-pressure belts creates a temporary impasse disrupting the simple convective transfer between the Equator and the poles. Thus, huge air masses begin to overturn in the middle latitudes to complete the exchange.
   a. Large masses of cold air break through the northern barrier moving south toward the Tropics.
   b. Large mid-latitude storms develop between cold outbreaks and carry warm air northward.

E. Friction
1. Friction between the wind and the Earth's terrain surface slows the wind.
   a. The rougher the terrain, the greater the frictional effect
   b. The stronger the wind speed, the greater the friction
2. As frictional force slows the wind speed, Coriolis force decreases. However, friction does not affect pressure gradient force.
   a. Since pressure gradient and Coriolis forces are no longer in balance, the stronger pressure gradient force turns the wind at an angle across the isobars toward lower pressure.

F. Jet Stream

1. Winds on the average increase with height throughout the troposphere, culminating in a maximum near the level of the tropopause.
    a. These maximum winds tend to be concentrated in narrow bands.
2. A jet stream is a narrow band of strong winds (50 kt. or more) meandering through the atmosphere in an easterly direction at a level near the tropopause.

G. Local and Small-Scale Winds

1. Until now, we have dealt with the general circulation and major wind systems. Local terrain features such as mountains and shorelines influence local winds and weather.
2. Valley and Mountain Winds
    a. Colder, denser air in the surroundings settles downward and forces the warmer air near the ground up the mountain slope.
        1) This wind is a valley wind because the air is flowing up out of the valley.
    b. At night, the air in contact with the mountain slope is cooled by terrestrial radiation and becomes heavier than the surrounding air, and sinks along the slope.
        1) This wind is a mountain wind because the air is flowing down the mountain slope.
3. Katabatic Wind
    a. A katabatic wind is any wind blowing down an incline (i.e., a mountain wind).
4. Sea and Land Breezes
    a. During the day the land is warmer than the sea.
        1) Sea breezes are caused by cooler and denser air moving inland off the water.
        2) Once over the warmer land, the air heats up and rises.
        3) Currents push the air out over the water where it cools and descends, starting the process over again.
    b. At night, the wind reverses from the cool land to the warmer water.
        1) This is called a land breeze.
    c. These breezes only occur when the overall pressure gradient is weak.

H. Wind Shear

1. Air currents of differing velocities and/or direction create friction between themselves.
    a. This friction creates eddies along a common shallow mixing zone.
    b. This zone of induced eddies and mixing is a shear zone.
2. Wind shear is the rate of change of wind velocity (direction and/or speed) per unit of distance.
    a. This may be expressed as vertical or horizontal wind shear.

I. Wind, Pressure Systems, and Weather

1. In the Northern Hemisphere, wind blows counterclockwise around a low pressure area and clockwise around a high. This is due to the Coriolis force. Remember that air flows outward from highs and inward to lows.
    a. At the surface, where winds cross the isobars at an angle, there is a movement of air from high to low pressure areas.
    b. Although winds are virtually parallel to contours on an upper air chart (due to the Coriolis force), there is still a slow movement of air from high to low pressure areas.

2. At the surface when air converges into a low, it cannot go outward against the pressure gradient, nor can it go downward into the ground. It must go upward. Therefore, a low or a trough is an area of rising air.
   a. Rising air is conducive to cloudiness and precipitation. Thus, low pressure areas are generally associated with bad weather.
3. Conversely, air moving out from a high or a ridge depletes the quantity of air and is an area of descending air.
   a. Descending air tends to dissipate clouds, so highs are usually associated with good weather.
4. Major weather is generally associated with upper air patterns rather than local surface influences.

## 7.6 MOISTURE, CLOUD FORMATION, AND PRECIPITATION

A. Water Vapor. Water evaporates and becomes an ever-present but variable constituent of the atmosphere. It is invisible like the other atmospheric gases, but we can still measure its quantity in the air. It is generally expressed as
   1. Relative humidity -- a ratio of how much actual water vapor is present to the amount that could be present. The amount of water that air can hold is a function of the air temperature. Cool air can hold less water vapor than warm air. At 100% relative humidity the air is saturated.
   2. Dew point -- the temperature to which air must be cooled to become saturated by the water vapor that is already present in that air.
      a. Dew point is compared to air temperature to determine how close the air is to saturation. This difference is referred to as the temperature-dew point spread.
      b. As the temperature and dew point converge, fog, clouds, or rain may be anticipated.

B. A change of state is the transformation of water from one form, i.e., solid (ice), liquid, or gaseous (water vapor), to any other form.
   1. There are six possible transformations designated by the five following terms.
      a. Condensation -- The change of water vapor to liquid water.
      b. Evaporation -- The change of liquid water to water vapor.
      c. Freezing -- The change of liquid water to ice.
      d. Melting -- The change of ice to liquid water.
      e. Sublimation -- The change of
         1) Ice to water vapor, or
         2) Water vapor to ice.
   2. Latent heat is the energy transferred during a change of state. It takes more energy to make the conversion from one state to another than the actual change in temperature before and after the conversion.
      a. The heat exchange needed to evaporate water thus cools surrounding matter. This is very like the cooling effect when perspiration evaporates.
   3. Condensation nuclei are the microscopic, solid particles of dust and other matter suspended in the atmosphere. They attract water vapor during periods of condensation and sublimation.
   4. Supercooled water consists of water droplets existing at temperatures below freezing.
      a. Supercooled water is dangerous because it immediately forms into heavy, clear ice when it strikes an airplane's surface.

5. Dew forms when the Earth's surface cools to below the dew point of adjacent air as a result of heat radiation. Then moisture forms (condenses) on leaves, grass, etc., as it does on a cold glass of water in warm, humid weather.

6. Frost forms in much the same way as dew. The difference is that the dew point of surrounding air must be colder than freezing. Water vapor then sublimates directly as ice crystals or frost rather than condensing as dew.

   a. Sometimes dew forms and later freezes. But frozen dew is easily distinguished from frost. Frozen dew is hard and transparent while frost is white and opaque.

C. Clouds are a visible aggregation of minute water or ice particles suspended in air. A cloud may be composed entirely of liquid water, of ice crystals, or a mixture of the two.

1. Cloud formation. Normally, air must become saturated for condensation or sublimation to occur. Saturation may result from cooling the temperature, increasing the dew point, or both. Cooling is far more predominant. There are three ways to cool air to saturation:

   a. Air moving over a colder surface.

   b. Stagnant air lying over a cooling surface.

   c. Expansional cooling in upward moving air. This process is the major cause of cloud formation.

2. If the cloud is on the ground, it is fog.

3. When entire layers of air cool to the point of saturation, fog or sheet-like clouds result.

4. Saturation of a localized updraft produces a towering cloud.

D. Precipitation is an all-inclusive term denoting drizzle, rain, snow, ice pellets, hail, and ice crystals. Precipitation occurs when any of these particles grow in size and weight until the atmosphere can no longer suspend them, and they fall.

1. These particles grow primarily in two ways.

   a. Once a water droplet or ice crystal forms, it continues to grow by added condensation or sublimation on its surface. This is a slow method. It usually results in drizzle or very light rain or snow.

   b. A more rapid process is the collision and merging of small particles into larger drops. This process is enhanced by upward moving air currents which build these particles into heavier rain, snow, and hail.

2. Precipitation can change its state as the temperature of its environment changes.

   a. Falling snow may melt to form rain in warmer layers of air at lower altitudes.

   b. Rain falling through colder air may become supercooled, freezing on impact as freezing rain.

      1) Freezing rain always indicates warmer air at higher altitudes.
      2) It may freeze during its descent, falling as ice pellets.

         a) Ice pellets always indicate freezing rain at higher altitudes.

   c. When supercooled water drops freeze and other drops freeze to them, hailstones are formed.

3. To produce significant precipitation, clouds must be at least 4,000 ft. thick.

E. Land and water surfaces underlying the atmosphere greatly affect cloud and precipitation development. Large bodies of water such as oceans and large lakes add water vapor to the air.

1. Expect the greatest frequency of low ceilings, fog, and precipitation in areas where prevailing winds have an over-water trajectory.

2. Be especially alert for these areas of poor visibility when moist winds are blowing upslope.

## 7.7 STABLE AND UNSTABLE AIR

A. A stable atmosphere resists any upward or downward displacement. An unstable atmosphere allows upward and downward disturbances to grow into vertical (convective) currents.

1. Any time air moves upward, it expands because of decreasing atmospheric pressure. Conversely, downward moving air is compressed by increasing pressure.
   a. When air expands, it cools, and when compressed, it warms.
   b. These changes are adiabatic, meaning that no heat is removed from or added to the air.
   c. The terms expansional or adiabatic cooling and compressional or adiabatic heating are commonly used.
2. Unsaturated air moving upward and downward cools and warms at about 3.0°C (5.4°F) per 1,000 ft.
   a. This rate of change is the "dry adiabatic rate of temperature change" and is independent of the temperature of the mass of air through which the vertical movements occur.
   b. That is, this is not the same as the standard temperature lapse rate discussed on page 166.
3. If air is forced upward, there are two possibilities:
   a. The air may become colder than the surrounding air, because its adiabatic rate of cooling is greater than the existing lapse rate of the surrounding air.
      1) The air begins to sink, and eventually settles into a stable condition because there is no tendency for any displacement to continue.
   b. The air may remain warmer than the surrounding air despite its cooling, because its adiabatic rate of cooling is less than the existing lapse rate.
      1) The air continues to rise, and is considered to be in an unstable condition.
      2) This instability could grow into a larger weather system.
4. Thus, the difference between the existing lapse rate of a given air mass and the adiabatic rate of cooling will determine whether the air is stable or unstable.

B. Stability and Instability

1. The stability of the atmosphere varies with location, altitude, and time.
   a. Certain air masses will be more stable or unstable than others.
   b. Often, air stability will be layered.
      1) A layer of stable air may overlie an unstable layer, or vice versa.
2. The stability of the air will be a predominant factor in the formation of clouds.
   a. Since stable air resists convection, clouds in stable air form in horizontal sheet-like layers or "strata." Thus, within a stable layer, clouds are stratiform.
   b. Unstable air favors convection. A "cumulus" cloud, meaning "heap," forms in a convective updraft and builds upward. Within an unstable layer, clouds are cumuliform. The vertical development depends on the depth of the unstable layer.
3. Stratiform and cumuliform clouds can merge if some updrafts are able to rise in a basically stable air mass. Convective clouds (i.e., thunderstorms) can be embedded in a stratiform layer and pose an unseen threat to pilots.

## 7.8 CLOUDS

A. There are four major classifications or families of clouds:

1. High clouds -- The high cloud family is cirriform. High clouds are composed almost entirely of ice crystals. The bases of these clouds usually range from about 16,500 ft. to 45,000 ft. in middle latitudes.
2. Middle clouds -- composed primarily of water, much of which may be supercooled. Cloud bases range from 6,500 ft. to 23,000 ft. in middle latitudes.
3. Low clouds -- composed almost entirely of water, but at times the water may be supercooled. They can also contain snow and ice particles if temperatures are below freezing. Cloud bases range from the surface to about 6,500 ft. in middle latitudes.
4. Clouds with extensive vertical development -- usually composed of supercooled water above the freezing level. Bases range from 1,000 ft. or less to above 10,000 ft.

B. The first three families are further classified according to the way they are formed, as mentioned in the previous module.

1. Clouds formed by vertical currents in unstable air are *cumulus*, and have a lumpy, billowy appearance.
2. Clouds formed by the cooling of a stable layer are *stratus*, and have a uniform, sheet-like appearance.
3. In addition, the prefix *nimbo* or the suffix *nimbus* means raincloud.
   a. For example, a cumulus cloud which produces precipitation is a *cumulonimbus*.

C. Estimating Bases of Cumulus Clouds

1. When air rises in a convective current, it cools at the rate of 5.4°F/1,000 ft. and its dew point decreases 1°F/1,000 ft.
   a. The temperature and dew point then are converging at 4.4°F/1,000 ft.
2. Since clouds form when the temperature-dew point spread is 0°, we can use this to estimate the bases of cumulus clouds.
   a. The surface temperature-dew point spread divided by 4.4°F equals the bases of cumulus clouds in thousands of feet above ground level (AGL).
3. EXAMPLE: Surface dew point 56°F, surface temperature 69°F results in an estimate of cumulus cloud bases at 3,000 ft. AGL: 69°F − 56°F = 13°F temperature-dew point spread; 13°F/4.4°F = approximately 3,000 ft. AGL.

## 7.9 AIR MASSES AND FRONTS

A. Air Masses. When a body of air comes to rest or moves slowly over an extensive area having uniform properties of temperature and moisture, the air takes on the same properties.

1. The area over which the air mass acquires its properties of temperature and moisture is its "source region." There are many source regions, the best examples being large snow or ice-covered polar regions, cold northern and tropical oceans, and large desert areas.
2. Just as an air mass takes on the properties of its source region, it tends to take on properties of the underlying surface when it moves away from its source region, thus becoming modified. Some ways in which air masses are modified include the following:
   a. Cool air moving over a warm surface is heated from below, generating instability and increasing the possibility of showers.
   b. Warm air moving over a cool surface is cooled from below, increasing stability. If air is cooled to its dew point, stratus clouds and/or fog forms.

c. Evaporation from water surfaces and falling precipitation adds water vapor to the air. When the water is warmer than the air, evaporation can raise the dew point sufficiently to saturate the air and form stratus clouds or fog.

d. Water vapor is removed by condensation and precipitation.

3. The stability of an air mass determines its typical weather characteristics. When one air mass overlies another, conditions change with height. Typical characteristics of stable and unstable air:

   a. Stable air -- stratiform clouds and fog, continuous precipitation, smooth air, and fair to poor visibility.

   b. Unstable air -- cumuliform clouds, showery precipitation, turbulence, and good visibility, except in blowing obstructions, e.g., dust, sand, snow, etc.

B. Fronts. The zone between two different air masses is a frontal zone or "front." Across this zone, temperature, humidity, and wind often change rapidly over short distances.

1. Discontinuities. When you pass through a frontal zone, these changes may be abrupt indicating a narrow front. A more subtle change indicates a broad and diffused front.

   a. Temperature -- The most easily recognizable indication that you are passing through a front will be a significant temperature change.

   b. Dew point -- temperature-dew point spread usually differ across a front.

   c. Wind -- always changes across a front. Direction, speed, or both will change. Wind shear is often associated with a frontal wind shift.

   d. Pressure -- may change abruptly as you move from one air mass to another. It is important to keep a current altimeter setting when in the vicinity of a front.

2. Types of fronts. There are three principal types of fronts.

   a. Cold front -- the leading edge of an advancing cold air mass. At the surface, cold air overtakes and replaces warm air.

   b. Warm front -- the leading edge of an advancing mass of warm air. Since cold air is more dense, it hugs the ground and the warm air slides up and over the cold mass. This elongates the frontal zone making it more diffuse. Warm fronts generally move about one-half as fast as cold fronts under the same wind conditions.

   c. Stationary front -- occurs when neither air mass is replacing the other and there is little or no movement. Surface winds tend to blow parallel to the front.

3. Frontolysis and frontogenesis

   a. As adjacent air masses converge, and as temperature and pressure differences equalize across a front, the front dissipates. This dissipation is called frontolysis.

   b. When two air masses come together and form a front the process is called frontogenesis.

4. Frontal weather. In and along fronts, flying weather varies from virtually clear skies to extreme hazards including hail, turbulence, icing, low clouds, and poor visibility. Weather occurring with a front depends on

   a. The amount of moisture available,
   b. The degree of stability of the air that is forced upward,
   c. The slope of the front,
   d. The speed of the frontal movement, and
   e. The upper wind flow.

5. An instability line is a narrow nonfrontal line or band of convective activity.
   a. If this line is a band of fully developed thunderstorms, it is called a squall line.
      1) Squall lines frequently develop ahead of a cold front.
6. A dew point front (also called a dry line) is a front between two air masses that differ significantly only with respect to moisture content.

## 7.10 TURBULENCE

A. A turbulent atmosphere is one in which air currents vary greatly over short distances. These currents range from rather mild eddies to strong currents of relatively large dimensions.

1. As an airplane moves through these currents, it undergoes changing accelerations which jostle it from its smooth flight path. This jostling is turbulence.
   a. An airplane's reaction to turbulence varies with the difference in wind speed in adjacent currents, size of the airplane, wing loading, airspeed, and altitude.
   b. The first rule in flying in turbulence is to reduce airspeed to the manufacturer's recommended turbulence penetration speed.
2. The main causes of turbulence are
   a. Convective currents,
   b. Obstructions to wind flow, and
   c. Wind shear.

B. Convective Currents

1. Convective currents are localized vertical (both up and down) air movements. For every rising current, there is a compensating downward current.
   a. This is a common cause of turbulence, especially at low altitudes.
   b. Convective currents are most active on warm summer afternoons when winds are light.
2. As air moves upward, it cools by expansion. A convective current continues upward until it reaches a level where its temperature cools to that of the surrounding air.
   a. If the air cools to saturation, a cloud forms.
      1) Cumulus clouds indicate convective turbulence.
      2) The cloud top marks the approximate upper limit of the convective current.
   b. Even when the air is too dry for clouds to form, convective currents can still be active.
3. Turbulence during an approach to a landing can cause abrupt changes in airspeed and may even result in a stall at a dangerously low altitude.
   a. Increase airspeed slightly over the normal approach speed during these conditions.

C. Obstructions to Wind Flow

1. Obstructions such as buildings, trees, and rough terrain disrupt smooth wind flow, which causes turbulence.
   a. The degree of turbulence depends on the wind speed and roughness of the obstructions. The higher the speed and/or the rougher the surface, the greater the turbulence.

b. When landing or taking off with a gusty crosswind, be alert for turbulence caused by airport structures upwind.

   1) Maintain an airspeed slightly over the normal approach/climb speed to allow for sudden changes in airspeed due to gusts.

c. Flying over rugged hills or mountains may present some turbulence problems.

   1) When wind speed across the mountain exceeds about 40 kt., anticipate turbulence.

   2) If the air is unstable, turbulence on the windward side is almost certain. As the air crosses the mountain, it spills down the leeward slope as a violent downdraft.

      a) Hazardous turbulence in unstable air generally does not extend a great distance downwind.

2. Mountain wave. When stable air crosses a mountain barrier, the air flowing up the windward side is relatively smooth and the wind across the barrier tends to flow in layers.

   a. The barrier may set up waves in these layers, thus the name mountain wave.

      1) The wave pattern may extend 100 mi. or more downwind from the barrier.

   b. Wave crests may be marked by stationary almond- or lens-shaped clouds known as standing lenticular clouds.

   c. Wave crests extend well above the highest mountain. Under each wave crest is a rotary circulation.

      1) The rotor forms below the elevation of the mountain peaks and turbulence can be violent in these rotors.

      2) Updrafts and downdrafts in the waves can also create violent turbulence.

D. Wind Shear

1. Wind shear generates eddies between two wind currents of differing velocities.

   a. The differences may be in speed and/or direction and may occur at any altitude.

2. Wind shear with a low-level temperature inversion

   a. A temperature inversion forms near the surface on a clear night with calm or light surface wind. Wind above the inversion may be relatively strong.

      1) A wind shear zone develops between the calm and the stronger winds above.

   b. Eddies in the shear zone cause airspeed fluctuations as an airplane climbs or descends through the inversion.

      1) Allow a margin of airspeed above normal climb or approach speed to alleviate danger of a stall in the event of turbulence or sudden change in wind velocity.

   c. When taking off or landing in calm wind under clear skies within a few hours before or after sunrise, be prepared for a temperature inversion.

      1) A shear zone in the inversion is relatively certain if the wind at 2,000 to 4,000 ft. is 25 kt. or greater.

3. Wind shear in a frontal zone

   a. Wind changes abruptly in the frontal zone and can induce wind shear turbulence.
   b. The degree of turbulence depends on the magnitude of the wind shear.

## 7.11 ICING

A. Icing is a cumulative hazard to airplanes. When ice builds up on the surface of an airplane, it increases weight and drag while reducing lift and thrust. These factors tend to slow the airplane and/or force it to descend. Icing can also seriously impair engine performance and flight instruments.

B. Structural icing will occur if two conditions are met:

1. The airplane is flying through visible water such as rain or cloud droplets.
2. The air temperature where the moisture strikes the aircraft is 0°C or cooler.

   a. Aerodynamic cooling can lower the temperature of an airfoil to 0°C even though ambient temperature is slightly higher.

      1) Ambient temperature is the surrounding (outside) air temperature.

      2) Aerodynamic cooling is a result of the decreased pressure on the top of an airfoil.

C. There are three types of ice that can form on an airplane:

1. Clear ice -- forms when water droplets which touch the airplane flow across the surface before freezing. Clear ice will accumulate as a smooth sheet. This type of ice forms when the water droplets are large, such as in rain or cumuliform clouds.

   a. Clear ice is very heavy and difficult to remove.
   b. It can substantially increase the gross weight of an airplane.

2. Rime ice -- forms when the drops are small, such as those in stratiform clouds or light drizzle, and freeze on impact without spreading. Rime ice is rough and opaque, similar to frost in your home freezer.

   a. Its irregular shape and rough surface greatly decrease the aerodynamic efficiency of an airplane's wings, thus reducing lift and increasing drag.

3. Mixed ice -- forms when the drops vary in size. Some freeze on impact and some spread before freezing. Mixed ice is opaque and has a very rough surface.

D. Induction System (and Carburetor) Icing

1. Forms under a variety of conditions on both piston and turbine aircraft. As air is ingested through the engine intakes, the moisture can freeze inside the induction system or carburetor and reduce or stop the flow of combustible air into the engine.

2. See Module 4.17, Induction System, on page 103.

E. Instrument Icing

1. If ice forms on the pitot tube opening, ram pressure is reduced and the airspeed indicator will be incorrect.

2. All the pitot-static system instruments will be unreliable if ice forms on the static ports.

3. Ice can also cause radio failure if it forms on the antennas.

F. Icing and Cloud Types

1. There is a potential for icing in any cloud whenever the temperature is subfreezing. The water drop size, drop distribution, and aerodynamic effects of the airplane all influence the nature of the ice buildup.

2. Small water droplets occur most often in fog and low-level clouds, as evidenced by drizzle and light rain. The most common type of icing in low-level stratus clouds is rime.

3. Thick, extensive stratified clouds producing continuous rain contain large droplets in abundance. Such systems may be very extensive in winter and present serious icing problems on long flights.

4. The upward currents in cumuliform clouds are favorable for the formation and support of large water droplets and clear ice.

G. Other Factors in Icing

1. Fronts. A condition favorable for rapid clear ice accumulation is freezing rain near weather fronts. The cold (heavy) air underlies warm air at a front. The rain forms in the higher warm air, falls through the cold air, becomes supercooled, and freezes on impact with an airplane surface.

2. Terrain. Air blowing upslope is cooled adiabatically. When moist air is cooled below the freezing point, the water it contains becomes supercooled and can be an icing hazard to airplanes in the area.

   a. Mountain ranges can cause severe icing when air is blown upward to cool. Also, the icing zone can extend more than 5,000 ft. above the ridge.

3. Seasons. Icing can occur during any season but is more common in winter because the freezing level is closer to the ground.

H. Ground Icing

1. Frost, ice pellets, frozen rain, or snow may accumulate on parked airplanes. All ice should be removed before takeoff.

2. Water blown by propellers or splashed by wheels during taxiing may result in serious icing of wheel wells, brakes, flap hinges, etc., and prevent proper operation of these components.

3. Ice on runways and taxiways can create traction and braking problems.

I. Frost

1. Frost should be removed from all airfoils before flight.

2. Even small amounts of frost can raise stall speeds and reduce lift because the roughness of its surface spoils the smooth flow of air over the wing.

## 7.12 THUNDERSTORMS

A. For a thunderstorm to form, the air must have

1. Sufficient water vapor.
2. An unstable lapse rate.
3. An initial upward boost (lifting) to start the storm process in motion.

   a. Surface heating, converging winds, sloping terrain, a frontal surface, or any combination of these can provide the necessary lifting.

B. A thunderstorm cell progresses through three stages during its life cycle.

1. The Cumulus Stage

   a. Although most cumulus clouds do not grow into thunderstorms, every thunderstorm begins as a cumulus.

   b. The key feature in the cumulus stage is the updraft.

   c. Early during the cumulus stage, water droplets are quite small but grow to raindrop size as the cloud grows.

      1) The rising air carries the liquid water above the freezing level, creating an icing hazard.

      2) As the raindrops grow still heavier, they fall. This cold rain drags air with it, creating a cold downdraft coexisting with the updraft.

2. The Mature Stage

   a. Precipitation beginning to fall from the cloud base is the sign that a downdraft has developed and a cell has entered the mature stage.

   b. Cold rain in the downdraft retards compressional heating, and the downdraft remains cooler than the surrounding air. Thus, its downward speed is accelerated.

   c. The downrushing air spreads outward at the surface, producing strong gusty surface winds, a sharp temperature drop, and a rapid rise in pressure.

      1) The surface wind surge is a "plow wind" and its leading edge is the "first gust."

   d. Updrafts and downdrafts in close proximity create strong vertical shear and a very turbulent environment.

      1) All thunderstorm hazards reach their greatest intensity during the mature stage.

3. The Dissipating Stage

   a. Downdrafts characterize the dissipating stage of the thunderstorm cell and the storm dies rapidly.

   b. When the rain has ended and downdrafts have abated, the dissipating stage is complete.

C. Size

1. Individual thunderstorms measure from less than 5 mi. to more than 30 mi. in diameter.
2. Cloud bases vary between a few hundred feet to more than 10,000 ft.
3. Tops generally range from 25,000 to 45,000 ft., but occasionally extend above 65,000 ft.

D. Types of Thunderstorms

1. Air Mass Thunderstorms

   a. Most often result from surface heating, and last only about 20 to 90 min.

2. Steady State Thunderstorms

   a. Usually associated with weather systems

      1) Fronts, converging winds, and troughs aloft force air upwards to initiate the storms.

   b. They may last for several hours.

E. Hazards

1. Tornadoes

   a. Violent thunderstorms draw air in at the base. If there is any rotation during this drawing, a vortex can develop.

   b. Vortex rotational velocity can exceed 200 kt.

      1) The pressure inside the vortex is very low which helps generate the funnel-shaped cloud.

   c. Tornadoes are usually associated with steady state thunderstorms.

2. Squall Lines

   a. Narrow bands of non-frontal active thunderstorms

   b. They often form in front of cold fronts in moist unstable air, but they may also develop in unstable air far removed from any fronts.

   c. They generally produce the most severe thunderstorm conditions (i.e., heavy hail, destructive winds, tornadoes, etc.).

3. Turbulence
   a. Present in all thunderstorms
   b. It is formed in the shear of updrafts and downdrafts.
   c. Turbulence can extend several thousand feet above and 20 mi. laterally from the storm.
   d. Wind shear turbulence cannot be seen, and is particularly hazardous for airplanes landing and taking off.
4. Icing
   a. Can be extremely hazardous in thunderstorms.
   b. Large amounts of water are carried up above the freezing level by the storm's updrafts and can be hazardous to aircraft.
5. Hail
   a. Should be anticipated with any thunderstorm.
   b. Supercooled water droplets above the freezing level freeze and build up until they fall, often miles from the parent storm.
   c. Hail can cause severe damage to an airplane.
6. Low Ceiling and Visibility
   a. Visibility is usually near zero within thunderstorms.
   b. Precipitation can reduce ceilings and visibilities beneath the cloud base.
7. Effect on Altimeter
   a. Pressure usually falls rapidly with the approach of a thunderstorm, then rises sharply with the onset of the first gust and cold downdrafts. Pressure returns to normal as the storm moves on.
   b. These pressure changes can occur within 15 min. and may induce over 100 ft. of error in the altimeter.
8. Thunderstorm Electricity
   a. Lightning. Always associated with a thunderstorm, although it is rarely a hazard to aircraft. It can puncture the airplane skin or cause damage to the radios, but is not really destructive unless fuel vapors that could cause an explosion have escaped. Nearby lightning, however, can momentarily blind a pilot.
   b. Precipitation static. A steady, high-level noise in the radios caused by the static buildup of the metal surfaces of the airplane passing through precipitation. It is harmless except for the difficulty in hearing over the noise.

F. Thunderstorms and Radar

1. Radar energy is reflected by droplet size precipitation.
   a. Larger drops and more intense precipitation cause stronger radar returns.
   b. Thunderstorms return the strongest echoes since the greatest rainfall rate is in thunderstorms.

G. Dos and Do Nots of Thunderstorm Flying

1. Avoiding thunderstorms is the best policy.
   a. Do not attempt to fly under or within about 20 mi. of severe thunderstorms because of hail and turbulence.
   b. Do not land or take off in the face of an approaching thunderstorm.
      1) A sudden wind shift or low-level turbulence could cause loss of control.

2. If it is not possible to avoid penetration of a thunderstorm:
   a. Tighten seat belts, secure all loose objects.
   b. Turn on pitot and carburetor heat to avoid icing and reduce speed to the recommended turbulence penetration speed (i.e., maneuvering speed).
   c. Turn up cockpit lights and keep your eyes on the instruments.
   d. Do not change power settings. Try to maintain a constant attitude and ride out the storm.
   e. Do not turn back after entry. Straight ahead is usually the quickest way out. Turning could induce additional/excess structural stress.

## 7.13 FOG

A. Fog is a surface-based cloud composed of either water droplets or ice crystals.
   1. It is the most frequent cause of IFR conditions, and is one of the most persistent weather hazards encountered in aviation.
   2. A small temperature-dew point spread is essential for fog to form.
      a. Abundant condensation nuclei, such as may be found in industrial areas, enhance the formation of fog.
   3. Fog is classified by the way it forms.

B. Radiation fog, or ground fog, is relatively shallow.
   1. It forms almost exclusively at night or near daybreak, under a clear sky, and with little or no wind and a small temperature-dew point spread.
   2. Terrestrial radiation cools the ground, which cools the air in contact with it.
      a. When the air is cooled to its dew point, fog forms.
   3. Radiation fog is restricted to land because water cools little at night.
      a. It is shallow when the wind is calm.
      b. It deepens in wind up to 5 kt.
      c. Stronger winds disperse the fog.

C. Advection fog forms when moist air moves over colder ground or water. At sea it is called sea fog.
   1. Advection fog deepens in wind speeds up to 15 kt.
   2. Wind much stronger than 15 kt. lifts the fog into a layer of low clouds.
   3. Advection fog is more persistent and extensive than radiation fog, and can appear during day or night.

D. Upslope fog forms as a result of moist, stable air being cooled adiabatically as it moves up sloping terrain.
   1. Once the upslope wind ceases, the fog dissipates.
   2. Upslope fog is often quite dense and extends to high altitudes.

E. When relatively warm rain falls through cool air, evaporation from the precipitation saturates the cool air and forms fog.
   1. Precipitation-induced fog can become quite dense and continue for a long time.
   2. It is most commonly associated with warm fronts.
   3. It occurs near other possible hazards such as icing, turbulence, and thunderstorms.

F. Steam fog forms in winter when cold, dry air passes from land areas over comparatively warm ocean waters.

   1. It is composed entirely of water droplets that often freeze quickly.
   2. Low-level turbulence and hazardous icing can occur.

## 7.14 WEATHER REPORT SERVICES

A. The rest of this chapter describes the sources and uses of the major weather reports and forecasts.

   1. Observed weather is contained in weather reports.
   2. Expected weather is reported in forecasts.

B. Aviation weather reports and forecasts are available nationwide at any Flight Service Station (FSS).

   1. To call the nearest FSS by telephone, dial 1-800-WX-BRIEF (1-800-992-7433). When calling for information, use the following procedures:

      a. Identify yourself as a pilot and give airplane identification number, if known.

      b. State your intended route, destination, proposed departure time, estimated time en route, type of airplane, and whether you will fly VFR or IFR.

   2. Flight Service Specialists are qualified and certificated by the NOAA/NWS as Pilot Weather Briefers.

      a. They are not authorized to make original forecasts.

      b. They are authorized to translate and interpret available forecasts and reports directly into terms of the weather conditions which you can expect along your flight route and at destination.

      c. They also will assist you in selecting an alternate course of action in case you encounter adverse weather.

C. While you are airborne, weather advisories are also available from several sources.

   1. You may radio the nearest FSS in your area on its assigned frequency which is indicated on the top of the communication box of the nearest VOR.

      a. This box appears near each VOR on navigation charts.
      b. See Module 9.3, Sectional Chart Legends, on page 275.

   2. En Route Flight Advisory Service (EFAS) or Flight Watch is a service specifically designed to provide en route aircraft with timely and meaningful weather advisories pertinent to the type of flight, route, and altitude.

      a. It is normally available throughout the contiguous U.S. from 6 a.m. to 10 p.m. to aircraft flying at 5,000 ft. AGL to 17,500 ft. MSL.

      b. EFAS is provided by specially trained specialists from FSSs controlling one or more remote communications outlets covering a large geographical area.

      c. All communications are conducted on the designated EFAS frequency, 122.0 MHz.

      d. To contact a Flight Watch facility, use the name of the Air Route Traffic Control Center serving the area of your location and the words FLIGHT WATCH or simply call FLIGHT WATCH and give the name of the VOR nearest your position.

   3. Transcribed Weather Broadcasts (TWEB) are provided at selected FSSs. Meteorological data and Notices to Airmen are recorded on tapes and broadcast continuously over certain ADF frequencies (190-535 kHz) and selected VORs (108.0 to 117.95 MHz).

## 7.15 SURFACE AVIATION OBSERVATION (SAO)

A. When a Surface Aviation Observation (SAO) is reported and transmitted, it is a weather report. An SAO report contains some or all of the following elements:

1. Station designator
2. Type and time of report
3. Sky condition and ceiling
4. Visibility
5. Weather and obstructions to vision
6. Sea level pressure (millibars)
7. Temperature and dew point
8. Wind direction, speed, and character
9. Altimeter setting
10. Remarks and coded data

B. An example of an SAO report is presented below. Its elements are numbered according to the above list and interpreted below.

| GNV | SA 1251 | M50 BKN | 3 | K | 175 | 75/68 | 3010 | 003 | VIRGA ALQDS |
|---|---|---|---|---|---|---|---|---|---|
| 1 | 2 | 3 | 4 | 5 | 6 | 7 | 8 | 9 | 10 |

1. Gainesville
2. Record observation at 1251Z
3. Measured ceiling 5,000 ft. broken
4. Visibility 3 SM
5. Smoke
6. Pressure 1017.5 millibars
7. Temperature 75°F, dew point 68°F
8. Wind 300° (true) at 10 kt.
9. Altimeter setting 30.03
10. Remarks: Virga exists in all quadrants

C. Elements not occurring at the time of observation or not pertinent are omitted. When an element should be included but is unavailable, the letter "M" is transmitted in lieu of the missing element.

D. Station designator (element 1). The station designator is a three-letter location identifier for the reporting station.

E. Type and time of report (element 2)

1. The two basic types of reports are:
   a. Record observations (SA) -- reports taken on the hour.
   b. Special reports (RS or SP) -- observations taken as needed to report significant changes in weather.
      1) A record special (RS) is a record observation that reports a significant change in weather.
      2) A special (SP) is an observation taken other than on the hour to report a significant change in weather.
2. All reports are transmitted with the time in Coordinated Universal Time (UTC) or Zulu (Z) along with the type of observation.

F. Sky condition and ceiling (element 3)

1. A clear sky or layer of clouds or obscuring phenomena aloft is reported by one of the first seven sky cover designators shown in the next table.

<table>
<tr><th>Designator</th><th colspan="2">Meaning</th><th>Spoken</th></tr>
<tr><td>CLR</td><td colspan="2">Clear (less than 0.1 sky cover)</td><td>CLEAR</td></tr>
<tr><td>SCT</td><td colspan="2">Scattered Layer Aloft (0.1 through 0.5 sky cover)</td><td>SCATTERED</td></tr>
<tr><td>BKN*</td><td colspan="2">Broken Layer Aloft (0.6 through 0.9 sky cover)</td><td>BROKEN</td></tr>
<tr><td>OVC*</td><td colspan="2">Overcast Layer Aloft (more than 0.9 or 1.0 sky cover)</td><td>OVERCAST</td></tr>
<tr><td>–SCT</td><td>Thin Scattered</td><td rowspan="3">At least 1/2 of the sky cover aloft is transparent at and below the level of the layer aloft.</td><td>THIN SCATTERED</td></tr>
<tr><td>–BKN</td><td>Thin Broken</td><td>THIN BROKEN</td></tr>
<tr><td>–OVC</td><td>Thin Overcast</td><td>THIN OVERCAST</td></tr>
<tr><td>X*</td><td colspan="2">Surface-Based Obstruction (all of sky is hidden by surface-based phenomena)</td><td>SKY OBSCURED</td></tr>
<tr><td>–X</td><td colspan="2">Surface-Based Partial Obscuration (0.1 or more, but not all, of sky is hidden by surface-based phenomena)</td><td>SKY PARTIALLY OBSCURED</td></tr>
</table>

* Sky condition represented by this designator will constitute a ceiling layer. Descriptions in capital letters are the usual phraseology in which these reports are broadcast.

a. The height of the base of a layer precedes the sky cover designator. Height is in hundreds of feet above ground level (AGL).

b. When more than one layer is reported, layers are given in ascending order according to height.

   1) EXAMPLE: 7 SCT 15 SCT E3Ø BKN, reports three layers:

      a) A scattered layer at 700 ft.

      b) Another scattered layer at 1,500 ft.

      c) A top layer at 3,000 ft. The total sky covered by all the layers is at least 6/10, and is reported as broken. This layer is estimated to be at 3,000 ft.

c. A scattered, broken, or overcast layer may be reported as "thin."

   1) To be classified as thin, a layer must be half or more transparent through which blue sky or higher sky cover is visible.

   2) EXAMPLE: E40 –OVC, reports an overcast layer estimated to be at 4,000 ft. AGL, at least 1/2 of which is transparent.

2. Any phenomenon based at the surface and hiding all or part of the sky is reported as SKY OBSCURED (X) or SKY PARTIALLY OBSCURED (–X). See table above.

   a. An obscuration or partial obscuration may be caused by precipitation, fog, dust, blowing snow, etc.

   b. No height value precedes the designator for partial obscuration since vertical visibility is not restricted overhead.

   c. A height value of the indefinite ceiling precedes the designator for a total obscuration and denotes the vertical visibility into the phenomena.

   d. EXAMPLE: W2 X, reports an indefinite ceiling of 200 ft. determined by the vertical visibility through an obscuration.

3. Ceiling
   a. A ceiling is defined as either
      1) Height of the lowest layer of clouds or obscuring phenomenon aloft that is reported as broken or overcast and not classified as thin, or
      2) Vertical visibility into a surface-based obscuration that is not classified as partial.
   b. A ceiling designator always precedes the height of the ceiling layer. The table below lists and explains ceiling designators.

| Coded | Meaning | Spoken |
|---|---|---|
| M | Measured. Identifies a ceiling height for a layer aloft determined by a ceiling light, ceilometer, or based on the known height of isolated objects in contact with the ceiling layer 1½ mi. or less from any runway. | MEASURED CEILING |
| E | Estimated. Identifies a ceiling height for a layer aloft determined by any other method not meeting criteria for measured ceiling. | ESTIMATED CEILING |
| W | Indefinite. Vertical visibility into a surface-based obstruction. Regardless of the method of determination, vertical visibility is classified as an indefinite ceiling. | INDEFINITE CEILING |

   c. The letter "V" appended to the ceiling height indicates a variable ceiling. The range of variability is shown in remarks. Variable ceiling is reported only when the ceiling height is below 3,000 ft.
      1) EXAMPLE: M12V OVC and in remarks CIG 10V14 means "measured ceiling 1,200 ft. variable overcast, ceiling variable between 1,000 and 1,400 ft."

G. Visibility (element 4). Prevailing visibility is the greatest distance at which objects can be seen and identified through at least 180° of the horizon. Visibility is reported in statute miles (SM) and fractions. Prevailing visibility always follows the sky condition and ceiling element.

1. EXAMPLE: 1 1/2 means "visibility 1½ SM."
2. When the visibility is less than 4 SM, the weather observation station and the control tower will both take visibility observations. The lower of the two observations will be the prevailing visibility and the other is reported in remarks.
   a. EXAMPLE: TWR VSBY 1/2 means "tower visibility ½ SM."
3. The letter "V" suffixed to the prevailing visibility denotes a variable visibility. The range of variability is shown in remarks. Variable visibility is reported only when it is critical to aircraft operations.
   a. EXAMPLE: 3/4V and in remarks VSBY 1/2V1 means "visibility ¾ SM variable, visibility variable between ½ and 1 SM."

H. Weather and obstructions to vision (element 5). When occurring at the station at the time of observation, weather and obstructions to vision are reported in the element immediately following visibility. If weather and obstructions to vision are observed at a distance from the station, they are reported in the remarks.

1. Weather refers only to those items in the next table.
   a. Precipitation is reported in one of three intensities. The intensity symbol follows the weather symbol.

| | |
|---|---|
| LIGHT | – |
| MODERATE | (No sign) |
| HEAVY | + |

| Coded | Spoken | Coded | Spoken |
|---|---|---|---|
| Tornado | TORNADO | ZL | FREEZING DRIZZLE |
| Funnel Cloud | FUNNEL CLOUD | A | HAIL |
| Waterspout | WATERSPOUT | IP | ICE PELLETS |
| T | THUNDERSTORM | IPW | ICE PELLET SHOWERS |
| T+ | SEVERE THUNDERSTORM | S | SNOW |
| R | RAIN | SW | SNOW SHOWERS |
| RW | RAIN SHOWER | SP | SNOW PELLETS |
| L | DRIZZLE | SG | SNOW GRAINS |
| ZR | FREEZING RAIN | IC | ICE CRYSTALS |

b. No intensity is reported for hail (A) or ice crystals (IC).

c. A thunderstorm is reported as "T" and a severe thunderstorm as "T+."

1) A *severe thunderstorm* is one in which surface wind is 50 kt. or greater and/or hail is ¾ in. or more in diameter.

2. Obstructions to vision include the phenomena listed below:

| Coded | Spoken |
|---|---|
| BD | BLOWING DUST |
| BN | BLOWING SAND |
| BS | BLOWING SNOW |
| BY | BLOWING SPRAY |
| D | DUST |
| F | FOG |
| GF | GROUND FOG |
| H | HAZE |
| IF | ICE FOG |
| K | SMOKE |
| VOLCANIC ASH | WRITTEN OUT IN FULL |

a. Obstructions to vision are only reported if visibility is 6 SM or less.

3. EXAMPLE: R+F means heavy rain (R+) as the weather and fog (F) as the obstruction to vision.

4. When obscuring phenomena are surface based and partially obscure the sky, a remark reports tenths of sky hidden.

a. D3 means 3/10 of the sky is hidden by dust.

b. RF2 means 2/10 of the sky is hidden by rain and fog.

I. Sea level pressure (element 6). Sea level pressure is separated from the preceding elements by a space and is transmitted in record hourly (SA) reports only.

1. Sea level pressure is in three digits to the nearest tenth of a millibar (mb), with the decimal point omitted.

2. Sea level pressure is normally greater than 960.0 mb and less than 1050.0 mb. The first 9 or 10 is omitted.

a. To decode, prefix a 9 or 10, whichever brings it closer to 1000.0 mb.

3. EXAMPLE:

| As Reported | Decoded |
|---|---|
| 980 | 998.0 mb. |
| 191 | 1019.1 mb. |
| 752 | 975.2 mb. |
| 456 | 1045.6 mb. |

J. Temperature and dew point (element 7). Temperature and dew point are in whole degrees Fahrenheit (F).

1. They are separated from sea level pressure by a slash (/). If sea level pressure is not transmitted, temperature is separated from the preceding elements by a space.
2. A slash also separates the temperature and dew point.
3. A minus sign precedes the temperature or dew point when either of these temperatures is below 0°F.
4. EXAMPLE: 82/59 means "temperature 82°F, dew point 59°F."

K. Wind (element 8). The surface wind follows dew point and is separated from it by a slash.

1. The wind is observed for 1 min. and the average direction and speed are reported in a four-digit group.
   a. The first two digits are the direction FROM which the wind is blowing. It is in tens of degrees referenced to TRUE north.
      1) EXAMPLE: 02 is 020°; 21 is 210°.
   b. The second two digits are the wind speed in knots.
      1) A calm wind is reported as 0000.
2. If wind speed is 100 kt. or greater, 50 is added to the direction code and the hundreds digit of the speed is omitted.
   a. EXAMPLE: 5908 means 090° (59 – 50) at 108 kt. (100 + 08).
3. A gust is a variation in wind speed of at least 10 kt. between peaks and lulls.
   a. A squall is a sudden increase in speed of at least 15 kt. in average wind speed to a sustained speed of 20 kt. or more which lasts for at least 1 min.
   b. Gusts or squalls are reported by the letter "G" or "Q" respectively following the average 1-min. speed and followed by the peak speed knots.
      1) EXAMPLE: 1522Q37 means wind 150° at 22 kt. with peak speed in squalls to 37 kt.
4. When any part of the wind report is estimated, the letter "E" precedes the wind group.
   a. EXAMPLE: E3122Q27 means estimated wind 310° at 22 kt. with peak speed in squalls to 27 kt.

L. Altimeter setting (element 9). Altimeter setting follows the wind group and is separated by a slash. The normal range for altimeter settings is from 28.00 to 31.00 in. Hg.

1. Only the last three digits are transmitted with the decimal point omitted.
2. To decode, prefix the coded value in the report with either a 2 or 3, whichever brings it closer to 30.00 in.
   a. EXAMPLES:
      1) 998 means altimeter setting 29.98 in. Hg.
      2) 025 means altimeter setting 30.25 in. Hg.

M. Remarks (element 10). Remarks, if any, follow the altimeter setting and are separated from it by a slash.

1. The first remark, when transmitted, should be runway visibility or runway visual range.
   a. Runway visibility (VV) is the visibility from a particular location along an identified runway. It is reported in statute miles and fractions of miles.
   b. Runway visual range (VR) is the maximum horizontal distance down a specified runway at which a pilot can see and identify standard high intensity runway lights. It is reported in hundreds of feet.

c. The report consists of a runway designator and the contraction VV or VR followed by the appropriate visibility or visual range.

1) Both the VV and VR reports are for a 10-min. period preceding observation time.

2) The remark usually reports the 10-min. extremes separated by the letter "V."

a) However, if the VV or VR has not changed significantly during the 10 min., a single value is sent.

d. EXAMPLES:

1) R36VV11/2 means "runway 36, visibility value 1½ SM."

2) R30VR10V20 means "runway 30, visual range variable between 1,000 ft. and 2,000 ft."

2. Coded remarks are used to report operationally significant information or elaborate on other coded data.

| Coded | Coded Remarks |
|---|---|
| FEW CU | Few cumulus clouds |
| HIR CLDS VSB | Higher clouds visible |
| BINOVC | Breaks in overcast |
| ACCAS ALQDS | Altocumulus castellanus all quadrants |
| ACSL SW-NW | Altocumulus standing lenticular southwest through northwest |
| ROTOR CLDS NW | Rotor clouds northwest |
| VIRGA E-SE | Virga (precipitation not reaching the ground) east through southeast |
| TCU W | Towering cumulus clouds west |
| CB N MOVG E | Cumulonimbus north moving east |
| CLDS TPG MTNS SW | Clouds topping mountains southwest |
| RDGS OBSCD W-N | Ridges obscured west through north |
| T W MOVG E FQT LTGCG | Thunderstorm west moving east, frequent lightning cloud to ground |
| RB30 | Rain began 30 min. after the hour |
| SB15E40 | Snow began 15, ended 40 min. after the hour |
| T OVHD MOVG E | Thunderstorm overhead, moving east |
| OCNL DSNT LTG NW | Occasional distant lightning northwest |
| HLSTO 2 | Hailstones 2 in. in diameter |
| INTMT R– | Intermittent light rain |
| OCNL RW | Occasional moderate rain shower |
| SNOINCR 1/4/8 | Snow increased 1 in. in past hour, 4 in. since last 6 hourly and 8 in. total on ground at time of observation |
| R– OCNLY R+ | Light rain occasionally heavy rain |
| RWU | Rain shower of unknown intensity |
| KOCTY | Smoke over city |
| PTCHY GF S | Patchy ground fog south |
| WSHFT 30 | Wind shifted at 30 min. past the hour |
| WND 27V33 | Wind variable between 270° and 330° |
| PK WND 3348/22 | Peak wind within the past hour from 330° at 48 kt. occurred 22 min. past the hour |
| PRESRR | Pressure rising rapidly |
| PRESFR | Pressure falling rapidly |

## 7.16 PILOT WEATHER REPORTS (PIREPs)

A. No more timely or helpful weather observation fills the gaps between reporting stations than those observations and reports made by fellow pilots during flight. Aircraft in flight are the only source of direct observations of cloud tops, icing, and turbulence.

1. ATC and FSSs are required to solicit PIREPs when the following conditions are reported or forecast:
   a. Ceilings at or below 5,000 ft.
   b. Visibility at or below 5 SM
   c. Thunderstorms and related phenomena
   d. Icing
   e. Turbulence that is moderate or greater
   f. Wind shear
2. Pilots are also urged to volunteer reports of the following:
   a. Cloud bases, tops, and layers
   b. Flight visibility
   c. Precipitation
   d. Visibility restrictions such as haze, smoke, and dust
   e. Wind and temperature aloft

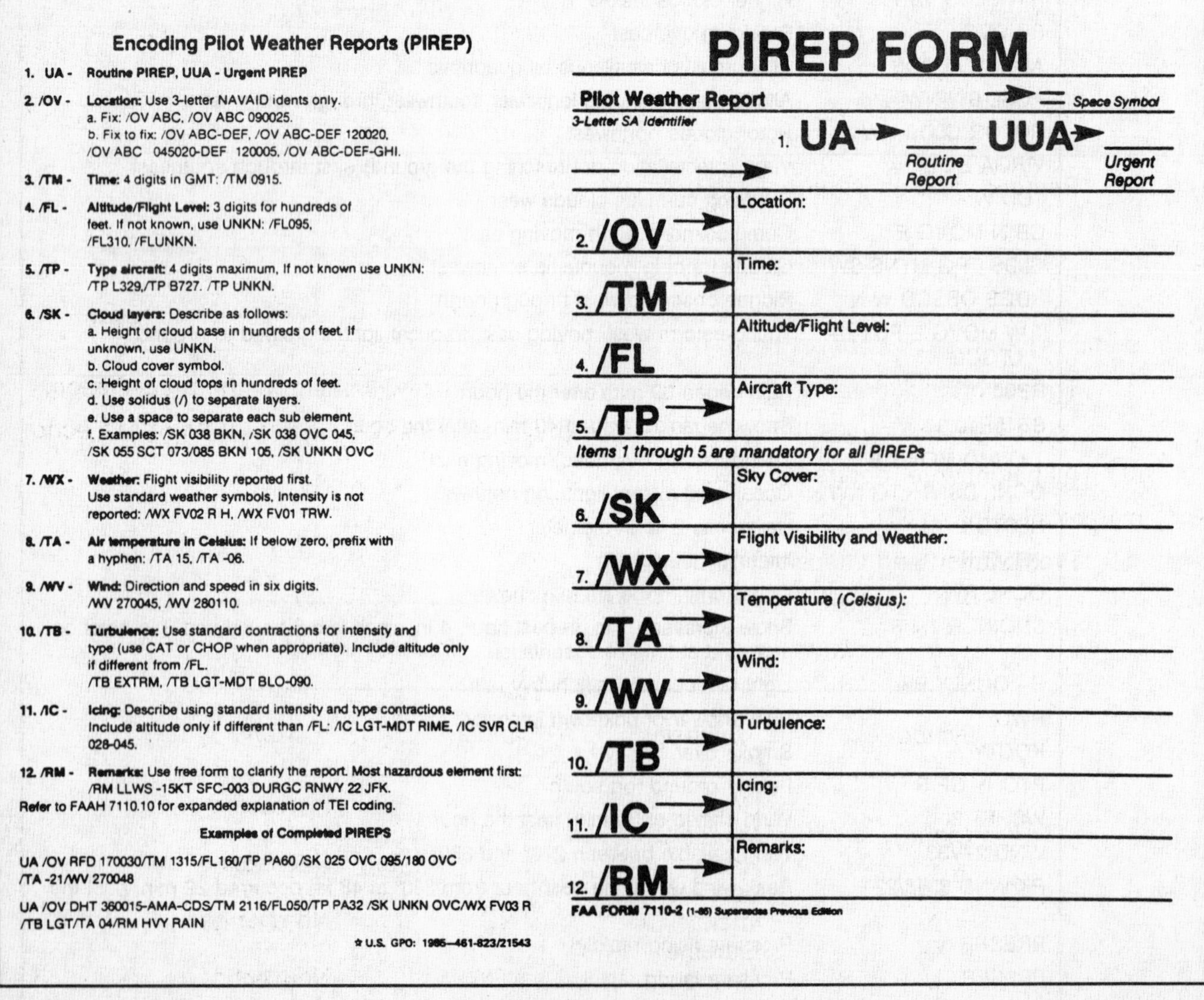

**Encoding Pilot Weather Reports (PIREP)**

1. UA - **Routine PIREP, UUA - Urgent PIREP**

2. /OV - **Location:** Use 3-letter NAVAID idents only.
a. Fix: /OV ABC, /OV ABC 090025.
b. Fix to fix: /OV ABC-DEF, /OV ABC-DEF 120020, /OV ABC 045020-DEF 120005, /OV ABC-DEF-GHI.

3. /TM - **Time:** 4 digits in GMT: /TM 0915.

4. /FL - **Altitude/Flight Level:** 3 digits for hundreds of feet. If not known, use UNKN: /FL095, /FL310, /FLUNKN.

5. /TP - **Type aircraft:** 4 digits maximum, If not known use UNKN: /TP L329,/TP B727. /TP UNKN.

6. /SK - **Cloud layers:** Describe as follows:
a. Height of cloud base in hundreds of feet. If unknown, use UNKN.
b. Cloud cover symbol.
c. Height of cloud tops in hundreds of feet.
d. Use solidus (/) to separate layers.
e. Use a space to separate each sub element.
f. Examples: /SK 038 BKN, /SK 038 OVC 045, /SK 055 SCT 073/085 BKN 105, /SK UNKN OVC

7. /WX - **Weather:** Flight visibility reported first. Use standard weather symbols, Intensity is not reported: /WX FV02 R H, /WX FV01 TRW.

8. /TA - **Air temperature in Celsius:** If below zero, prefix with a hyphen: /TA 15, /TA -06.

9. /WV - **Wind:** Direction and speed in six digits. /WV 270045, /WV 280110.

10. /TB - **Turbulence:** Use standard contractions for intensity and type (use CAT or CHOP when appropriate). Include altitude only if different from /FL. /TB EXTRM, /TB LGT-MDT BLO-090.

11. /IC - **Icing:** Describe using standard intensity and type contractions. Include altitude only if different than /FL: /IC LGT-MDT RIME, /IC SVR CLR 028-045.

12. /RM - **Remarks:** Use free form to clarify the report. Most hazardous element first: /RM LLWS -15KT SFC-003 DURGC RNWY 22 JFK.

Refer to FAAH 7110.10 for expanded explanation of TEI coding.

**Examples of Completed PIREPS**

UA /OV RFD 170030/TM 1315/FL160/TP PA60 /SK 025 OVC 095/180 OVC /TA -21/WV 270048

UA /OV DHT 360015-AMA-CDS/TM 2116/FL050/TP PA32 /SK UNKN OVC/WX FV03 R /TB LGT/TA 04/RM HVY RAIN

☆ U.S. GPO: 1985—461-823/21543

# PIREP FORM

**Pilot Weather Report** → = Space Symbol

*3-Letter SA Identifier*

1. UA → ___ UUA → ___
*Routine Report* *Urgent Report*

2. /OV → Location:

3. /TM → Time:

4. /FL → Altitude/Flight Level:

5. /TP → Aircraft Type:

*Items 1 through 5 are mandatory for all PIREPs*

6. /SK → Sky Cover:

7. /WX → Flight Visibility and Weather:

8. /TA → Temperature *(Celsius)*:

9. /WV → Wind:

10. /TB → Turbulence:

11. /IC → Icing:

12. /RM → Remarks:

FAA FORM 7110-2 (1-85) Supersedes Previous Edition

B. A PIREP is usually transmitted as part of a group of PIREPs collected by state or as a remark appended to an SAO.

1. A PIREP is usually transmitted in a prescribed format, as shown in the example below.

   a. The letters "UA" identify the message as a routine PIREP. The letters "UUA" identify an urgent PIREP.

   b. All altitude references are MSL unless otherwise noted. Distances are in nautical miles (NM), and time is in UTC.

C. EXAMPLE: UA /OV DSM 320012/TM 1735/FL 080/TP C172/SK 020 BKN 030/042 BKN-OVC/TA -04/WV 245040/TB LGT/IC LGT CLR 045-055/RM IN CLR

1. Routine Pilot Report
2. Location: 12 NM out on 320° radial from Des Moines VOR
3. Time: 1735 UTC
4. Altitude: 8,000 ft. MSL
5. Type aircraft: Cessna 172
6. Cloud layers: first layer is 2,000 ft. broken with tops at 3,000 ft.; second layer is 4,200 ft. broken, occasionally overcast, with no tops reported.
7. Air temperature: –4°C
8. Wind: 245° at 40 kt.
9. Turbulence: Light
10. Icing: light, clear; between 4,500 and 5,500 ft.
11. Remark: Aircraft is currently in clear skies.

## 7.17 RADAR WEATHER REPORT (SD)

A. Thunderstorms and general areas of precipitation can be observed by radar. Most radar stations report each hour at H+35 with special reports issued as required.

1. The report includes the type, intensity, intensity trend, and location of the precipitation.

   a. Also included is the echo top of the precipitation and, if significant, the base echo.

2. All heights are reported in MSL.

B. Interpretation of an SD

1. Precipitation and Intensity Trend

| *Intensity* | | *Intensity Trend* | |
|---|---|---|---|
| *Symbol* | *Intensity* | *Symbol* | *Trend* |
| – | Light | + | Increasing |
| (none) | Moderate | | |
| + | Heavy | – | Decreasing |
| ++ | Very Heavy | | |
| X | Intense | NC | No change |
| XX | Extreme | | |
| U | Unknown | NEW | New echo |

2. EXAMPLE: OKC 1934 LN 8TRW++/+ 86/40 164/60 199/115 15W L2425 MT570 AT 159/65 2 INCH HAIL RPRTD THIS CELL ^ MO1 NO2 ON3 PM34 QM3 RL2 SL9
   a. Location identifier and time of radar observation [Oklahoma City (OKC) SD at 1934 UTC].
   b. Echo pattern (LN). The radar echo pattern or configuration may be a
      1) Line (LN) -- a line of precipitation echoes at least 30 NM long, at least five times as long as it is wide and at least 30% coverage within the line.
      2) Fine Line (FINE LN) -- a unique clear air echo (usually precipitation free and cloud free) in the form of a thin or fine line on the radar scope. It represents a strong temperature/moisture boundary such as an advancing dry cold front.
      3) Area (AREA) -- a group of echoes of similar type and not classified as a line.
      4) Spiral Band Area (SPRL BAND AREA) -- an area of precipitation associated with a hurricane that takes on a spiral band configuration around the center.
      5) Single Cell (CELL) -- a single isolated convective echo such as a rain shower.
      6) Layer (LYR) -- an elevated layer of stratiform precipitation not reaching the ground.
   c. Coverage in tenths (8/10 in the example).
   d. Type, intensity, and intensity trend of weather. In the example, the radar depicted thunderstorms (T) and very heavy rainshowers (RW++) that are increasing in intensity (/+). Note that the intensity is separated from intensity trend by a slash.
   e. Azimuth (reference true N) and range in NM of points defining the echo pattern (86/40 164/60 199/115 in the example).
   f. Dimension of echo pattern (15W in the example). The dimension of an echo pattern is given when azimuth and range define only the center line of the pattern. In this example, 15W means the line has a total width of 15 NM, 7½ NM either side of a center line drawn from the points given. D15 would mean a convective echo is 15 NM in diameter around a given center point.
   g. Pattern movement (the LINE is moving *from* 240° at 25 kt. in the example). This element may also show movement of individual storms or cells with a "C" or movement of an area with an "A."
   h. Maximum top (MT) and location (57,000 ft. MSL on radial 159° at 65 NM in the example).
   i. Remarks are self-explanatory using plain-language contractions.
   j. The digital section is used for preparing the radar summary chart.

C. When an SD is transmitted, but does not contain any encoded weather observation, a contraction is sent which indicates the operational status of the radar.
   1. Contractions of radar operational status

| *Contraction* | *Operational Status* |
|---|---|
| PPINE | Equipment normal and operating in PPI (Plan Position Indicator) mode; no echoes observed. |
| PPIOM | Radar inoperative or out-of-service for preventative maintenance. |
| PPINA | Observations not available for reasons other than PPINE or PPIOM. |

| Contraction | Operational Status |
|---|---|
| ROBEPS | Radar operating below performance standards. |
| ARNO | "A" scope or azimuth/range indicator inoperative. |
| RHINO | Radar cannot be operated in RHI (Range-Height Indicator) mode. Height data not available. |

2. EXAMPLE: OKC 1135 PPINE means Oklahoma City's radar at 1135 UTC detects no echoes.

D. Remember that when weather radar detects objects in the atmosphere, it only detects those of precipitation size or greater.

1. An area may be blanketed with fog or low stratus, but unless precipitation is also present, the radar will be clear of echoes.

## 7.18 SATELLITE WEATHER PICTURES

A. Before weather satellites came into use, weather observations were limited to ground weather reports and PIREPs. Now weather satellites provide pictures of cloud cover every 30 min.

1. These satellite photos are available in FSSs, on TV weather broadcasts, in newspapers, etc.
2. They provide a photograph of weather (clouds) which may adversely affect your flight.

B. Infrared photos are also available to provide information about cloud top temperatures which is used to determine cloud heights.

## 7.19 AREA FORECAST (FA)

A. An FA is a forecast of general weather conditions over an area the size of several states or portions of states.

1. It is used to determine expected en route weather conditions and also to obtain an insight to weather conditions that might be expected at airports where weather reports or forecasts are not issued.
2. FAs are issued three times a day.

B. The FA is comprised of two sections, each of which has a unique communications header which allows replacement of individual sections, due to amendments or corrections, instead of replacing the entire FA.

1. Hazards/Flight Precautions (H)

   a. This is a 12-hr. forecast that identifies and locates the aviation weather hazards which meet In-Flight Advisory criteria (see Module 7.21, In-Flight Advisories, beginning on page 200) and the thunderstorms that are forecast to be at least scattered in area coverage.

   b. This section serves only as a flag alerting you of any of the following hazards that meet or are expected to meet AIRMET, SIGMET, or Convective SIGMET criteria.

      1) IFR conditions
      2) Icing (ICG)
      3) Turbulence (TURBC)
      4) Mountain obscurement (MTN OBSCN)
      5) Thunderstorms (TSTMS)

2. Synopsis and VFR Clouds/Weather (C)
   a. The synopsis gives a brief summary of the location and movement of fronts, pressure systems, and circulation patterns for an 18-hr. period.
      1) References to low ceilings and/or visibilities, strong winds, or any other phenomena the forecaster considers useful may also be included.
   b. The VFR clouds/weather (CLDS/WX) section contains a 12-hr. specific forecast, followed by a 6-hr. categorical outlook, giving a total forecast period of 18 hr.
      1) This section is usually several paragraphs long, and the breakdown may be by states or by well-known geographic areas.
      2) Two Flight Precautions from the Hazards section, IFR and MTN OBSCN, will be indicated by a lead sentence that refers you to AIRMET SIERRA.
      3) The specific forecast provides a general description of clouds and weather that is significant to flight operations.
      4) Surface visibility and obstructions to vision are included when the forecast visibility is 6 SM or less.
      5) Precipitation, thunderstorms, and sustained winds of 20 kt. or greater are always included when forecast.

C. EXAMPLE: The following is an excerpt from an FA.

1. MIAH FA 231945 AMD 1
   HAZARDS VALID UNTIL 240700

2. NC SC GA FL AND CSTL WTRS
   .

3. FLT PRCTNS . . . IFR . . . NC SC GA AND CSTL WTRS
   . . . MTN OBSCN . . . NC SC GA
   . . . TURBC . . . NC SC GA
   . . . TSTMS . . . NC SC GA FL AND CSTL WTRS
   .

4. TSTMS IMPLY SVR OR GTR TURBC SVR ICG LLWS AND IFR CONDS.

5. NON MSL HGTS NOTED BY AGL OR CIG.
   . . . .

6. MIAC FA 231845
   SYNOPSIS AND VFR CLDS/WX
   SYNOPSIS VALID UNTIL 241300
   CLDS/WX VALID UNTIL 240700 . . . OTLK VALID 240700-241300
   .

7. SYNOPSIS . . . SFC LOW MOVG EWD ACRS TN THRU 06Z AND ACRS SRN VA 06-13Z. A WMFNT E OF THE LOW MOVG NEWD ACRS NRN GA/CAROLINAS. DEEP MSTR N OF THE LOW/WMFNT MOVG SPRDG NWD. DRY STBL AMS SPRDG INTO WRN GA AT 19Z SPRDG EWD ACRS GA/SC AND NEWD INTO NC BY 13Z.
   .

8. NC
   SEE AIRMET SIERRA FOR IFR AND MTN OBSCN.
   MTNS . . . 30 BKN-OVC 50 OVC LYRD 240. VSBY 3-5R-F. 22-00Z BCMG 30 SCT-BKN 50 BKN LYRD 150. OCNL VSBY 3-5 IN SCT RW–. ISOLD TRW–. CB TOPS TO 350. OTLK . . . MVFR CIG RW F.
   RMNDR . . . 15-30 OVC. VSBY 3-5R-F. WDLY SCT EMBDD TRW PSBLY SVR. CB TOPS TO 450. 02-06Z BCMG 25 SCT-BKN 50 BKN LYRD 150. OCNL VSBY 3-5 IN SCT RW–. ISOLD TRW–. OTLK . . . MVFR CIG RW F.

Interpretation:

1. The heading of the example states that this section of the FA deals with the Hazards/Flight Precautions (H) section and was issued on the 23rd day of the month at 1945 UTC for the Miami (MIA) forecast area. The hazards listed may be valid for the forecast period or for only a portion of the time period.
   a. Note that this is amendment 1 (AMD 1) to the FA for this section. This section was updated from the original forecast at 1900 UTC.
2. Forecast area includes NC, SC, GA, FL, and coastal waters (CSTL WTRS).
3. Flight Precaution statement. This states that IFR conditions, MTN OBSCN, TURBC, and TSTMS are forecast within the forecast period for the listed states.
4. "Thunderstorms imply severe or greater turbulence, severe icing, low-level wind shear, and IFR conditions." This statement is a reminder of the hazards existing in all thunderstorms, and thus, these hazards are not spelled out within the body of the FA.
5. All heights are above MSL, unless noted by AGL or CIG.
   a. AGL means above ground level.
   b. CIG is a contraction for ceiling, which by definition is always expressed above ground.
6. Synopsis and VFR Clouds/Weather (C) section also states the valid times of the synopsis, clouds/weather, and the outlook.
7. The synopsis briefly summarizes the location and movements of fronts, pressure systems, and circulation patterns for an 18-hr. period.
   a. In the example, a surface low is moving eastward across TN through 0600Z (UTC) and across southern VA. From 0600Z-1300Z a warm front east of the low will be moving northeastward across northern GA and the Carolinas. Deep moisture north of the low pressure area and warm front moving and spreading northward. Dry stable air mass will be spreading into western GA at 1900Z, then spreading eastward across GA and SC and northeastward into NC by 1300Z.
8. VFR CLDS/WX section is a state-by-state (or well-known geographical areas) summary of the forecast.
   a. All heights are abbreviated by omitting the last two zeros. For example, 10,000 ft. is written as 100 and 1,500 ft. is written as 15.
   b. The following is a list of contractions and their definitions used to denote sky conditions in Area Forecasts (FA). These are listed along with the contractions or designators used in Terminal Forecasts (FT) so that a comparison can be made. Terminal Forecasts are discussed in Module 7.20, Terminal Forecast, beginning on page 198.

| FA Contraction | FT Designator | Definition |
|---|---|---|
| CLR | CLR | Sky Clear |
| SCT | SCT | Scattered |
| BKN | BKN | Broken |
| OVC | OVC | Overcast |
| OBSC | X | Obscured, obscure, or obscuring |
| PTLY OBSC | –X | Partially Obscured |
| THN | – | Thin |
| VRBL | V | Variable |
| CIG | C | Ceiling |
| INDEF | W | Indefinite |

1) The following is a list of adjectives and their meanings as used to describe area coverage of showers and thunderstorms:

| Adjectives | Coverage |
|---|---|
| Isolated | Single cells (no percentage) |
| Widely scattered | Less than 25% of area affected |
| Scattered | 25% to 54% of area affected |
| Numerous | 55% or more of area affected |

2) The following identifies the variability terms used.

| Term | Description |
|---|---|
| OCNL | Greater than 50% probability of the phenomenon occurring but for less than ½ of the forecast period |
| CHC | 30 to 50% probability (precipitation only) |
| SLGT CHC | 10 to 20% probability (precipitation only) |

c. The categorical outlook on the FA, identified by the contraction "OTLK," is found at the end of each paragraph in this section. It describes the outlook (valid for 6 hr.) for that particular area.

1) Both FAs and FTs group ceiling and visibilities into categories which are used in the categorical outlook for these forecasts. The categorical outlook extends the FAs and the FTs for 6 hr. These outlooks are intended primarily for advanced flight planning.

| | |
|---|---|
| LIFR (Low IFR) | Ceiling less than 500 ft. and/or visibility less than 1 SM |
| IFR | Ceiling 500 to less than 1,000 ft. and/or visibility 1 to less than 3 SM |
| MVFR (Marginal VFR) | Ceiling 1,000 to 3,000 ft. and/or visibility 3 to 5 SM inclusive |
| VFR | No ceiling or ceiling greater than 3,000 ft. and visibility greater than 5 SM |

2) In the example, the outlook (from 0700Z to 1300Z on the 24th) for NC (for both mountains and remainder) is marginal VFR due to ceilings in rain showers and fog.

D. Amendments to the FA are issued as needed and only that section of the FA being revised is transmitted as an amendment.

1. FAs are also amended and updated by in-flight advisories.
2. An amended FA is identified by "AMD," a corrected FA is identified by "COR," and a delayed FA is identified by "RTD."

## 7.20 TERMINAL FORECAST (FT)

A. A terminal forecast (FT) is a description of the surface weather expected to occur at an airport.

1. The forecast includes cloud heights and amounts, visibility, weather, and winds related to flight operations within 5 NM of the center of the runway complex.

   a. The term vicinity (VCNTY) covers the area from 5 to 25 NM beyond the center of the runway complex.

2. Scheduled FTs are issued three times daily and are valid for a 24-hr. period.

   a. The last 6 hr. of the forecast is a categorical outlook.

B. EXAMPLE: STL FT 251010 C5 X 1/2S-BS 3325G35 OCNL C0 X 0S+BS. 16Z C30 BKN 3BS 3320 CHC SW-. 22Z 30 SCT 3315. 00Z CLR. 04Z VFR WND..

1. To aid in the discussion, we have divided the FT into elements lettered a. through i.

STL FT 251010 C5 X 1/2 S-BS 3325G35 OCNL C0 X 0S+BS
a. b. c. d. e. f. g.

16Z C30 BKN 3BS 3320 CHC SW-. 22Z 30 SCT 3315. 00Z CLR.
h.

04Z VFR WND..
i.

2. Interpretation

   a. Station identifier. STL identifies Lambert/St. Louis International Airport. The FT identifies this as a terminal forecast.

   b. Date-time group. The forecast is valid beginning on the 25th day of the month at 1000Z and is valid until 1000Z the following day.

   c. Sky and ceiling. "C5 X" means ceiling 500 ft., sky obscured. The letter "C" always identifies a forecast ceiling.

      1) Cloud heights are always in reference to above ground level (AGL).

      2) Sky cover designators and height coding are identical to those used in SAOs. See Module 7.15, Surface Aviation Observation, beginning on page 186.

   d. Visibility. Visibility is in SM and fractions. "1/2" means visibility ½ SM.

      1) Absence of a visibility entry specifically implies visibility is more than 6 SM.

   e. Weather and obstruction to vision. These elements are in symbols identical to those used in SAO reports and are entered only when forecast. "S-BS" means light snow and blowing snow.

   f. Wind. "3325G35" means the wind is from 330° at 25 kt. gusting to 35 kt.

      1) Omission of a wind entry implies wind less than 6 kt.

   g. Remarks. Remarks may be added to more completely describe forecast weather by indicating variations from prevailing conditions. "OCNL C0 X 0S+BS" means occasional conditions of ceiling zero, sky obscured, visibility zero, heavy snow and blowing snow.

      1) See the table on page 198 for the definitions of the variability terms used in remarks.

   h. Expected changes. When changes are expected, preceding conditions are followed by a period before the time of the expected change. In the example, by 1600Z the prevailing conditions will be ceiling 3,000 ft. broken, visibility 3 SM, blowing snow, wind 330° at 20 kt., and a 30% to 50% chance of light snow showers.

   i. 6-hour categorical outlook. The last 6 hr. of the forecast is a categorical outlook. "04Z VFR WND.." means that from 0400Z until 1000Z (the end of the forecast period), the weather will be no ceiling or ceiling higher than 3,000 ft. and visibility greater than 5 SM (VFR) with wind 25 kt. or stronger. The double period (..) signifies the end of the forecast.

      1) The term "WND" is used when the sustained winds or gusts are forecast to be 25 kt. or stronger.

      2) See the table on page 198 for the definition of the categories.

## 7.21 IN-FLIGHT ADVISORIES (WST, WS, WA, CWA)

A. In-Flight Advisories are unscheduled forecasts to advise aircraft in flight of the development of potentially hazardous weather.

1. These advisories are available from weather service outlets.
   a. They are an excellent source of information for preflight planning and briefing.
2. ATC will generally broadcast the issuance of an advisory and direct you to contact FSS for further information.
3. All heights are stated MSL unless otherwise noted.
   a. Ceilings (CIG) are always AGL.

B. There are four types of In-flight Advisories:

1. Convective SIGMET (WST).
2. SIGMET (WS).
3. AIRMET (WA).
4. Center Weather Advisories (CWA).

C. The format of these advisories consists of a heading and text.

1. The heading identifies the
   a. Issuing WSFO (Weather Service Forecast Office).
   b. Type of advisory.
   c. Valid period.
2. The text of the advisory contains
   a. A message identifier, e.g., SIGMET ALPHA 2.
   b. A flight precautions statement; e.g., statement about location, size, and movement of an area of thunderstorms.

D. Convective SIGMETs (WST). Convective SIGMET bulletins are issued for the Eastern (E), Central (C), and Western (W) United States.

1. Convective SIGMETs are used for any of the following:
   a. Severe thunderstorms due to
      1) Surface winds greater than or equal to 50 kt.,
      2) Hail greater than or equal to ¾ in. in diameter, or
      3) Tornadoes.
   b. Lines of thunderstorms.
   c. Embedded thunderstorms.
   d. Thunderstorms greater than or equal to VIP (Video Integrator Processor) level 4.
      1) Thunderstorms are reported as level 1, 2, 3, 4, or 5 depending on their intensity. Level 1 is least intense and level 5 is most intense.
2. Any Convective SIGMET implies severe or greater turbulence, severe icing, and low-level wind shear (LLWS).
   a. A Convective SIGMET may be issued for any convective situation which the forecaster feels is hazardous to all categories of aircraft.

3. Convective SIGMET bulletins are issued hourly at H+55.

   a. Special bulletins are issued at any time as required and updated at H+55.

   b. If no criteria meeting a Convective SIGMET is observed or forecast, the message "CONVECTIVE SIGMET...NONE" will be issued for each area at H+55.

   c. On an hourly basis (H+55), an outlook is made for each of the three regions. This outlook is a forecast for thunderstorm systems that are expected to require Convective SIGMET issuances during a time period of 2 to 6 hr. into the future.

      1) An outlook will always be made, even if it is a negative statement.

4. EXAMPLE:

   MKCC WST 221855
   CONVECTIVE SIGMET 20C
   VALID UNTIL 2055Z
   ND SD
   FROM 90W MOT-GFK-ABR-90 MOT
   INTSFYG AREA SVR TSTMS MOVG FROM 2445. TOP ABV 450. WIND GUSTS TO 60 KTS RPRTD. TORNADOES...HAIL TO 2 IN...WIND GUSTS TO 65 KTS PSBL ND PTN.
   OUTLOOK VALID 222055-230055
   AREA 1...FROM INL-MSP-ABR-MOT-INL
   SVR TSTMS CONT TO DVLP IN AREA OVER ND. AREA IS XPCD TO RMN SVR AND SPRD INTO MN AS STG PVA MOVS OVR VRY UNSTBL AMS CHARACTERIZED BY -12 LIFTED INDEX

   Interpretation: Issued at 1855Z on the 22nd day of the month. It is the 20th Convective SIGMET of the day in the Central U.S. The message indicates an area of severe thunderstorms in North and South Dakota. These storms have produced wind gusts to 60 kt. with the possibility of tornadoes, hail up to 2 in., and 65-kt. winds over North Dakota. The outlook provides the forecast from 2 to 6 hr. into the future over North and South Dakota.

E. SIGMET (WS). A SIGMET is issued to advise pilots of nonconvective weather considered potentially hazardous to all categories of aircraft. SIGMETs are valid for 4 hr.

1. SIGMETs are based specifically on forecasts of

   a. Severe icing.

   b. Severe or extreme turbulence.

   c. Duststorms, sandstorms, or volcanic ash lowering surface or in-flight visibilities to below 3 SM.

   d. Volcanic eruption.

   e. Tropical storms or hurricanes.

2. SIGMETs are identified by an alphanumeric designator which consists of an alphabetic identifier (NOVEMBER through YANKEE, except SIERRA and TANGO) and issuance number, e.g., PAPA 1.

   a. The first issuance of a SIGMET will be labeled UWS (Urgent Weather SIGMET) and subsequent issuances at the forecaster's discretion.

   b. Issuances for the same phenomenon will be sequentially numbered using the original designator until the phenomenon ends, e.g., PAPA 1, PAPA 2.

3. EXAMPLE:

DFWA UWS 051710
SIGMET NOVEMBER 1 VALID UNTIL 052110
AR LA MS
FROM MEM TO 30N MEI TO BTR TO MLU TO MEM
OCNL SVR ICING ABV FRZLVL EXPCD.
FRZLVL 080 E TO 120 W.
CONDS CONTG BYD 2100Z.

Interpretation: The SIGMET was issued for the DFW area at 1710Z on the 5th and is valid until 2110Z (Note maximum forecast period of 4 hr. for a SIGMET). The designator NOVEMBER identifies the phenomenon, in this case, severe icing. This is the first issuance of the SIGMET as indicated by UWS (Urgent Weather SIGMET) and the issuance number of 1. The affected states within the DFW area are Arkansas, Louisiana, and Mississippi. VORs outline the entire area to be affected by occasionally severe icing above the freezing level expected during the forecast period. Freezing level data and notation that conditions are expected to continue beyond 4 hr. are included.

F. AIRMET (WA). AIRMETs are weather advisories issued only to amend the area forecast (FA) concerning weather phenomena which are of operational interest to all aircraft and potentially hazardous to aircraft having limited capability because of lack of equipment, instrumentation, or pilot qualification. AIRMETs are valid for 6 hr.

1. AIRMETs are based specifically on forecasts of
   a. Moderate icing.
   b. Moderate turbulence.
   c. Sustained surface winds of 30 kt. or more.
   d. Ceiling less than 1,000 ft. and/or visibility less than 3 SM affecting over 50% of the area at one time.
   e. Extensive mountain obscurement.
2. AIRMETs have the following fixed alphanumeric designators:
   a. SIERRA for IFR conditions and mountain obscuration
   b. TANGO for turbulence, strong surface winds, and low-level wind shear
   c. ZULU for icing and freezing level
3. EXAMPLE:

MIAZ WA 231945
AIRMET ZULU FOR ICG AND FRZLVL VALID UNTIL 240200
.
NO SGFNT ICG XPCD OUTSIDE CNVTV ACTVTY.
.
FRZLVL . . . NC/SC/NRN-CNTRL GA . . . 95-115.
SRN GA/NRN FL . . . 115-130. SRN FL . . . 130-150.

Interpretation: Issued for the Miami (MIA) FA at 1945Z on the 23rd day of the month. AIRMET ZULU is for icing and freezing level and is valid until 0200Z on the 24th. No significant icing is expected outside convective activity. Freezing level for NC/SC/northern and central GA is 9,500 ft. to 11,500 ft.; southern GA/northern FL is 11,500 ft. to 13,000 ft.; and southern FL is 13,000 ft. to 15,000 ft.

G. Center Weather Advisory (CWA)

1. A Center Weather Advisory (CWA) is an unscheduled in-flight flow control, air traffic and air crew advisory for use in anticipating and avoiding adverse weather conditions in the en route and terminal areas.

2. The CWA is *not* a flight planning forecast but a *nowcast* for conditions beginning within the next 2 hr.

   a. Maximum valid time of a CWA is 2 hr., i.e., no more than 2 hr. between issuance time and "valid until time."

3. A CWA may be issued for the following three situations:

   a. As a supplement to an *existing* in-flight advisory or area forecast (FA) section for the purpose of improving or updating the definition of the phenomenon in terms of location, movement, extent, or intensity *relevant* to the Air Route Traffic Control Center (ARTCC) area of responsibility. This is important for the following reason. A SIGMET for severe turbulence may outline the entire ARTCC area for the total 4-hr. valid period but may only be covering a relatively small portion of the ARTCC area at any one time during the 4-hr. period.

   b. When an in-flight advisory has not yet been issued but conditions meet in-flight advisory criteria based on current pilot reports (PIREPs) and the information must be disseminated sooner than a Convective SIGMET, SIGMET, or AIRMET can be issued. In this case of an impending SIGMET, the CWA will be issued as urgent "UCWA" to allow the fastest possible dissemination.

   c. When in-flight advisory criteria are not met but conditions are or will shortly be adversely affecting the safe flow of air traffic within the ARTCC area of responsibility.

4. Format of a CWA heading:

   ARTCC Designator and Phenomenon number (numbers 1 through 6 used for replaceability)/"CWA"/issuance number (2 digits)/in-flight advisory alphanumeric designator (if applicable)/date and time issued/"–"/valid until time.

5. Example of a CWA:

   ZFW3 CWA 03 032140-2340
   ISOLD SVR TSTM OVR MLU MOVG
   SWWD 10 KTS. TOP 610. WND GUSTS TO
   55 KTS. HAIL TO 1 INCH RPRTD AT MLU.
   SVR TSTM CONTG BYND 2340.

   Interpretation: CWA 03 was issued from the Dallas-Ft. Worth ARTCC at 2140Z on the 3rd day of the month and is valid until 2340Z on the same day. Isolated severe thunderstorm over Monroe, LA (MLU) moving southwest at 10 kt. Cloud tops are at 61,000 ft. MSL. Monroe Regional Airport reported wind gusts to 55 kt. and hail to 1 in. in diameter. Severe thunderstorms will continue after 2340Z.

## 7.22 WINDS AND TEMPERATURES ALOFT FORECAST (FD)

A. The winds and temperatures aloft are forecast for specific locations in the contiguous United States. They consist of a heading followed by forecasts at nine altitudes for each location.

B. EXAMPLE: A Winds and Temperatures Aloft Forecast (FD) giving the heading and six locations:

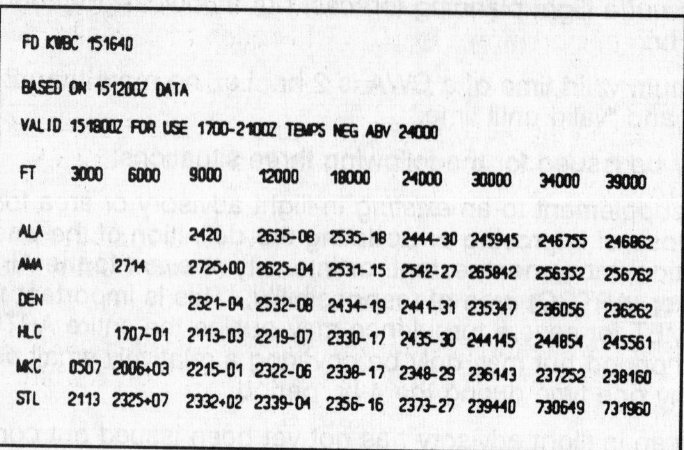

FD KWBC 151640

BASED ON 151200Z DATA

VALID 151800Z FOR USE 1700-2100Z TEMPS NEG ABV 24000

| FT | 3000 | 6000 | 9000 | 12000 | 18000 | 24000 | 30000 | 34000 | 39000 |
|---|---|---|---|---|---|---|---|---|---|
| ALA | | | 2420 | 2635-08 | 2535-18 | 2444-30 | 245945 | 246755 | 246862 |
| AMA | | 2714 | 2725+00 | 2625-04 | 2531-15 | 2542-27 | 265842 | 256352 | 256762 |
| DEN | | | 2321-04 | 2532-08 | 2434-19 | 2441-31 | 235347 | 236056 | 236262 |
| HLC | | 1707-01 | 2113-03 | 2219-07 | 2330-17 | 2435-30 | 244145 | 244854 | 245561 |
| MKC | 0507 | 2006+03 | 2215-01 | 2322-06 | 2338-17 | 2348-29 | 236143 | 237252 | 238160 |
| STL | 2113 | 2325+07 | 2332+02 | 2339-04 | 2356-16 | 2373-27 | 239440 | 730649 | 731960 |

C. Heading

1. The first line is "FD WBC 151640."
   a. FD identifies this as a Winds and Temperatures Aloft Forecast.
   b. WBC indicates that the forecast is prepared at the National Meteorological Center.
   c. In 151640, the first two digits (15) mean the 15th day of the month; 1640 indicates the time of the forecast in Coordinated Universal Time (UTC or Z).
2. The second line DATA BASED ON 151200Z indicates that the forecast is based on data collected at 1200Z on the 15th day of the month.
3. The third line VALID 151800Z FOR USE 1700-2100Z,
   a. Means the forecast data are valid at 1800Z on the 15th, and are to be used by pilots between 1700Z and 2100Z.
   b. The notation TEMPS NEG ABV 24,000 is always included. Since temperatures above 24,000 ft. are always negative, no sign preceding the temperature above this level is included unless it is positive.
4. Forecast levels. The line labeled "FT" shows the nine standard levels in feet for which the winds and temperatures apply. The levels through 12,000 ft. are based on true altitude, and the levels at 18,000 ft. and above are based on pressure altitude.

D. Body of the Forecast

1. The station identifiers denoting the location for which the forecast applies are arranged in alphabetical order in a column down the left side of the data sheet.
2. The coded wind and temperature information in digits for each station is found in columns under each level.
3. Note that at some of the lower levels the wind and temperature information is omitted.
   a. Winds aloft are not forecast for levels within 1,500 ft. of the station elevation.
   b. No temperatures are forecast for the 3,000-ft. level or for any level within 2,500 ft. of the station elevation.

4. A four-digit group shows the wind direction in reference to true north and the wind speed in knots (kt.).
   a. EXAMPLE: In the Atlanta (ATL) forecast for the 3,000-ft. level, the group 2611 means the wind is forecast to be from 260° true at a speed of 11 kt.
   b. Note that to decode, you add a zero to the end of the first two digits giving the direction in increments of 10°. The second two digits give speed in knots.
5. A six-digit group includes the forecast temperature aloft in degrees Celsius.
   a. EXAMPLE: In the Abilene (ABI) forecast for the 6,000-ft. level, the group 2213 + 19 means the wind is forecast to be from 220° true at 13 kt. with a temperature of +19°C.
6. If the wind speed is forecast to be 100 to 199 kt., the forecaster adds 50 to the direction and subtracts 100 from the speed. To decode, you must do the reverse: Subtract 50 from the direction and add 100 to the speed.
   a. EXAMPLE: If the forecast for the 39,000-ft. level appears as 731960, subtract 50 from 73 and add 100 to 19. The wind would be 230° true at 119 kt. with a temperature of –60°C.
   b. It is easy to know when the coded direction has been increased by 50. Coded direction (in tens of degrees) normally ranges from 01 (010°) to 36 (360°). Any coded direction with a numerical value greater than 36 indicates a wind of 100 kt. or greater. The coded direction for winds of 100 to 199 kt. thus ranges from 51 through 86.
7. If the wind speed is forecast to be 199 kt. or more, the wind group is coded as 199 kt., e.g., 7799 means the wind is forecast to be from 270° true at 199 kt. or more.
8. When the forecast speed is less than 5 kt., the coded group is 9900 which means LIGHT AND VARIABLE.
9. EXAMPLES: Decode these FD winds and temperatures:

| Coded | Decoded |
|---|---|
| 9900 + 00 | Winds light and variable, temperature 0°C |
| 2707 | 270° true at 7 kt. |
| 850552 | 85 – 50 = 35; 05 + 100 = 105<br>350° true at 105 kt., temperature –52°C |

## 7.23 SURFACE ANALYSIS CHART

A. The Surface Analysis Chart (see page 207), often referred to as a surface weather chart, is the basic weather chart. The chart is prepared by the NWS from reports of existing weather conditions. The chart is transmitted every 3 hr. The valid time of the map corresponds to the time of the plotted observations.

1. A date and time (UTC) group gives the actual time of conditions portrayed on the map.
2. The Surface Analysis Chart displays weather information (as of chart time) such as
   a. Surface wind direction and speed
   b. Temperature
   c. Dew point
   d. Position of fronts
   e. Areas of high or low pressure
3. It gives a pictorial overview of the weather situation. You should keep in mind that weather systems move and conditions change.

B. Each reporting station is depicted on the chart by a small circle. Weather information pertaining to the station is placed in a standard pattern around this circle. This pattern is called a station model. The standard pattern of a station model follows with the explanation of the symbols.

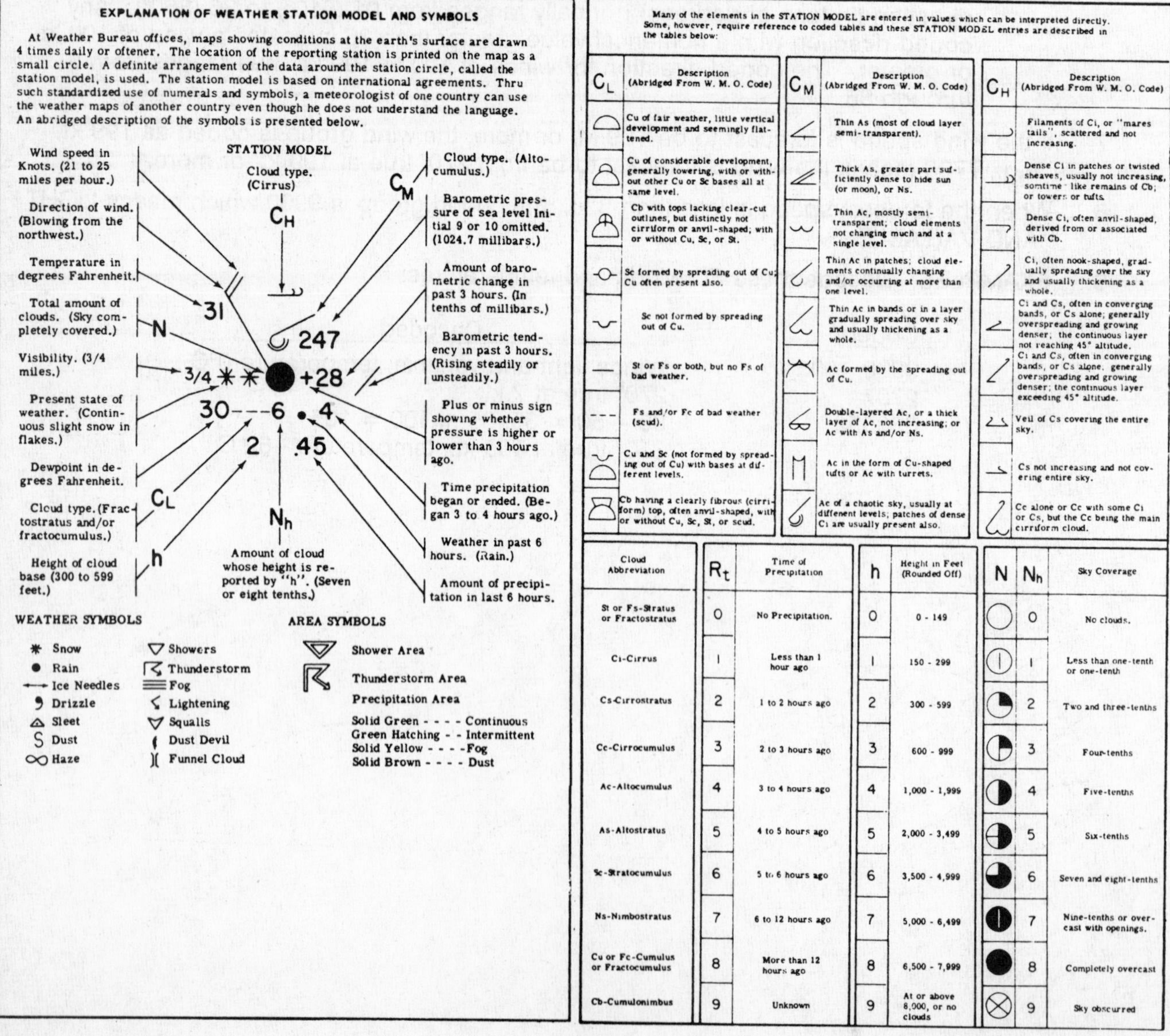


| $C_L$ | Description (Abridged From W. M. O. Code) |
|---|---|
| | Cu of fair weather, little vertical development and seemingly flattened. |
| | Cu of considerable development, generally towering, with or without other Cu or Sc bases all at same level. |
| | Cb with tops lacking clear-cut outlines, but distinctly not cirriform or anvil-shaped; with or without Cu, Sc, or St. |
| | Sc formed by spreading out of Cu; Cu often present also. |
| | Sc not formed by spreading out of Cu. |
| | St or Fs or both, but no Fs of bad weather. |
| | Fs and/or Fc of bad weather (scud). |
| | Cu and Sc (not formed by spreading out of Cu) with bases at different levels. |
| | Cb having a clearly fibrous (cirriform) top, often anvil-shaped, with or without Cu, Sc, St, or scud. |

| $C_M$ | Description (Abridged From W. M. O. Code) |
|---|---|
| | Thin As (most of cloud layer semi-transparent). |
| | Thick As, greater part sufficiently dense to hide sun (or moon), or Ns. |
| | Thin Ac, mostly semi-transparent; cloud elements not changing much and at a single level. |
| | Thin Ac in patches; cloud elements continually changing and/or occurring at more than one level. |
| | Thin Ac in bands or in a layer gradually spreading over sky and usually thickening as a whole. |
| | Ac formed by the spreading out of Cu. |
| | Double-layered Ac, or a thick layer of Ac, not increasing; or Ac with As and/or Ns. |
| | Ac in the form of Cu-shaped tufts or Ac with turrets. |
| | Ac of a chaotic sky, usually at different levels; patches of dense Ci are usually present also. |

| $C_H$ | Description (Abridged From W. M. O. Code) |
|---|---|
| | Filaments of Ci, or "mares tails", scattered and not increasing. |
| | Dense Ci in patches or twisted sheaves, usually not increasing, sometime like remains of Cb; or towers or tufts. |
| | Dense Ci, often anvil-shaped, derived from or associated with Cb. |
| | Ci, often hook-shaped, gradually spreading over the sky and usually thickening as a whole. |
| | Ci and Cs, often in converging bands, or Cs alone; generally overspreading and growing denser; the continuous layer not reaching 45° altitude. |
| | Ci and Cs, often in converging bands, or Cs alone, generally overspreading and growing denser; the continuous layer exceeding 45° altitude. |
| | Veil of Cs covering the entire sky. |
| | Cs not increasing and not covering entire sky. |
| | Cc alone or Cc with some Ci or Cs, but the Cc being the main cirriform cloud. |

| Cloud Abbreviation | $R_t$ | Time of Precipitation | h | Height in Feet (Rounded Off) | N | $N_h$ | Sky Coverage |
|---|---|---|---|---|---|---|---|
| St or Fs-Stratus or Fractostratus | 0 | No Precipitation. | 0 | 0 - 149 | | 0 | No clouds. |
| Ci-Cirrus | 1 | Less than 1 hour ago | 1 | 150 - 299 | | 1 | Less than one-tenth or one-tenth |
| Cs-Cirrostratus | 2 | 1 to 2 hours ago | 2 | 300 - 599 | | 2 | Two and three-tenths |
| Cc-Cirrocumulus | 3 | 2 to 3 hours ago | 3 | 600 - 999 | | 3 | Four-tenths |
| Ac-Altocumulus | 4 | 3 to 4 hours ago | 4 | 1,000 - 1,999 | | 4 | Five-tenths |
| As-Altostratus | 5 | 4 to 5 hours ago | 5 | 2,000 - 3,499 | | 5 | Six-tenths |
| Sc-Stratocumulus | 6 | 5 to 6 hours ago | 6 | 3,500 - 4,999 | | 6 | Seven and eight-tenths |
| Ns-Nimbostratus | 7 | 6 to 12 hours ago | 7 | 5,000 - 6,499 | | 7 | Nine-tenths or overcast with openings. |
| Cu or Fc-Cumulus or Fractocumulus | 8 | More than 12 hours ago | 8 | 6,500 - 7,999 | | 8 | Completely overcast |
| Cb-Cumulonimbus | 9 | Unknown | 9 | At or above 8,000, or no clouds | | 9 | Sky obscured |

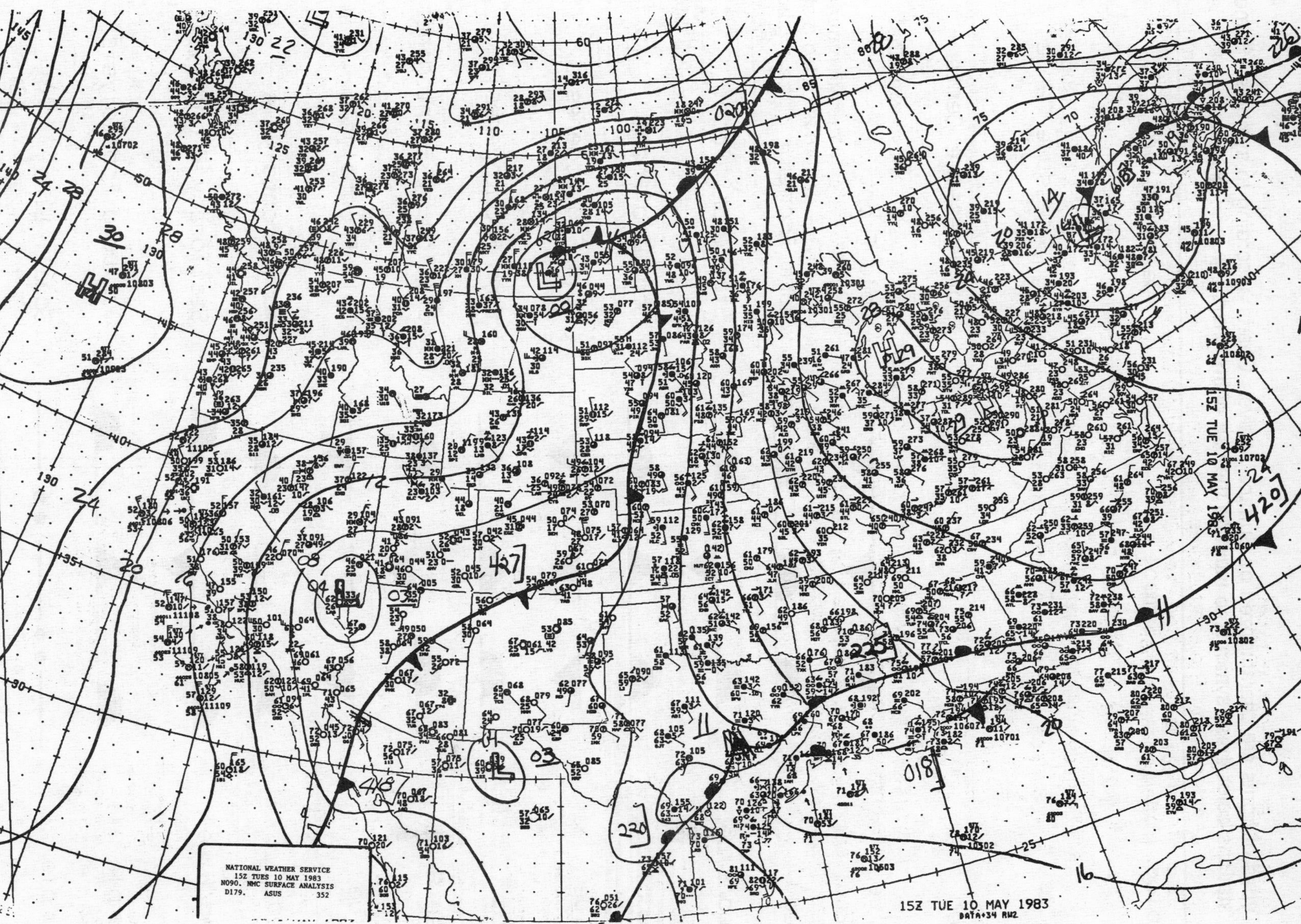


FIGURE 5-1. Surface Weather Analysis Chart.

C. Types of fronts are characterized on Surface Analysis Charts according to symbols. Some stations color these symbols to facilitate the use of the chart.

| Color | Symbol | Description |
|---|---|---|
| Blue | H | High Pressure Center |
| Red | L | Low Pressure Center |
| Blue | | Cold Front |
| Red | | Warm Front |
| Red/Blue | | Stationary Front |
| Purple | | Occluded Front |
| Blue | | Cold Frontogenesis |
| Red | | Warm Frontogenesis |
| Red/Blue | | Stationary Frontogenesis |
| Blue | | Cold Frontolysis |
| Red | | Warm Frontolysis |
| Red/Blue | | Stationary Frontolysis |
| Purple | | Occluded Frontolysis |
| Purple | | Squall Line |
| Brown | | Trough |
| Yellow | | Ridge |

1. A three-digit number along the front indicates type, intensity, and character as shown below.

   a. Type of front

| Code Figure | Description |
|---|---|
| 0 | Quasi-stationary at surface |
| 1 | Quasi-stationary above surface |
| 2 | Warm front at surface |
| 3 | Warm front above surface |
| 4 | Cold front at surface |
| 5 | Cold front above surface |
| 6 | Occlusion |
| 7 | Instability line |
| 8 | Intertropical front |
| 9 | Convergence line |

   b. Intensity of front

| Code Figure | Description |
|---|---|
| 0 | No specification |
| 1 | Weak, decreasing |
| 2 | Weak, little or no change |
| 3 | Weak, increasing |
| 4 | Moderate, decreasing |
| 5 | Moderate, little or no change |
| 6 | Moderate, increasing |
| 7 | Strong, decreasing |
| 8 | Strong, little or no change |
| 9 | Strong, increasing |

   c. Character of front

| Code Figure | Description |
|---|---|
| 0 | No specification |
| 1 | Frontal area activity, decreasing |
| 2 | Frontal area activity, little change |
| 3 | Frontal area activity, increasing |
| 4 | Intertropical |
| 5 | Forming or existence expected |
| 6 | Quasi-stationary |
| 7 | With waves |
| 8 | Diffuse |
| 9 | Position doubtful |

D. Solid lines depicting the pressure pattern are called isobars. They denote lines of equal pressure. Think of them as similar to terrain contour lines on geographic maps. Isobars usually encircle a high- or low-pressure area.

   1. The two-digit numbers on the isobars denote the pressure in millibars (mb). To decode, simply add either a 9 or a 10 before the two digits, whichever brings it closer to 1000 mb (e.g., 04 means 1004 mb; 96 means 996 mb).

E. The letter "H" on the chart marks the center of a high-pressure area. "L" marks the center of a low-pressure area. The actual pressure at each center is indicated by an underlined two-digit number which is decoded like the number along the isobars.

## 7.24 WEATHER DEPICTION CHART

A. The Weather Depiction Chart is a national map (of the contiguous U.S.) giving a quick picture of the weather conditions as of the valid time stated on the chart. It is prepared from Surface Aviation Observations (SAOs).

1. Areas affected by clouds and weather can be seen at a glance.
2. A weather depiction chart is illustrated on the opposite page.

B. An abbreviated station model is used to plot data consisting of total sky cover, cloud height or ceiling, weather and obstructions to vision, visibility, and an analysis.

1. The amount of sky cover is shown by the shading in the station circle as shown below.

| *Symbol* | *Total sky cover* |
|---|---|
| ○ | Sky Clear (less than 1/10) |
| ◔ | 1/10 to 5/10 inclusive (Scattered) |
| ◕ | 5/10 to 9/10 inclusive (Broken) |
| ● | 10/10 (Overcast) |
| ⊗ | Sky obscured or partially obscured |

2. Cloud height above ground level (AGL) is entered under the station circle in hundreds of feet.
   a. Broken or greater total sky cover without a height entry indicates thin sky cover.
3. Weather and obstructions to vision symbols are entered to the left of the station circle using the same symbols as on the Surface Analysis Chart.
4. When visibility is 6 SM or less, it is entered to the left of the weather or obstructions to vision symbol. Visibility is entered in whole miles and fractions of a mile.
5. The chart shows an analysis of observed ceiling and visibility by categories as follow:
   a. IFR -- Ceiling less than 1,000 ft. and/or visibility less than 3 SM; hatched area outlined by a smooth line.
   b. MVFR (Marginal VFR) -- Ceiling 1,000 to 3,000 ft. inclusive and/or visibility 3 to 5 SM inclusive; non-hatched area outlined by a smooth line.
   c. VFR -- No ceiling or ceiling greater than 3,000 ft. and visibility greater than 5 SM; not outlined.

C. The weather depiction chart is a choice place to begin your weather briefing and flight planning. It gives you a bird's-eye view at chart time of areas of favorable and adverse weather and frontal systems associated with the weather.

1. After you initially size up the general picture, your flight planning must consider all available weather reports and forecasts.

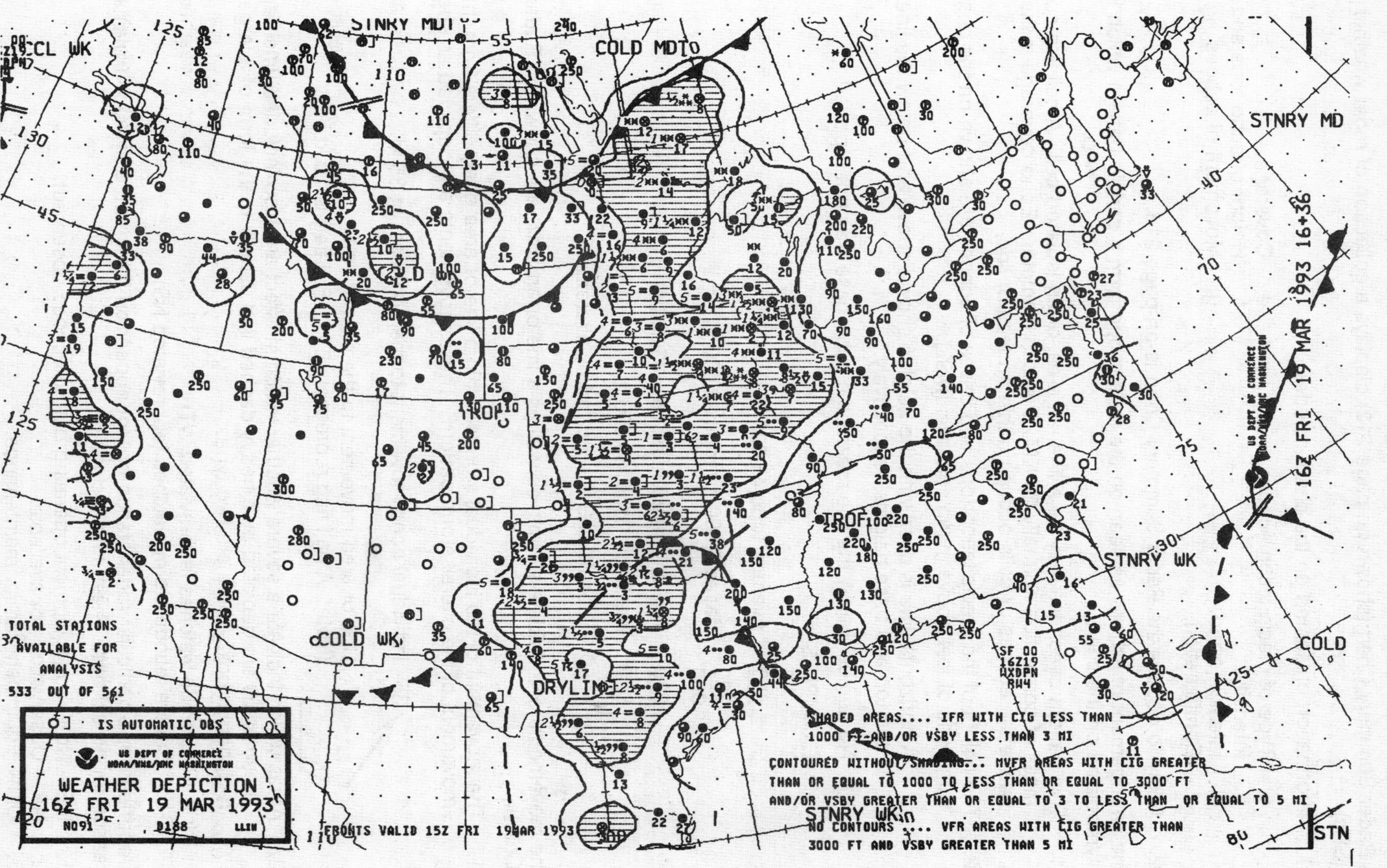
WEATHER DEPICTION
16Z FRI 19 MAR 1993
US DEPT OF COMMERCE
NOAA/NWS/NMC WASHINGTON
IS AUTOMATIC OBS
TOTAL STATIONS AVAILABLE FOR ANALYSIS
533 OUT OF 561
FRONTS VALID 15Z FRI 19MAR 1993
16Z FRI 19 MAR 1993 16+36
SHADED AREAS.... IFR WITH CIG LESS THAN 1000 FT AND/OR VSBY LESS THAN 3 MI
CONTOURED WITHOUT SHADING... MVFR AREAS WITH CIG GREATER THAN OR EQUAL TO 1000 TO LESS THAN OR EQUAL TO 3000 FT AND/OR VSBY GREATER THAN OR EQUAL TO 3 TO LESS THAN OR EQUAL TO 5 MI
NO CONTOURS .... VFR AREAS WITH CIG GREATER THAN 3000 FT AND VSBY GREATER THAN 5 MI
CL WK
COLD MDTO
STNRY MD
COLD WK
STNRY WK
TROF
DRYLINE
COLD
STN

## 7.25 RADAR SUMMARY CHART

A. A Radar Summary Chart (shown on page 213) displays a collection of radar weather reports (SDs).

1. Information presented on the chart includes

   a. Type of precipitation echoes.
   b. Intensity.
   c. Intensity trend.
   d. Configuration.
   e. Coverage.
   f. Height of echo tops and bases.
   g. Movement of echoes.

2. A key to decode the Radar Summary Chart is on page 213.

B. The arrangement of echoes as seen on the radarscope form a certain pattern which is symbolized on the chart.

1. This pattern of echoes may be a line, an area, or an isolated cell. A cell is a concentrated mass of convection normally 20 NM or less in diameter. Echo coverage is the amount of space the echoes or cells occupy within an area or line.

2. The height of the precipitation tops and bases of echoes are shown on the chart in hundreds of feet above mean sea level (MSL).

   a. A horizontal line is used with the heights shown above and below the line denoting the top and base heights, respectively.

   b. No number below the line means the echo base was not reported.

   c. EXAMPLES:

| | |
|---|---|
| <u>450</u> | Average tops 45,000 ft. |
| <u>220</u><br>080 | Bases 8,000 ft.; tops 22,000 ft. |
| <u>330</u> | Top of an individual cell, 33,000 ft. |
| <u>650/</u> | Maximum tops, 65,000 ft. |
| <u>A350</u> | Tops 35,000 ft. reported by aircraft. |

C. The movements of individual storms, as well as a line or an area, are shown on Radar Summary Charts.

1. The movement of the individual storms within a line or area often differs from the movement of the overall storm pattern. These movements are depicted as shown:

35 Individual echo movement to the northeast at 35 kt.

Line or area movement to the east at 15 kt.
(Note: A half flag represents 5 kt. Full flag is 10 kt.)

2. Areas which indicate a severe weather watch in effect are also included when appropriate. These areas are depicted by a heavy dashed line usually in the form of a large rectangular box. There are two types.

   a. Tornado watches (abbreviated WT)
   b. Severe thunderstorm watches (abbreviated NS)

D. If reports from a particular radar station do not appear on the chart, a symbol explains the reason for no echoes. These may include

1. NE -- No echo (equipment operating but no echoes observed).
2. NA -- Observation not available.
3. OM -- Equipment out for maintenance.

1*

2

3

450

Highest precipitation top in area in hundreds of feet MSL (45,000 FEET MSL)

| VIP LEVEL | ECHO INTENSITY | PRECIPITATION INTENSITY | RAINFALL RATE in/hr STRATIFORM | RAINFALL RATE in/hr CONVECTIVE |
|---|---|---|---|---|
| 1 | WEAK | LIGHT | LESS THAN 0.1 | LESS THAN 0.2 |
| 2 | MODERATE | MODERATE | 0.1 - 0.5 | 0.2 - 1.1 |
| 3 | STRONG | HEAVY | 0.5 - 1.0 | 1.1 - 2.2 |
| 4 | VERY STRONG | VERY HEAVY | 1.0 - 2.0 | 2.2 - 4.5 |
| 5 | INTENSE | INTENSE | 2.0 - 5.0 | 4.5 - 7.1 |
| 6 | EXTREME | EXTREME | MORE THAN 5.0 | MORE THAN 7.1 |

* The numbers representing the intensity level do not appear on the chart. Beginning from the first contour line, bordering the area, the intensity level is 1-2, second contour is 3-4, and the third contour is 5-6.

## SYMBOLS USED ON CHARTS

| SYMBOL | MEANING |
|---|---|
| R | RAIN |
| RW | RAIN SHOWER |
| HAIL | HAIL |
| S | SNOW |
| IP | ICE PELLETS |
| SW | SNOW SHOWER |
| L | DRIZZLE |
| T | THUNDERSTORM |
| ZR, ZL | FREEZING PRECIPITATION |
| NE | NO ECHOES OBSERVED |
| NA | OBSERVATIONS UNAVAILABLE |
| OM | OUT FOR MAINTENANCE |
| STC | STC ON - all precipitation may not be seen |
| ROBEPS | RADAR OPERATING BELOW PERFORMANCE STANDARDS |
| RHINO | RANGE HEIGHT INDICATOR NOT OPERATING |

| SYMBOL | MEANING |
|---|---|
| + | INTENSITY INCREASING OR NEW ECHO |
| - | INTENSITY DECREASING |
| NO SYMBOL | NO CHANGE IN INTENSITY |
| 35 | CELL MOVEMENT TO NE AT 35 KNOTS |
|  | LINE OR AREA MOVEMENT TO EAST AT 20 KNOTS |
| LM | LITTLE MOVEMENT |
| MA | ECHOES MOSTLY ALOFT |
| PA | ECHOES PARTLY ALOFT |

| SYMBOL | MEANING |
|---|---|
|  | LINE OF ECHOES |
| SLD | 8/10 OR GREATER COVERAGE IN A LINE |
| WS999 | SEVERE THUNDERSTORM WATCH |
| WT999 | TORNADO WATCH |
| LEWP | LINE ECHO WAVE PATTERN |
| HOOK | HOOK ECHO |
| BWER | BOUNDED WEAK ECHO REGION |
| PCLL | PERSISTENT CELL |
| FNLN | FINE LINE |

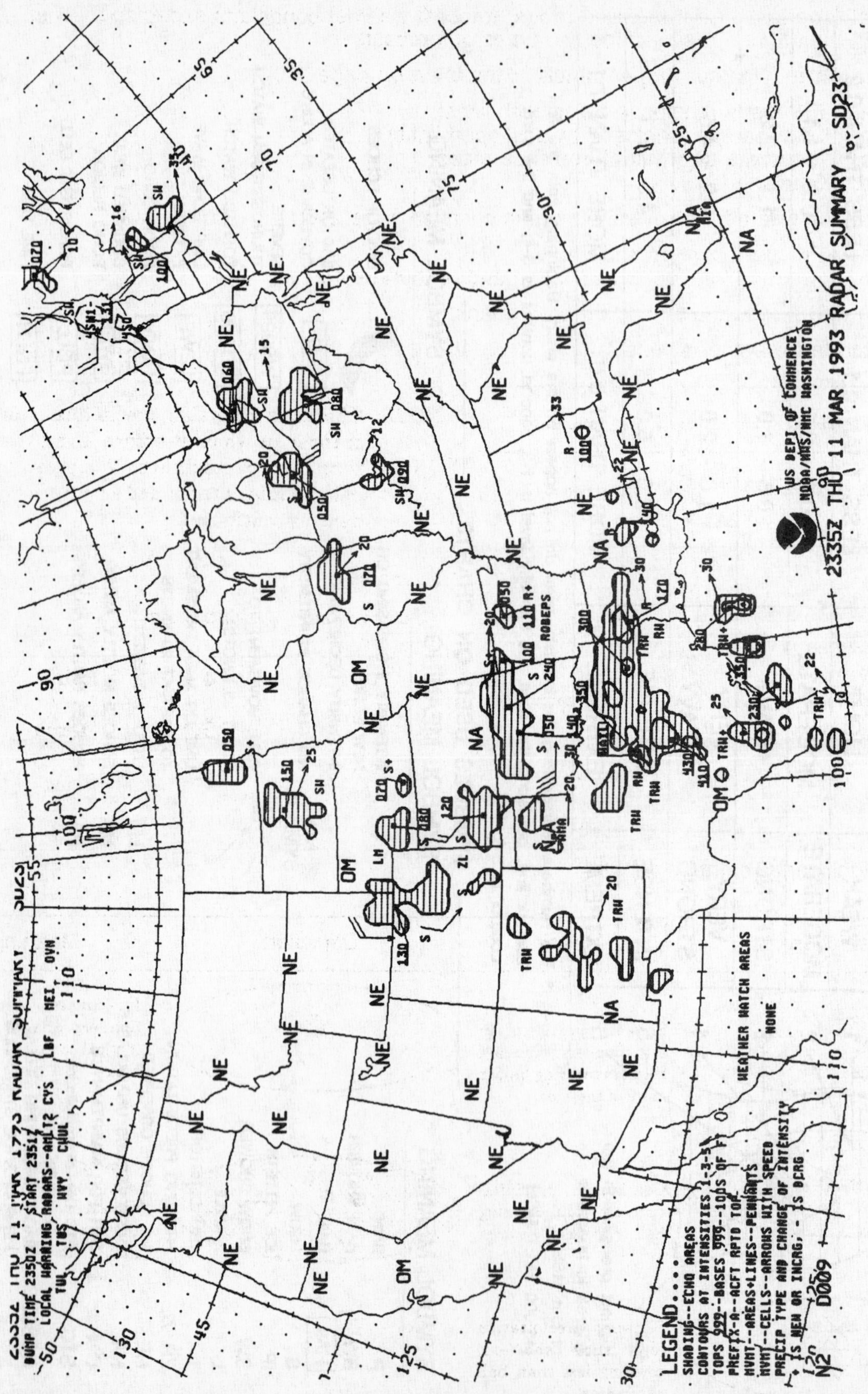
LEGEND....
SHADING--ECHO AREAS
CONTOURS AT INTENSITIES 1-3-5
TOPS 999--BASES 999--100S OF FT
PREFIX-A--ACFT RPTD TOP
MVMT--AREAS+LINES--PENNANTS
MVMT--CELLS--ARROWS WITH SPEED
PRECIP TYPE AND CHANGE OF INTENSITY
+ IS NEW OR INCRG, - IS DCRG
WEATHER WATCH AREAS
NONE
US DEPT OF COMMERCE
NOAA/NWS/NMC WASHINGTON
2335Z THU 11 MAR 1993 RADAR SUMMARY
SD23

## 7.26 LOW-LEVEL SIGNIFICANT WEATHER PROGNOSTIC CHARTS

A. Low-level Prognostic Charts (called progs) forecast weather conditions expected to exist 12 and 24 hr. in the future. They include two types of forecasts.

1. Significant weather (upper panels of the chart on page 216).
   a. IFR areas (enclosed by smooth lines).
   b. MVFR areas (enclosed by scalloped lines).
   c. Moderate or greater turbulence areas.
   d. Freezing levels.
2. Surface weather (lower panels of the chart on page 216).
   a. Pressure centers and fronts.
   b. Areas of forecast precipitation and/or thunderstorms.

B. The following symbols are used on prog charts:

1. Standard weather symbols

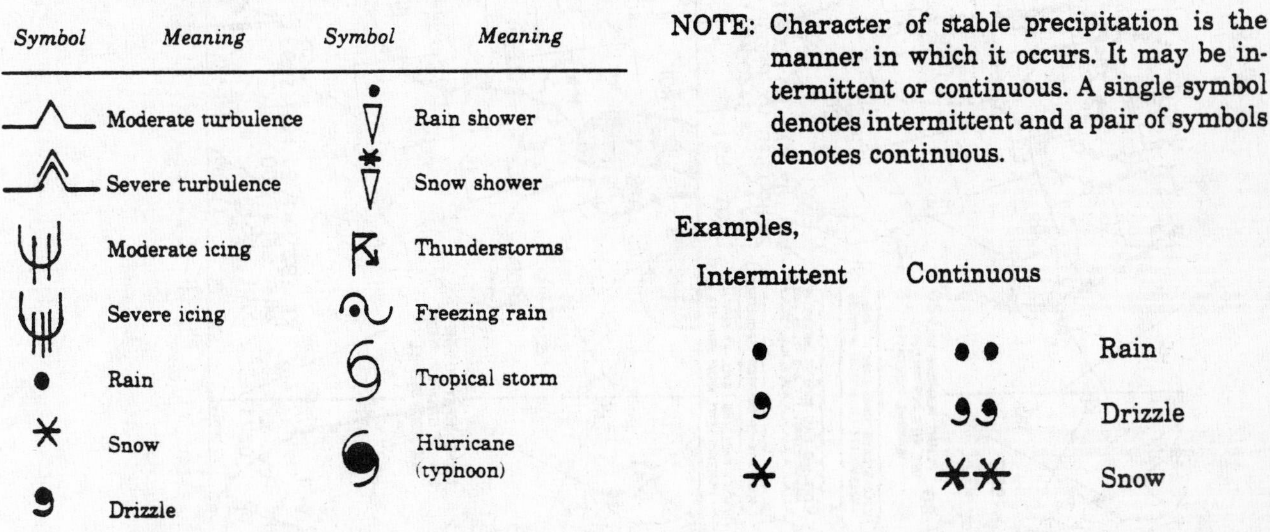


2. Significant weather symbols

| Depiction | Meaning | Depiction | Meaning |
|---|---|---|---|
| | Showery precipitation (e.g. thunderstorms/rain showers covering half or more of the area | | Intermittent precipitation (e.g. drizzle) covering less than half of the area |
| | Continuous precipitation (e.g. rain) covering half or more of the area | | Showery precipitation (e.g. rain showers) embedded in an area of continuous rain covering half or more of the area |
| | Showery precipitation (e.g. snow showers) covering less than half of the area | | |

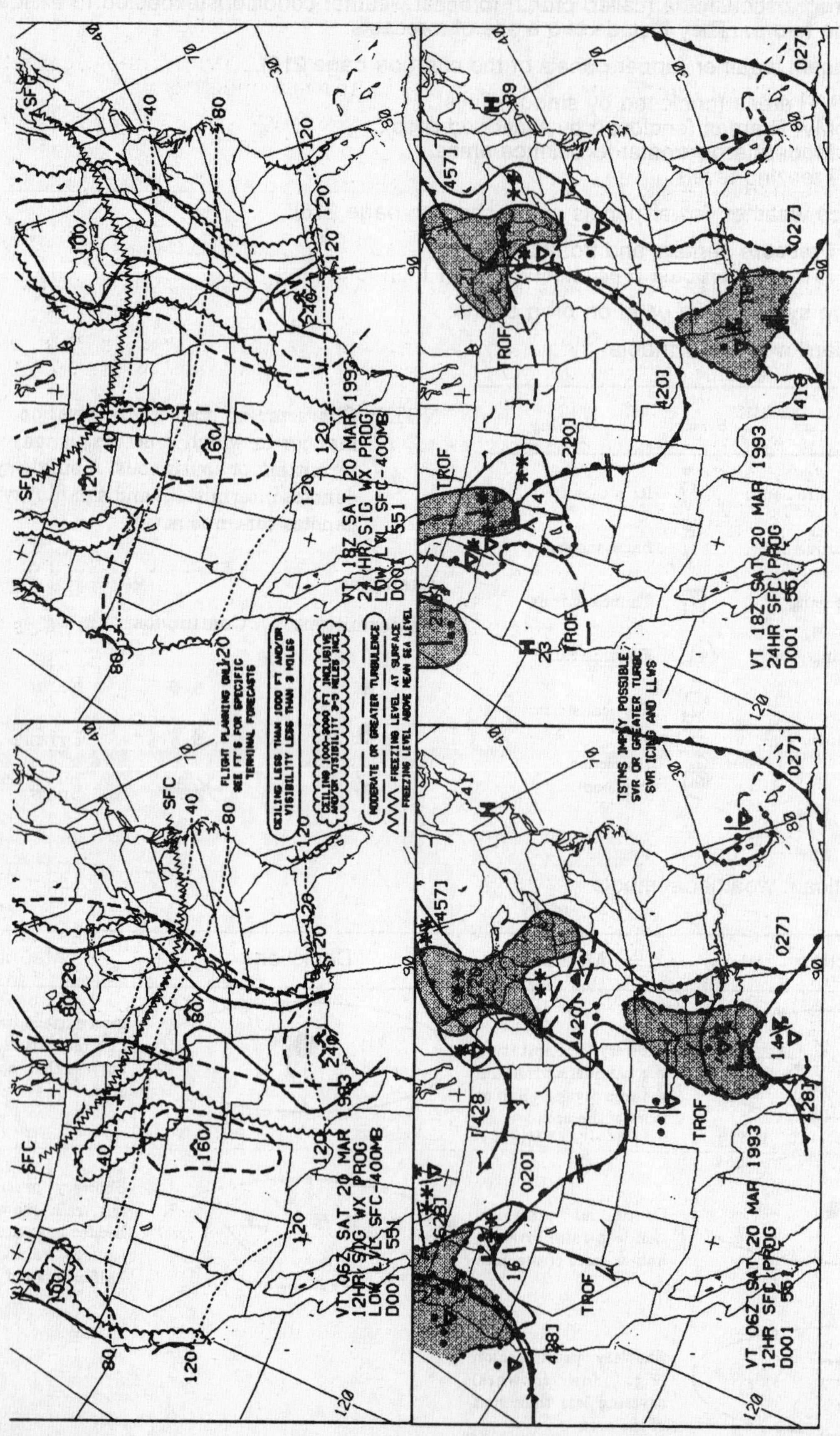
VT 18Z SAT 20 MAR 1993
24 HR SIG WX PROG
LOW LVL SFC-400MB
D001 551
FLIGHT PLANNING ONLY
SEE FT'S FOR SPECIFIC
TERMINAL FORECASTS
CEILING LESS THAN 1000 FT AND/OR
VISIBILITY LESS THAN 3 MILES
CEILING 1000-3000 FT INCLUSIVE
AND/OR VISIBILITY 3-5 MILES INCL
MODERATE OR GREATER TURBULENCE
FREEZING LEVEL AT SURFACE
FREEZING LEVEL ABOVE MEAN SEA LEVEL
VT 18Z SAT 20 MAR 1993
24HR SFC PROG
D001 551
TSTMS IMPLY POSSIBLE
SVR OR GREATER TURBC
SVR ICING AND LLWS
VT 06Z SAT 20 MAR 1993
12HR SIG WX PROG
LOW LVL SFC-400MB
D001 551
VT 06Z SAT 20 MAR 1993
12HR SFC PROG
D001 551

## 7.27 SEVERE WEATHER OUTLOOK CHART

A. A Severe Weather Outlook Chart (shown below) is a 48-hr. outlook for thunderstorm activity presented in two panels. This chart is issued once daily at about 0800Z.

1. The upper panel covers the first 24-hr. period beginning at 1200Z and depicts areas of possible general thunderstorm activity as well as severe thunderstorms.
2. The lower panel covers the following day beginning at 1200Z and is an outlook for the possibility of severe thunderstorms only.

B. General thunderstorms. A line with an arrowhead delineates an area of probable general thunderstorm activity.

1. When you face in the direction of the arrow, activity is expected to the right of the line.
2. An area labeled APCHG indicates probable general thunderstorm activity may approach severe intensity.
3. Approaching means that, at the surface, winds are greater than or equal to 35 kt. but less than 50 kt. and/or hail is greater than or equal to ½ in. in diameter but less than ¾ in.

C. Severe thunderstorms. The hatched area indicates possible severe thunderstorms.

1. Slight risk (SLGT) -- 2 to 5% coverage or 4 to 10 radar grid boxes containing severe thunderstorms per 100,000 square mi.
2. Moderate risk (MDT) -- 6 to 10% coverage or 11 to 21 radar grid boxes containing severe thunderstorms per 100,000 square mi.
3. High risk -- More than 10% coverage or more than 21 radar grid boxes containing severe thunderstorms per 100,000 square mi.

D. The Severe Weather Outlook Chart is strictly for advanced planning. It alerts all interests to the possibility of future storm development.

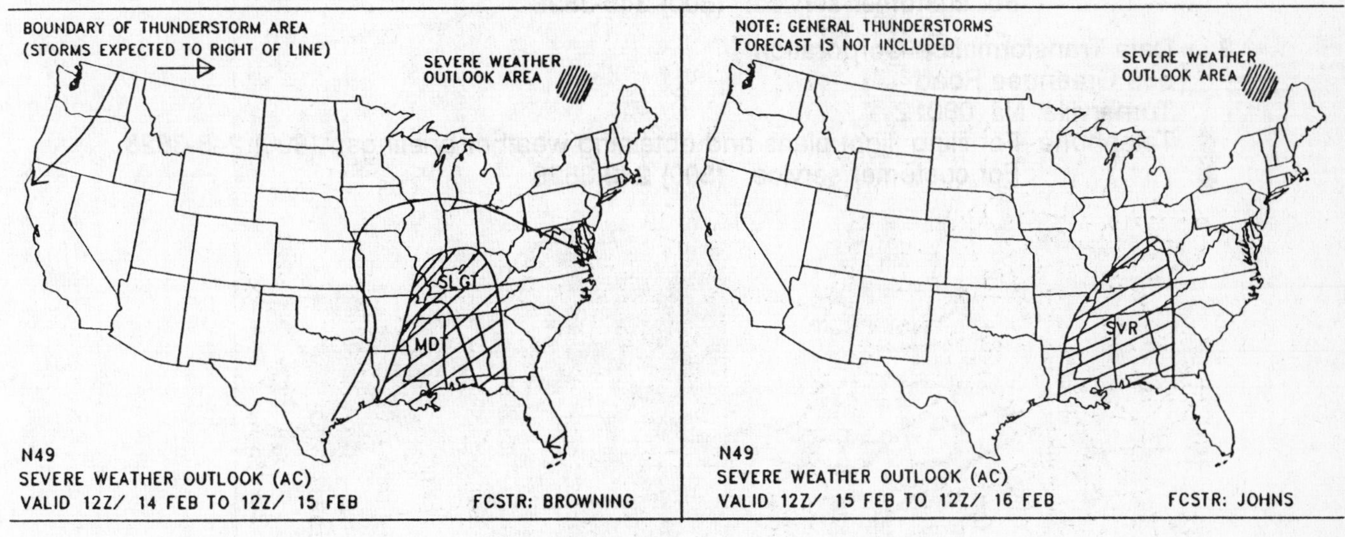

## 7.28 A.M. WEATHER

A. AM Weather is a 15-min. weather program aired Monday through Friday mornings on the PBS television network.

B. Professional meteorologists from the National Weather Service (NWS) provide weather information primarily for pilots to enable them to make better go or no-go flight decisions.

   1. National and regional weather maps are provided along with
      a. Satellite sequences.
      b. Radar reports.
      c. Winds aloft.
      d. Weather watches.

C. The program draws on the U.S. weather observations, satellite data, and computer analysis to produce daily forecasts with 85% to 90% accuracy.

## 7.29 DUATS (DIRECT USER ACCESS TERMINAL SERVICE)

A. DUATS can be accessed by pilots with a current medical certificate toll-free in the 48 contiguous states via personal computer.

   1. You can receive the same weather reports and forecasts that are available from the FSSs.
   2. The system will also allow you to file flight plans.

B. The FAA has contracted with the following two companies to provide up to 20 min. access at no cost to you (even use of the telephone line is free). Call one or both (customer service numbers) for user manuals and other data.

   1. GTE
      15000 Conference Center Drive
      Chantilly, VA 22021-3808
      Telephone--For filing flight plans and obtaining weather briefings: (800) 767-9989
      For customer service: (800) 345-3828

   2. Data Transformation Corporation
      559 Greentree Road
      Turnerville, NJ 08012
      Telephone--For filing flight plans and obtaining weather briefings: (800) 245-3828
      For customer service: (800) 243-3828

# CHAPTER EIGHT
# FEDERAL AVIATION REGULATIONS, OUTLINED



(Continued)

(Continued)

## 8.1 FEDERAL AVIATION REGULATIONS

The first purpose of this chapter is to outline (paraphrase) the FARs we feel are particularly relevant to private pilots. These include Parts 1, 61, 67, 91, and NTSB 830. Many parts of the FARs are not relevant to private pilots (e.g., Part 103, Ultralight Vehicles). Those sections not outlined are listed at the end of this chapter for your information.

The scope of this chapter is to acquaint you with the FARs. You should obtain your own copy of the FARs to use as your official reference to the regulations. Reprints of Parts 1, 61, 67, 91, etc., are available at most FBOs and pilot shops for $5 to $10.

Most Flight Service Stations (FSSs), Flight Standard District Offices (FSDOs), and other FAA offices have complete sets of the FARs available for public use. The FAA issues an Advisory Circular (AC) listing the current publication status, prices (single issue and subscriptions), and order forms for the FARs. The AC number is AC 00-44, which is available at no charge from:

U.S. Department of Transportation
Utilization and Storage Section
M-443.2
Washington, DC 20590

## 8.2 Part 1 -- DEFINITIONS AND ABBREVIATIONS

A. This Part contains several pages of definitions of terms and abbreviations used throughout the FARs.

B. You should use Part 1 any time you do not understand the meaning of a word and/or abbreviation.

### 1.1 General Definitions

Only selected terms most relevant to the private certificate are included here.

1. **Administrator** means the FAA administrator or any person to whom (s)he has delegated his authority in the matter concerned.
2. **Aircraft** means a device that is used or intended to be used for flight in the air.
3. **Airframe** means the fuselage, booms, nacelles, cowlings, fairings, airfoil surfaces (excluding propellers of engines), and landing gear of an aircraft and their accessories and controls.
4. **Airplane** means an engine-driven fixed-wing aircraft heavier than air that is supported in flight by the dynamic reaction of the air against its wings.
5. **Airport** means an area of land or water that is used or intended to be used for the landing and takeoff of aircraft, and includes its buildings and facilities, if any.
6. **Air traffic** means aircraft operating in the air or on an airport surface, exclusive of loading ramps and parking areas.
7. **Air traffic clearance** means an authorization by air traffic control, for the purpose of preventing a collision between known aircraft, for an aircraft to proceed under specified traffic conditions within controlled airspace.
8. **Air traffic control** means a service operated by appropriate authority to promote the safe, orderly, and expeditious flow of air traffic.
9. **Alternate airport** means an airport at which an aircraft may land if a landing at the intended airport becomes inadvisable.
10. **Category**
    a. As used with respect to the certification, ratings, privileges, and limitations of airmen, means a broad classification of aircraft.
        1) EXAMPLES: Airplane, rotorcraft, glider, and lighter-than-air.
    b. As used with respect to the certification of aircraft, means a grouping of aircraft based upon intended use or operating limitations.
        1) EXAMPLES: Transport, normal, utility, acrobatic, limited, restricted, and provisional.
11. **Ceiling** means the height above the Earth's surface of the lowest layer of clouds or obscuring phenomena that is reported as "broken," overcast," or "obscuration," and not classified as "thin" or "partial."
12. **Civil aircraft** means aircraft other than public aircraft.
13. **Class**
    a. As used with respect to the certification, ratings, privileges, and limitations of airmen, means a classification of aircraft within a category having similar operating characteristics.
        1) EXAMPLES: Single-engine, multiengine, land, water, gyroplane, helicopter, airship, and free balloon.

b. As used with respect to certification of aircraft, means a broad grouping of aircraft having similar characteristics of propulsion, flight, or landing.

1) EXAMPLES: Airplane, rotorcraft, glider, balloon, landplane, and seaplane.

14. **Controlled airspace** means an airspace of defined dimensions within which air traffic control is provided to IFR flights and to VFR flights in accordance with the airspace classification.

a. Note: Controlled airspace is a generic term that covers Class A, Class B, Class C, Class D, and Class E airspace.

15. **Crewmember** means a person assigned to perform duty in an aircraft during flight time.

16. **Flight plan** means specified information, relating to the intended flight of an aircraft, that is filed orally or in writing with air traffic control.

17. **Flight time** means the time from the moment the aircraft first moves under its own power for the purpose of flight until the moment it comes to rest at the next point of landing ("block-to-block" time).

18. **Flight visibility** means the average forward horizontal distance, from the cockpit of an aircraft in flight, at which prominent unlighted objects may be seen and identified by day and prominent lighted objects may be seen and identified by night.

19. **Ground visibility** means prevailing horizontal visibility near the Earth's surface as reported by the United States National Weather Service or an accredited observer.

20. **IFR conditions** means weather conditions below the minimum for flight under visual flight rules.

21. **Instrument** means a device using an internal mechanism to show visually or aurally the attitude, altitude, or operation of an aircraft or aircraft part.

22. **Large aircraft** means aircraft of more than 12,500 lb., maximum certificated takeoff weight.

23. **Load factor** means the ratio of a specified load to the total weight of the aircraft.

24. **Maintenance** means inspection, overhaul, repair, preservation, and the replacement of parts, but excludes preventive maintenance.

25. **Major alteration** means an alteration not listed in the aircraft, aircraft engine, or propeller specifications

a. That might appreciably affect weight, balance, structural strength, performance, powerplant operation, flight characteristics, or other qualities affecting airworthiness; or

b. That is not done according to accepted practices or cannot be done by elementary operations.

26. **Major repair** means a repair

a. That, if improperly done, might appreciably affect weight, balance, structural strength, performance, powerplant operation, flight characteristics, or other qualities affecting airworthiness; or

b. That is not done according to accepted practices or cannot be done by elementary operations.

27. **Manifold pressure** means absolute pressure as measured at the appropriate point in the induction system and usually expressed in inches of mercury.

28. **Medical certificate** means an acceptable evidence of physical fitness on a form prescribed by the Administrator.

29. **Minor alteration** means an alteration other than a major alteration.

30. **Minor repair** means a repair other than a major repair.
31. **Night** means the time between the end of evening civil twilight and the beginning of morning civil twilight, as published in the *American Air Almanac*, converted to local time.
32. **Operator** is a person who uses or authorizes use of an aircraft.
33. **Over-the-top** means above the layer of clouds or other obscuring phenomena forming the ceiling.
34. **Pilot in Command (PIC)** means the pilot responsible for the operation and safety of an aircraft during flight time.
35. **Pilotage** means navigation by visual reference to landmarks.
36. **Positive control** means control of all air traffic, within designated airspace, by air traffic control.
37. **Preventive maintenance** means simple or minor preservation operations and the replacement of small standard parts not involving complex assembly operations.
38. **Rating** means a statement that, as part of a certificate, sets forth special conditions, privileges, and limitations.
39. **Small aircraft** means aircraft of 12,500 lb. or less, maximum certificated takeoff weight.
40. **Traffic pattern** means the traffic flow that is prescribed for aircraft landing at, taxiing on, or taking off from, an airport.
41. **VFR over-the-top,** with respect to the operation of aircraft, means the operation of an aircraft over-the-top under VFR when it is not being operated on an IFR flight plan.

## 1.2 Abbreviations and Symbols

**AGL** means above ground level.
**ATC** means air traffic control.
**CAS** means calibrated airspeed.
**DME** means distance measuring equipment compatible with TACAN.
**FAA** means Federal Aviation Administration.
**HIRL** means high-intensity runway light system.
**IAS** means indicated airspeed.
**ICAO** means International Civil Aviation Organization.
**IFR** means instrument flight rules.
**ILS** means instrument landing system.
**MSL** means mean sea level.
**NDB(ADF)** means nondirectional beacon (automatic direction finder).
**PAR** means precision approach radar.
**RAIL** means runway alignment indicator light system.
**RBN** means radio beacon.
**RCLM** means runway centerline marking.
**RCLS** means runway centerline light system.
**REIL** means runway end identification lights.
**TACAN** means ultra-high frequency tactical air navigational aid.
**TAS** means true airspeed.
**TDZL** means touchdown zone lights.
$V_A$ means design maneuvering speed.
$V_{FE}$ means maximum flap extended speed.
$V_{LE}$ means maximum landing gear extended speed.
$V_{LO}$ means maximum landing gear operating speed.
$V_{NE}$ means never-exceed speed.
$V_{NO}$ means maximum structural cruising speed.
$V_R$ means rotation speed.
$V_{S0}$ means the stalling speed or the minimum steady flight speed in the landing configuration.
$V_{S1}$ means the stalling speed or the minimum steady flight speed obtained in a specific configuration.
$V_X$ means speed for best angle of climb.
$V_Y$ means speed for best rate of climb.
**VFR** means visual flight rules.
**VHF** means very high frequency.
**VOR** means very high frequency omnirange station.
**VORTAC** means collocated VOR and TACAN.

## 8.3 Part 61 -- CERTIFICATION: PILOTS AND FLIGHT INSTRUCTORS

Part 61 contains seven subparts, labeled A through G. Parts E, F, and G are not immediately related to private pilots.

Subpart A -- General
Subpart B -- Aircraft Ratings and Special Certificates
Subpart C -- Student and Recreational Pilots
Subpart D -- Private Pilots
Subpart E -- Commercial Pilots
Subpart F -- Airline Transport Pilots
Subpart G -- Flight Instructors

Subpart E is thoroughly covered in Gleim's *Commercial Pilot FAA Practical Test Prep*. Subpart G is thoroughly covered in Gleim's *Flight Instructor FAA Practical Test Prep*. **Note:** Only selected sections are outlined below through page 239. Pages 239 and 240 contain the section titles of Part 61 that are not outlined.

### Subpart A -- General

#### 61.1 Applicability

1. Part 61 prescribes the requirements for issuing pilot and flight instructor certificates and ratings, the conditions under which these certificates and ratings are necessary, and the privileges and limitations of these certificates and ratings.
2. For a certificate or rating, you must meet the requirements in Part 61, unless you are enrolled in a Part 141 flight school.
   a. Part 141 schools have different requirements (e.g., flight time).

#### 61.3 Requirement for Certificates, Rating, and Authorizations

1. Both the appropriate pilot certificate and a current and appropriate medical certificate are required to be in your personal possession when acting as pilot in command or as a required flight crewmember.

#### 61.5 Certificates and Ratings Issued under This Part

1. The following ratings may be placed on a pilot certificate.
   a. Aircraft Category Ratings
      1) Lighter-Than-Air
      2) Airplane
      3) Rotorcraft
      4) Glider
   b. Airplane Class Ratings
      1) Single-Engine Land
      2) Multiengine Land
      3) Single-Engine Sea
      4) Multiengine Sea

**61.13 Application and Qualification**

1. If you want to apply for a certificate or rating, or to add a rating to an existing certificate, you must do so in the manner and on the form designated by the FAA.
2. If you are not a citizen or resident alien, you must also show proof that you have paid the fee prescribed by Part 187 (fee for processing services provided by the FAA in Oklahoma City).
3. If you meet all the requirements of Part 61, you are entitled to the certificate or rating sought.
4. If you cannot comply with certain requirements for a certificate or rating, except for flight proficiency, you may apply for the certificate or rating with limitations placed on it.
5. If your pilot certificate has been suspended, you may not apply for any certificate or rating during the suspension.
6. If your pilot certificate has been revoked, you may not apply for any certificate or rating for 1 year after the revocation.

**61.15 Offenses Involving Alcohol or Drugs**

1. Conviction for a violation of any law relating to drugs or alcohol is the basis for:
   a. The denial of an application for a certificate or rating for up to 1 year after the final conviction.
   b. The suspension or revocation of any existing certificates or ratings.

**61.16 Refusal to Submit to an Alcohol Test or to Furnish Test Results**

1. If you refuse to submit test results for drugs or alcohol when requested by the FAA, you may not receive a certificate or rating for a period of 1 year.
2. This is also grounds to suspend or revoke existing certificates or ratings.

**61.17 Temporary Certificate**

1. A temporary certificate is issued to you after successful completion of your practical test. It is valid for a maximum of 120 days or until
   a. You receive your permanent certificate.
   b. Notice is given that the certificate or rating sought is denied.

**61.19 Duration of Pilot and Flight Instructor Certificates**

1. All pilot certificates (except a student pilot certificate) issued under Part 61 are issued without an expiration date.
2. Any pilot certificate is no longer valid if it is surrendered, suspended, or revoked.
   a. The FAA may request that a suspended or revoked certificate be returned to it.

**61.23 Duration of Medical Certificates**

1. For private pilot purposes, a medical certificate expires at the end of the last day of the 24th month after the month of the date of examination shown on the certificate.

**61.25 Change of Name**

1. To change your name on your pilot certificate, you must submit your current certificate and a copy of the marriage license, court order, or other document verifying the change.
   a. The documents will be returned after inspection.

## 61.29 Replacement of Lost or Destroyed Certificate

1. An application for a replacement pilot certificate must be made by letter to the Department of Transportation • FAA Airman Certification Branch • P.O. Box 25082 • Oklahoma City, OK 73125.
   a. It must include your name, social security number, date and place of birth, any available information concerning the type of certificate and ratings, and $2.00.
2. An application for a replacement medical certificate must be made by letter to the Department of Transportation • FAA Aeromedical Certification Branch • P.O. Box 25082 • Oklahoma City, OK 73125.
   a. Include a check or money order for $2.00.
3. A telegram from the FAA showing that the certificate (pilot and/or medical) was issued may be used for a period not to exceed 60 days, pending the arrival of the replacement certificate.

## 61.31 General Limitations

1. Type ratings are required when operating any turbojet-powered airplane or airplane having a gross weight of 12,500 lb.
2. To act as pilot in command of a high-performance airplane (retractable landing gear, flaps, a controllable propeller, and/or more than 200 horsepower), you must receive flight instruction in such an airplane and obtain a logbook endorsement of competence.
3. To act as pilot in command of a pressurized airplane that has a service ceiling or maximum operating altitude, whichever is lower, above 25,000 ft. MSL, you must have both ground and flight instruction in such an airplane and obtain a logbook endorsement.
4. To act as pilot in command of a tailwheel airplane you must receive flight instruction in such an airplane and obtain a logbook endorsement of competence. Training must include:
   a. Normal and crosswind takeoffs and landings,
   b. Wheel landings, unless manufacturer does not recommend them, and
   c. Go-around procedures.

## 61.35 Written Test: Prerequisites and Passing Grades

1. To take a written test you must:
   a. Show that you have satisfactorily completed the ground or home-study course required by Part 61.
   b. Present personal identification such as an Airman Certificate, driver license, or other official document.
      1) NOTE: Advisory Circular (AC) 61-65C, *Certification: Pilots and Flight Instructors*, requires that the identification presented must include your photograph, signature, and actual residential address, if different from the mailing address. This information may be present in more than one form of identification.
   c. Present a birth certificate or other official document showing that the age requirements of Part 61 are met or will be met within 2 years of taking the test. A driver license will suffice.
2. The minimum passing grade for the test specified by the FAA is printed on the test booklets (usually 70%).
3. This section does not pertain to the written test for an ATP certificate. The ATP written test requires an authorization from the FAA.

**61.37 Written Tests: Cheating or Other Unauthorized Conduct**

1. You may not:
   a. Copy or intentionally remove a written test from the testing site.
   b. Give to another or receive from another a copy of the test.
   c. Give help to another or receive help from another while taking the test.
   d. Take the test on behalf of another.
   e. Use any material as an aid during the test.
      1) NOTE: You are permitted to take and use a flight computer, plotter, and calculator (you must erase all memory in the calculator before you start your test).
   f. Intentionally cause, assist, or participate in any act contrary to this part.
2. If caught in any of these acts you will be ineligible to take a test or receive any certificates or ratings for a period of 1 year.
3. These are also grounds to suspend or revoke any certificate or ratings you already possess.

**61.39 Prerequisites for Flight Tests**

1. To be eligible for a flight test, you must have:
   a. Passed any required written tests within the preceding 24 months.
   b. Have the required instruction and aeronautical experience as prescribed in Part 61.
   c. Have a current and appropriate medical certificate for the rating sought.
   d. Meet the minimum age requirements as given in Part 61.
   e. Have a written statement from a CFI certifying that (s)he has given you flight instruction in preparation for the flight test within the preceding 60 days and finds you competent to pass the test and that you have satisfactory knowledge of the areas shown to be deficient on the written test.

**61.43 Flight Tests: General Procedures**

1. When you apply for a new certificate or rating, you are judged by your ability to:
   a. Execute procedures and maneuvers within your airplane's performance capabilities and limitations, and use the airplane's systems.
   b. Execute emergency procedures and maneuvers appropriate to your airplane.
   c. Pilot your airplane with smoothness and accuracy.
   d. Exercise judgment.
   e. Apply your aeronautical knowledge.
   f. Show that you are the master of your airplane and that the outcome of any maneuver is never seriously in doubt.
2. If you fail any of the required pilot operations, the entire checkride is failed.
3. Either you or the examiner may discontinue the flight test at any time when the failure of a pilot operation has caused the failure of the checkride.

### 61.45 Flight Tests: Required Aircraft and Equipment

1. For your practical (flight) test you must furnish an appropriate U.S. registered airplane that has a current airworthiness certificate.
2. Aircraft furnished for the flight test must have:
   a. The equipment for each pilot operation required by the flight test.
   b. No operating limitations precluding the performance of a required pilot operation.
   c. Pilot seats with adequate outside visibility for each pilot to operate the aircraft safely.
   d. All flight and power controls accessible and easily controlled by both pilots.
   e. For testing of flight by reference to instruments only, you must provide a satisfactory view-limiting device, e.g., a hood or a pair of foggles.

### 61.47 Flight Tests: Status of FAA Inspectors and Other Authorized Flight Examiners

1. An FAA inspector or a designated examiner conducts the flight test for certificates and ratings.
2. The FAA inspector/examiner is not the pilot in command unless (s)he acts in that capacity in order to perform the flight test, e.g., your practical test is for a second in command for an airplane that requires more than one pilot. This determination must be made prior to starting the checkride.
   a. For most practical tests (e.g., instrument, commercial, etc.) you are the pilot in command.
3. Neither you nor your examiner are considered a passenger of one another and are thereby not responsible for the passenger-carrying provisions of the FARs.

### 61.49 Retesting after Failure

1. If you fail a written or flight test you may not apply for retesting until 30 days have passed since the failure.
2. In the case of a first-time failure, you may apply within the 30-day period if a written statement is presented from a CFI stating that (s)he has given you additional instruction and finds you competent to pass the test.

### 61.51 Pilot Logbooks

1. All the aeronautical training and experience used to meet the requirements for a certificate or rating must be shown by a reliable record, e.g., a logbook.
   a. All flight time used to meet the recent flight requirements must also be logged (e.g., three takeoffs and landings within the preceding 90 days).
   b. All other time need only be logged at your discretion.
2. Each logbook entry shall include:
   a. Date.
   b. Total time of flight.
   c. Points of departure and arrival.
   d. Type and identification of aircraft.
   e. Type of pilot time (e.g., PIC, SIC, solo, dual, etc.).
   f. Conditions of flight (e.g., day or night).

3. Types of flight time:
   a. Solo is logged when you are the sole occupant of the airplane in which you are training before obtaining your private pilot certificate.
   b. PIC is logged when you are the sole manipulator of the controls in an airplane in which you are rated, or when you are the PIC during a flight in which an SIC is required.
   c. SIC time is logged when you are acting as a second in command on an aircraft requiring more than one pilot by the type certificate or FARs.
   d. Instrument time is logged when you operate the aircraft solely by reference to instruments under actual or simulated conditions.
   e. All time logged as instruction must be certified by an appropriately rated and certificated instructor giving the instruction.
4. You must present your logbook upon reasonable request by the FAA, or a member of the NTSB, or a local or state law enforcement officer.
5. As a student pilot, you must carry your logbook with you on all solo cross-country flights.

**61.53 Operations during Medical Deficiency**

1. You may not act as a pilot in command or required crewmember while you have a known medical problem which would make you unable to meet the requirements of your current medical certificate (i.e., Class I, II, or III).

**61.55 Second-in-Command Qualifications**

1. To serve as second in command of an airplane certified for operation by more than one required pilot flight crewmember, you must hold at least a private pilot certificate with appropriate category and class ratings.

**61.56 Flight Review**

1. To act as pilot in command of an aircraft, you must have:
   a. Satisfactorily accomplished a flight review or completed a proficiency check or a practical test for a new certificate/rating within the preceding 24 calendar months, or
   b. Satisfactorily completed one or more phases of an FAA-sponsored pilot proficiency award program.
      1) This is commonly known as the "Wings" program.
         a) There are nine levels and satisfactory completion of a level will qualify as a flight review.
         b) Requires 3 hr. of flight instruction and attendance of one FAA-sponsored safety seminar.
      2) For more information visit your nearest FSDO or your local accident prevention counselor.
2. The FAA is currently deciding if an annual flight review will be required for all recreational pilots and noninstrument-rated private pilots with fewer than 400 hr. of flight time.
   a. As of now, the annual flight review requirement will be effective on August 31, 1993.

### 61.57 Recent Flight Experience: Pilot in Command

1. You may not act as pilot in command of an airplane carrying passengers, or of an airplane certificated for more than one required pilot flight crewmember, unless you have:
   a. Made three takeoffs and landings within the preceding 90 days in an aircraft of the same category and class of the aircraft to be flown, and if a type rating is required, in the same type.
      1) In a tailwheel airplane, the landings must have been made to a full stop.
   b. To carry passengers at night, you must have made three takeoffs and landings to a full stop at night within the preceding 90 days in the category and class of aircraft to be used.
      1) Here, night refers to the period beginning 1 hour after sunset to 1 hour before sunrise.

### 61.59 Falsification, Reproduction, or Alteration of Applications, Certificates, Logbooks, Reports, or Records

1. You may not make a false or fraudulent statement on any:
   a. Application for a certificate or rating,
   b. Required record,
   c. Required logbook,
   d. Existing certificate or rating.
2. Any commission of one of the above acts is grounds to suspend or revoke any existing certificate or rating, and can be used to deny any application for a certificate or rating.

### 61.60 Change of Address

1. If you make a change in your permanent address, you may not exercise the privileges of your pilot certificate after 30 days (from the day you move) unless you notify the FAA in writing to the Department of Transportation • FAA Airman Certification Branch • P.O. Box 25082 • Oklahoma City, OK 73125.

## Subpart C -- Student and Recreational Pilots

### 61.81 Applicability

1. This subpart prescribes the requirements for the issuance of student pilot and recreational pilot certificates, the conditions under which those certificates are necessary, and the general rules for holders of those certificates.

### 61.83 Eligibility Requirements: Student Pilots

1. To be eligible for a student pilot's certificate, you must:
   a. Be at least 16 yr. old.
   b. Be able to read, speak, and understand the English language or you will have limitations placed on the certificate as necessary for safety.
   c. Hold at least a current third-class medical certificate issued under FAR Part 67.

### 61.85 Application

1. An application for a student pilot certificate is made on a form and in a manner approved by the FAA.
2. It is submitted to a designated aviation medical examiner when applying for an FAA medical certificate, or to an FAA inspector or designated examiner when it is accompanied by a current FAA medical certificate.

## 61.87 Solo Flight Requirements for Student Pilots

1. You must pass a written test administered by your CFI on FAR Parts 61 and 91 and the operational characteristics of the make and model of airplane you will fly.
2. You must receive flight instruction in the following 15 flight maneuvers:

(1) Flight preparation procedures, including preflight inspections, powerplant operation, and aircraft systems;

(2) Taxiing or surface operations, including runups;

(3) Takeoffs and landings, including normal and crosswind;

(4) Straight-and-level flight, shallow, medium, and steep banked turns in both directions;

(5) Climbs and climbing turns;

(6) Airport traffic patterns including entry and departure procedures, and collision and wake turbulence avoidance;

(7) Descents with and without turns using high and low drag configurations;

(8) Flight at various airspeeds from cruising to minimum controllable airspeed;

(9) Emergency procedures and equipment malfunctions;

(10) Ground reference maneuvers;

(11) Approaches to the landing area with engine power at idle and with partial power;

(12) Slips to a landing;

(13) Go-arounds from final approach and from the landing flare in various flight configurations including turns;

(14) Forced landing procedures initiated on takeoff, during initial climb, cruise, descent, and in the landing pattern; and

(15) Stall entries from various flight attitudes and power combinations with recovery initiated at the first indication of a stall, and recovery from a full stall.

3. Your logbook must be endorsed every 90 days by your CFI indicating:
   a. Flight instruction in the make and model of the plane to be used for solo flight.
   b. Proficiency in the above maneuvers.
   c. Competency for safe solo flight in that make and model.
4. Your student pilot certificate must be endorsed by your CFI for solo flight in the make and model of airplane you are flying.

## 61.89 General Limitations

1. As a student pilot you may **not** act as a pilot in command of an aircraft:
   a. Carrying passengers.
   b. Carrying property for compensation or hire.
   c. In return for compensation or hire.
   d. In furtherance of a business.
   e. On an international flight.
   f. If visibility is below 3 SM during daylight hours or below 5 SM at night.
   g. Above an overcast, i.e., without visual reference to the surface.
   h. In violation of any CFI-imposed limitations in your logbook.
2. You may not act as a crewmember on an aircraft requiring more than one pilot unless you are receiving dual instruction on board the aircraft and no passengers are carried.

## 61.93 Cross-Country Flight Requirements (For Student and Recreational Pilots Seeking Private Pilot Certification)

1. You may not operate an aircraft in solo cross-country unless properly authorized by an instructor.
   a. The term cross-country flight, as used in this section, means a flight beyond a radius of 25 NM from the point of departure.
2. You may not make a solo landing (except in an emergency) other than at the airport from which you are authorized to depart.

a. Your CFI may, however, authorize you to practice solo takeoffs and landings at an airport within 25 NM of the base airport after
   1) (S)he determines that you are competent and proficient to make those takeoffs and landings.
   2) (S)he has flown with you prior to authorizing those takeoffs and landings.
   3) (S)he endorses your logbook with an authorization to make those takeoffs and landings.

3. You must receive training from your CFI in the following areas before being authorized to conduct solo cross-country flights:
   a. The use of aeronautical charts for VFR navigation using pilotage and dead reckoning with the aid of a magnetic compass.
   b. Aircraft cross-country performance, and procurement and analysis of aeronautical weather reports and forecasts, including
      1) Recognition of critical weather situations, and
      2) Estimating visibility while in flight.
   c. Cross-country emergency procedures including
      1) Lost procedures,
      2) Adverse weather conditions, and
      3) Simulated precautionary off-airport approaches and landing procedures.
   d. Traffic pattern procedures including
      1) Normal area arrival and departure,
      2) Collision avoidance, and
      3) Wake turbulence precautions.
   e. Recognition of operational problems caused by peculiar terrain features in your area.
   f. Proper operation of instruments and equipment installed in your airplane.
   g. Short- and soft-field takeoff, approach, and landing procedures, including crosswind takeoffs and landings.
   h. Takeoffs at best rate and best angle of climb.
   i. Control and maneuvering solely by reference to flight instruments.
      1) Straight-and-level flight, turns, descents, and climbs.
      2) Use of radio aids and radar directives.
   j. The use of radio VFR navigation and two-way communication.
   k. For solo night cross-country privileges: night takeoffs, landings, go-arounds, and VFR navigation.

4. Your student pilot certificate must be endorsed by your CFI attesting that you have received the above instruction and have demonstrated an acceptable level of competency and proficiency.

5. A CFI must also endorse your logbook for each solo cross-country flight after
   a. Reviewing your preflight planning and preparation,
   b. Certifying that you are prepared to make a safe flight under the known circumstances and any CFI-imposed limitations listed in the endorsement.

6. An endorsement can be made for repeated solo cross-country flight to an airport less than 50 NM after dual cross-country flight in both directions with landings and takeoffs at the airports to be used, with any given conditions set by your CFI.

**61.95 Operations in Class B Airspace and at Airports Located within Class B Airspace**

1. In order for you to solo in Class B airspace (formerly a TCA) or at a specific airport within Class B airspace, you must have:
   a. Received both ground and flight instruction on that Class B airspace area. The flight instruction must have been given in the specific Class B airspace area or at the specific airport in the Class B airspace area where you will be operating.
   b. A current 90-day logbook endorsement from the CFI who gave the training which says that you have received the required training and have been found competent to operate in the specific Class B airspace area or at the specific airport within the Class B airspace area.
   c. Solo student operations are not allowed at the primary airports of certain Class B airspace areas.

**61.96 Eligibility Requirements: Recreational Pilots**

1. To be eligible to be a recreational pilot you must:
   a. Be at least 17 yr. of age.
   b. Be able to read, speak, and understand the English language, or you will have limitations placed on the certificate as necessary for safety.
   c. Hold at least a valid third-class medical certificate issued under Part 67.
   d. Pass a written examination (covered by Gleim's *Private Pilot and Recreational Pilot Written Exam* book).
   e. Pass a practical test (both oral and flight) appropriate to the rating sought (e.g., Airplane Single-Engine Land).

**61.97 Aeronautical Knowledge**

1. As an applicant for a recreational pilot certificate you must have logged ground instruction from an authorized instructor, or
2. You must present evidence showing you have satisfactorily completed a course of instruction or home study in the following areas of aeronautical knowledge appropriate to the category and class of aircraft for which the rating is sought:
   a. The Federal Aviation Regulations applicable to recreational pilot privileges, limitations, and flight operations, the accident reporting requirements of the National Transportation Safety Board, and the use of the *Airman's Information Manual* and FAA advisory circulars.
   b. The use of aeronautical charts for VFR navigation using pilotage with the aid of a magnetic compass.
   c. The recognition of critical weather situations from the ground and in flight and the procurement and use of aeronautical weather reports and forecasts.
   d. The safe and efficient operation of aircraft including collision and wake turbulence avoidance.
   e. The effects of density altitude on takeoff and climb performance.
   f. Weight and balance computations.
   g. Principles of aerodynamics, powerplants, and aircraft systems.
   h. Stall awareness, spin entry, spins, and spin recovery techniques. (Actual spin training for recreational pilot applicants is not required.)

**61.98 Flight Proficiency**

1. As an applicant for a recreational pilot certificate you must have logged instruction from an authorized flight instructor in at least the following pilot operations for airplanes:
   a. Preflight operations, including weight and balance determination, line inspection, airplane servicing, powerplant operations, and aircraft systems.
   b. Airport and traffic pattern operations, collision and wake turbulence avoidance.
   c. Flight maneuvering by reference to ground objects.
   d. Pilotage with the aid of a magnetic compass.
   e. Flight at slow airspeeds with realistic distractions and the recognition of and recovery from stalls entered from straight flight and from turns.
   f. Emergency operations, including simulated aircraft and equipment malfunctions.
   g. Maximum performance takeoffs and landings.
   h. Normal and crosswind takeoffs and landings.

**61.99 Airplane Rating: Aeronautical Experience**

1. As an applicant for a recreational pilot certificate with an airplane rating you must have a total of 30 hr. of total flight time.
   a. 15 hr. of flight instruction given by an authorized flight instructor, including at least:
      1) 2 hr. outside of the vicinity of the airport at which instruction is given, including at least three landings at another airport that is located more than 25 NM from the airport of departure.
      2) 2 hr. in airplanes in preparation for the recreational pilot practical test within the 60-day period before the test.
   b. 15 hr. of solo flight time in airplanes.
2. If you are located on an island from which the required flight of 25 NM cannot be accomplished without flying over water more than 10 NM from the nearest shoreline, you are not required to make it.
   a. If airports are available without flying over water more than 10 NM from the nearest shoreline, you must complete a flight with your instructor between those two airports, which must include three landings at the other airport.
   b. A certificate issued under these conditions will contain the following endorsement:

      *Passenger carrying prohibited in flights more than 10 NM from (name of island).*
   c. This will be removed if you present satisfactory evidence of compliance with the flight requirement to an FAA inspector or designated pilot examiner.

**61.101 Recreational Pilot Privileges and Limitations**

1. As a recreational pilot you may only:
   a. Carry one passenger.
   b. Share the operating expenses of the flight with your passenger.
   c. Act as pilot in command when
      1) The flight is within 50 NM of an airport at which you received ground and flight instruction from an authorized flight instructor;
      2) The flight lands at an airport within 50 NM of the departure airport; and
      3) You carry your logbook which has been endorsed by your instructor attesting to the ground and flight instruction given.

2. As a recreational pilot you may NOT act as pilot in command of an airplane:
    a. That is certificated for more than four occupants, with more than one powerplant, with a powerplant of more than 180 HP, or with retractable landing gear.
    b. That is classified as a glider, airship, or balloon.
    c. That is carrying a passenger or property for compensation or hire.
    d. For compensation or hire.
    e. In furtherance of a business.
    f. Between sunset and sunrise.
    g. In airspace in which communications with air traffic control (ATC) are required.
    h. At an altitude of more than 10,000 ft. MSL or 2,000 ft. AGL, whichever is higher.
    i. When the flight or surface visibility is less than 3 SM.
    j. Without visual reference to the surface.
    k. On a flight outside the U.S.
    l. To demonstrate that aircraft in flight to a prospective buyer.
    m. That is used in a passenger-carrying airlift and sponsored by a charitable organization.
    n. That is towing any object.
3. As a recreational pilot you may not act as a required pilot flight crewmember on any aircraft for which more than one pilot is required by the type certificate of the aircraft or the regulations under which flight is conducted.
    a. The exception is when you are receiving flight instruction from an authorized flight instructor on board an airship and no person other than the required flight crewmember is on board.
4. A recreational pilot who has logged fewer than 400 flight hr. and who has not logged pilot-in-command time in an aircraft within the preceding 180 days may not act as pilot in command of an aircraft until the pilot has received flight instruction from an authorized flight instructor who certifies in the pilot's logbook that the pilot is competent to act as pilot in command of the aircraft.
5. The recreational pilot certificate states "Holder does not meet ICAO requirements."
6. For the purpose of obtaining additional certificates or ratings, while under the supervision of an authorized flight instructor, as a recreational pilot you may fly as sole occupant of an aircraft:
    a. For which you do not hold an appropriate category or class rating.
    b. Within airspace that requires communication with ATC.
    c. Between sunset and sunrise, provided flight or surface visibility is at least 5 SM.
    d. In excess of 50 NM from an airport at which flight instruction is received.
    e. For any of these situations you must carry your logbook that has been properly endorsed for each flight by an authorized flight instructor.

## Subpart D -- Private Pilots

### 61.102 Applicability

1. This subpart prescribes the requirements for the issuance of private pilot certificates and ratings, the conditions under which those certificates are necessary, and the general rules for holders of those certificates.

**61.103 Eligibility Requirements: General**

1. To be eligible to be a private pilot, you must:
   a. Be at least 17 yr. of age.
   b. Be able to read, speak, and understand the English language or you will have limitations placed on the certificate as necessary for safety.
   c. Hold at least a valid third-class medical certificate issued under Part 67.
   d. Pass a written examination (covered by Gleim's *Private Pilot FAA Written Exam* book).
   e. Pass a practical test appropriate to the rating sought (e.g., Airplane Single-Engine Land).

**61.105 Aeronautical Knowledge**

1. As an applicant for a private pilot certificate you must have logged ground instruction from an authorized instructor, or
2. Must present evidence showing you have satisfactorily completed a course of instruction for home study in the following areas of aeronautical knowledge for airplanes:
   a. The accident reporting requirements of the National Transportation Safety Board and the Federal Aviation Regulations applicable to private pilot privileges, limitations, and flight operations for airplanes or rotorcraft, as appropriate, the use of the *Airman's Information Manual*, and FAA advisory circulars.
   b. VFR navigation using pilotage, dead reckoning, and radio aids.
   c. The recognition of critical weather situations from the ground and in flight, the procurement and use of aeronautical weather reports and forecasts.
   d. The safe and efficient operation of airplanes, including high-density airport operations, collision avoidance precautions, and radio communication procedures.
   e. Basic aerodynamics and the principles of flight.
   f. Stall awareness, spin entry, spins, and spin recovery techniques for airplanes. (Actual spin training for private pilot applicants is not required.)

**61.107 Flight Proficiency**

1. As an applicant for a private pilot certificate you must have logged instruction from an authorized flight instructor in at least the following pilot operations:
   a. Preflight operations, including weight and balance determination, line inspection, and airplane servicing.
   b. Airport and traffic pattern operations, including operations at controlled airports, radio communications, and collision avoidance precautions.
   c. Flight maneuvering by reference to ground objects.
   d. Flight at slow airspeeds with realistic distractions, and the recognition of and recovery from stalls entered from straight flight and from turns.
   e. Normal and crosswind takeoffs and landings.
   f. Control and maneuvering of an airplane solely by reference to instruments, including descents and climbs using radio aids or radar directives.
   g. Cross-country flying, using pilotage, dead reckoning, and radio aids, including one 2-hour flight.
   h. Maximum performance takeoffs and landings.
   i. Night flying, including takeoffs, landings, and VFR navigation.
   j. Emergency operations, including simulated aircraft and equipment malfunctions.

## 61.109 Airplane Rating: Aeronautical Experience

1. As an applicant for a private pilot certificate with an airplane rating you must have a total of at least 40 hr. of total flight time.
   a. 20 hr. of flight instruction given by an authorized flight instructor, including at least:
      1) 3 hr. of cross-country.
      2) 3 hr. at night, including 10 takeoffs and landings if you are seeking night flying privileges.
      3) 3 hr. in airplanes in preparation for the private pilot flight test within 60 days prior to your practical test.
   b. 20 hr. of solo flight time, including at least:
      1) 10 hr. in an airplane.
      2) 10 hr. of cross-country flights.
         a) Each flight with a landing more than 50 NM from the point of departure.
         b) One flight of 300 NM, with landings at a minimum of three points, one of which is more than 100 NM from the original departure point.
      3) Three takeoffs and landings to a full stop at an airport with an operating control tower.

## 61.111 Cross-Country Flights: Pilots Based on Small Islands

1. If you are located on an island from which the required cross-country flights cannot be made without flying over water more than 10 NM from the nearest shoreline you need not comply with 61.109(b)(2).
   a. If airports are available without flying over water more than 10 NM from the nearest shoreline, you must complete two round trip solo flights between the two airports that are farthest apart.
      1) You must make a landing at each airport on both flights.
   b. A certificate issued under these conditions will contain the following endorsement:

      *Passenger carrying prohibited on flights more than 10 NM from (name of island).*
2. If you do not have 3 hr. of solo cross-country flight time, including a round trip flight to an airport at least 50 NM from the place of departure with at least two full stop landings at different points along the route, the certificate will be endorsed as follows:

   *Holder does not meet the cross-country flight requirements of ICAO.*

## 61.118 Private Pilot Privileges and Limitations: Pilot in Command

1. As a private pilot you may not act as pilot in command of an aircraft that is carrying passengers or property for compensation or hire, nor may you be paid to act as pilot in command, **except**
   a. You may act as pilot in command, for compensation or hire, of an aircraft in connection with any business or employment if the flight is only incidental to that business or employment and the aircraft does not carry passengers or property for compensation or hire.
   b. You may share the operating expenses of a flight with your passengers.
   c. If you are an aircraft salesperson and have at least 200 hr. of logged flight time you may demonstrate an aircraft to a prospective buyer.

d. You may act as pilot in command of an aircraft used in a passenger-carrying airlift sponsored by a charitable organization for which passengers make a donation if

1) The sponsor of the airlift notifies the appropriate FAA FSDO at least 7 days before the flight,

2) The flight is conducted from a public airport, or an airport approved by an FAA inspector,

3) You have logged at least 200 hr. of flight time,

4) No acrobatic or formation flights are conducted,

5) Each aircraft used is certificated in the standard category and complies with the 100-hr. inspection requirement, and

6) The flight is made under VFR during the day.

**61.120 Private Pilot Privileges and Limitations: Second in Command of Aircraft Requiring More Than One Required Pilot**

1. You may not be paid to act as second in command of an aircraft type certificated for more than one required pilot, except under 61.118.

   a. Nor may you act in such capacity if the aircraft is operated for compensation or hire.

Part 61 sections not outlined above and on pages 225 through 238:

**Subpart A -- General**

61.2 Certification of foreign pilots and flight instructors
61.7 Obsolete certificates and ratings
61.9 Exchange of obsolete certificates and ratings for current certificates and ratings
61.11 Expired pilot certificates and reissuance
61.14 Refusal to submit to a drug test
61.21 Duration of Category II pilot authorization
61.27 Voluntary surrender or exchange of certificate
61.33 Tests: General procedure
61.41 Flight instruction received from flight instructors not certificated by FAA
61.58 Pilot-in-command proficiency check: Operation of aircraft requiring more than one required pilot

**Subpart B -- Aircraft Ratings and Special Certificates**

61.61 Applicability
61.63 Additional aircraft ratings (other than airline transport pilot)
61.65 Instrument rating requirements
61.67 Category II pilot authorization requirements
61.69 Glider towing: Experience and instruction requirements
61.71 Graduates of certificated flying schools: Special rules
61.73 Military pilots or former military pilots: Special rules
61.75 Pilot certificate issued on basis of a foreign pilot license
61.77 Special purpose pilot certificate: Operation of U.S.-registered civil airplanes leased by a person not a U.S. citizen

**Subpart C -- Student and Recreational Pilots**

61.91 Aircraft limitations: Pilot in command
61.100 Rotorcraft rating: Aeronautical experience

Part 61 sections not outlined on pages 225 through 239:

**Subpart D -- Private Pilots**

61.113 Rotorcraft rating: Aeronautical experience
61.115 Glider rating: Aeronautical experience
61.117 Lighter-than-air rating: Aeronautical experience
61.119 Free balloon rating: Limitations

**Subpart E -- Commercial Pilots**

61.121 Applicability
61.123 Eligibility requirements: General
61.125 Aeronautical knowledge
61.127 Flight proficiency
61.129 Airplane rating: Aeronautical experience
61.131 Rotorcraft ratings: Aeronautical experience
61.133 Glider rating: Aeronautical experience
61.135 Airship rating: Aeronautical experience
61.137 Free balloon rating: Aeronautical experience
61.139 Commercial pilot privileges and limitations: General
61.141 Airship and free balloon ratings: Limitations

**Subpart F -- Airline Transport Pilots**

61.151 Eligibility requirements: General
61.153 Airplane rating: Aeronautical knowledge
61.155 Airplane rating: Aeronautical experience
61.157 Airplane rating: Aeronautical skill
61.159 Rotorcraft rating: Aeronautical knowledge
61.161 Rotorcraft rating: Aeronautical experience
61.163 Rotorcraft rating: Aeronautical skill
61.165 Additional category ratings
61.167 Tests
61.169 Instruction in air transportation service
61.171 General privileges and limitations

**Subpart G -- Flight Instructors**

61.181 Applicability
61.183 Eligibility requirements: General
61.185 Aeronautical knowledge
61.187 Flight proficiency
61.189 Flight instructor records
61.191 Additional flight instructor ratings
61.193 Flight instructor authorizations
61.195 Flight instructor limitations
61.197 Renewal of flight instructor certificates
61.199 Expired flight instructor certificates and ratings
61.201 Conversion to new system of instructor ratings

## 8.4 Part 67 -- MEDICAL STANDARDS AND CERTIFICATION

The following summary of selected paragraphs from Part 67 is presented for your information. Page 242 contains the section titles of Part 67 that have not been outlined.

### 67.1 Applicability

1. This subpart prescribes the medical standards for issuing medical certificates for airmen.

## 67.17 Third-Class Medical Certificate

1. To be eligible for a third-class medical certificate, you must meet the following requirements:
   a. Eyes
      1) Distant Vision: 20/50 or better in each eye separately or corrected to 20/30 or better in each eye with corrective lenses (glasses or contacts)
      2) No serious pathology of the eye
      3) Ability to distinguish aviation signal red, aviation signal green, and white
   b. Ear, Nose, Throat, and Equilibrium
      1) Ability to hear the whispered voice at 3 ft.
      2) No acute or chronic disease of the internal ear
      3) No disease or malformation of the nose or throat that might interfere with, or be aggravated by, flying
      4) No disturbance in equilibrium
   c. Mental and Neurologic
      1) Mental -- No established medical history or clinical diagnosis of any of the following:
         a) A personality disorder
         b) A psychosis
         c) Alcoholism, unless there is established clinical evidence of recovery, including sustained total abstinence from alcohol of at least 2 yr.
         d) Drug dependence
      2) Neurologic -- No established medical history or clinical diagnosis of the following:
         a) Epilepsy
         b) A disturbance of consciousness without satisfactory medical explanation of the cause
   d. Cardiovascular
      1) No established medical history or clinical diagnosis of:
         a) Myocardial infarction
         b) Angina pectoris
         c) Coronary heart disease that has required treatment or, if untreated, that has been symptomatic or clinically significant
   e. General medical condition
      1) No established medical history or clinical diagnosis of diabetes mellitus that requires insulin or any other hypoglycemic drug for control
      2) No other organic, functional, or structural disease, defect, or limitation that the Federal Air Surgeon finds would cause you to be unable to perform your pilot duties safely
   f. If you do not meet the conditions for a medical certificate you may apply for a discretionary issuance of a certificate under 67.19.

**67.19 Special Issuance of Medical Certificates**

1. The Federal Air Surgeon may issue a medical certificate to you (if you do not meet the standards) if you show that you can perform the duties authorized by the certificate without endangering air commerce during that period (e.g., two years for a third-class medical certificate).
   a. The Federal Air Surgeon may authorize a special medical flight test, practical test, or medical evaluation for this purpose.
2. In issuing a medical certificate under this section, the Federal Air Surgeon may do any or all of the following:
   a. Limit the duration of the certificate.
   b. Condition the continued effect of the certificate on the result of subsequent medical tests, examinations, or evaluations.
   c. Impose any operational limitation on the certificate needed for safety.
   d. Condition the continued effect of a third-class medical certificate on compliance with a statement of functional limitations issued to you in coordination with the Director, Flight Standards Service.

**67.23 Medical Examinations: Who May Give**

1. Any aviation medical examiner may give the examination for the third-class certificate.
2. You may obtain a list of aviation medical examiners in your area from your local FSDO.

Part 67 sections not outlined above and on pages 240 and 241:

**Subpart A -- General**

67.3 Access to the National Driver Register
67.11 Issue
67.12 Certification of foreign airmen
67.13 First-class medical certificate
67.15 Second-class medical certificate
67.20 Applications, certificates, logbooks, reports, and records: Falsification, reproduction or alteration.

**Subpart B -- Certification Procedures**

67.21 Applicability
67.25 Delegation of authority
67.27 Denial of medical certificate
67.29 Medical certificates by senior flight surgeons of armed forces
67.31 Medical records

## 8.5 Part 91 -- GENERAL OPERATING AND FLIGHT RULES

### Subpart A -- General

**91.1 Applicability**

1. This part prescribes rules governing the operation of most aircraft within the U.S., including the waters within 3 NM of the U.S. coast.

**91.3 Responsibility and Authority of the Pilot in Command**

1. As the pilot in command of an aircraft you are directly responsible for, and are the final authority as to, the operation of that aircraft.
2. Thus, in emergencies, you may deviate from the FARs to the extent needed to maintain the safety of the airplane and passengers.
3. If you do deviate from the FARs in such an emergency, you may be required to file a written report with the FAA.

**91.7 Civil Aircraft Airworthiness**

1. You may not operate an aircraft that is not in an airworthy condition.
2. You, as the pilot in command, are responsible for determining whether the aircraft is fit for safe flight.

**91.9 Civil Aircraft Flight Manual, Marking, and Placard Requirements**

1. You may not operate an aircraft that has an approved flight manual unless that manual is aboard the aircraft.
2. You may not operate contrary to any limitations specified in that manual.

**91.11 Prohibition against Interference with Crewmembers**

1. No person may intimidate, assault, threaten, or interfere with a crewmember while (s)he is performing his/her duties aboard an aircraft.

**91.13 Careless or Reckless Operation**

1. You may not operate an aircraft in a careless or reckless manner so as to endanger the life or property of another.

**91.15 Dropping Objects**

1. Dropping objects from an airplane is not prohibited provided you take reasonable precautions to avoid injury or damage to persons or property.

**91.17 Alcohol or Drugs**

1. You may not act, or attempt to act, as a crewmember of a civil aircraft:
   a. While under the influence of drugs or alcohol.
   b. Within 8 hr. after the consumption of any alcoholic beverage.
   c. While having .04% by weight or more alcohol in your blood.
   d. While using any drug that affects your faculties in any way contrary to safety.
2. Except in an emergency, no person who appears to be under the influence of drugs or alcohol (except those under medical care) may be carried aboard an aircraft.

**91.19 Carriage of Narcotic Drugs, Marihuana, and Depressant or Stimulant Drugs or Substances**

1. You may not operate an aircraft within the United States with knowledge that any of these substances are aboard. This does not apply to flights that are authorized by the Federal government or a state government or agency.

**91.25 Aviation Safety Reporting Program: Prohibition against Use of Reports for Enforcement Purposes**

1. The FAA will not use reports submitted to the National Aeronautics and Space Administration (NASA) under the Aviation Safety Reporting Program (ASRP) in any enforcement action except those concerning criminal offenses and/or accidents.
   a. ASRP is a voluntary program designed to encourage a flow of information concerning deficiencies and discrepancies in the aviation system. It is explained in AC 00-46, *Aviation Safety Reporting Program.*
   b. The primary objective is to obtain information to evaluate and enhance the safety and efficiency of the present system. Operations covered include:
      1) Departure, en route, approach, and landing operations and procedures.
      2) ATC procedures.
      3) Pilot/controller communications.
      4) Aircraft movement on the airport.
      5) Near midair collisions.
   c. NASA acts as an independent third party to receive and analyze these reports.
      1) NASA ensures that no information which might reveal the identity of any party involved in an occurrence or incident reported under the ASRP is released to the FAA, except:
         a) Information concerning criminal offenses, and
         b) Information concerning accidents.
         c) Reports concerning criminal activities or accidents are not de-identified prior to their referral to the appropriate agency.
      2) Each report (see page 245) has a tear-off portion which contains your name and address. This portion is returned to you with a date indicating NASA's receipt of the report.
   d. The filing of a report concerning an incident or occurrence involving a violation of the FARs is considered by the FAA to be an indication of a constructive attitude. Such an attitude will help prevent future violations. Accordingly, although a finding of a violation may be made, neither a civil penalty nor certificate suspension will be imposed if:
      1) The violation was inadvertent and not deliberate.
      2) The violation did not involve a criminal offense or action which shows a lack of qualification or competency.
      3) The person has not been found in any prior FAA enforcement action to have committed a violation of the FARs for a period of 5 years prior to the date of the occurrence.
      4) The person proves (by the returned identification portion) that, within 10 days after the violation, (s)he completed and delivered or mailed a written report of the incident to NASA under the ASRP.
2. If you believe you have violated an FAR and may be subject to an enforcement action, you can complete and mail a NASA ARC Form 277 (available from FSS and FSDO offices) within 10 days and avoid possible enforcement action.
   a. You should also use the form to report any deficiencies and discrepancies in our aviation system.
   b. NASA ARC Form 277 is reproduced on page 245.

Form Approved. OMB No. 04–R0206

**IDENTIFICATION STRIP:** *Please fill in all blanks. This section will be returned to you promptly; no record will be kept.*

TELEPHONE NUMBERS where we may reach you for further details of this occurrence:

AREA______NO.______________HOURS__________ TYPE OF OCCURRENCE/INCIDENT:__________

AREA______NO.______________HOURS__________

DATE OF OCCURRENCE__________

TIME *(local, 24-hr. clock)*__________

NAME______________________

ADDRESS______________________

*(This space reserved for NASA receipt stamp)*

*Please fill in appropriate spaces and circle or check all terms which apply to this occurrence or incident.*

1. Location: *(Geographic (including State), airport, runway, ATC facility and sector, navigation aid reference, etc.)*

2. Type of operation:

| SCHEDULED AIR CARRIER | | SUPPLEMENTAL CARRIER | | CORPORATE AVIATION | | MILITARY: ARMY | |
|---|---|---|---|---|---|---|---|
| DOMESTIC OPERATION | | CHARTER OPERATION | | PERSONAL BUSINESS | | NAVY/CG/MC | |
| INTERNATIONAL OPN. | | UTILITY OPERATION | | PLEASURE FLIGHT | | AIR FORCE | |
| AIR TAXI | | AGRICULTURAL OPN. | | TRAINING FLIGHT | | GOVERNMENT | |

3. Type of aircraft:

| FIXED WING, LOW | RETRACTABLE GEAR | RECIPROCATING | GROSS WT.: <2500 | 25,000-50,000 |
|---|---|---|---|---|
| HIGH WING | CONST. SPEED PROP | TURBOPROP | 2500-5000 | 50,000-100,000 |
| ROTARY WING | FLAPS | TURBOJET | 5000-12,500 | 100,000-300,000 |
| NO. OF SEATS: | NO. OF ENGINES: | WIDE BODY JET | 12,500-25,000 | OVER 300,000 |

4. Second aircraft TYPE: *(if two aircraft involved)*

FIRST FOLD HERE

5. Reported by: PILOT CREWMEMBER CONTROLLER OTHER *(specify)*
If pilot: TOTAL HOURS: HRS. LAST 90 DAYS:

6. Light conditions: DAWN DAYLIGHT DUSK NIGHT | 7. Altitude: FEET MSL.

8. Flight plan: IFR VFR DVFR SVFR NONE | 9. Flight conditions: VFR IFR

10. Flight phase: PREFLIGHT TAXI TAKEOFF CLIMB CRUISE DESCENT HOLDING TRAFFIC PATTERN APPROACH LANDING MISSED APPROACH

11. Airspace: POSITIVE CONTROL AREA (PCA) TERMINAL CONTROL AREA (TCA) ON AIRWAYS AIRPORT TRAFFIC AREA UNCONTROLLED AIRSPACE

12. Air Traffic Control: GROUND TOWER DEPARTURE CENTER APPROACH FSS NONE

13. Weather factors: RESTRICTED VISIBILITY TURBULENCE THUNDERSTORM AIRCRAFT ICING CROSSWIND PRECIPITATION NONE OTHER *(specify)*

14. *(Circle all which you believe apply to this occurrence)*
AIRPORT AIR TRAFFIC CONTROL AIR NAVIGATION FACILITY AIRCRAFT
FLIGHT CREW AERONAUTICAL PUBLICATIONS/CHARTS OTHER *(specify below)*

15. NARRATIVE DESCRIPTION: *(Please describe the occurrence as clearly and precisely as possible. Include information on: what happened . . . how was the problem discovered . . . what actions were taken . . . was evasive action required . . . what factors contributed to the situation . . . why do you believe the situation occurred . . . your suggestions as to how to prevent a recurrence.*
*USE BOTH SIDES OF THE FORM, AS REQUIRED.)*

Continue on other side.

NASA ARC Form 277 (March 1976)

## Subpart B -- Flight Rules

### 91.101 Applicability

1. This subpart prescribes flight rules governing the operation of aircraft within the U.S. and within 12 NM from the coast of the U.S.

### 91.103 Preflight Action

1. Prior to every flight, you are required to familiarize yourself with all available information concerning that flight and specifically to determine:
   a. Runway lengths at airports of intended use and your airplane's takeoff and landing requirements.
   b. On cross-country flights, weather, fuel requirements, alternate airports available, and any known traffic delays.

### 91.105 Flight Crewmembers at Stations

1. Required flight crewmembers' seatbelts must be fastened while the crewmembers are at their stations.
2. Required flight crewmembers' shoulder harnesses, if installed, must be fastened during takeoff and landing.

### 91.107 Use of Safety Belts

1. You may not take off without first briefing your passengers on how to use their seatbelts and shoulder harnesses, if installed.
   a. You must also notify them to fasten their seatbelts before each takeoff and landing.
2. During takeoff and landing, each passenger who is 2 years of age or older must be in a seat with the seatbelt and shoulder harness, if installed, fastened.

### 91.111 Operating near Other Aircraft

1. You may not operate your airplane so close to another aircraft as to create a collision hazard.
2. You may not operate your airplane in formation flight except by arrangement with the pilot in command of each aircraft in the formation.

### 91.113 Right-of-Way Rules: Except Water Operations

1. *Converging*. When aircraft of the same category are converging at approximately the same altitude (except head-on), the aircraft to the right has the right-of-way.
   a. Balloons, gliders, and airships have the right-of-way over an airplane.
   b. Aircraft towing or refueling other aircraft have the right-of-way over all other engine-driven aircraft.
2. *Approaching head-on*. The pilot of each aircraft shall alter course to the right.
3. *Overtaking*. An aircraft that is being overtaken has the right-of-way.
   a. The overtaking aircraft shall alter course to the right.

4. *Landing*. Aircraft while on final approach to land or while landing have the right-of-way over other aircraft in flight or on the ground.
    a. When two or more aircraft are approaching the airport for landing, the lower aircraft has the right-of-way.
        1) You may not take advantage of this rule to cut in front of another aircraft which is on final approach or to overtake that aircraft.

**91.117 Aircraft Speed**

1. You may not operate an airplane at an indicated airspeed greater than 250 kt. if you are under 10,000 ft. MSL or operating within Class B airspace.
2. You may not operate an aircraft at or below 2,500 ft. above the surface within 4 NM of the primary airport of a Class B, Class C, or Class D airspace area at an indicated airspeed of more than 200 kt.
3. You may not operate under Class B airspace or in a VFR corridor through such a Class B airspace area at an indicated airspeed greater than 200 kt.
4. If your minimum safe speed in your airplane is faster than the speed normally allowed, you may operate at that minimum safe speed.

**91.119 Minimum Safe Altitudes: General**

1. Except for takeoff and landing, the following altitudes are required:
    a. You must have sufficient altitude for an emergency landing without undue hazard to persons or property on the surface if your engine fails.
    b. Over congested areas of a city, town, or settlement, or over an open-air assembly of persons, you must have 1,000 ft. of clearance over the highest obstacle within 2,000-ft. radius of your airplane.
    c. Over other than congested areas, an altitude of 500 ft. above the surface.
    d. Over open water or sparsely populated areas, you must remain at least 500 ft. from any person, vessel, vehicle, or structure.

**91.121 Altimeter Settings**

1. At all times you must maintain an altitude by reference to an altimeter that has been set to
    a. The current reported altimeter setting of a station along your route and within 100 NM of your aircraft,
    b. An appropriate available station, or
    c. The elevation of your departure airport or an appropriate altimeter setting available before departure.

**91.123 Compliance with ATC Clearances and Instructions**

1. Once you have been given ATC instructions or a clearance, you may not deviate from it unless you obtain an amended clearance or instructions, except in an emergency.
    a. If you deviate from a clearance in an emergency, you must notify ATC as soon as possible.
    b. If you are given priority by ATC in an emergency, you must submit a detailed report of the emergency within 48 hr. to the manager of that ATC facility, if requested.
        1) This may be requested even if you do not deviate from any rule of Part 91.
2. If you are uncertain about the meaning of an ATC clearance, you should immediately ask for clarification from ATC.

## 91.125 ATC Light Signals

1. ATC light signals have the meaning shown in the following table:

| Light Signal | On the Ground | In the Air |
|---|---|---|
| Steady Green | Cleared for takeoff | Cleared to land |
| Flashing Green | Cleared to taxi | Return for landing *(to be followed by steady green at proper time)* |
| Steady Red | Stop | Give way to other aircraft and continue circling |
| Flashing Red | Taxi clear of landing area (runway) in use | Airport unsafe -- Do not land |
| Flashing White | Return to starting point on airport | Not applicable |
| Alternating Red and Green | General warning signal -- Exercise extreme caution | General warning signal -- Exercise extreme caution |

## 91.126 Operating on or in the Vicinity of an Airport in Class G Airspace

1. When operating an aircraft on or in the vicinity of an airport in Class G (uncontrolled) airspace, you must make all turns in the traffic to the left, unless the airport displays light signals or markings indicating right turns.

## 91.127 Operating on or in the Vicinity of an Airport in Class E Airspace

1. When operating on or in the vicinity of an airport in a Class E airspace area, you should make all turns in the traffic pattern to the left unless the airport displays light signals or markings indicating right turns.
   a. When departing, you must comply with the established traffic pattern for that airport.

## 91.129 Operations in Class D Airspace

1. Communications with ATC in Class D Airspace
   a. You must establish two-way radio communication with the ATC facility providing air traffic services prior to entering and while operating within the Class D airspace area.
   b. When departing from the primary airport or a satellite airport with an operating control tower, you must establish and maintain two-way radio communication with the control tower.
      1) The primary airport is the airport for which the Class D airspace area is designated.
      2) A satellite airport is any other airport within the Class D airspace area.
   c. When departing from a satellite airport without an operating control tower, you must establish and maintain two-way radio communication with the ATC facility providing air traffic services to the Class D airspace area as soon as practicable after departing.
   d. If your radio fails in flight, you may operate your airplane and land if weather conditions are at or above basic VFR weather minimums, visual contact with the tower is maintained, and a clearance to land is received (e.g., light signal).

2. When you are approaching to land on a runway served by a visual approach slope indicator, you must remain at or above the glide slope until a lower altitude is necessary for a safe landing.
   a. This does not prohibit you from making normal bracketing maneuvers above or below the glide slope for the purpose of remaining on the glide slope.
3. When approaching to land you should make left turns in the traffic pattern unless directed otherwise by the tower.
4. When departing you must comply with any departure procedures established for that airport by the FAA.
5. You may not, at any airport with an operating control tower, operate your airplane on a runway or taxiway, or take off or land, unless an appropriate clearance is received from ATC.

**91.130 Operations in Class C Airspace**

1. You must establish two-way radio communication with the appropriate ATC facility before entering Class C airspace (formerly ARSA), and maintain communication while you are within the Class C airspace area.
2. If you depart from the primary airport (the airport for which the Class C airspace area is designated) or satellite airport (any other airport within the Class C airspace area) with an operating control tower, two-way radio communication must be established and maintained with the tower and as instructed by ATC while in the Class C airspace area.
   a. From a satellite airport without an operating control tower, you must establish two-way radio communication with ATC as soon as practicable after departing.
3. Unless otherwise authorized by the ATC facility having jurisdiction over the Class C airspace area, you must have a transponder with altitude encoding while operating in the Class C airspace area, and the airspace above the ceiling and within the lateral boundaries of the Class C airspace area.

**91.131 Operations in Class B Airspace**

1. You must have an ATC clearance to operate within a Class B airspace area (formerly TCA).
2. If it is necessary to conduct training operations within a Class B airspace area, procedures established for these flights within the Class B airspace area must be followed.
3. In order to land at an airport within a Class B airspace area or even operate within the Class B airspace area, you must:
   a. Be at least a private pilot; or
   b. Be a student pilot who has been instructed and authorized to operate in that specific Class B airspace area by a flight instructor (a specific CFI logbook signoff is required).
4. However, there are certain Class B airspace area primary airports that require the pilot to hold at least a private pilot certificate to land or take off. These are the busiest airports such as Atlanta Hartsfield and Chicago O'Hare.
5. The equipment aboard your aircraft must include operative two-way radio communications, and transponder with altitude encoding (Mode C).

**91.133 Restricted and Prohibited Areas**

1. You may not operate your airplane within a restricted area contrary to the restrictions imposed, or within a prohibited area, unless you have the permission of the using or controlling agency, as appropriate.

**91.137 Temporary Flight Restrictions**

1. The FAA may issue a Notice to Airmen (NOTAM) to establish temporary flight restrictions
   a. To protect persons and property from a hazard associated with an incident on the surface.
   b. To provide a safe environment for the operation of disaster relief aircraft.
   c. In airspace above events generating a high degree of public interest.
2. When a NOTAM is issued under 1.a., you may not operate your airplane in the area unless it is directed by an official in charge of on-scene emergency activities.
3. When a NOTAM is issued under 1.b., you may not operate your airplane in that area unless one of the following conditions is met:
   a. Your airplane is involved in relief activity and directed by an official in charge on the scene.
   b. Your airplane is carrying law enforcement officials.
   c. The operation is conducted directly to or from an airport in the area or is necessitated because VFR flight is impracticable; notice is given to the proper authority for receiving disaster relief advisories; relief activities are not hampered; and the flight is not solely for observation of the disaster.
   d. Your airplane is carrying properly accredited news representatives; a proper flight plan is filed; and the flight is above the altitude used by relief aircraft.
4. When a NOTAM is issued under 1.c., you may not operate your airplane in the area unless one of the following conditions is met:
   a. See 3.c., except for the notice requirement.
   b. Your airplane is carrying incident or event personnel or law enforcement officials.
   c. See relevant portions of 3.d.
5. Flight plans filed and notice given must include the following:
   a. Aircraft identification, type, and color
   b. Radio frequencies to be used
   c. Times of entry and exit from the area
   d. Name of news organization and purpose of flight
   e. Any other information requested by ATC

**91.139 Emergency Air Traffic Rules**

1. When the Administrator determines that an emergency condition exists, or will exist, relating to the FAA's ability to operate the ATC system and during which normal flight operations conducted under Part 91 cannot be done at the required level of safety and efficiency, the following will be done.
   a. The Administrator immediately issues an air traffic rule or regulation in response to the emergency.
   b. The Administrator or Associate Administrator for Air Traffic may utilize the NOTAM system to provide notification of the issuance of the rule or regulation.
      1) The NOTAMs will have information concerning the rules and regulations that govern flight operations, navigational facilities, and the designation of that airspace in which the rules and regulations apply.
2. When a NOTAM has been issued under this section, you may not operate your airplane within the designated airspace, except in accordance with the authorizations, terms, and conditions prescribed in the regulation covered by the NOTAM.

**91.141 Flight Restrictions in the Proximity of the Presidential and Other Parties**

1. You may not operate your airplane over or in the vicinity of any area to be visited or travelled by the President, the Vice President, or other public figures contrary to the restrictions established by the FAA in a NOTAM.

**91.143 Flight Limitations in the Proximity of Space Flight Operations**

1. You may not operate your airplane within the areas designated by NOTAM for space flight operation except when authorized by ATC.

**91.151 Fuel Requirements for Flight in VFR Conditions**

1. You may not fly VFR during the day unless there is enough fuel to fly to the destination and then at least 30 min. beyond that.
2. You may not fly VFR at night unless there is enough fuel to fly to the destination and at least 45 min. beyond that.

**91.153 VFR Flight Plan; Information Required**

1. Unless authorized by ATC, when filing a VFR flight plan you must include the following information:
   a. Aircraft identification number and, if different, radio call sign
   b. Type aircraft
   c. Full name and address of pilot in command
   d. Point and proposed time of departure
   e. Proposed route, cruising altitude, and true airspeed
   f. Point of first intended landing and the estimated time en route
   g. Amount of fuel on board (in hours)
   h. Number of persons in the airplane
   i. Any other information you or ATC believes is necessary
2. If a flight plan has been activated, you should notify the appropriate authority (i.e., Flight Service Station) upon canceling or completing the flight.

**91.155 Basic VFR Weather Minimums**

1. Except as provided in this section and 91.157, you may not operate your airplane under VFR when the flight visibility is less, or at a distance from clouds that is less, than prescribed for the corresponding altitude in the following table:

Cloud Clearance and Visibility Required for VFR

<table>
<tr><th rowspan="2">Altitudes</th><th colspan="4">Classes of Airspace</th></tr>
<tr><th>B</th><th>C, D, and E<br>G (Night)</th><th colspan="2">G (Day)</th></tr>
<tr><td>Below 1,200 ft. AGL</td><td rowspan="2">Clear of clouds<br>3 SM visibility</td><td rowspan="2">500 ft. below<br>1,000 ft. above<br>2,000 ft. horizontal<br>3 SM visibility</td><td rowspan="2">1 SM<br>visibility</td><td>Clear of clouds</td></tr>
<tr><td>Above 1,200 ft. AGL<br>and<br>Below 10,000 ft. MSL</td><td>500 ft. below<br>1,000 ft. above<br>2,000 ft. horizontal</td></tr>
<tr><td>Above 1,200 ft. AGL<br>and<br>Above 10,000 ft. MSL</td><td colspan="4">1,000 ft. below<br>1,000 ft. above<br>1 SM horizontal<br>5 SM visibility</td></tr>
</table>

2. You may operate your airplane in Class G airspace below 1,200 ft. AGL when the visibility is less than 3 SM but not less than 1 SM at night if you are operating in an airport traffic pattern within ½ mi. of the runway.
3. Except as provided in 91.157, you may not operate your airplane under VFR within the lateral boundaries of the surface areas of Class B, Class C, Class D, or Class E airspace designated for an airport when the ceiling is less than 1,000 ft.
   a. You may not take off, land, or enter the traffic pattern of an airport unless ground visibility is at least 3 SM. If ground visibility is not reported, flight visibility must be at least 3 SM.

**91.157 Special VFR Weather Minimums**

1. These special minimums apply to VFR traffic operating within the lateral boundaries of the surface areas of Class B, Class C, Class D, or Class E airspace designated for an airport with a special ATC clearance.
2. You must be clear of clouds.
3. Flight visibility must be at least 1 SM.
4. To take off or land under VFR, ground visibility must be at least 1 SM. If that is not reported, flight visibility during landing or takeoff must be at least 1 SM.
5. Operation under special VFR at night is prohibited unless both the pilot and aircraft are IFR rated and equipped.

**91.159 VFR Cruising Altitude or Flight Level**

1. All VFR aircraft above 3,000 ft. AGL and below 18,000 ft. MSL in level cruising flight must maintain specified altitudes.
2. The altitude prescribed is based upon the magnetic course (not magnetic heading).
3. For magnetic courses of 0° to 179°, use odd thousand foot MSL altitudes plus 500 ft., e.g., 3,500, 5,500, or 7,500.
4. For magnetic courses of 180° to 359°, use even thousand foot MSL altitudes plus 500 ft., e.g., 4,500, 6,500, or 8,500.

**Subpart C -- Equipment, Instrument, and Certificate Requirements**

**91.203 Civil Aircraft: Certifications Required**

1. You may not operate a civil aircraft unless it has in it:
   a. An appropriate and current airworthiness certificate which is posted near the aircraft entrance for passengers and crew to see.
   b. A registration certificate issued to the aircraft owner.

**91.205 Powered Civil Aircraft with Standard Category U.S. Airworthiness Certificates: Instrument and Equipment Requirements**

1. You may not operate a powered civil aircraft with a standard category U.S. airworthiness certificate without the specified operable instruments and equipment.
2. Required Equipment: VFR - day
   a. Airspeed indicator
   b. Altimeter
   c. Magnetic direction indicator (compass)
   d. Tachometer for each engine

e. Oil pressure gauge for each engine using a pressure system

f. Temperature gauge for each liquid-cooled engine

g. Oil temperature gauge for each air-cooled engine

h. Manifold pressure gauge for each altitude engine

i. Fuel gauge indicating the quantity of fuel in each tank

j. Landing gear position indicator if the aircraft has a retractable landing gear

k. Approved flotation gear for each occupant and one pyrotechnic signaling device if the aircraft is operated for hire over water beyond power-off gliding distance from shore

l. Safety belt with approved metal to metal latching device for each occupant

m. For small civil airplanes manufactured after July 18, 1978, an approved shoulder harness for each front seat

n. An emergency locator transmitter (ELT), if required by FAR 91.207

3. Required Equipment: VFR - night

a. All equipment listed in 2. on page 252

b. Approved position (navigation) lights

c. Approved aviation red or white anticollision light system on all U.S.-registered civil aircraft

d. If the aircraft is operated for hire, one electric landing light

e. An adequate source of electricity for all electrical and radio equipment

f. A set of spare fuses or three spare fuses for each kind required which are accessible to the pilot in flight

**91.207 Emergency Locator Transmitters**

1. ELT batteries must be replaced after 1 cumulative hr. of use or after 50% of their useful life expires.
2. Airplanes may be operated for training purposes within 50 NM of the originating airport without an ELT.
3. The expiration date for batteries used in an ELT must be legibly marked on the outside of the transmitter.

**91.209 Aircraft Lights**

1. During the period from sunset to sunrise, you may not operate an aircraft unless it has lighted position (navigation) lights.
2. You may not park or move an aircraft in, or in dangerous proximity to, a night flight operations area of an airport unless the aircraft:

   a. Is clearly illuminated,
   b. Has lighted position lights, or
   c. Is in an area which is marked by obstruction lights.

3. During the period of sunset to sunrise you must use anticollision lights (i.e., rotating beacon and/or strobe lights) if your airplane is so equipped.

   a. The anticollision light may be turned off if you (the pilot in command) determine that it would be in the interest of safety, given the operating conditions, to turn it off.

**91.211 Supplemental Oxygen**

1. At cabin pressure altitudes above 12,500 ft. MSL up to and including 14,000 ft. MSL, the required minimum crew must use oxygen after 30 min. at those altitudes.
2. At cabin pressure altitudes above 14,000 ft. MSL, the required minimum flight crew must continuously use oxygen.
3. At cabin pressure altitudes above 15,000 ft. MSL, each passenger must be provided supplemental oxygen.

**91.213 Inoperative Instruments and Equipment**

1. You may not take off in an aircraft with inoperable instruments or equipment installed unless:
   a. An approved minimum equipment list (MEL) exists for that specific aircraft. Note that the MEL is a list of equipment that does NOT have to be operable.
      1) This includes the different flight limitations placed upon the aircraft when that equipment is inoperative, e.g., you cannot fly at night if the landing light is out.
   b. The aircraft has within it a letter of authorization, issued by the FAA FSDO in the area where the operator is based, authorizing operation of the aircraft under the minimum equipment list. The MEL and authorization letter constitute an STC (supplemental type certificate) for the aircraft.
   c. The approved MEL must:
      1) Be prepared in accordance with specified limitations.
      2) Provide how the aircraft is to be operated with the instruments and equipment in an inoperable condition.
   d. The aircraft records available to you must include an entry describing the inoperable instruments and equipment.
   e. The aircraft must be operated under all applicable conditions and limitations contained in the MEL.
2. The following instruments and equipment may NOT be included in an MEL:
   a. Instruments and equipment that are specifically or otherwise required by the airworthiness requirements under which the aircraft is type-certificated and which are essential to the safe operation of the aircraft.
   b. Instruments and equipment required by an Airworthiness Directive.
   c. Instruments and equipment required for operations by the FARs.
3. Except as described above, you may take off in a light, piston-driven airplane with inoperative equipment and NO MEL under any of the following conditions:
   a. An FAA Master MEL (MMEL) has not been developed by the FAA and the inoperative equipment is not required by the aircraft manufacturer's equipment list, any other FARs, ADs, etc.
   b. If an FAA MMEL exists, and the inoperative equipment is not required by the MMEL, the aircraft manufacturer's equipment list, any other FARs, ADs, etc.
   c. The inoperative equipment is removed, or deactivated and placarded "inoperative."
   d. You or an appropriate maintenance person determines that the inoperative equipment does not constitute a hazard.
   e. Then the aircraft is deemed to be in a "properly altered condition" by the FAA.

4. Special flight permits (from the FAA) are possible under FAR 21 when the requirements previously noted cannot be met.
5. Author's note: 91.213 applies the MEL concept to all aircraft but provides an "out" for Part 91 operations if an FAA Master MEL has not been developed for a particular type of aircraft **or** the equipment is not required by the Master MEL, the aircraft manufacturer's equipment list, FARs, ADs, etc.

**91.215 ATC Transponder and Altitude Reporting Equipment and Use**

1. Mode C transponder equipment is required in all Class A, Class B, and Class C airspace areas.
2. All aircraft certified with an engine-driven electrical system must have Mode C transponder equipment
   a. Within 30 NM of the primary airport of a Class B airspace area from the surface up to 10,000 ft. MSL.
   b. Above 10,000 ft. MSL, excluding airspace at or below 2,500 ft. AGL.
3. All aircraft must have Mode C transponder equipment
   a. Within Class C airspace area and when above the ceiling and within the lateral limits of the Class C airspace area.
   b. Within 10 NM of certain specified airports (except below 1,200 ft. AGL outside of the airport traffic area).
4. If the airplane you are flying is equipped with a Mode C transponder, you must have it on in all controlled airspace, not just the airspace specified above.

**91.217 Data Correspondence between Automatically Reported Pressure Altitude Data and the Pilot's Altitude Reference**

1. You may not operate your transponder on Mode C (automatic pressure altitude reporting equipment):
   a. When ATC directs you to turn off Mode C, or
   b. Unless, as installed, the equipment was tested and calibrated to transmit altitude data within 125 ft. of the altimeter used to maintain flight altitude for altitudes ranging from sea level to maximum operating altitude of the airplane, or
   c. Unless the altimeters and digitizers in that equipment meet certain specified standards.

## Subpart D -- Special Flight Operations

**91.303 Aerobatic Flight**

1. Aerobatic flight is not permitted
   a. Over any congested area of a city, town, or settlement.
   b. Over an open air assembly of persons.
   c. Within the lateral boundaries of the surface areas of Class B, Class C, Class D, or Class E airspace designated for an airport.
   d. Within 4 NM of the centerline of any Federal airway.
   e. Below an altitude of 1,500 ft. AGL.
   f. When flight visibility is less than 3 SM.
2. Aerobatic flight means an intentional maneuver involving an abrupt change in an aircraft's attitude, an abnormal attitude, or abnormal acceleration, not necessary for normal flight.

**91.305 Flight Test Areas**

1. Flight tests may only be conducted over open water or sparsely populated areas having light air traffic.

**91.307 Parachutes and Parachuting**

1. Emergency parachutes cannot be carried aboard an airplane unless they meet FAA specifications.
2. Except in emergencies, persons may not make parachute jumps from airplanes unless in accordance with FAR Part 105.
3. Unless each occupant of the aircraft is wearing an approved parachute, no pilot carrying another person may execute any intentional maneuver that exceeds
   a. A bank of 60° relative to the horizon, or
   b. A nose-up or nose-down attitude of 30° relative to the horizon.
4. Paragraph 3. does not apply to flight tests for pilot certifications or ratings, or to spins and other flight maneuvers required for any certificate or rating if given by a CFI.

**Subpart E -- Maintenance, Preventive Maintenance, and Alterations**

**91.401 Applicability**

1. This subpart gives the rules governing maintenance, preventive maintenance, and the alteration of U.S. registered aircraft.

**91.403 General**

1. The owner or operator of an aircraft is primarily responsible for maintaining the aircraft in an airworthy condition.
2. You may not perform work on aircraft in a manner contrary to this subpart.
3. You may not operate an aircraft contrary to any airworthiness limitations specified by the manufacturer. This includes following the required replacement time, inspection intervals, and related procedures.

**91.405 Maintenance Required**

1. Each owner or operator shall have the aircraft inspected as prescribed in 91.409, 91.411, and 91.413.
2. Between inspections, any discrepancies shall be dealt with in accordance with FAR Part 43.

**91.407 Operation after Maintenance, Preventive Maintenance, Rebuilding, or Alteration**

1. You may not operate an aircraft that has undergone any maintenance, preventive maintenance, rebuilding, or alteration unless:
   a. It has been approved for return to service by a person authorized by FAR 43.7.
   b. The logbook entry required by FARs 43.9 and 43.11 has been made.
2. You may not operate an aircraft that has significantly been altered or rebuilt, to the extent that it changes its flight characteristics, until it has been test-flown by an appropriately rated pilot with at least a Private Pilot certificate.

**91.409 Inspections**

1. Annual inspections are good through the last day of the 12th calendar month after the previous annual inspection.
   a. An annual inspection must be performed by a certified mechanic (A & P) who also has an inspection authorization (IA).

2. For commercial operations, an inspection is also required every 100 hr.
   a. The 100 hr. may not be exceeded by more than 10 hr. if necessary to reach a place at which an inspection can be performed.
   b. The next inspection, however, is due 200 hr. from the prior inspection; e.g., if the inspection is done at 105 hr., the next inspection is due in 95 hr.
   c. If you have an inspection done prior to 100 hr., you cannot add the time remaining to 100 hr. to the next inspection.

**91.413 ATC Transponder Tests and Inspections**

1. You may not use an ATC Transponder unless it has been tested within the last 24 calendar months and found to comply with the required standards.
2. This test must be done by a certified repair shop.

**91.415 Changes to Aircraft Inspection Programs**

1. Whenever the FAA determines that a change is required in the approved aircraft inspection program is necessary to maintain safety, the owner or operator shall, after notification, make the required changes.
2. The owner or operator may petition against this change within 30 days of receiving the notice of the change.

**91.417 Maintenance Records**

1. Each owner or operator shall keep the following records:
   a. Alteration or rebuilding records
   b. 100-hr. inspections
   c. Annual inspections
   d. Progressive and other required inspections
2. The records must be kept for each aircraft (airframe), engine, propeller, and appliance.
3. Each record shall include a description of the work performed, the date of completion, and the signature and certificate number of the person performing the work.

**91.419 Transfer of Maintenance Records**

1. Any owner or operator who sells as U.S. registered aircraft must, at the time of the sale, transfer to the new owner the following records:
   a. Records of maintenance, preventive maintenance, and alteration
   b. Records of all 100-hr., annual, progressive, and other required inspections

**91.421 Rebuilt Engine Maintenance Records**

1. The owner or operator may use a new maintenance record for an aircraft engine rebuilt by the manufacturer or a shop approved by the manufacturer.
2. Each shop that grants zero time to an engine shall enter in the new record:
   a. A signed statement of the date it was rebuilt
   b. Each change made as required by an Airworthiness Directive
   c. Each change made in compliance with a Manufacturer's Service Bulletin
3. A rebuilt engine is one that is completely disassembled, inspected, repaired, reassembled, tested, and approved to the same tolerances as new.

Part 91 sections not outlined on pages 242 through 257:

**Subpart A -- General**

91.5 Pilot in command of aircraft requiring more than one required pilot
91.21 Portable electronic devices
91.23 Truth-in-leasing clause requirement in leases and conditional sales contracts

**Subpart B -- Flight Rules**

General
91.109 Flight instruction; Simulated instrument flight and certain flight tests
91.115 Right-of-way rules: Water operations
91.135 Operations in Class A airspace

Instrument Flight Rules
91.167 Fuel requirements for flight in IFR conditions
91.169 IFR flight plan: Information required
91.171 VOR equipment check for IFR operations
91.173 ATC clearance and flight plan required
91.175 Takeoff and landing under IFR
91.177 Minimum altitudes for IFR operations
91.179 IFR cruising altitude or flight level
91.181 Course to be flown
91.183 IFR radio communications
91.185 IFR operations: Two-way radio communications failure
91.187 Operation under IFR in controlled airspace: Malfunction reports
91.189 Category II and III operations: General operating rules
91.191 Category II manual
91.193 Certificate of authorization for certain Category II operations

**Subpart C -- Equipment, Instrument, and Certificate Requirements**

91.219 Altitude alerting system or device: Turbojet-powered civil airplanes
91.221 Traffic alert and collision avoidance system equipment and use

**Subpart D -- Special Flight Operations**

91.309 Towing: Gliders
91.311 Towing: Other than under § 91.309
91.313 Restricted category civil aircraft: Operating limitations
91.315 Limited category civil aircraft: Operating limitations
91.317 Provisionally certificated civil aircraft: Operating limitations
91.319 Aircraft having experimental certificates: Operating limitations
91.321 Carriage of candidates in Federal elections
91.323 Increased maximum certificated weights for certain airplanes operated in Alaska

**Subpart E -- Maintenance, Preventive Maintenance, and Alterations**

91.411 Altimeter system and altitude reporting equipment tests and inspections

**Subpart F -- Large and Turbine-Powered Multiengine Airplanes**

91.501 Applicability
91.503 Flying equipment and operating information
91.505 Familiarity with operating limitations and emergency equipment
91.507 Equipment requirements: Over-the-top or night VFR operations
91.509 Survival equipment for overwater operations
91.511 Radio equipment for overwater operations
91.513 Emergency equipment
91.515 Flight altitude rules
91.517 Smoking and safety belt signs
91.519 Passenger briefing
91.521 Shoulder harness
91.523 Carry-on baggage

Part 91 sections not outlined on pages 242 through 257:

91.525 Carriage of cargo
91.527 Operating in icing conditions
91.529 Flight engineer requirements
91.531 Second-in-command requirements
91.533 Flight attendant requirements

**Subpart G -- Additional Equipment and Operating Requirements for Large and Transport Category Aircraft**

91.601 Applicability
91.603 Aural speed warning device
91.605 Transport category civil airplane weight limitations
91.607 Emergency exits for airplanes carrying passengers for hire
91.609 Flight recorders and cockpit voice recorders
91.611 Authorization for ferry flight with one engine inoperative
91.613 Materials for compartment interiors

**Subpart H -- Foreign Aircraft Operations and Operations of U.S.-Registered Civil Aircraft Outside of the United States**

91.701 Applicability
91.703 Operations of civil aircraft of U.S. registry outside of the United States
91.705 Operations within the North Atlantic Minimum Navigation Performance Specifications Airspace
91.707 Flights between Mexico or Canada and the United States
91.709 Operations to Cuba
91.711 Special rules for foreign civil aircraft
91.713 Operation of civil aircraft of Cuban registry
91.715 Special flight authorizations for foreign civil aircraft

**Subpart I -- Operating Noise Limits**

91.801 Applicability: Relation to Part 36
91.803 Part 125 operators: Designation of applicable regulations
91.805 Final compliance: Subsonic airplanes
91.807 Phased compliance under Parts 121, 125, and 135: Subsonic airplanes
91.809 Replacement airplanes
91.811 Service to small communities exemption: Two-engine, subsonic airplanes
91.813 Compliance plans and status: U.S. operations of subsonic airplanes
91.815 Agricultural and fire fighting airplanes: Noise operating limitations
91.817 Civil aircraft sonic boom
91.819 Civil supersonic airplanes that do not comply with Part 36
91.821 Civil supersonic airplanes: Noise limits
91.851 Definitions
91.853 Final compliance: Civil subsonic airplanes
91.855 Entry and nonaddition rule
91.857 Airplanes imported to points outside the contiguous United States
91.859 Modification to meet Stage 3 noise levels
91.861 Base level
91.863 Transfers of Stage 2 airplanes with base level
91.865 Phased compliance for operators with base level
91.867 Phased compliance for new entrants
91.869 Carry-forward compliance
91.871 Waivers from interim compliance requirements
91.873 Waivers from final compliance
91.875 Annual progress reports

**Subpart J -- Waivers**

91.903 Policy and procedures
91.905 List of rules subject to waivers

## 8.6 NTSB Part 830 -- NOTIFICATION AND REPORTING OF AIRCRAFT ACCIDENTS OR INCIDENTS AND OVERDUE AIRCRAFT, AND PRESERVATION OF AIRCRAFT WRECKAGE, MAIL, CARGO, AND RECORDS

### Subpart A -- General

### 830.1 Applicability

1. This part concerns reporting accidents, incidents, and certain other occurrences involving U.S. civil aircraft and preservation of the wreckage, mail, cargo, and records.

### 830.2 Definitions

1. Aircraft Accident -- an occurrence that takes place between the time any person boards an aircraft with the intention of flight until such time as all such persons have disembarked, and in which
   a. Any person suffers death or serious injury as a result of being in or upon the aircraft or by direct contact with the aircraft or anything attached thereto, or
   b. The aircraft receives substantial damage.
2. Fatal injury -- an injury resulting in death within 30 days of the accident.
3. Incident -- an occurrence other than an accident, associated with the operation of an aircraft, that affects or could affect the safety of operations.
4. Operator -- any person who causes or authorizes the operation of an aircraft, such as the owner, lessee, or bailee of an aircraft.
5. Serious injury -- any injury that
   a. Requires hospitalization for more than 48 hr., commencing within 7 days from the date the injury was received.
   b. Results in a fracture of any bone (except simple fractures of fingers, toes, or nose).
   c. Causes severe hemorrhages, nerve, muscle, or tendon damage.
   d. Involves injury to any internal organ.
   e. Involves second- or third-degree burns, or any burns affecting more than 5% of the body surface.
6. Substantial damage -- damage or failure that adversely affects the structural strength, performance, or flight characteristics of the aircraft, and that would normally require major repair or replacement of the affected component.
   a. Engine failure, damage limited to an engine, bent fairings or cowling, dented skin, small punctured holes in the skin or fabric, ground damage to rotor or propeller blades, damage to landing gear, wheels, tires, flaps, engine accessories, brakes, or wingtips are not considered "substantial damage."

**Subpart B -- Initial Notification of Aircraft Accidents, Incidents, and Overdue Aircraft**

**830.5 Immediate Notification**

1. The nearest NTSB office (see page 262 for a list of offices) must be notified immediately when an aircraft is overdue and believed to be involved in an accident, when an accident occurs, or when any of the following incidents occurs:
   a. Flight control system malfunction or failure
   b. Inability of any required flight crewmember to perform normal flight duties as a result of injury or illness
   c. Failure of structural components of a turbine engine excluding compressor and turbine blades and vanes
   d. Inflight fire
   e. Aircraft collision in flight
   f. Damage to property, other than the aircraft, estimated to exceed $25,000 for repair (including materials and labor) or fair market value in the event of total loss, whichever is less

**830.6 Information to Be Given in Notification**

1. The notification required in NTSB Part 830.5 above must contain the following information, if available:
   a. Type, nationality, and registration marks of the aircraft.
   b. Name of owner, and operator of the aircraft.
   c. Name of the pilot in command.
   d. Date and time of the accident.
   e. Last point of departure and point of intended landing of the aircraft.
   f. Position of the aircraft with reference to some easily defined geographical point.
   g. Number of persons aboard, number killed, and number seriously injured.
   h. Nature of the accident, the weather and the extent of damage to the aircraft, so far as is known.
   i. A description of any explosives, radioactive materials, or other dangerous articles carried.

**Subpart C -- Preservation of Aircraft Wreckage, Mail, Cargo, and Records**

**830.10 Preservation of Aircraft Wreckage, Mail, Cargo, and Records**

1. The operator of an aircraft is responsible for preserving any aircraft wreckage, cargo, mail, and all records until the Board takes custody.
2. The wreckage may only be disturbed to
   a. Remove persons injured or trapped.
   b. Protect the wreckage from further damage.
   c. Protect the public from injury.
3. When it is necessary to disturb or move aircraft wreckage or mail or cargo, sketches, descriptive notes, and photographs shall be made if possible of the accident locale, including original position and condition of the wreckage and any significant impact marks.
4. The operator of an aircraft involved in an accident or incident shall retain all records and reports, including all internal documents and memoranda dealing with the event, until authorized by the NTSB to the contrary.

## Subpart D -- Reporting of Aircraft Accidents, Incidents, and Overdue Aircraft

### 830.15 Reports and Statements to Be Filed

1. The operator of an aircraft shall file a report on NTSB Form 6120.1/2 within 10 days after an accident, or after 7 days if an overdue aircraft is still missing.
   a. The form can be obtained by contacting the nearest NTSB office (see listing below) or FSDO.
   b. NTSB Form 6120.1/2 is a very detailed 7-page form, of which only the first page has been reproduced on page 263.
   c. The report shall be filed at the nearest NTSB office.
2. A report on an incident for which notification is required by NTSB Part 830.5 must be filed only as requested by an authorized representative of the Board.
3. Each crewmember shall, as soon as physically able, attach a statement concerning the facts, conditions, and circumstances relating to the accident or incident.

### NTSB District Offices

ANCHORAGE
222 West 7th Avenue
Room 142, Box 11
Anchorage, AK 99513
(907) 271-5001

ARLINGTON
1200 Copeland Road, Suite 300
Arlington, TX 76011
(817) 885-6800

ATLANTA
1720 Peachtree Street, NW
Suite 321
Atlanta, GA 30309
(404) 347-7385

CHICAGO
31 West 775 N. Avenue
West Chicago, IL 60185
(708) 377-8177

DENVER
4760 Oakland Street
Suite 500
Denver, CO 80239
(303) 361-0611

LOS ANGELES
Federal Building
1515 W. 190th Street
Suite 555
Gardena, CA 90248
(213) 297-1041

MIAMI
8405 N.W. 53rd Street
Suite B-103
Miami, FL 33166
(305) 597-4610

NEW YORK
2001 Route 46
Suite 203
Parsippany, NJ 07054
(201) 334-6420

SEATTLE
19518 Pacific Highway South
Room 201
Seattle, WA 98188
(206) 764-3782

WASHINGTON (Home Office)
490 L'Enfant Plaza East, S.W.
Washington, D.C. 20594
(202) 382-6714

FORM APPROVED FOR USE THROUGH 11/30/90 BY OMB NO. 3147-0001.

# NATIONAL TRANSPORTATION SAFETY BOARD
## PILOT/OPERATOR AIRCRAFT ACCIDENT REPORT
**This Form To Be Used For Reporting Civil Aircraft Accidents Involving Commercial and General Aviation Aircraft**

**Location**

| **Nearest City/Place, State, Zip Code** | **Date of Accident** | **Local Time** (24 HOUR CLOCK) | **Zone** | **Elevation At Accident Site** ______ **Feet MSL** **Feet MSL** |
|---|---|---|---|---|

If The Accident Occurred On Approach, Takeoff Or Within 3 Miles Of An Airport, Complete The Following Information

**Proximity To Airport:**

1. ☐ On Airport
2. ☐ Within 1/4 Mile
3. ☐ Within 1/2 Mile
4. ☐ Within 3/4 Mile
5. ☐ Within 1 Mile
6. ☐ Within 2 Miles
7. ☐ Within 3 Miles
8. ☐ Beyond 3 Miles

| Airport Name | Airport Ident | Runway/Landing Surface And Conditions: 1. Direction: 2. Length: 3. Width: 4. Surface: 5. Condition: |
|---|---|---|

**Phase Of Operation:**

1. ☐ Standing
2. ☐ Taxi
3. ☐ Takeoff
4. ☐ Climb
5. ☐ Cruise
6. ☐ Descent
7. ☐ Approach
8. ☐ Landing
9. ☐ Hover/Maneuver
10. ☐ Altitude Of In-Flight Occurrence ______ Feet MSL

**Aircraft Information**

| **Registration Mark** | **Aircraft Manufacturer** | **Aircraft Type/Model** | **Serial Number** | **Cert Max Gross WT** |
|---|---|---|---|---|

**Type Of Aircraft**
1. ☐ Airplane
2. ☐ Helicopter
3. ☐ Glider
4. ☐ Balloon
5. ☐ Blimp/Dirigible
6. ☐ Ultralight
7. ☐ Gyroplane
8. Specify ______

**Type Of Airworthiness Certificate**
1. ☐ Normal
2. ☐ Utility
3. ☐ Acrobatic
4. ☐ Transport
5. ☐ Restricted
6. ☐ Limited
7. ☐ Experimental
8. Specify

**Amateur Built**
1. ☐ Yes
2. ☐ No

**Landing Gear**
1. ☐ Tricycle—Fixed
2. ☐ Tricycle—Retractable
3. ☐ Tailwheel—Fixed
4. ☐ Tailwheel—Retractable
5. ☐ Tailwheel—Retractable Mains
6. ☐ Amphibian
7. ☐ Skid
8. ☐ Ski/Wheel
9. Specify ______

**No. Of Seats**
Flight/Cabin
Crew ______
Pax ______

**Stall Warning System Installed**
1. ☐ Yes
2. ☐ No

**IFR Equipped**
1. ☐ Yes
2. ☐ No

**Engine Type**
1. ☐ Reciprocating—Carburetor
2. ☐ Reciprocating—Fuel Injected
3. ☐ Turbo Prop
4. ☐ Turbo Jet
5. ☐ Turbo Fan
6. ☐ Turbo Shaft

| **Engine Manufacturer** | **Engine Model/Series** | **Engine Rated Power** 1. ______ Horsepower 2. ______ Lbs. Thrust | **Type Of Fire Extinguishing System Used** 1. ☐ None 2. Specify ______ |
|---|---|---|---|

| **Engine(s)** | **Date of Mfg.** | **Mfg. Serial No.** | **Total Time** | **Time Since Inspection** | **Time Since Overhaul** |
|---|---|---|---|---|---|
| Engine No. 1 | | | Hours | Hours | Hours |
| Engine No. 2 | | | Hours | Hours | Hours |
| Engine No. 3 | | | Hours | Hours | Hours |
| Engine No. 4 | | | Hours | Hours | Hours |

**Type Of Maintenance Program**
1. ☐ Annual
2. ☐ Manufacturer's Inspection Program
3. ☐ Other Approved Inspection Program (AAIP)
4. ☐ Continuous Airworthiness
5. Specify ______

**Type Of Last Inspection**
1. ☐ Annual
2. ☐ 100 Hour
3. ☐ AAIP
4. ☐ Continuous Airworthiness

**Date Last Inspection Performed**
______ (M/D/Y)
Time Since Last Inspection
______ Hours
Airframe Total Time
______ Hours

| **Emergency Locator Transmitter (ELT)** | **ELT Manufacturer** | **Model/Series** | **Serial Number** | **Battery Date** (M/D/Y) |
|---|---|---|---|---|
| | **Switch** 1. ☐ On 2. ☐ Off 3. ☐ Armed | **Operated** 1. ☐ Yes 2. ☐ No | **Aided In Accident Location** 1. ☐ Yes 2. ☐ No | |

| **Registered Aircraft Owner** | **Address** ______ |
|---|---|
| **Operator Of Aircraft** 1. ☐ Same As Registered Owner 2. Name 3. DBS: | **Address** 1. ☐ Same As Registered Owner 2. ______ |

## 8.7 SUMMARY OF CURRENT FAR PART NUMBERS

The purpose of this section is to provide a brief description of the various "Parts" of the Code of Federal Regulations that are commonly called the Federal Aviation Regulations (FARs). This section is intended as a reference so when an FAR Part is mentioned you will have a general notion of how the FARs are organized. Currently, the FARs have 73 parts organized under the following 13 subchapters:

A -- Definitions
B -- Procedural Rules
C -- Aircraft
D -- Airmen
E -- Airspace
F -- Air Traffic and General Operating Rules
G -- Air Carriers, Air Travel Clubs, and Operators for Compensation or Hire: Certification and Operations
H -- Schools and Other Certificated Agencies
I -- Airports
J -- Navigational Facilities
K -- Administrative Regulations
N -- War Risk Insurance
O -- Aircraft Loan Guarantee Program

### A -- DEFINITIONS

1 - **Definitions and Abbreviations** -- several pages of definitions of terms and abbreviations used throughout the FARs.

### B -- PROCEDURAL RULES

11 - **General Rule-Making Procedures** -- applies to the issue, amendment, and repeal of rules and orders for airspace assignment and use, and other substantive rules.

13 - **Investigation and Enforcement Procedures** -- prescribes the procedures to be used by the FAA in enforcing the FARs.

14 - **Rules Implementing the Equal Access to Justice Act of 1980** -- prescribes the parties eligible for the award of attorney fees and other expenses who are parties to certain administrative proceedings before the FAA, and the proceedings that are covered under the Equal Access to Justice Act. It also explains how to apply for awards, and the procedures and standards used to make them.

15 - **Administrative Claims under Federal Tort Claims Act** -- applies to claims asserted under the Federal Tort Claims Act for money damages against the U.S. for injury, loss of property, or for personal injury or death caused by the negligent or wrongful act or omission of an FAA employee.

## C -- AIRCRAFT

21 - **Certification Procedures for Products and Parts** -- prescribes procedural requirements for the issue of type certificates and changes to those certificates, the issue of production certificates, the issue of airworthiness certificates, and the issue of export airworthiness approvals. It also prescribes the procedure requirements for the approval of certain materials, parts, processes, and appliances.

23 - **Airworthiness Standards: Normal, Utility, Acrobatic, and Commuter Category Airplanes** -- prescribes airworthiness standards for the issue of type certificates, and changes to those certificates, for airplanes in the normal, utility, acrobatic, and commuter categories.

25 - **Airworthiness Standards: Transport Category Airplanes** -- prescribes airworthiness standards for the issue of type certificates, and changes to those certificates, for transport category airplanes.

27 - **Airworthiness Standards: Normal Category Rotorcraft** -- prescribes airworthiness standards for the issue of type certificates, and changes to those certificates, for normal category rotorcraft with maximum weights of 6,000 lb. or less.

29 - **Airworthiness Standards: Transport Category Rotorcraft** -- prescribes airworthiness standards for the issue of type certificates, and changes to those certificates, for transport category rotorcraft.

31 - **Airworthiness Standards: Manned Free Balloons** -- prescribes airworthiness standards for the issue of type certificates, and changes to those certificates, for manned free balloons.

33 - **Airworthiness Standards: Aircraft Engines** -- prescribes airworthiness standards for the issue of type certificates, and changes to those certificates, for aircraft engines.

35 - **Airworthiness Standards: Propellers** -- prescribes airworthiness standards for the issue of type certificates, and changes to those certificates, for propellers.

36 - **Noise Standards: Aircraft Type and Airworthiness Certification** -- prescribes noise standards for the issue of the following certificates: type certificates, and changes to those certificates, and standard airworthiness certificates for all aircraft.

39 - **Airworthiness Directives** -- prescribes airworthiness directives that apply to aircraft, aircraft engines, propellers, or appliances (referred to as "products") when an unsafe condition exists in a product, and that condition is likely to exist or develop in other products of the same type design. It also prescribes inspections and the conditions and limitations, if any, under which those products may continue to be operated.

43 - **Maintenance, Preventive Maintenance, Rebuilding and Alteration** -- prescribes rules governing the maintenance, preventive maintenance, rebuilding, and alteration of any

a. Aircraft having a U.S. airworthiness certificate.
b. Airframe, aircraft engine, propeller, or appliance of such an aircraft.

45 - **Identification and Registration Marking** -- prescribes the requirements for

a. Identification of aircraft, and identification of aircraft engines and propellers that are manufactured under the terms of a type or production certificate.

b. Identification of certain replacement and modified parts produced for installation on type certificated products.

c. Nationality and registration marking of U.S. registered aircraft.

47 - **Aircraft Registration** -- prescribes the requirements for registering aircraft, Certificate of Aircraft Registrations, and Dealers' Aircraft Registration Certificates.

49 - **Recording of Aircraft Titles and Security Documents** -- applies to the recording of certain conveyances affecting title to or any interest in any registered aircraft, any specifically identified aircraft engine of 750 or more rated takeoff horsepower, or any specifically identified aircraft propeller able to absorb 750 or more rated takeoff shaft horsepower.

## D -- AIRMEN

61 - **Certification: Pilots and Flight Instructors** -- prescribes the requirements for issuing pilot and flight instructor certificates and ratings, the conditions under which those certificates and ratings are necessary, and the privileges and limitations of those certificates and ratings.

63 - **Certification: Flight Crewmembers Other Than Pilots** -- prescribes the requirements for issuing flight engineer and flight navigator certificates and the general operating rules for holders of those certificates.

65 - **Certification: Airmen Other Than Flight Crewmembers** -- prescribes the requirements for issuing the following certificates and associated ratings and the general operating rules for the holders of those certificates and ratings:

a. Air traffic control tower operators.
b. Aircraft dispatchers.
c. Mechanics.
d. Repairmen.
e. Parachute riggers.

67 - **Medical Standards and Certification** -- prescribes the medical standards for issuing medical certificates for airmen.

a. Sets forth the medical standards and certification procedures for first-class, second-class, and third-class medical certificates, and indicates who may administer these medical examinations.

## E -- AIRSPACE

71 - **Designation of Class A, Class B, Class C, Class D, and Class E Airspace Areas; Airways; Routes; and Reporting Points** -- defines Class A, Class B, Class C, Class D, and Class E airspace areas; airways; routes; and reporting points.

73 - **Special Use Airspace** -- prescribes the requirements for the use of restricted and prohibited areas.

77 - **Objects Affecting Navigable Airspace** --

a. Establishes standards for determining obstructions in navigable airspace.
b. Sets forth the requirements for notice to the FAA of certain proposed construction or alteration.
c. Provides for aeronautical studies of obstructions to air navigation, to determine their effect on the safe and efficient use of airspace.
d. Provides for public hearings on the hazardous effect of proposed construction or alteration on air navigation.
e. Provides for establishing antenna farm areas.

## F -- AIR TRAFFIC AND GENERAL OPERATING RULES

91 - **General Operating and Flight Rules** -- prescribes rules governing the operation of aircraft (other than moored balloons, kites, unmanned rockets, and unmanned free balloons) within the United States.

93 - **Special Air Traffic Rules and Airport Traffic Patterns** -- prescribes special airport traffic patterns and airport traffic areas. It also prescribes special air traffic rules for operating aircraft in those traffic patterns, traffic areas, and in the vicinity of those airports.

95 - **IFR Altitudes** -- prescribes altitudes governing the operation of aircraft under IFR on Federal airways, jet routes, area navigation low or high routes, or other direct routes for which an MEA (minimum en route altitude) is designated in this Part. In addition, it designates mountainous areas and changeover points.

97 - **Standard Instrument Approach Procedures** -- prescribes standard instrument approach procedures for instrument letdown to airports in the United States and the weather minimums that apply to takeoffs and landings under IFR at those airports.

99 - **Security Control of Air Traffic** -- prescribes rules for operating civil aircraft in a defense area, or into, within, or out of the United States through an Air Defense Identification Zone (ADIZ). ADIZs are areas of airspace over land or water in which the ready identification, location, and control of civil aircraft is required in the interest of national security.

101 - **Moored Balloons, Kites, Unmanned Rockets and Unmanned Free Balloons** -- prescribes the operation of moored balloons, kites, unmanned rockets, and unmanned free balloons.

103 - **Ultralight Vehicles** -- prescribes rules governing the operation of ultralight vehicles in the United States.

105 - **Parachute Jumping** -- prescribes rules governing parachute jumps made in the United States except parachute jumps necessary because of an in-flight emergency.

107 - **Airport Security** -- prescribes aviation security rules governing the operation of each airport regularly serving the scheduled passenger operations of a domestic and/or foreign air carrier required by the FARs to have a security program.

108 - **Airplane Operator Security** -- prescribes aviation security rules governing the operations of holders of FAA air carrier operating certificates engaging in scheduled or public charter passenger operations, including each person aboard the airplane or on the airport at which these operations are conducted. This does not apply to helicopter or all-cargo operations.

109 - **Indirect Air Carrier Security** -- prescribes aviation security rules governing each air carrier, including each air freight forwarder and each cooperative shippers' association, engaged indirectly in air transportation of property (i.e., any package cargo).

## G -- AIR CARRIERS, AIR TRAVEL CLUBS, AND OPERATORS FOR COMPENSATION OR HIRE: CERTIFICATION AND OPERATIONS

121 - **Certification and Operations: Domestic, Flag, and Supplemental Air Carriers and Commercial Operators of Large Aircraft** -- prescribes the rules governing the certification and operations of domestic, flag, and supplemental air carriers and commercial operators of large aircraft.

125 - **Certification and Operations: Airplanes Having a Seating Capacity of 20 or More Passengers or a Maximum Payload Capacity of 6,000 Pounds or More** -- prescribes rules governing the operations of U.S.-registered civil airplanes which have a seating configuration of 20 or more passengers, or a maximum payload capacity of 6,000 lb. or more when common carriage is not involved.

127 - **Certification and Operations of Scheduled Air Carriers with Helicopters** -- prescribes rules governing each air carrier holding a certificate of public convenience and necessity issued by the U.S. Department of Transportation when that air carrier engages in scheduled interstate air transportation using helicopters within the 48 contiguous states and the District of Columbia.

129 - **Operations: Foreign Air Carriers and Foreign Operators of U.S.-Registered Aircraft Engaged in Common Carriage** -- prescribes the rules governing the operation within the United States of each foreign air carrier holding a permit issued by the U.S. Department of Transportation.

a. It also applies to U.S.-registered aircraft operated in common carriage by a foreign person or foreign air carrier solely outside the U.S.

133 - **Rotorcraft External-Load Operations** -- prescribes airworthiness certification rules and operating and certification rules for civil rotorcraft conducting external-load operations.

135 - **Air Taxi Operators and Commercial Operators** -- prescribes the rules governing the carriage of persons or property for compensation or hire as a commercial operator (not an air carrier) in aircraft having a maximum seating capacity of less than 20 passengers or a maximum payload capacity of less than 6,000 lb., or common carriage operations solely between points entirely within any state of the U.S. in aircraft having a maximum seating capacity of 30 seats or less or a maximum payload capacity of 7,500 lb. or less.

137 - **Agricultural Aircraft Operations** -- prescribes rules governing agricultural aircraft operations within the United States and the issue of commercial and private agricultural aircraft operator certificates for those operations.

139 - **Certification and Operations: Land Airports Serving Certain Air Carriers** -- prescribes rules governing the certification and operation of land airports which serve any scheduled or unscheduled passenger operation of an air carrier that is conducted with an aircraft having a seating capacity of more than 30 passengers.

**H -- SCHOOLS AND OTHER CERTIFICATED AGENCIES**

141 - **Pilot Schools** -- prescribes the requirements for issuing pilot school certificates, provisional pilot school certificates, and associated ratings and the general operating rules for the holders of those certificates and ratings.

142 - **Training Centers** -- this is a **proposed** new part to the FARs. The proposed new regulations would contain certification and operating rules for training centers that would provide additional use of aircraft flight simulators and flight training devices for pilot training, testing, and training as required under Parts 61, 63, 121, 125, 127, 135, and 137.

143 - **Ground Instructors** -- prescribes the requirements for issuing ground instructor certificates and associated ratings, and the general operating rules for the holders of those certificates and ratings.

145 - **Repair Stations** -- prescribes the requirements for issuing repair station certificates and associated ratings to facilities for the maintenance and alteration of airframes, powerplants, propellers, or appliances. It also prescribes the general operating rules for the holders of those certificates and ratings.

147 - **Aviation Maintenance Technician Schools** -- prescribes the requirements for issuing aviation maintenance technician school certificates and associated ratings, and the general operating rules for the holders of those certificates and ratings.

149 - **Parachute Lofts** -- prescribes the requirements for issuing parachute loft certificates and associated ratings, and the general operating rules for the holders of those certificates and ratings.

**I -- AIRPORTS**

150 - **Airport Noise Compatibility Planning** -- prescribes the procedures, standards, and methodology governing the development, submission, and review of airport noise exposure maps and airport noise compatibility programs by operators of public use airports (including heliports), including the process for evaluating and approving or disapproving those programs.

151 - **Federal Aid to Airports** -- prescribes the policies and procedures for administering the Federal-aid Airport Program under the Federal Airport Act, as amended.

152 - **Airport Aid Program** -- prescribes the policies and procedures for administering the Airport Aid Program for airport development and planning grant projects under the Airport and Airway Development Act of 1970, as amended.

153 - **Acquisition of U.S. Land for Public Airports** -- applies to the acquisition by public agencies, under section 16 of the Federal Airport Act, of property interests in land owned or controlled by the United States, the use of which is necessary to carry out a project under the Federal-aid Airport Program or to operate a public airport.

154 - **Acquisition of U.S. Land for Public Airports under the Airport and Airway Development Act of 1970** -- applies to the acquiring by public agencies, under Section 23 of the Airport and Airway Development Act of 1970, of property interest in land owned or controlled by the U.S., the use of which is reasonably necessary to carry out a project for airport development under part II of that act or to operate a public airport, including lands reasonably necessary to meet future development of an airport in accordance with the national airport system plan.

155 - **Release of Airport Property from Surplus Property Disposal Restrictions** -- applies to releases from terms, conditions, etc., in any deed, surrender of leasehold, or other instrument of transfer or conveyance by which some right, title, or interest of the United States in real or personal property was conveyed to a non-Federal public agency to be used by that agency in developing, improving, operating, or maintaining a public airport or to provide a source of revenue from non-aviation business at a public airport.

156 - **State Block Grant Pilot Program** -- applies to grant applicants for the state block grant pilot program and to those states receiving block grants available under the Airport and Airway Improvement Act of 1982, as amended. This part prescribes the procedures by which a state may apply to participate and describes the administration, responsibilities, and enforcement of the program by the participating state.

157 - **Notice of Construction, Alteration, Activation, and Deactivation of Airports** -- applies to persons proposing to construct, alter, activate, or deactivate a civil or joint-use (civil/military) airport, and sets forth requirements for notice to the Administrator.

158 - **Passenger Facility Charges (PFCs)** -- applies to PFCs as may be approved by the FAA and imposed by a public agency that controls a commercial service airport. This part also describes the procedures for reducing funds apportioned under section 507(a) of the Airport and Airway Improvement Act of 1982 (as amended) to a large or medium hub airport that imposes a PFC.

159 - **National Capital Airports** -- prescribes the rules governing the use and occupancy of Washington National Airport and Dulles International Airport.

161 - **Notice and Approval of Airport Noise and Access Restrictions** -- implements the Airport Noise and Capacity Act of 1990 and applies to airports imposing restrictions on Stage 2 and Stage 3 aircraft (as defined in Part 36) operations and the FAA procedures of evaluating these restrictions imposed by airport operators.

169 - **Expenditures of Federal Funds for Nonmilitary Airports or Air Navigational Facilities Thereon** -- prescribes the requirements for issuing a written recommendation and certification that a proposed project is reasonably necessary for use in air commerce or in the interests of national defense.

## J -- NAVIGATIONAL FACILITIES

170 - **Establishment and Discontinuance Criteria for Air Traffic Control Services and Navigational Facilities** -- sets forth establishment and discontinuance criteria for navigation aids and Air Traffic Control Towers.

171 - **Non-Federal Navigation Facilities** -- sets forth minimum requirements for the approval and operation of non-Federal VOR, NDB, ILS, and other navigational facilities that are to be involved in the approval of instrument flight rules and air traffic control procedures related to those facilities.

## K -- ADMINISTRATIVE REGULATIONS

183 - **Representatives of the Administrator** -- describes the requirements for designating private persons to act as representatives of the Administrator (FAA) in examining, inspecting, and testing persons and aircraft for the purpose of issuing airman and aircraft certificates.

185 - **Testimony by Employees and Production of Records in Legal Proceedings and Service of Legal Process and Pleadings** -- names the FAA officials upon whom legal process or pleadings may be served in any legal proceeding concerning the FAA and who otherwise perform the functions in legal proceedings concerning the FAA with respect to testimony by FAA employees and production of FAA records in legal proceedings.

187 - **Fees** -- prescribes fees only for FAA services for which fees are not prescribed in other parts of the FARs.

189 - **Use of Federal Aviation Administration Communications System** -- describes the kinds of messages that may be transmitted by FAA communications stations and prescribes the charges therefor.

191 - **Withholding Security Information from Disclosure under the Air Transportation Security Act of 1974** -- governs the release of any record, and any information contained therein, in the possession of the FAA which has been obtained or developed in the conduct of research and development activities to develop, modify, test, and evaluate systems, procedures, facilities, and devices to protect persons and property aboard aircraft in air transportation against acts of criminal violence and aircraft privacy.

## N -- WAR RISK INSURANCE

198 - **Aviation Insurance** -- prescribes the eligibility, types of insurance, and amount of insurance coverage available for aircraft operating outside the U.S. and under the direction of the U.S. government that is necessary to carry out the foreign policy of the U.S.

## O -- AIRCRAFT LOAN GUARANTEE PROGRAM

199 - **Aircraft Loan Guarantee Program** -- applies to applications for aircraft loan guarantees and to requests for approval of deviations from the terms of guarantee and loan agreements.

# CHAPTER NINE
# NAVIGATION CHARTS AND AIRSPACE



## 9.1 VFR NAVIGATION CHARTS

A. The National Ocean Service (NOS) publishes and sells aeronautical charts of the United States and foreign areas. The type of charts most commonly used by pilots flying VFR include

1. Sectional Charts. The scale is 1:500,000 (1 in. = 6.86 NM).
   a. This chart is normally used for VFR navigation.
2. VFR Terminal Area Charts. The scale is 1:250,000 (1 in. = 3.43 NM).
   a. VFR Terminal Area Charts depict the airspace designated as Class B airspace (formerly a Terminal Control Area or TCA). The information found on these charts is similar to that found on sectional charts, but in greater detail. They exist for large metropolitan areas such as Atlanta and New York.
   b. Most of the sectional and VFR Terminal Area charts are revised semiannually.
3. World Aeronautical Charts. The scale is 1:1,000,000 (1 in. = 13.7 NM). These are very similar to sectional charts except they cover larger areas so they have a smaller scale.
   a. These charts are generally revised annually.

B. The Sectional and VFR Terminal Area charts are designed for visual navigation by slow and medium speed aircraft.

1. The topographical information featured on these charts portrays surface elevation levels and a great number of visual checkpoints used for VFR flight.
   a. Checkpoints include populated places, drainage, roads, railroads, and other distinctive landmarks.
2. The aeronautical information on sectional charts includes visual and radio aids to navigation, airports, controlled airspace, restricted areas, obstructions, and related data.

C. Each rectangle on the U.S. map (shown below) is an area covered by one sectional chart. Most, but not all, VFR Terminal Area Charts are indicated by a black dot.

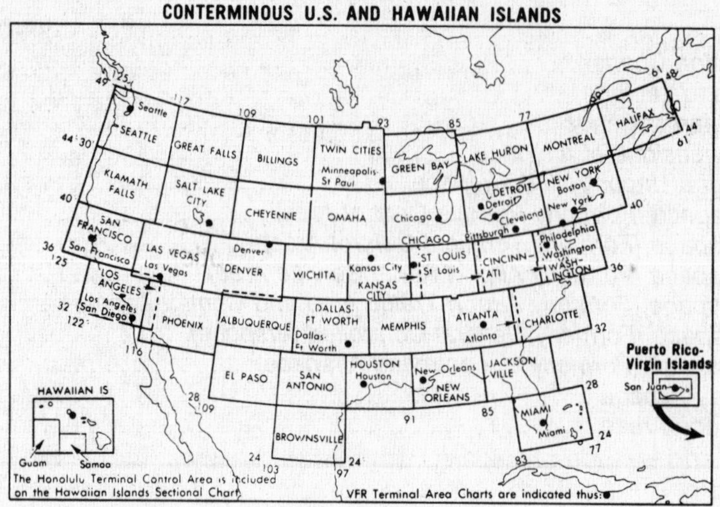


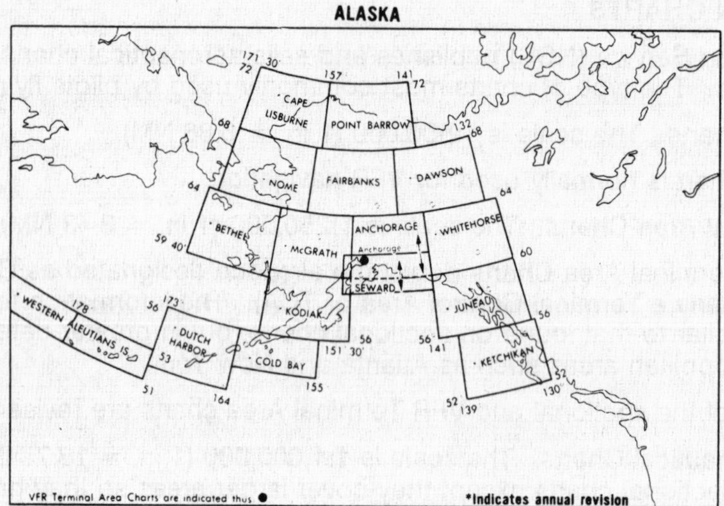


D. Obsolete charts must be discarded and replaced by new editions. This is important because revisions in aeronautical information occur constantly.

1. These revisions include changes in radio frequencies, new obstructions, temporary or permanent closing of certain runways and airports, and other temporary or permanent hazards to flight.

E. VFR aeronautical charts are available from the following sources.

1. The Aircraft Owners and Pilots Association (AOPA) on an individual or subscription basis. Call 1-800-872-2672 for information or to order.
2. The National Ocean Service on an individual or subscription basis. For information contact:

   NOAA Distribution Branch (N/CG33)
   National Ocean Service
   Riverdale, MD 20737-1199
   Telephone: (301) 436-6990 for individual orders
   (301) 436-6993 for subscriptions

3. Charts are also available at most FBOs and pilot supply stores.

## 9.2 LONGITUDE AND LATITUDE

A. Lines of longitude and latitude provide a common grid system that is the key to navigation. The location of any point on the Earth can be determined by the intersection of the lines of longitude and latitude.

1. Parallels, or lines of latitude, are imaginary circles parallel to the Equator. They are drawn as lines on charts running east and west around the world.
   a. They are used to measure degrees of latitude north (N) or south (S) of the Equator.
   b. The angular distance from the Equator to the pole is one-fourth of a circle or 90°.
   c. The 48 conterminous states of the United States are located between 25° and 49°N latitude.
2. Meridians, or lines of longitude, are drawn from the North Pole to the South Pole and are at right angles to the Equator and the parallels.
   a. The Prime Meridian, which passes through Greenwich, England, is used as the zero line from which measurements are made in degrees east (E) and west (W) to 180°.
   b. The 48 conterminous states of the United States are located between 67° and 125°W longitude.
   c. Because lines of longitude connect the poles, they mark the direction of true north and south.

B. Any specific geographical point on Earth can thus be located by reference to its latitude and longitude.

1. EXAMPLES: Washington, D.C. is approximately 39°N latitude, 77°W longitude, and Chicago is approximately 42°N latitude, 88°W longitude.
2. The lines of longitude and latitude are printed on aeronautical (e.g., sectional) charts with each degree subdivided into 60 equal segments called minutes, i.e., ½° is equal to 30′ (the "′" is the symbol for min.).

C. The meridians are also useful for designating time zones.

1. A day is defined as the time required for the Earth to make one complete revolution of 360°. Since the day is divided into 24 hr., the Earth revolves at the rate of 15° an hour.
   a. When the sun is directly above a meridian:
      1) It is noon at that meridian.
      2) To the west of that meridian it is forenoon.
      3) To the east of that meridian it is afternoon.

2. The standard practice is to establish a time belt for each 15° of longitude. This makes a difference of exactly 1 hr. between each belt.
   a. The Continental United States has four time belts: Eastern (75°), Central (90°), Mountain (105°), and Pacific (120°).

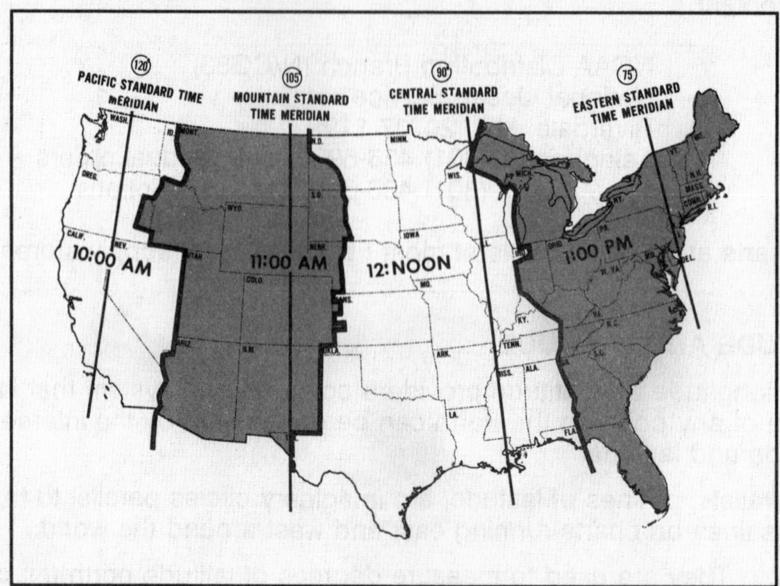


3. The actual dividing lines are somewhat irregular because communities near the boundaries often find it more convenient to use the time designations of neighboring communities or trade centers.

D. Measurement of Direction. By using the meridians, direction from one point to another can be measured in degrees, in a clockwise direction from true north.
   1. To indicate a course to be followed in flight, draw a line on the chart from the point of departure to the destination and measure the angle that this line forms with a meridian.
      a. Direction is expressed in degrees.
      b. Course measurement should be taken at a meridian near the midpoint of the course.
   2. The course you measure on your sectional chart is known as the true course. It is the direction measured by reference to a meridian or to true north. Put another way, it is the direction of intended flight as measured in degrees clockwise from true north.

## 9.3 SECTIONAL CHART LEGENDS

A. The following information appears (in color) on the front of every sectional chart. Study it here! Few pilots take time to study the whole legend because they are in a hurry to look at the chart itself.

1. Airports

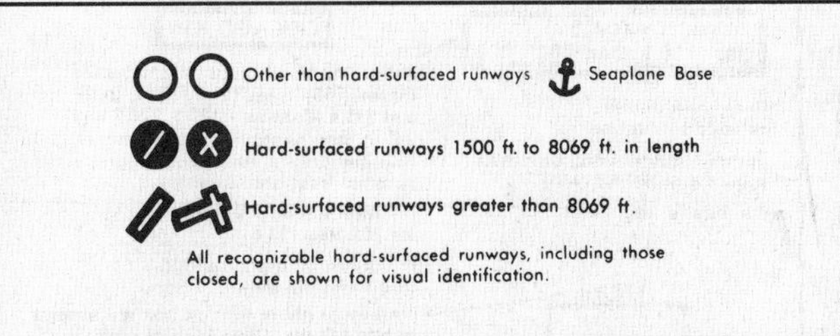


NOTE: On sectional charts, airports having control towers are illustrated in blue, all others are illustrated in magenta.

a. Additional Airport Information

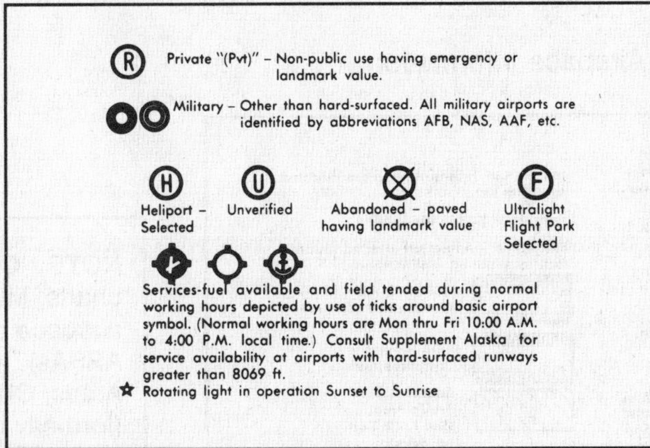


NOTE: On sectional charts, airports having control towers are illustrated in blue, all others are illustrated in magenta.

2. Airport Data

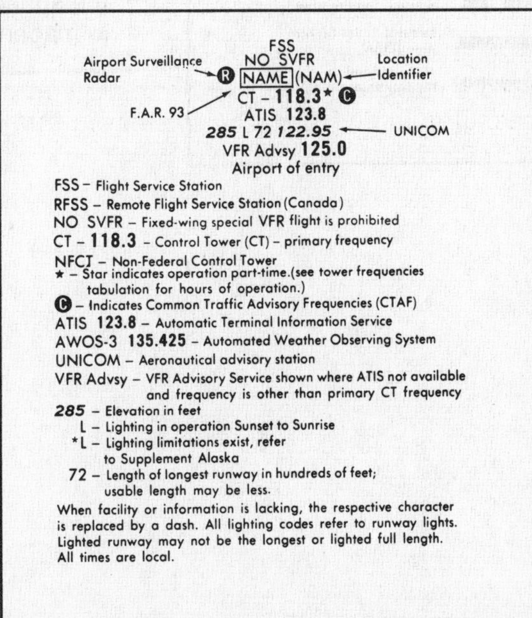

3. Radio Aids to Navigation and Communication Boxes

   a. On sectional charts, the Non-Directional Radiobeacon is illustrated in magenta.

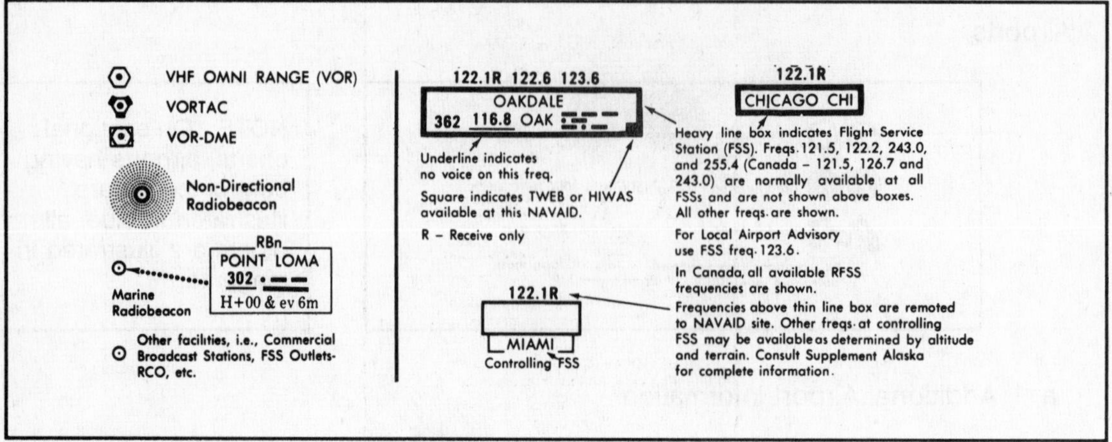


4. Airport Traffic Service and Airspace Information

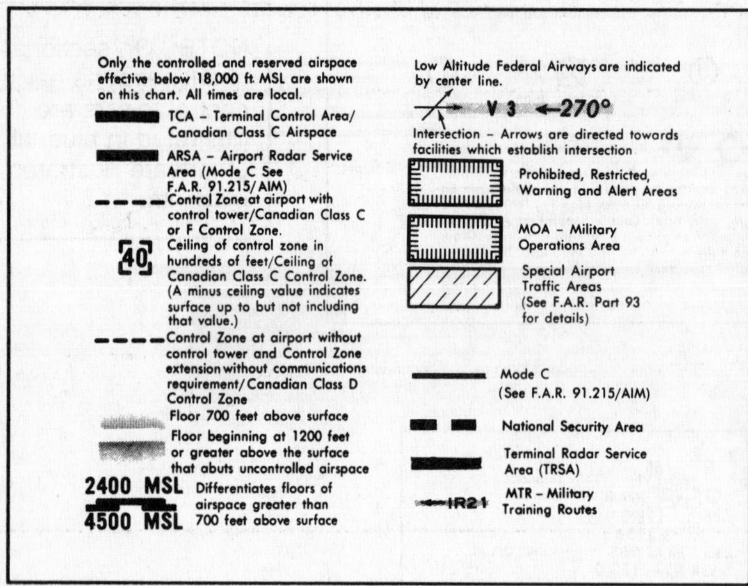


NOTE: On sectional charts, MOAs, Class C airspace areas (formerly ARSAs), National Security Areas, Class E airspace (formerly control zones at airports without control towers), and Class E airspace floors 700 ft. above the surface are illustrated in magenta.

## 5. Obstructions

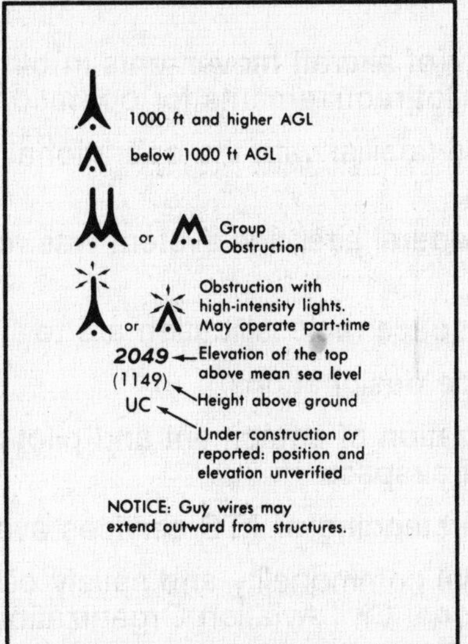


## 6. Topographic Information. NOTE: On sectional charts, roads, road markers, and bridges are illustrated in magenta.

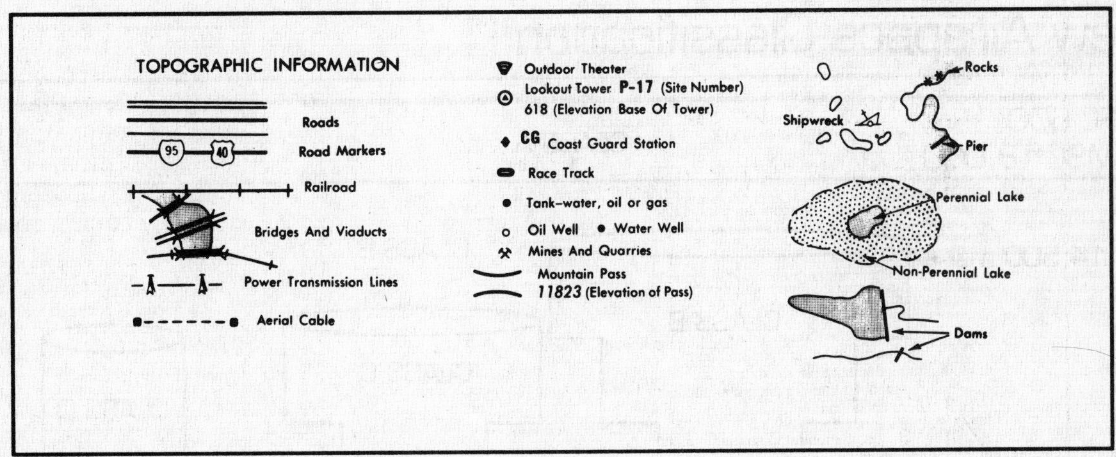


## 7. Miscellaneous

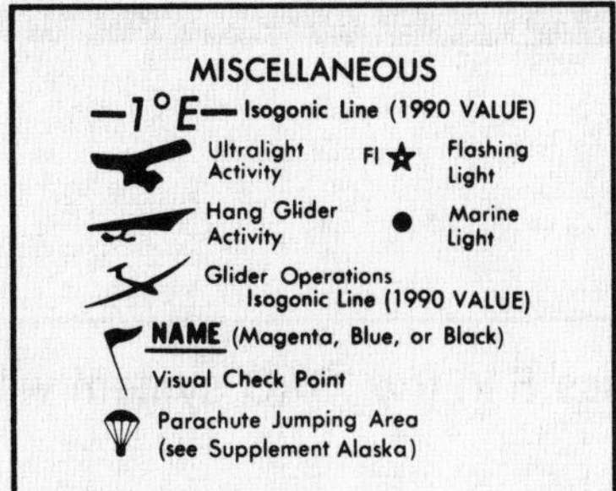


NOTE: On sectional charts, Isogonic Lines are illustrated in magenta.

## 9.4 GENERAL DIMENSIONS OF AIRSPACE

A. Because of the nature of operations within certain airspace areas, restrictions are required for safety reasons.

1. The complexity or density of aircraft movements in other airspace areas may result in additional aircraft and pilot requirements for operation within such airspace.
2. It is important that you be familiar with the operational requirements for the various airspace segments.

B. On September 16, 1993[1], the federal airspace system was reclassified, establishing six class designations.

1. The objectives of this airspace reclassification are to
   a. Simplify the airspace designations.
   b. Increase standardization of equipment and pilot requirements for operations in various classes of airspace.
   c. Promote pilot understanding of ATC services available.
   d. Achieve international commonality and satisfy our responsibilities as a member state of ICAO (International Civil Aviation Organization).
2. The diagram below and the table on page 279 show the new airspace system and summarize the new classifications with regard to the requirements and services available in each class of airspace.

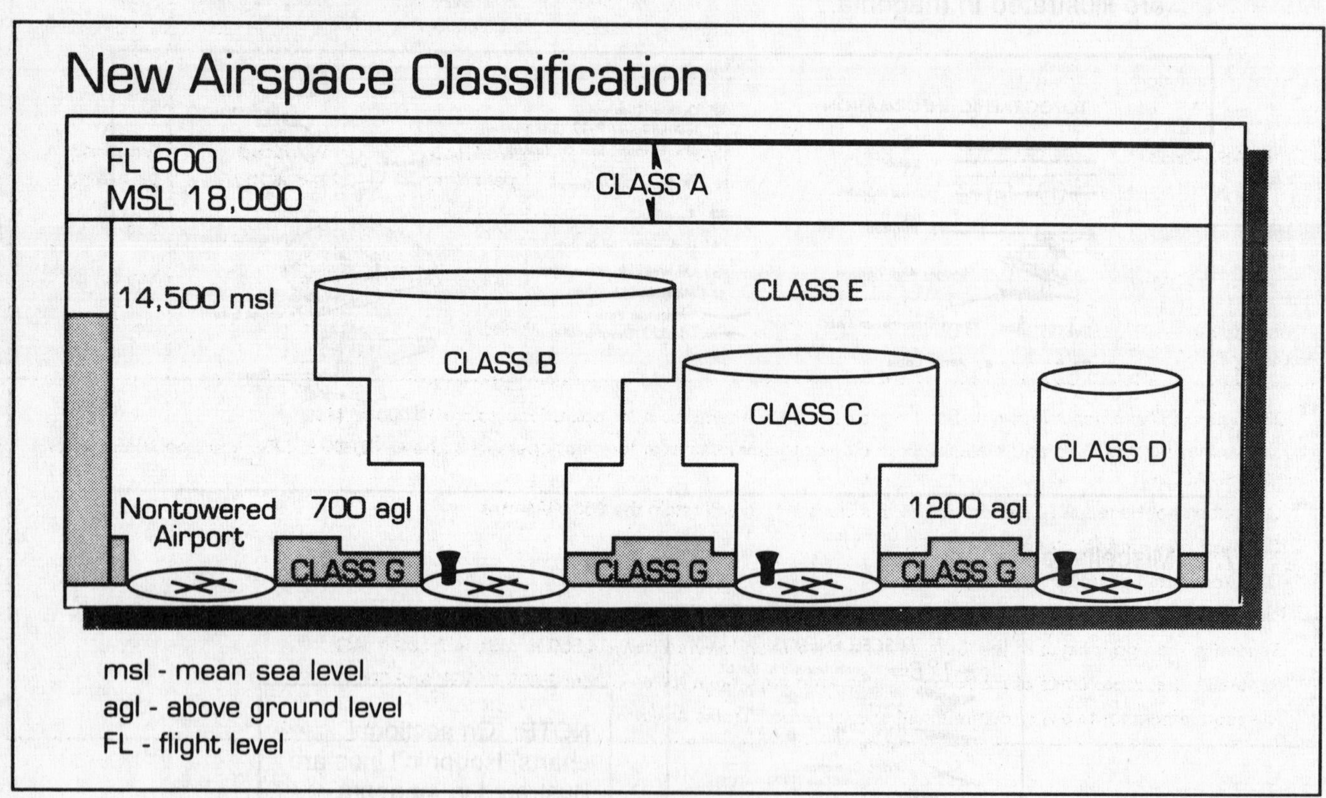


3. Note that the airspace designated as Class F in the ICAO system will not be used in the U.S.
4. This new airspace classification conforms with the International Civil Aviation Organization's (ICAO) airspace system.

---

[1] We published this Fourth Edition in April 1993, 5 months prior to the airspace change. If you are studying this chapter before September 16, 1993, note that this chapter contains cross-references to the old airspace titles (PCA, TCA, TRSA, etc.).

| Airspace Features | Class A | Class B | Class C | Class D | Class E | Class G |
|---|---|---|---|---|---|---|
| Former Airspace Equivalent | Positive Control Area (PCA) | Terminal Control Area (TCA) | Airport Radar Service Area (ARSA) | Airport Traffic Area (ATA) and Control Zone (CZ) | General Controlled Airspace | Uncontrolled Airspace |
| Operations Permitted | IFR | IFR and VFR | IFR and VFR | IFR and VFR | IFR and VFR | IFR and VFR |
| Entry Requirements | ATC clearance | ATC clearance | ATC clearance for IFR. All require radio contact. | ATC clearance for IFR. All require radio contact. | ATC clearance for IFR. All IFR require radio contact. | None |
| Minimum Pilot Qualifications | Instrument Rating | Private or student certificate | Student certificate | Student certificate | Student certificate | Student certificate |
| Two-way Radio Communications | Yes | Yes | Yes | Yes | Yes for IFR | No |
| VFR Minimum Visibility | N/A | 3 statute miles | 3 statute miles | 3 statute miles | 3 statute miles[1] | 1 statute mile[2] |
| VFR Minimum Distance from Clouds | N/A | Clear of clouds | 500 ft. below, 1,000 ft. above, and 2,000 ft. horizontal | 500 ft. below, 1,000 ft. above, and 2,000 ft. horizontal | 500 ft. below[1], 1,000 ft. above, and 2,000 ft. horizontal | Clear of clouds |
| Aircraft Separation | All | All | IFR, SVFR, and runway operations | IFR, SVFR, and runway operations | IFR and SVFR | None |
| Conflict Resolution | N/A | N/A | Between IFR and VFR ops | No | No | No |
| Traffic Advisories | N/A | N/A | Yes | Workload permitting | Workload permitting | Workload permitting |
| Safety Advisories | Yes | Yes | Yes | Yes | Yes | Yes |
| Differs from ICAO | No | Yes[3] | Yes[3,4] | Yes for VFR[4] | No | Yes for VFR[5] |
| Changes the Existing Rule | No | Yes for VFR[6] | No | Yes[7,8,9] | No | No |

1 Different visibility minima and distance from cloud requirements exist for operations above 10,000 ft. MSL

2 Different visibility minima and distance from cloud requirements exist for night operations above 10,000 ft. MSL and operations below 1,200 ft. AGL

3 ICAO does not have speed restrictions in this class -- U.S. will retain the 250 KIAS rule

4 ICAO requires an ATC clearance for VFR

5 ICAO requires 3 statute miles visibility

6 Reduces the cloud clearance distance from standard to clear of clouds

7 Generally, the upper limits of the Control Zone have been lowered from 14,500 ft. MSL to 2,500 ft. AGL

8 Generally, the upper limits of the Airport Traffic Area have been lowered from 2,999 ft. AGL to 2,500 ft. AGL

9 The requirement for two-way communications for Airport Traffic Areas

## 9.5 CONTROLLED AND UNCONTROLLED AIRSPACE

A. FAR Part 1.1 defines controlled airspace as an area within which ATC service is provided to IFR and VFR flights in accordance with the airspace classification.

1. Controlled airspace is designated as Class A, Class B, Class C, Class D, and Class E airspace.
2. Class G airspace is considered to be uncontrolled.

B. The distinction between uncontrolled airspace and the various types of controlled airspace relates to the following factors (refer to the airspace table on page 279).

1. ATC clearance requirements
2. Pilot qualification requirements
3. VFR flight visibility and distance from clouds requirements

Cloud Clearance and Visibility Required for VFR

<table>
<tr><th rowspan="2">Altitudes</th><th colspan="4">Classes of Airspace</th></tr>
<tr><th>B</th><th>C, D, and E<br>G (Night)</th><th colspan="2">G (Day)</th></tr>
<tr><td>Below 1,200 ft. AGL</td><td rowspan="2">Clear of clouds<br><br>3 SM visibility</td><td rowspan="2">500 ft. below<br>1,000 ft. above<br>2,000 ft. horizontal<br><br>3 SM visibility</td><td rowspan="2">1 SM visibility</td><td>Clear of clouds</td></tr>
<tr><td>Above 1,200 ft. AGL and Below 10,000 ft. MSL</td><td>500 ft. below<br>1,000 ft. above<br>2,000 ft. horizontal</td></tr>
<tr><td>Above 1,200 ft. AGL and Above 10,000 ft. MSL</td><td colspan="4">1,000 ft. below<br>1,000 ft. above<br>1 SM horizontal<br><br>5 SM visibility</td></tr>
</table>

a. In addition, when within the surface area of Class B, C, D, or E airspace (i.e., the area around a controlled airport), you may not operate VFR beneath a ceiling that is less than 1,000 ft.

1) Thus, a controlled airport is IFR when the ceiling is less than 1,000 ft. **or** the visibility is less than 3 SM.

b. Special VFR (SVFR) is an ATC clearance to operate within the lateral boundaries of the surface areas of Class B, Class C, Class D, or Class E airspace designated for an airport when the ground visibility (if not reported, then the flight visibility) is less than 3 SM.

1) Ground visibility (or flight visibility if no ground report) must be at least 1 SM, and you must remain clear of clouds.

2) You must request an SVFR clearance; ATC cannot assign it.

   a) A student pilot cannot request an SVFR.

3) You must be instrument rated and your airplane must be instrument equipped to receive an SVFR clearance at night.

4) SVFR for fixed wing (airplane) operations is prohibited at certain airports marked as shown below.

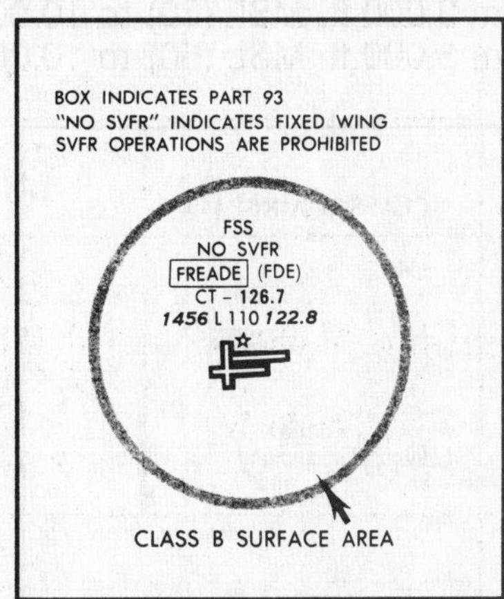


5) NOTE: On sectional charts, Class B Surface Areas are illustrated in blue.

## 9.6 CLASS A AIRSPACE

A. Formerly known as the Positive Control Area (PCA), Class A airspace is most of the airspace within the continental U.S. from 18,000 ft. MSL up to and including FL 600.

B. Operating Rules and Pilot/Equipment Requirements

1. An IFR clearance to enter and operate within Class A airspace is mandatory.

   a. VFR operations are prohibited.

2. Two-way radio communication and appropriate navigational capability are required.

3. Mode C transponder is required, since Class A airspace is above 10,000 ft. MSL.

4. You must be instrument-rated to act as pilot in command of an aircraft in Class A airspace.

## 9.7 CLASS B AIRSPACE

A. Formerly known as a Terminal Control Area (TCA), Class B airspace is an area of controlled airspace which consists of varying lateral and vertical limits, as well as a 30-NM ring (or veil) encircling the primary Class B airport.

1. The geographic area of Class B airspace is depicted by heavy blue lines on a sectional or terminal area chart.
    a. The vertical limits of each section of Class B airspace are shown in hundreds of feet MSL.
2. The 30-NM veil is marked by a thinner blue circle.
3. Class B airspace is shown on the chart as in the example below.
    a. Class B vertical limits in this example are
        1) From the surface (SFC) to 10,000 ft. MSL (100) in the inner circle.
        2) From 3,000 ft. MSL (30) to 10,000 ft. MSL in the middle circle.
        3) From 5,000 ft. MSL (50) to 10,000 ft. MSL in the outer circle.

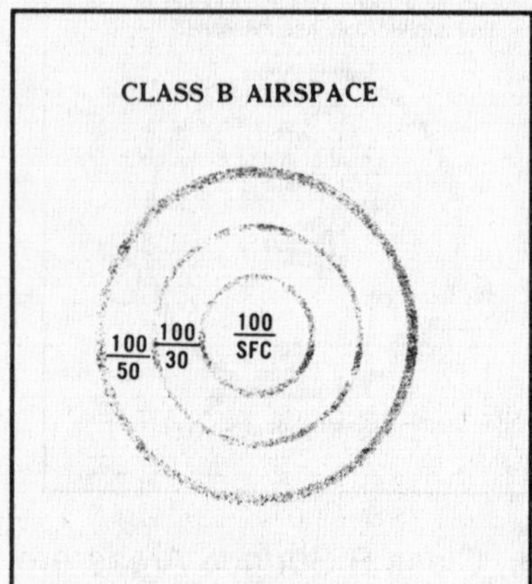


NOTE: On sectional charts, Class B airspace boundaries are illustrated in blue.

B. Operating Rules and Pilot/Equipment Requirements

1. An ATC clearance to enter and operate within Class B airspace is mandatory.
2. Two-way radio communication capability is required.
3. Mode C transponder is required within Class B airspace and also within the 30-NM veil.
4. You may not act as pilot in command of an aircraft within Class B airspace unless you hold at least a private pilot certificate, or you are a student pilot and you have the necessary endorsement(s) from your CFI in your logbook (see FAR 61.95 on page 234).
    a. Also, the following Class B primary airports require that the pilot in command hold at least a private pilot certificate.

Atlanta Hartsfield Airport, GA
Boston Logan Airport, MA
Chicago O'Hare Int'l Airport, IL
Dallas/Ft. Worth Int'l Airport, TX
Los Angeles Int'l Airport, CA
Miami Int'l Airport, FL
Newark Int'l Airport, NJ
New York Kennedy Airport, NY
New York La Guardia Airport, NY
San Francisco Int'l Airport, CA
Washington National Airport, DC
Andrews Air Force Base, MD

## 9.8 CLASS C AIRSPACE

A. Formerly known as an Airport Radar Service Area (ARSA), Class C airspace is an area of controlled airspace which consists of two circles (an inner and an outer circle) centered on the primary Class C airport.

1. The general dimensions of Class C airspace are as shown in the following diagram.

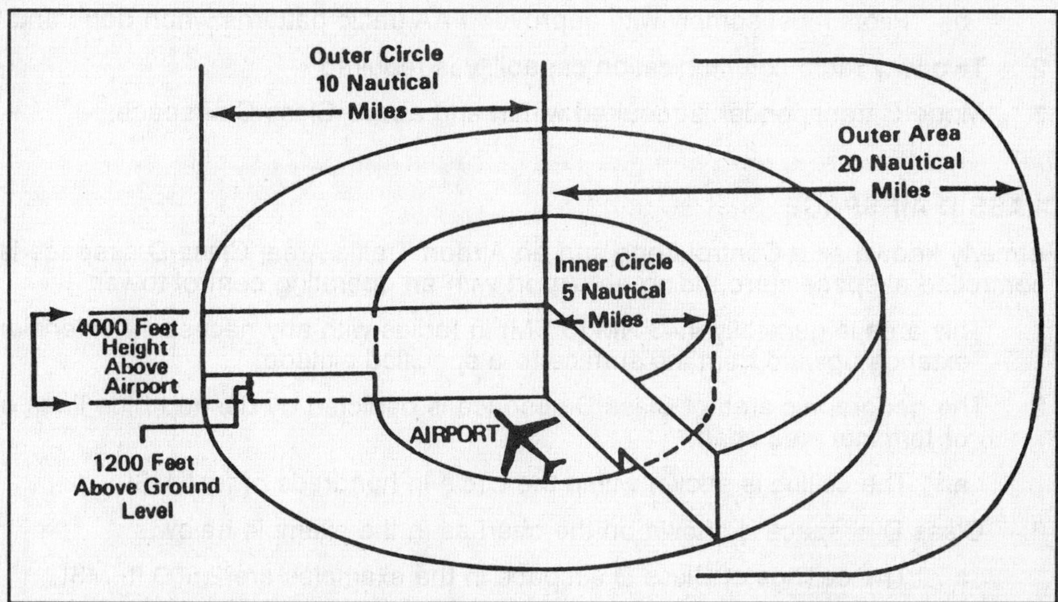


a. The outer area, which is the airspace area between 10 NM and 20 NM from the primary Class C airport, is not considered Class C airspace.

1) Radar services in this area are available, but not mandatory.

2. The geographic area of Class C airspace is depicted by solid magenta lines on sectional and some terminal area charts.

a. The vertical limits of each circle are shown in hundreds of feet MSL.

3. Class C airspace is shown on the chart as in the example below.

a. Class C airspace vertical limits in the example extend

1) From the surface (SFC) to 4,500 ft. MSL (45) in the inner circle.
2) From 1,200 ft. MSL (12) to 4,500 ft. MSL in the outer circle.

b. The dashed magenta line shows an area of Class E airspace extending upward from the surface to the overlying Class C airspace (see Module 9.10, Class E Airspace, on page 285).

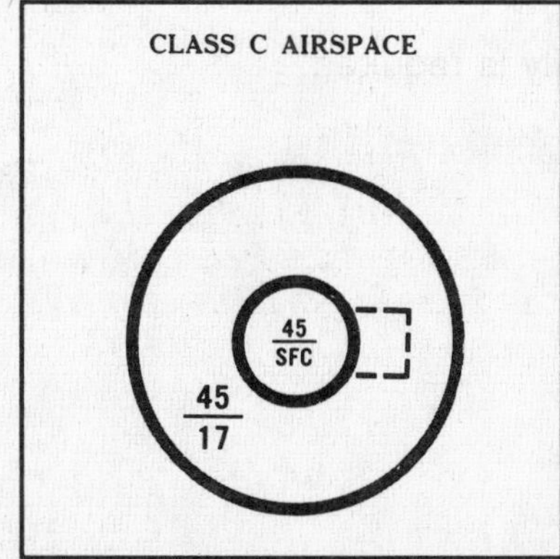


NOTE: On sectional charts, Class C airspace boundaries are illustrated in magenta.

B. Operating Rules and Pilot/Equipment Requirements

1. Two-way radio communication must be maintained with ATC while within Class C airspace.
    a. Aircraft departing satellite airports within the Class C surface area must establish two-way communication with ATC as soon as possible.
    b. Pilots must comply with approved FAA traffic patterns when departing these airports.
2. Two-way radio communication capability is required.
3. Mode C transponder is required within and above Class C airspace.

## 9.9 CLASS D AIRSPACE

A. Formerly known as a Control Zone and an Airport Traffic Area, Class D airspace is an area of controlled airspace surrounding an airport with an operating control tower.

1. This area is generally 4.43 NM (5 SM) in radius with any necessary extensions, and extends upward from the surface to a specified altitude.
2. The geographic area of Class D airspace is depicted by dashed blue lines on a sectional or terminal area chart.
    a. The ceiling is shown within the circle in hundreds of feet MSL.
3. Class D airspace is shown on the chart as in the example below.
    a. The ceilings of Class D airspace in the examples are 2,600 ft. MSL.
    b. On sectional charts, a dashed magenta line (see right side of the example on the right) illustrates an area of Class E airspace extending upward from the surface.

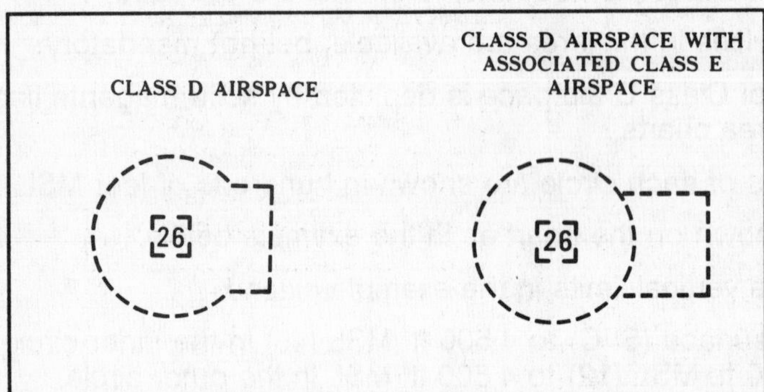


NOTE: On sectional charts, Class D airspace boundaries are illustrated in blue and Class E airspace boundaries are illustrated in magenta.

B. Operating Rules and Equipment Requirements

1. Two-way radio communication must be maintained with ATC while within Class D airspace.
2. Two-way radio communication capability is required.

## 9.10 CLASS E AIRSPACE

A. Formerly known as general controlled airspace, Class E airspace is an area of controlled airspace with no communications requirements under VFR.

1. This area begins at 1,200 ft. AGL throughout the conterminous U.S. unless otherwise indicated, or unless superseded by Class B, C, or D airspace, and extends upward to the floor of Class A airspace.

   a. A dashed magenta line around an airport indicates Class E airspace extending upward from the surface.

      1) This was formerly a control zone at an uncontrolled airport.

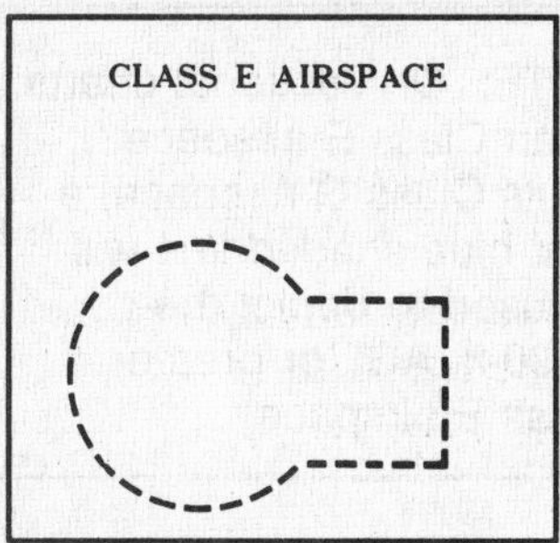


NOTE: On sectional charts, Class E airspace boundaries are illustrated in magenta.

   b. A light-magenta shaded line indicates Class E airspace extending upward from 700 ft. AGL.

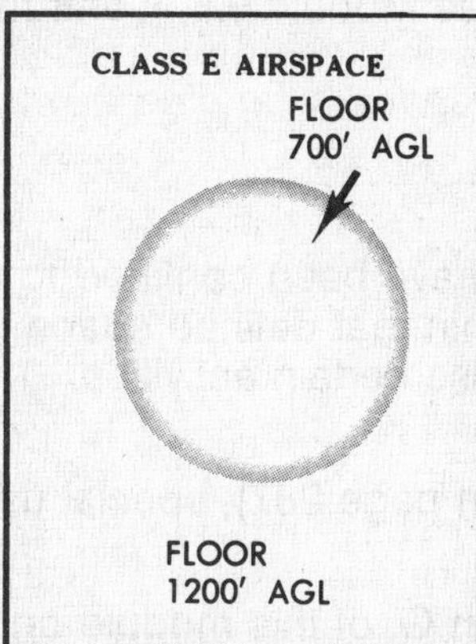


NOTE: Where the outer edge of the 700-ft. AGL transition area ends (illustrated on sectional charts in magenta shading), the 1,200-ft. AGL or greater area automatically begins.

   c. The symbol shown below indicates Class E airspace extending upward from the indicated altitude. On sectional charts, it is illustrated in blue.

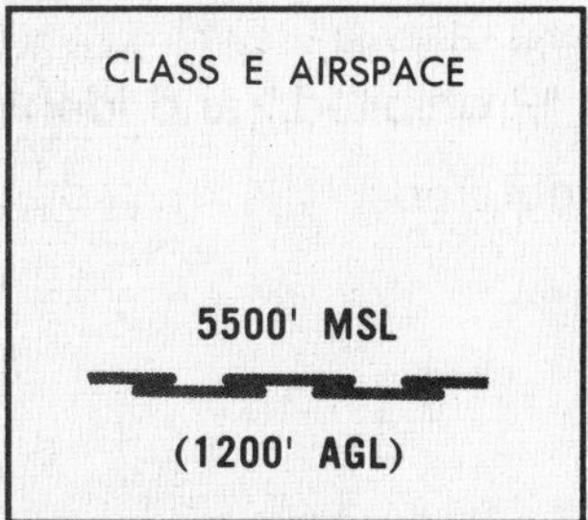


B. The only operating rules in Class E airspace under VFR are the basic VFR visibility and cloud clearance requirements for Class E airspace. (See Module 9.5, Controlled and Uncontrolled Airspace, on page 280.)

## 9.11 CLASS G AIRSPACE

A. Class G airspace is airspace that is not controlled airspace (i.e., Class A, B, C, D, or E airspace).

1. It exists beneath the floor of controlled airspace in areas where that airspace does not extend down to the surface.
2. Class G airspace that extends upward to the floor of Class A airspace (FL 180) is depicted by the distinct side of a light-blue shaded line on a sectional or terminal area chart, as shown below.
    a. Note that Class E airspace begins at 1,200 ft. AGL or higher on the fuzzy side of the blue line.

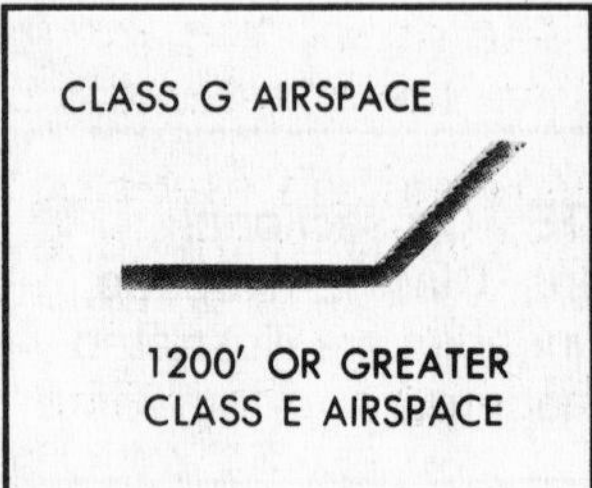


NOTE: On sectional charts, when Class E airspace abuts Class G airspace, a light-blue shaded line will be used to depict the 1,200-ft. AGL or greater Class E airspace.

    b. Class G airspace that underlies Class B, C, D, or E airspace is implied -- it is not indicated on the chart.

B. The only operating rules in Class G airspace under VFR are the basic VFR visibility and cloud clearance requirements for Class G airspace. (See Module 9.5, Controlled and Uncontrolled Airspace, on page 280.)

## 9.12 SPECIAL USE AIRSPACE

A. Special use airspace means that certain activities have been confined to an airspace with defined dimensions because of their nature. Within that defined space, limitations are imposed upon aircraft operations that are not a part of those certain activities. There are several kinds of special use airspace.

1. Except for Controlled Firing Areas (see G. on page 287), special use airspace areas are depicted on sectional charts.
    a. Controlled Firing Areas are explained in G. of this module on page 287.
2. A tabulation at the bottom of each sectional chart lists each special use airspace by number or name, its hours and altitudes of use, and its controlling agency.

B. *Prohibited Areas* -- airspace within which flight is prohibited. Such areas are established for security or other reasons of national welfare.

1. A Prohibited Area is charted in blue, labeled "Prohibited," and identified by a number, i.e., P-73.

C. *Restricted Areas* -- airspace within which flight, while not wholly prohibited, is subject to restrictions.

1. Restricted Areas denote the existence of unusual, often invisible hazards to aircraft such as artillery firing, aerial gunnery, or guided missiles.
2. Entering Restricted Areas without authorization from the using or controlling agency may be extremely hazardous.
3. A Restricted Area is charted in blue, labeled "Restricted," and identified by a number, i.e., R-2403.
   a. Contact the controlling agency to determine whether a Restricted Area is in use.

D. *Warning Areas* -- airspace which may contain hazards to nonparticipating aircraft in international airspace. Warning Areas extend from 3 to 12 NM from the coast of the U.S.

1. Warning Areas cannot be legally designated as Restricted Areas because they are over international waters, but the activities conducted within Warning Areas may be as hazardous as those in Restricted Areas.
2. A Warning Area is charted in blue, labeled "Warning," and identified by a number, i.e., W-497B.
   a. Contact the controlling agency to determine whether a Warning Area is in use.

E. *Military Operations Areas (MOA)* -- airspace established to separate certain military training activities from IFR traffic.

1. Most military training activities necessitate acrobatic or abrupt flight maneuvers. Military pilots conducting flight in Department of Defense aircraft within a designated and active MOA are exempted from FAR 91.303, which prohibits acrobatic flight within Federal airways and Control Zones.
2. Pilots operating under VFR should exercise extreme caution while flying within an MOA when military activity is being conducted.
   a. First contact any FSS within 100 NM of the area to obtain accurate real-time information concerning the MOA hours of operation.
   b. Prior to entering an active MOA, contact the controlling agency for traffic advisories.
3. An MOA is charted in magenta, labeled "MOA," and identified by a name, i.e., Columbus 4 MOA.

F. *Alert Areas* -- depicted on aeronautical charts to inform nonparticipating pilots of areas that may contain a high volume of pilot training or an unusual type of aerial activity.

1. An Alert Area is charted in blue, labeled "Alert," and identified by a number, i.e., A-440.

G. *Controlled Firing Areas* -- contain activities which, if not conducted in a controlled environment, could be hazardous to nonparticipating aircraft.

1. The activities are suspended immediately when spotter aircraft, radar, or ground lookout positions indicate an aircraft might be approaching the area.
2. Controlled Firing Areas are not charted since they do not cause a nonparticipating aircraft to change its flight path.

## 9.13 OTHER AIRSPACE AREAS

A. An *airport advisory area* is the area within 10 SM of an airport that has no operating control tower, but where an FSS is located. At such locations, the FSS provides advisory service to arriving and departing aircraft. Participation is recommended but not required.

B. *Military training routes (MTRs)* are developed for use by the military for the purpose of conducting low-altitude, high-speed training.

1. The routes above 1,500 ft. AGL are flown, to the maximum extent possible, under IFR.
   a. The routes at 1,500 ft. AGL and below are flown under VFR.
2. MTRs are charted in grey and labeled as follows:
   a. "IR" for IFR or "VR" for VFR.
   b. Routes below 1,500 ft. AGL use 4-digit identifiers, e.g., IR 1006, VR 1007.
   c. Routes above 1,500 ft. AGL use 3-digit identifiers, e.g., IR 008, VR 009.
3. Extreme vigilance should be exercised when flying through or near these routes.
   a. You should contact the FSS within 100 NM of a particular MTR to obtain current information on route use in the vicinity.
   b. Available information includes times of scheduled activity, altitudes in use on each route segment, and actual route width.

C. Temporary flight restrictions (FAR 91.137) may be put into effect in the vicinity of any incident or event which by its nature may generate such a high degree of public interest that hazardous congestion of air traffic is likely.

1. A Notice to Airmen (NOTAM) implementing temporary flight restrictions will contain a description of the area in which the restrictions apply.
2. Normally the area will include the airspace below 2,000 ft. above the surface within a 2-NM radius of the site of the incident. The exact dimensions will be included in the NOTAM.

D. Flight limitations in the proximity of Space Flight Operations (FAR 91.143) are designated in a NOTAM.

1. This provides protection from potentially hazardous situations for pilots and space flight crews and costly delays of shuttle operations.

E. Flight Restrictions in the proximity of Presidential and Other Parties (FAR 91.141) are put into effect by a regulatory NOTAM to establish flight restrictions.

1. This is required because numerous aircraft and large assemblies of persons may be attracted to areas to be visited or traveled by the President or Vice President, heads of foreign states, and other public figures.
2. In addition, restrictions are imposed in the interest of providing protection to these public figures.

F. Tabulations of parachute jump areas in the U.S. are contained in the *Airport/Facility Directory* (see Chapter 10, Other Navigation Publications, on page 289).

# CHAPTER TEN
# OTHER NAVIGATION PUBLICATIONS



## 10.1 FAA ADVISORY CIRCULAR (AC)

A. The FAA issues advisory circulars (AC) to provide a systematic means for issuing nonregulatory material of interest to the aviation public.

1. Unless incorporated into a regulation by reference, the contents of an AC are not binding (i.e., they are only advisory in nature).

2. An AC is issued to provide guidance and information in its designated subject area or to show a method acceptable to the FAA for complying with a related FAR.

B. ACs are issued in a numbered system of general subject matter areas that correspond with the subject areas in Federal Aviation Regulations (FARs).

1. The general subject number and the subject areas are as follows:

00 -- General
10 -- Procedural Rules
20 -- Aircraft
60 -- Airmen
70 -- Airspace
90 -- Air Traffic and General Operating Rules
120 -- Air Carriers, Air Travel Clubs, and Operators for Compensation or Hire: Certification and Operations
140 -- Schools and Other Certificated Agencies
150 -- Airport Noise Compatibility Planning
170 -- Navigational Facilities
180 -- Administrative Regulations
190 -- Withholding Security Information; War Risk Insurance; Aircraft Loan Guarantee Program
210 -- Flight Information (Note: This series is about aeronautical charts and does not relate to an FAR Part.)

C. If you wish, you may order a free list of the ACs. It is called the "Advisory Circular Checklist," AC 00-2. See order form on page 291.

D. If no price is listed after the AC, it is free.

E. If a price is listed after the AC description, the AC is sold by the Superintendent of Documents, U.S. Government Printing Office. When "(Sub.)" is included with the price, the AC is available on a subscription basis only. This means that supplements or changes to the basic document will be sent to you at no additional charge until the subscription expires.

## 10.2 AIRMAN'S INFORMATION MANUAL (AIM)

A. The *AIM* provides pilots with a vast amount of basic flight information and Air Traffic Control (ATC) procedures in the United States.

1. This information is vital to you as a pilot so that you may understand the structure and operation of the ATC system and your part in it.

2. Your CFI will explain how best to use this book.
3. The *AIM* is an 8 x 10½ in. paperback published approximately every 3 months by the FAA.
4. Subscriptions are available from the Government Printing Office (202) 783-3238 for $26 per year (three issues). MasterCard and VISA are accepted.
5. Other aviation publishers reprint the last *AIM* each calendar year and label it as the *AIM* for the next calendar year, e.g., reprint the October 15, 1992 *AIM* and call it 1993 *AIM*. The cost of these single issues is $5 to $10 and these are adequate for most pilots.

B. Chapters and section titles



C. Each issue of *AIM* has a comprehensive and useful index to help you find topics of interest. The index is to paragraph numbers, not page numbers.

**ORDER BLANK [Free Publications]** **DATE ____/____/____**

***For Faster Service Use A Self-Addressed Mailing Label When Not Using This Blank. Please Print Or Type All Information.***

***Mail To:***
***DOT, M-443.2***
***GENERAL SERVICES, SECTION***
***WASHINGTON, D.C. 20590***

| NUMBER | TITLE | QUANTITY |
|---|---|---|
| AC 00-2 | Advisory Circular Checklist | 1 |
| | | |
| | | |
| | | |
| | | |
| | | |
| | | |
| | | |
| | | |

**M-443.2**
**Request Filled By: ____________________** **Date ____/____/____**

**1. Out of Stock [reorder in days]* *** **3. Cancelled, no replacement**

**2. Being revised** **4. Cancelled by ____________[enclosed]**

**5. Other: ____________________**

*** * IF YOU DO NOT RECEIVE DESIRED PUBLICATION(S) AFTER YOUR <u>SECOND</u> REQUEST PLEASE CALL FAA'S TOLL-FREE CONSUMER HOTLINE: 1-800 FAA-SURE.**

**TO COMPLETE ORDER: Enter Name and Address. DO NOT DETACH.**

**NAME**

**STREET ADDRESS**

**CITY** **STATE** **ZIP CODE**

## 10.3 AIRPORT/FACILITY DIRECTORY (A/FD)

A. *The Airport/Facility Directory* (A/FD) is a Civil Flight Information Publication published and distributed every 8 weeks by the National Ocean Service (NOS), a division of the National Oceanic and Atmospheric Administration (NOAA).

1. It is a directory of all airports, seaplane bases, and heliports open to the public; communications data; navigational facilities; and certain special notices and procedures.
2. Subscriptions to the publication are for sale by the

   National Ocean Service
   NOAA Distribution Branch, N/CG33
   Riverdale, MD 20737-1199
   Telephone: (301) 436-6993

3. One of these directories is published for each of seven geographical districts:
   a. Northwest.
   b. Southwest.
   c. North Central.
   d. South Central.
   e. East Central.
   f. Northeast.
   g. Southeast.

B. Use of the *A/FD* is a vital part of your cross-country flight planning.

1. All pertinent information regarding airports, FSS contact information, etc., is contained in this volume.
2. The *A/FD* also contains National Weather Service telephone numbers listed alphabetically by state.

C. Table of contents of each issue

1. Abbreviations.
2. Legend for the Airport/Facility Directory.
3. Airport/Facility Directory.
4. Heliports.
5. Seaplane Bases.
6. Notices.
7. FSS and National Weather Service Telephone Numbers.
8. Air Route Traffic Control Centers.
9. GADO (General Aviation District Office) and FSDO (Flight Standards District Office) Addresses/Telephone Numbers.
10. Preferred IFR Routes.
11. VOR Receiver Checkpoints.
12. Parachute Jumping Areas.
13. Aeronautical Chart Bulletin.
14. Tower En Route Control (TEC).
15. National Weather Service (NWS) Upper Air Observing Stations.
16. En Route Flight Advisory Service (EFAS).

D. A sample *A/FD* legend and explanations are reproduced in Chapter 10 of *Private Pilot and Recreational Pilot FAA Written Exam.*

E. VOR checkpoints

1. VOR receiver checkpoints are listed in a separate section of the *A/FD* as the excerpt below illustrates. They include

    a. Facility (airport) name.
    b. Frequency and identification.
    c. Type of checkpoint: identified as ground (G) or airborne (A).

        1) Includes altitude if an airborne checkpoint

    d. Checkpoint's magnetic direction from the VOR (i.e., radial).
    e. Checkpoint's distance from the VOR in nautical miles.
    f. Checkpoint description.

2. Example listing

**KENTUCKY**

**VOR RECEIVER CHECK POINTS**

| Facility Name (Arpt Name) | Freq/Ident | Type Check Pt. Gnd. AB/ALT | Azimuth from Fac. Mag | Dist. from Fac. N.M. | Check Point Description |
|---|---|---|---|---|---|
| Bowling Green-Warren Co | 117.9/BWG | G | 023 | 2.2 | On twy in front of Admin Bldg. |
| Central City (Muhlenberg Co) | 109.8/CCT | A/2500 | 149 | 11.0 | Over intersection of rwy 23 and central taxiway. |
| Cincinnati (Greater Cincinnati) | 117.3/CVG | G | 045 | 2.5 | On twy m E of twy B. |
| Clarksville (Campbell AAF) | 110.6/CKV | G | 298 | 5 | On end of old rwy 36 near Maltese Cross. |
| Clarksville (Hopkinsville-Christian Co) | 110.6/CKV | A/2000 | 345 | 13.5 | Over hangar. |
| Cunningham (Barkley) | 113.6/CNG | G | 043 | 4.6 | Intersection of taxiways and west corner of ramp. |
| London (London-Corbin Arpt-Magee Fld) | 116.1/LOZ | G | 034 | 3.8 | On parking ramp taxiway entry. |

## 10.4 NOTICE TO AIRMEN (NOTAM)

A. NOTAMs offer time-critical aeronautical information which is of a temporary nature not sufficiently known in advance to permit publication on aeronautical charts or on other operational publications. These notices are disseminated immediately via telecommunications. They are published biweekly or held for local use depending on their urgency and applicability.

B. NOTAMs are categorized into three types:

1. NOTAM (D) -- runway or airport closures, interruptions in service of navigational aids, radar service availability, and other information essential to planning. This information could affect your decision to make a flight.

    a. This information is disseminated for all navigational facilities that are part of the National Airspace System (NAS), all public use airports, seaplane bases, and heliports listed in the A/FD.

    b. In addition to local distribution, they are given distant (D) distribution beyond the FSS's area of responsibility.

2. NOTAM (L) -- covers information that is "handy to know," such as taxiway closings, men and equipment near or crossing runways, and information on airports. These are local NOTAMs. They are kept by local FBOs, towers, etc., for transmittal to pilots.
   a. This information is distributed locally only and a separate file of local (L) NOTAMs is maintained at each FSS for facilities in their area only.
   b. NOTAM (L) information for other FSS areas must be specifically requested directly from that FSS.
3. FDC NOTAMs -- Regulatory in nature. Examples would be notices to amend current aeronautical charts or instrument approach procedures, or to restrict flight.
   a. FSSs are responsible for maintaining a file of current, unpublished FDC NOTAMs concerning conditions within 400 NM of their facilities.
   b. FDC information concerning conditions beyond 400 NM from the FSS, or that is already published, is given to you only when you request it.

C. An integral part of the NOTAM system is the biweekly Notices to Airmen publication (NTAP). Once published, the information is NOT provided during pilot weather briefings unless specifically requested by you.
1. The NTAP consists of two sections.
   a. The first section contains NOTAMs (D) that are expected to remain in effect for an extended period and FDC NOTAMs that are current at the time of publication.
      1) Occasionally, some NOTAMs (L) and other unique information are included in this section when they will contribute to flight safety.
   b. The second section contains special notices that are either too long or concern a wide or unspecified geographic area.
2. All new NOTAMs entered, excluding FDC NOTAMs, will be published only if the information is expected to remain in effect for at least 7 days after the effective date of the NTAP.

D. Note that NOTAMs of a temporary nature and those not yet published (in the NTAP) are part of the hourly SA (weather) reports.
1. Only the NOTAMs (D) and FDC NOTAMs are included in the SA reports.
2. Sample NOTAMs
   a. !TLH 04/009 TLH 9-27 CLSD TIL 07182359
   b. !TLH 04/011 TLH 27 ALS OTS TIL 07182359
   c. !TLH 04/012 TLH 27 ILS GS OTS TIL 07182359

# CHAPTER ELEVEN
# RADIO NAVIGATION



Radio navigation is a method of navigation by which the pilot follows a predetermined flight path over the Earth's surface by utilizing the properties of radio waves. This is commonly done by ground facilities transmitting signals to navigation radio receivers installed in the airplane. The pilot determines and controls ground track on the basis of the instrument indications.

Before learning the operational procedures of radio navigation, you should have a knowledge of the basic radio principles to increase your understanding of their use and limitations.

## 11.1 BASIC RADIO PRINCIPLES

A. Definitions

1. A *wave* is a pulse of energy traveling through a medium (e.g., air) by means of vibrations from particle to particle.
   a. EXAMPLE: A stone is dropped into water. The energy of motion disturbs the water causing the water to rise and fall. Energy waves travel outward from the source of disturbance, but the water itself does not move outward.
      1) This rise and fall above and below the normal undisturbed level can be pictured as a curved line, as shown below.

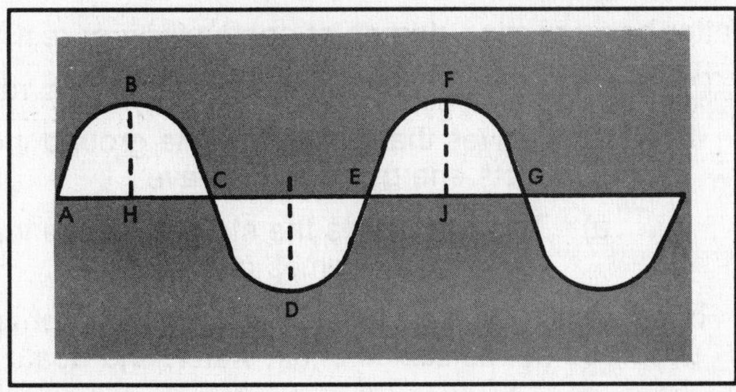


2. The *amplitude* of a wave is a linear distance measuring the extreme range of fluctuation from the highest or lowest point to the midpoint between them (i.e., from Point B to point H in the diagram above).
3. A *cycle* is the interval between any two points measuring the completion of a single wave movement (i.e., from points A to E, B to F, or C to G in the diagram above).
4. The *wavelength* is the linear distance of a cycle.

5. The *frequency* of a wave is the number of cycles completed in 1 sec.
   a. Since radio wave frequencies involve very high numbers of cycles per second, they are generally expressed in one of the following terms
      1) Hertz (Hz) or cycles per second.
      2) Kilohertz (kHz) or thousands of cycles per second.
      3) Megahertz (MHz) or millions of cycles per second.
   b. A frequency of 1,000 Hz equals 1 kHz, and 1,000 kHz equals 1 MHz.
6. A *current* is the flow of electrons through a conductor and is either direct current (DC) or alternating current (AC).
   a. DC flows only in one direction.
   b. AC flows in one direction during a given time interval, then flows in the opposite direction for the same time interval, reversing continuously.
7. Radio waves are produced by sending a high-frequency alternating current (AC) through a conductor (i.e., antenna).
   a. The frequency of the radio wave is equal to the frequency of the AC.
   b. The radio wave moves at a velocity equal to the speed of light (approximately 186,000 miles per second).
8. Frequency bands. Since radio frequencies extend from approximately 3 kHz to over 30,000 MHz, and different groups of frequencies within this range produce different effects in transmission, radio frequencies are classified into frequency bands. Some are shown below.

| Frequency Band | Frequency Range |
|---|---|
| Very Low Frequency (VLF) | 3 to 30 kHz |
| Low Frequency (LF) | 30 to 300 kHz |
| Medium Frequency (MF) | 300 to 3,000 kHz |
| High Frequency (HF) | 3 to 30 MHz |
| Very High Frequency (VHF) | 30 to 300 MHz |
| Ultra High Frequency (UHF) | 300 to 3,000 MHz |

B. Characteristics of Radio Waves

1. All matter has a varying degree of conductivity or resistance to radio waves.
   a. The Earth itself acts as the greatest resistor to radio waves.
      1) Radio waves that travel near the ground induce a voltage in the ground that subtracts energy from the wave.
         a) This decreases the strength of the wave as the distance from the antenna becomes greater.
   b. Radio waves that travel into the upper atmosphere are also affected as energy is absorbed by molecules of air, water, and dust.
2. A radio wave normally radiates from an antenna in all directions.
   a. Part of the energy travels along the ground (ground wave) until its energy is dissipated.
   b. The remainder of the transmitted energy travels upward into space (sky wave).
3. The characteristics of radio waves vary according to their frequency, as do the behaviors of their ground and sky waves.
   a. This determines the design, use, and limitations of both ground and airborne equipment.

4. Low Frequency (LF) Radio Waves

   a. At frequencies below 300 kHz, there is substantial energy in the ground and sky waves.

   b. The sky wave is reflected by the ionosphere by highly charged particles (ions) caused by the Sun's radiation.

      1) This reflection of the radio wave permits reception of the signals at varying distances from the antenna.

      2) The transmission distance is determined by factors such as the height and density of the ionosphere (which varies with the time of day, seasons, and latitude due to the Sun's radiation) and the angle at which the radio wave strikes the ionosphere.

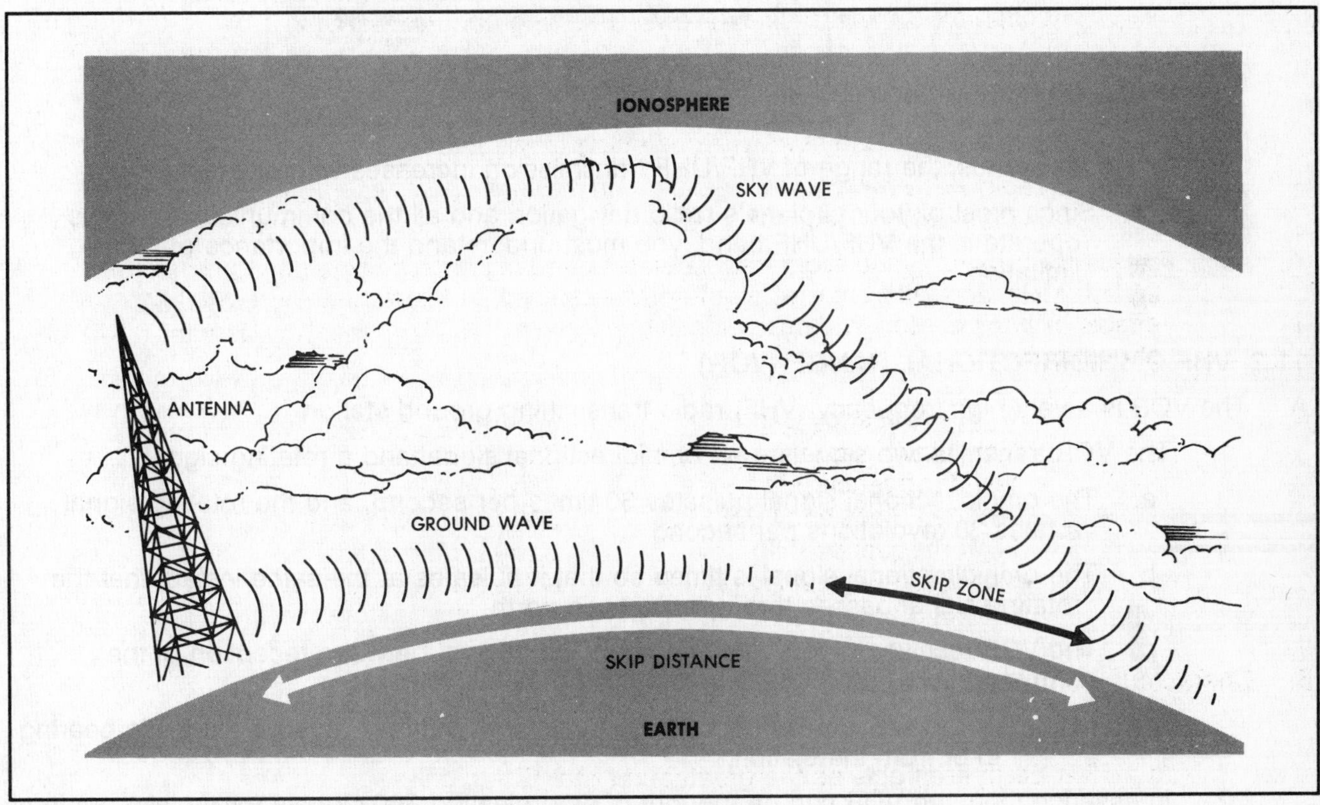


   c. The distance between the transmitting antenna and the point where the sky wave first returns to the ground is called the skip distance.

      1) The distance between the point where the ground wave can no longer be received and the sky wave returns is the skip zone.

   d. Since solar radiation varies the height and density of the ionosphere, great changes in skip distances occur at dawn and dusk when fading of signals is more prevalent.

5. Very High Frequency (VHF) and Ultra High Frequency (UHF) Radio Waves

   a. At frequencies above 30 MHz, there is practically no ground wave and ordinarily no reflection of the sky wave by the ionosphere.

   b. Use of VHF/UHF signals is possible only if the transmitting and/or receiving antennas are raised sufficiently above the surface of the Earth to allow the use of a direct wave.

      1) This is known as "line-of-sight" transmission.

c. The use of VHF/UHF radio waves is limited by the position of the receiver in relation to the transmitter, as shown below.

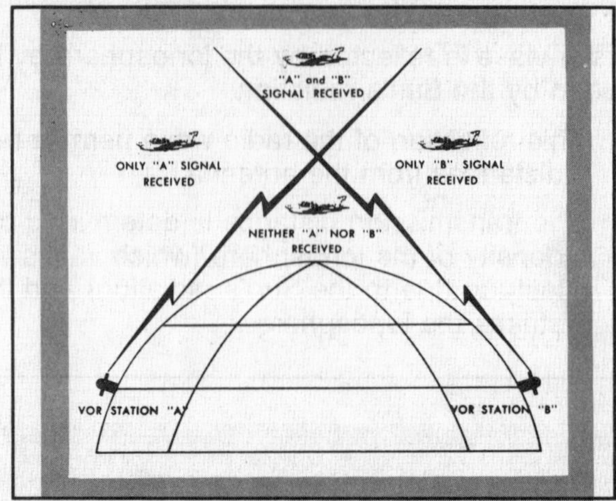


1) Thus, the range of VHF/UHF transmission increases with altitude.

d. Since most of your airplane's radio navigation and all the communication radios operate in the VHF/UHF band, you must understand the importance of this limitation.

## 11.2 VHF OMNIDIRECTIONAL RANGE (VOR)

A. The VOR is a very high frequency (VHF) radio transmitting ground station.

1. The VOR transmits two signals -- an omnidirectional signal and a rotating signal.

   a. The omnidirectional signal pulsates 30 times per second, and the rotating signal rotates 30 revolutions per second.

   b. The omnidirectional signal is timed so that it pulsates at the same instant that the rotating signal passes through magnetic north.

   c. The VOR receiver in your airplane times the interval between reception of the omnidirectional pulse and the rotating signal.

      1) The receiver converts this time interval into degrees as your magnetic bearing to or from the station.

2. In essence then, the VOR can be thought of as projecting 360 signals (or radials) out in all directions from the station.

   a. From a top view, the radials can be visualized as being similar to the spokes from the hub of a wheel.

   b. The radials are referenced to magnetic north.

      1) Thus, a radial is defined as a line of magnetic bearing extending FROM the VOR.

   c. To aid in orientation, a compass rose reference to magnetic north is superimposed on sectional charts at the station location.

3. The VOR ground station is a small, low building topped with a flat white disk upon which are located the antennas and a fiberglass antenna shelter. It has the appearance of an inverted ice cream cone about 30 ft. in height.

   a. VOR ground stations transmit within a VHF band of 108.00 to 117.95 MHz.

      1) Since VHF signals are subject to line-of-sight restrictions, the reception range varies proportionally to the altitude of the receiving equipment.

4. For the purpose of this discussion, the term VOR will be used to include the following types of ground stations.
   a. VOR -- provides azimuth (i.e., magnetic course) information.
   b. VORTAC (VOR/Tactical Air Navigation) -- provides azimuth in addition to range information from the Tactical Air Navigation (TACAN) component.
      1) If your airplane is equipped with distance measuring equipment (DME), your distance from the station in nautical miles (NM) will be displayed on the instrument.
      2) TACAN is used by military aircraft.
   c. VOR/DME -- provides azimuth and range information, similar to the VORTAC, but does not have the TACAN component.
5. VORs appear on aeronautical charts.
   a. A compass rose surrounding each VOR indicates magnetic headings.
   b. Some radials between VORs are marked in blue and are called Victor airways.
   c. Near each VOR compass rose is a radio communication box indicating the VOR name, frequency, and other information.

B. The VOR equipment in your airplane includes an antenna, a receiver with a tuning device, and a VOR navigation instrument.
1. VOR signals from the ground station are received through the antenna to the receiver, which interprets and separates the navigation information. Then this information is displayed on the navigation instrument.
2. The VOR navigation instrument consists of
   a. An omnibearing selector (OBS), sometimes referred to as the course selector.
      1) By turning the OBS knob (lower left of the diagram below), the desired course is selected. In the diagram below, the course is under the index at the top of the instrument, i.e., approximately 328°.

b. A course deviation indicator (CDI), referred to as the needle.
   1) The CDI needle is hinged to move laterally across the face of the instrument.
   2) It indicates the position of the selected course relative to your airplane.
   3) The CDI needle centers when your airplane is on the selected radial, as shown in the diagram on page 299.
c. A TO/FROM indicator, also called a sense indicator or ambiguity indicator.
   1) The TO/FROM indicator shows whether the selected course will take your airplane TO or FROM the station.
      a) It does not indicate whether the airplane is heading to or from the station.
      b) In the diagram on page 299, the selected course of 328° will take the airplane TO the station.

C. Using the VOR
1. Determine the frequency of the ground station.
   a. This is normally done during your cross-country planning. See Chapter 13, Cross-Country Flying, beginning on page 337.
   b. Frequencies can be found in the *Airport/Facility Directory* or on the appropriate sectional chart.
2. Tune and identify the station.
   a. Tune the appropriate frequency in the VOR receiver.
   b. The only positive method of identifying a VOR station is by its three-letter Morse code identification or by the recorded voice identification, which is always indicated by the use of the word "V-O-R" following its name.
      1) During periods of maintenance, the VOR station may transmit the word "T-E-S-T" (- . ... -) or the identifier may be removed.
      2) To monitor the station identifier, select the ident feature on the VOR receiver.
   c. Do not use a VOR station for navigation unless you can positively identify it.

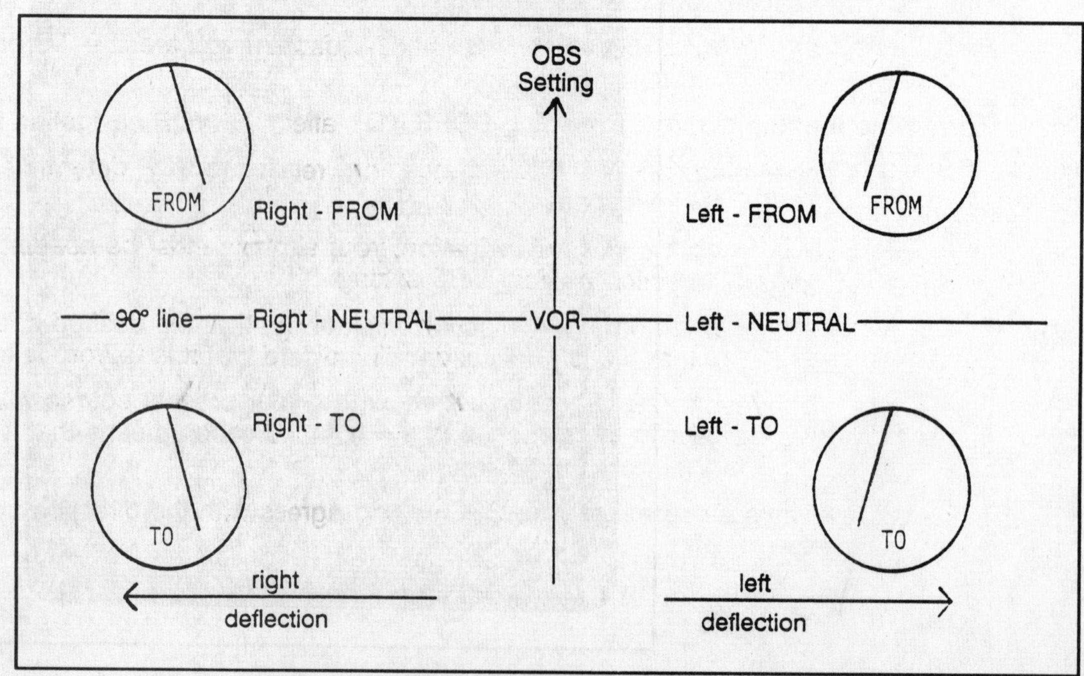

3. Interpreting VOR Indications (see the diagram at the bottom of the opposite page)
   a. When you select a course in the OBS, imagine that you have drawn a line through the VOR station in the direction of the course.
      1) The line should extend outward from the VOR both in the direction of the selected course and the direction of its reciprocal.
      2) Imagine an arrowhead at the end of the line in the direction of the desired course, as in the diagram.
      3) Now look at the diagram and imagine the VOR in the center.
         a) Rotate the diagram until the arrowhead points in the direction of your OBS setting.
         b) Note that when you are facing in the direction of the OBS setting, the CDI needle points to the right if you are left of the course, and points to the left if you are right of the course.
         c) If you are directly on the course line, the CDI needle will be centered.
   b. Imagine also a line drawn through the VOR perpendicular to the selected course, as shown in the diagram.
      1) Again, rotate the diagram until the arrowhead points in the direction of the OBS setting, and imagine that you are facing in that same direction.
         a) If you are below the 90° line, the TO/FROM indicator will read TO.
         b) If you are above the 90° line, it will read FROM.
         c) If you are anywhere on the 90° line, you will see a neutral (i.e., a blank TO/FROM window, NAV, OFF, or red flag) indication.
            i) You will also see a neutral indication if the VOR signal is too weak for reliable navigation.
   c. The diagram should be used to interpret VOR indications in flight. Remember that you must rotate the diagram so the omnibearing direction is pointed in the direction in which your OBS is set (i.e., the selected course).
      1) When flying, interpret the needle by envisioning your airplane being on a heading indicated by the OBS.
         a) You can immediately tell which quadrant you are in -- TO or FROM, left or right.
   d. Note that the airplane's heading DOES NOT affect the VOR navigation instrument.
      1) The airplane's POSITION (not heading) relative to VOR determines the CDI and TO/FROM indications.
      2) Thus, to obtain a useful indication, your airplane must be heading in the same general direction as your OBS setting.
         a) Then a right CDI deflection will indicate that the desired course is to your right, and a left deflection will indicate that it is to your left.
         b) Also, a TO indication will show that your present course will move you closer to the station, and a FROM indication means that it will take you farther from the station.
      3) Always be sure that your OBS setting agrees with the direction you intend to fly.

D. Navigating with the VOR

1. Using the VOR for navigation will generally require some combination of the following procedures.
   a. Flying directly to a VOR station from an unknown position
   b. Intercepting a desired VOR radial, either inbound or outbound
   c. Tracking a VOR course
   d. Determining your position using two VOR stations
2. Flying Directly to a VOR Station
   a. Tune and identify the station.
   b. Turn the OBS until a TO indication is shown and the CDI needle is centered. Then turn the airplane to the heading indicated by the OBS setting.
   c. Once you are on the desired radial, you must track that course (i.e., keep the CDI needle centered) by using crosswind corrections.
   d. If necessary, adjust the OBS once more to center the needle.
   e. Track the course you are on inbound to the station as outlined below.
3. Intercepting a Desired VOR Radial, either Inbound or Outbound
   a. Tune and identify the station.
   b. Turn to a heading to parallel the desired course, in the same direction as the course to be flown.
   c. Center the CDI needle and determine the difference between the radial to be intercepted and the radial on which you are located.
   d. Double the difference to determine the interception angle but do not use less than 20° or greater than 90°.
   e. Rotate the OBS to the desired course.
   f. Turn toward the CDI needle the amount determined in step d. above.
   g. Hold this magnetic heading constant until the CDI begins to center, indicating that you are on the desired radial or course.
   h. Turn to the magnetic heading corresponding to the selected course and track that radial.
      1) With practice, you will learn to lead the turn to prevent overshooting the course.
4. Tracking a VOR Radial
   a. In the diagram on page 303, you are tracking inbound on the 170° radial (magnetic course of 350° to the station).
   b. If a heading of 350° is maintained with a wind from the right, as shown at the bottom of the diagram, the airplane will drift to the left of the intended track.
      1) As the airplane drifts off course, the CDI needle will gradually move to the right of center and indicate the direction of the desired radial.
   c. To return to the desired radial, the airplane heading must be altered 20° to the right. As the airplane returns to the desired track, the CDI needle will slowly return to center.
      1) When the CDI is centered, the airplane will be on the desired radial and a left turn must be made toward, but not totally to, the original heading of 350°, in order to establish a wind drift correction.

a) The amount of correction depends upon the strength of the wind. If the wind velocity is unknown, a trial and error method (i.e., bracketing) can be used to find the correct heading.

b) Assume, for this example, a 10° correction or a heading of 360° is maintained.

d. While maintaining a heading of 360°, assume that the CDI needle begins to move to the left. This means that the wind correction of 10° is too great and the airplane is flying to the right of course.

1) A turn to the left to a heading of 350° should be made to permit the airplane to return to the desired radial.

2) When the CDI needle centers, a smaller wind drift correction of 5°, or a heading of 355°, should be flown.

a) If this correction is adequate, the airplane will remain on the radial.

b) If not, small heading variations should be made to keep the CDI needle centered, and consequently keep the airplane on the radial.

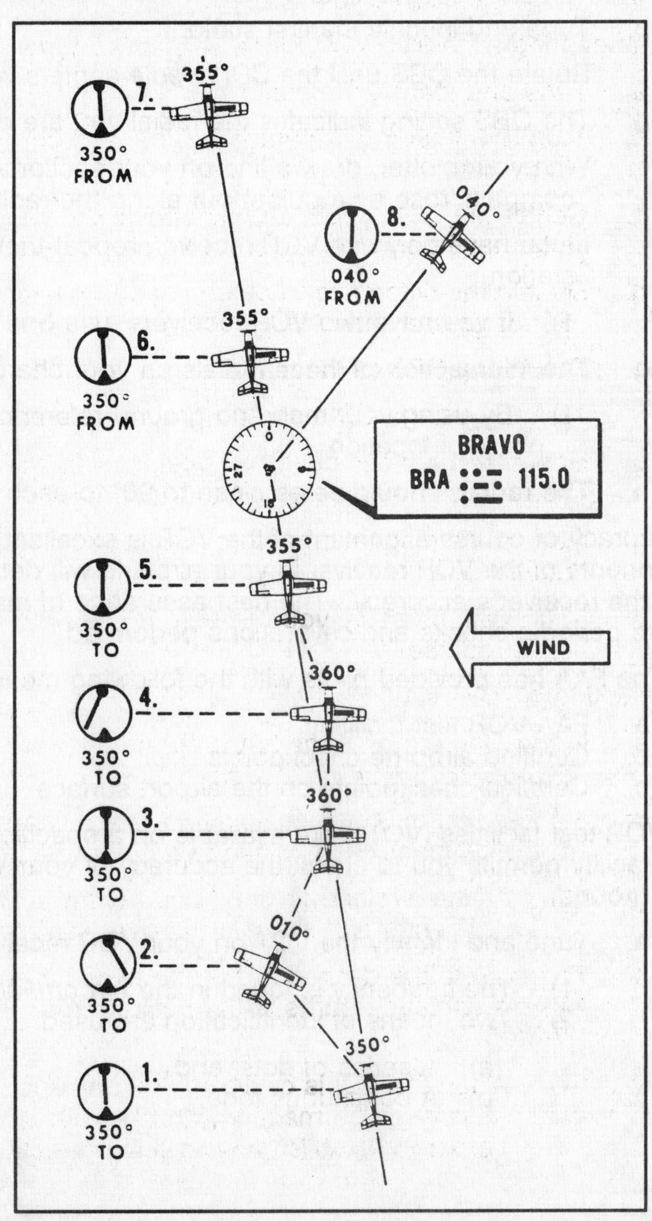

e. As the VOR station is passed, the TO indication will change to FROM. If the aircraft passes to one side of the station, the CDI needle will deflect in the direction of the station as the indicator changes to FROM.

f. Generally, the same techniques apply when tracking outbound as those used for tracking inbound.

1) If the intent is to fly over the station and track outbound on the reciprocal of the inbound radial, the course selector should not be changed. Corrections are made in the same manner to keep the CDI needle centered. The only difference is that the TO-FROM indicator will indicate FROM.

2) If tracking outbound on a course other than the reciprocal of the inbound radial, this new course or radial must be set in the course selector and a turn made to intercept this course. After this course is reached, tracking procedures are the same as previously discussed.

5. Determining Your Position Using Two VOR Stations

a. This is most convenient if your airplane is equipped with two VOR receivers, but can also be done easily using only one VOR receiver.

b. Tune and identify the first station.

c. Rotate the OBS until the CDI needle centers with a FROM indication.

d. The OBS setting indicates the radial you are on.

e. With your plotter, draw a line on your sectional chart from the VOR (using the compass rose as a guide) out along the radial you are on.

f. If you have only one VOR receiver, repeat these steps using the second VOR station.

1) If you have two VOR receivers, use one VOR receiver for each VOR station.

g. The intersection of these radials on your chart is your approximate location.

1) By using your map and ground references you should be able to establish your location.

h. The radials should be as close to 90° to each other for the most accurate location.

E. The accuracy of course alignment of the VOR is excellent, generally within ±1°. However, components of the VOR receiver in your airplane will deteriorate over time and will adversely affect the receiver's accuracy. The best assurance of maintaining an accurate VOR receiver is to have periodic checks and calibrations performed.

1. The FAA has provided pilots with the following means of checking VOR receiver accuracy:

a. FAA VOR test facilities
b. Certified airborne checkpoints
c. Certified checkpoints on the airport surface

2. VOR test facilities (VOTs) are available on a specific frequency at certain airports. The facility permits you to check the accuracy of your VOR receiver while you are on the ground.

a. Tune and identify the VOT on your VOR receiver.

1) The frequency is found in the *Airport/Facility Directory*.
2) Two means of identification are used.

a) A series of dots, and
b) A continuous tone.

b. Turn the OBS until the CDI needle centers.
   1) The indicated course should be either 0° or 180°, regardless of your position on the airport.
   2) If 0°, the TO/FROM indicator should indicate FROM.
   3) If 180°, the TO/FROM indicator should indicate TO.

c. Accuracy of the VOR receiver should be ±4°.

3. Certified airborne and ground checkpoints consist of certified radials that should be received (i.e., CDI needle centered and a FROM indication) over specific points or landmarks while airborne in the immediate vicinity of the airport or at a specific point on the airport surface.
   a. Accuracy of the VOR receiver should be
      1) ±6° for airborne checks.
      2) ±4° for ground checks.
4. If your airplane is equipped with two separate VOR receivers, you may check one system against the other.
   a. Tune, identify, and center the CDI needle of each VOR receiver to the same VOR station. Ensure each has the same TO/FROM indication.
   b. The maximum variation between the two indicated bearings should be ±4°.
5. Locations of VOTs, airborne, and ground checkpoints are published in the *Airport/Facility Directory*.
6. It is possible for the VOR receiver to display acceptable accuracy close into the VOR or VOT and display out-of-tolerance readings when located at greater distances where weaker signal areas exist.
   a. A certified repair facility should recalibrate the VOR receiver on a yearly basis.
7. While VOR receiver accuracy checks are not required for VFR flight, it is good to follow the IFR guidelines, as discussed above.

F. Tips on Using the VOR

1. Positively identify the station by its code or voice identification.
2. Keep in mind that VOR signals are line-of-sight. A weak signal or no signal at all will be received if the airplane is too low or too far from the station.
3. When navigating TO a station, determine the inbound radial and use it. If the airplane drifts, do not reset the OBS, but correct for drift and fly a heading that will compensate for wind drift.
4. If minor needle fluctuations occur, avoid changing headings immediately. Wait momentarily to see if the needle recenters. If it does not, then correct.
5. When flying TO a station, always fly the selected course with a TO indication. When flying FROM a station, always fly the selected course with a FROM indication.
   a. If this is not done, the action of the CDI needle will be reversed (i.e., reverse sensing).
      1) If the airplane is flown toward a station with a FROM indication or away from a station with a TO indication, the CDI needle will indicate in a direction opposite to that which it should.
      2) EXAMPLE: If the airplane drifts to the right of a radial being flown, the needle will move to the right or point away from the radial. If the airplane drifts to the left of the radial being flown, the needle will move left or in the opposite direction of the radial.

6. When flying from one VOR to another, fly FROM the first VOR until about the halfway point. Then tune in to the next VOR and fly TO it.
   a. Changing to the next VOR may require a slight adjustment to your OBS to center the CDI needle.
   b. Relying on a VOR for only one-half the distance will help prevent weak signals.

## 11.3 DISTANCE MEASURING EQUIPMENT (DME)

A. VORTAC and VOR/DME ground stations provide distance information to those airplanes equipped with distance measuring equipment (DME).
   1. DME operates on a UHF band of 962 to 1213 MHz, and like the VOR signal, it is subject to line-of-sight restrictions.
   2. To use DME, you select the VORTAC or VOR/DME frequency band as you do with the VOR. The DME will then be tuned to the correct UHF band. This is called a paired frequency.
   3. When using both VOR and DME, you must ensure that each is operating properly by listening for the identifiers.
      a. The DME identifier is transmitted one time for each three or four times the VOR identifier is transmitted.
      b. A single coded identification transmitted every 30 sec. indicates the DME is operative, but the VOR is inoperative.
         1) The absence of the single coded identification every 30 sec. indicates the DME is inoperative.

B. The DME equipment in the airplane includes a transceiver and a small shark fin-type antenna. The DME display is on the face of the transceiver and may be part of the VOR receiver or a separate unit, as shown below.

   1. Many DMEs show distance, time, and speed on separate displays as opposed to only one display as in the figure above.

C. In the operation of DME, your airplane first transmits a signal (integration) to the ground station. The ground station (transponder) then transmits a signal back to your airplane.
   1. The DME in your airplane records the round trip time of this signal exchange. From this it can compute
      a. Distance (NM) to the station.
      b. Groundspeed (kt.) relative to the station.
      c. Time (min.) to the station at the current groundspeed.
   2. The mileage readout is the direct distance from the airplane to the DME ground facility. This is commonly referred to as slant-range distance.
      a. The difference between a measured distance on the surface and the DME slant-range distance is known as slant-range error.

1) It is smallest at low altitude and long range.
2) This error is greatest when the airplane is at a high altitude close to, or over, the ground station, at which time the DME receiver will display altitude in NM above the station.
3) Slant-range error is negligible if the airplane is 1 NM or more from the ground facility for each 1,000 ft. of altitude above the elevation of the facility.

3. To use the groundspeed and/or time to station function of the DME, you must be flying directly to or from the station.
   a. Flying in any other direction will provide you with false groundspeed and time to station information.

## 11.4 AUTOMATIC DIRECTION FINDER (ADF)

A. Many airplanes are equipped with an ADF radio which receives radio signals in the low to medium frequency bands of 190 kHz to 1750 kHz.
   1. There are two types of ground stations that may be used with the ADF.
      a. Nondirectional radio beacons (NDB) which operate in the frequency band of 190 to 535 kHz.
      b. Commercial broadcast (AM) radio stations which operate in the frequency band of 540 to 1620 kHz.

B. The equipment in the airplane includes two antennas, a receiver with a tuning device, and a navigational display.
   1. The two antennas are
      a. A loop antenna which is used as the directional antenna.
         1) The loop antenna determines the direction in which the signal is the strongest, but it cannot determine whether the station is in front of or behind the airplane (i.e., known as loop ambiguity).
      b. The sense antenna is nondirectional and allows the ADF to solve the problem of loop ambiguity and the ADF can determine the direction of the signal.
   2. The receiver allows you to tune the correct frequency, and function selectors, as shown below.

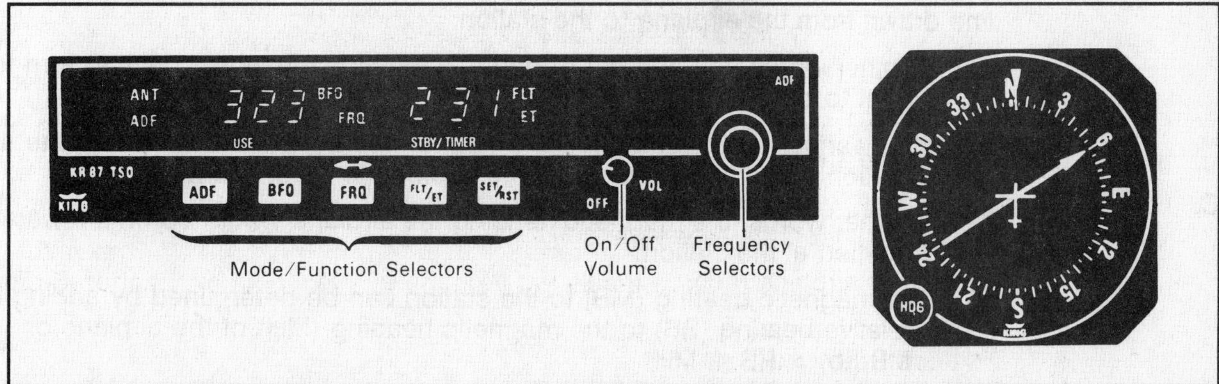




   3. The navigational display, which consists of a dial upon which the azimuth (0° to 360°) is printed, and a needle which rotates around the dial and points to the station to which the receiver is tuned.
      a. Some ADF dials can be rotated to align the azimuth with the airplane heading (as shown above). This is called a movable card indicator.

b. Other ADF dials are fixed, with the 0° - 180° points on the azimuth aligned with the longitudinal axis of the airplane. On these, the 0° position on the azimuth represents the nose of the airplane. This is called a fixed-card indicator.

1) Our discussion will be based on the fixed-card indicator.

C. Using the ADF

1. Determine the frequency of the ground station.

a. This is normally done during your cross-country planning. See Chapter 13, Cross-Country Flying, beginning on page 337.

b. Frequencies for NDBs can be found in the *Airport/Facility Directory* or on the appropriate sectional chart.

1) Some major commercial broadcast station locations and frequencies are shown on sectional charts.

2. Tune and identify the station.

a. Use the function selector to select the ANT or REC position. This selects the sense antenna only and allows maximum sensitivity to radio signals.

b. Next tune the desired frequency and increase the volume until you can hear background noise, then readjust it for comfort.

c. Positively identify the ground station.

1) All NDBs transmit a continuous two- or three-letter identification in Morse code.

a) Some NDBs may have voice transmissions which override the identifier.

2) Commercial broadcast stations are identified at random times, although 15-min. intervals are common.

d. While using the ADF for navigation you should continuously monitor the identifier, as this is the only means of verifying that the proper station is being received.

3. Next, select the ADF mode, which uses both the loop and sense antennas.

a. This mode allows navigation information to be displayed on the navigational display.

4. ADF Orientation (see diagram on page 309)

a. Relative bearing is the value to which the indicator (needle) points on the azimuth dial. This value is the angle measured clockwise from the nose of the airplane to a line drawn from the airplane to the station.

1) In other words, the number of degrees the airplane would have to turn to the right to be pointed at the station.

b. Magnetic bearing to the station is the angle formed by a line drawn from the airplane to the station and a line drawn from the airplane to magnetic north.

1) In other words, the magnetic heading the airplane would be on if it were pointed at the station.

2) The magnetic bearing (MB) to the station can be determined by adding the relative bearing (RB) to the magnetic heading (MH) of the airplane or MB (to) = RB + MH.

a) EXAMPLE: If the relative bearing is 060° and the magnetic heading is 130°, the magnetic bearing to the station is 190° (060° + 130°). This means that in still air a magnetic heading of approximately 190° would be flown to the station.

3) If the total is greater than 360°, subtract 360° from the total to obtain the magnetic bearing to the station.

   a) EXAMPLE: If the relative bearing is 270° and magnetic heading is 300°, 360° is subtracted from the total, or 570° – 360° = 210°, which is the magnetic bearing to the station.

c. To determine the magnetic bearing from the station, 180° is added to or subtracted from the magnetic bearing to the station. You would use this reciprocal bearing when plotting your position.

d. You will orient yourself more readily if you think in terms of nose/tail and left/right needle indications, visualizing the ADF dial in terms of the longitudinal axis of the airplane.

   1) When the needle points to 0°, the nose of the airplane points directly to the station.

   2) With the needle on 210°, the station is 30° to the left of the tail.

   3) With the needle on 090°, the station is off the right wingtip.

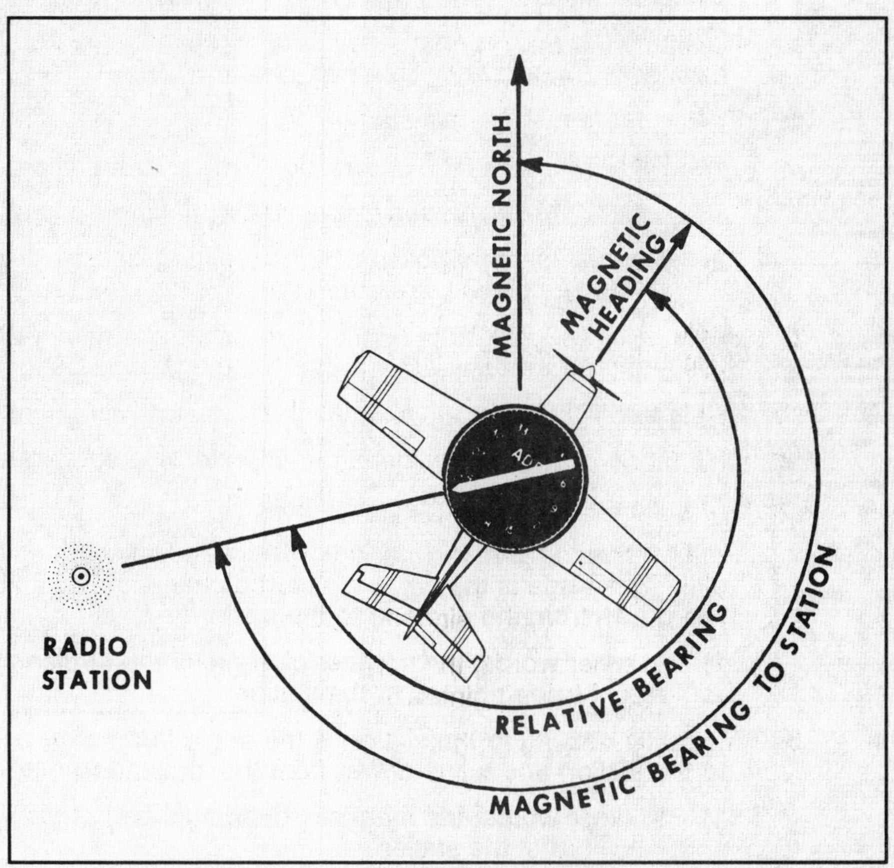

NDB Tracking -- Inbound

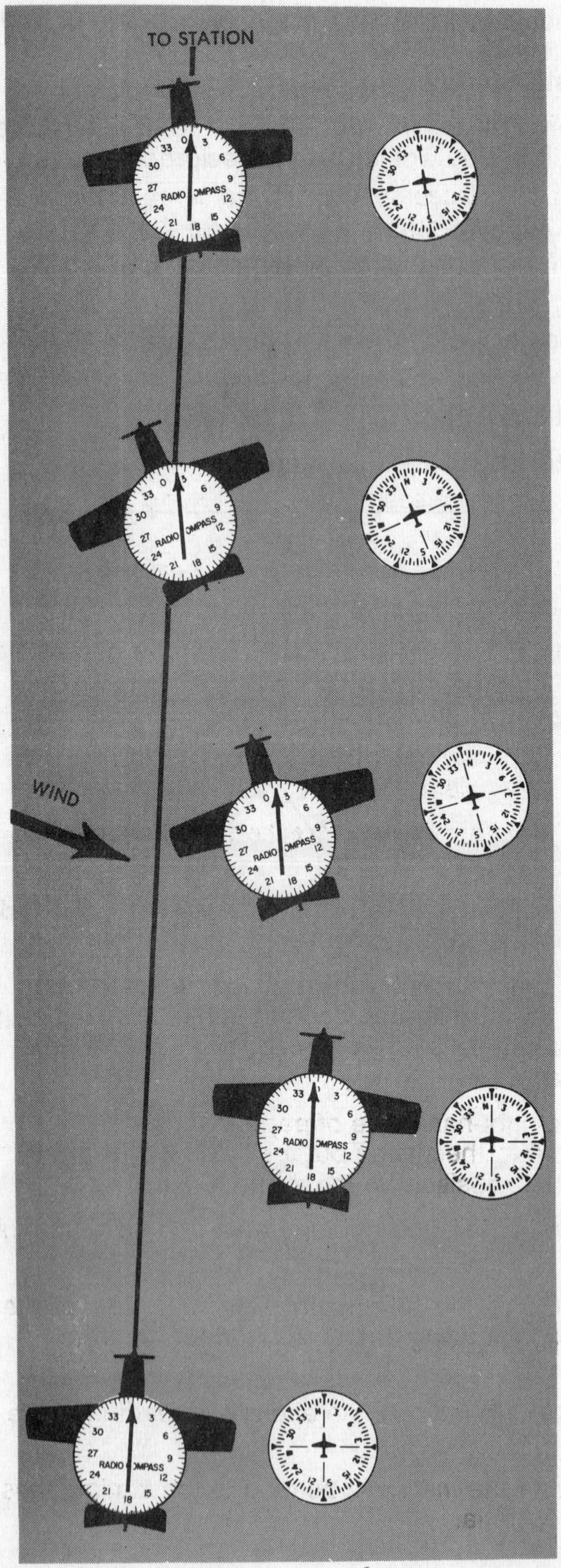

TO STATION

WIND

RADIO COMPASS

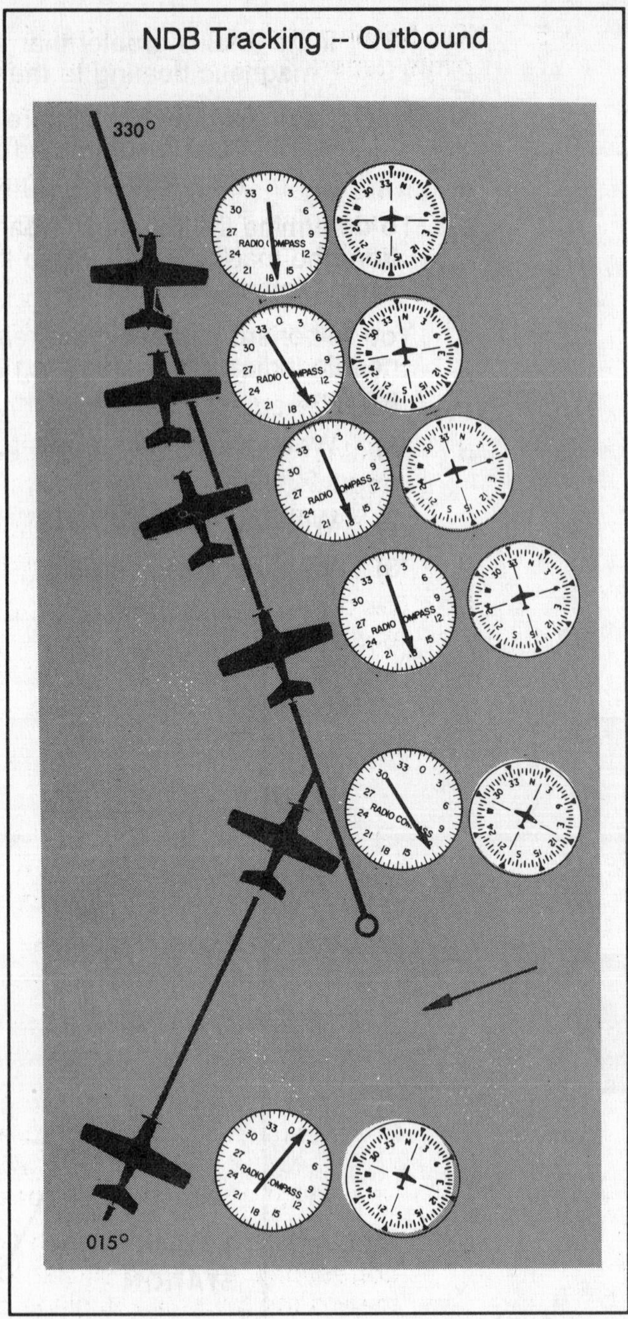

5. NDB bearing interception and tracking are explained here even though student and private pilots generally are **not** required to learn them.
   a. Determine your position in relation to the station by turning to the magnetic heading of the bearing to be intercepted.
   b. Note whether the station is to the right or left of the nose to track inbound. Determine the number of degrees of needle deflection from the 0° position, and double this amount for the interception angle.
      1) Interception of an outbound bearing is accomplished in the same manner, except you substitute the 180° position for the 0° position on the ADF dial.
   c. Turn your airplane toward the desired magnetic bearing the number of degrees determined for the interception angle.
   d. Maintain the interception heading until the needle is deflected the same number of degrees from the zero position as the angle of interception (minus lead appropriate to the rate of bearing change).
   e. Turn inbound and continue with tracking.
   f. The procedures to track inbound are as follows (see figure on left-hand side of page 310):
      1) Turn airplane until the needle is on zero. Hold this heading until off-course drift is indicated by left or right needle deflection.
      2) When a 5° change in needle deflection is observed, turn 20° in the direction of needle deflection.
      3) When the needle is deflected 20° (deflection = interception angle), track has been intercepted. Turn 10° back toward the inbound course. You are now inbound with a 10° drift correction angle.
      4) If you observe off-course deflection in the original direction, turn again to the original interception heading.
      5) When the desired course has been reintercepted, turn 5° toward the inbound course, proceeding inbound with a 15° drift correction.
      6) If the initial 10° drift correction is excessive, as shown by needle deflection away from the wind, turn to parallel the desired course and let the wind drift you back on course. When the needle is again zeroed, turn into the wind with a reduced drift correction angle.
   g. When tracking outbound (see figure on right-hand side of page 310), wind corrections are made similar to tracking to the station but the ADF needle points toward the tail of the airplane or the 180° position on the azimuth dial.
      1) Even though the needle points to the tail, you still turn toward the direction of the deflection.
      2) Attempting to keep the ADF needle on the 180° position during winds results in the airplane flying a curved flight leading further and further from the desired track.
6. The movable-card ADF can be manually rotated to indicate the airplane's heading at the top of the instrument.
   a. By doing this the needle will then indicate the magnetic bearing to the station, thus it does not require you to use the ADF formula.

D. Advantages and Limitations

1. Advantages
   a. ADF does not rely on line-of-sight, which may allow reliable navigational signals at lower altitudes than VOR and may also provide greater reception range.
   b. ADF can be used to determine your airplane's position. This can be done by using two NDBs or, if the airplane is equipped, using a VOR station and an NDB.
      1) This is helpful if there is not an off-course VOR station available.
2. Disadvantages are mainly due to the characteristics of low or medium frequency radio waves.
   a. During the period just before and after sunrise or sunset, the radio waves may be reflected by the ionosphere, which causes erratic needle movements.
      1) Stations transmitting on frequencies lower than 350 kHz are least affected by this phenomenon.
   b. Radio waves may be bent when they cross shorelines at small angles.
   c. In mountainous areas, the radio waves can be reflected by mountains.
   d. Near thunderstorms, the ADF needle has a tendency to point toward lightning discharges.
   e. At night, it is possible to receive signals from a distant station which could interfere with the station being used.

## 11.5 AREA NAVIGATION (RNAV)

A. Area navigation (RNAV) allows a pilot to fly a selected course to a predetermined point without the need to overfly ground-based navigation facilities. The most common types of RNAV equipment used by small general aviation aircraft are

1. VORTAC-based,
2. LORAN (long-range navigation), and
3. GPS (Global Positioning System).

B. RNAV allows you to fly directly from your departure airport to your destination airport, or from waypoint to waypoint.

1. A waypoint is a geographical position that is determined by a radial and distance from a VORTAC station or in terms of latitude/longitude coordinates.
2. Flying direct routes saves time and fuel, and lowers operating expenses.

## 11.6 VORTAC-BASED RNAV

A. VORTAC-based RNAV is based on azimuth (i.e., a VOR radial) and distance information (DME) generated by VORTAC ground stations.
   1. A waypoint is defined by a radial and distance from the VORTAC.
   2. Navigation is to these waypoints rather than the VORTAC stations.

B. VORTAC RNAV is a method of "moving" VORs. That is, when the position of a waypoint is entered into the RNAV, the display unit (which resembles a VOR receiver) allows the pilot to navigate to the waypoint using the RNAV unit as if it were a VOR.
   1. This is known as the Course Line Computer (CLC).

C. For example, as shown in the figure below, the value of side (A) is the measured DME distance to the VORTAC from the airplane.
   1. You set the following information into the RNAV unit.
      a. The radial (1) and the distance (B) from the VORTAC to the waypoint.
   2. The bearing from the VORTAC to the airplane, angle (2), is measured by the VOR receiver.
   3. The CLC in the VORTAC RNAV unit compares angles (1) and (2) and determines angle (3).
   4. With this information, the CLC, by means of simple trigonometric functions, continuously solves for side (C), the distance in NM and magnetic course from the airplane to the waypoint. The result is presented on the cockpit display (i.e., VOR indicator) of the RNAV unit.

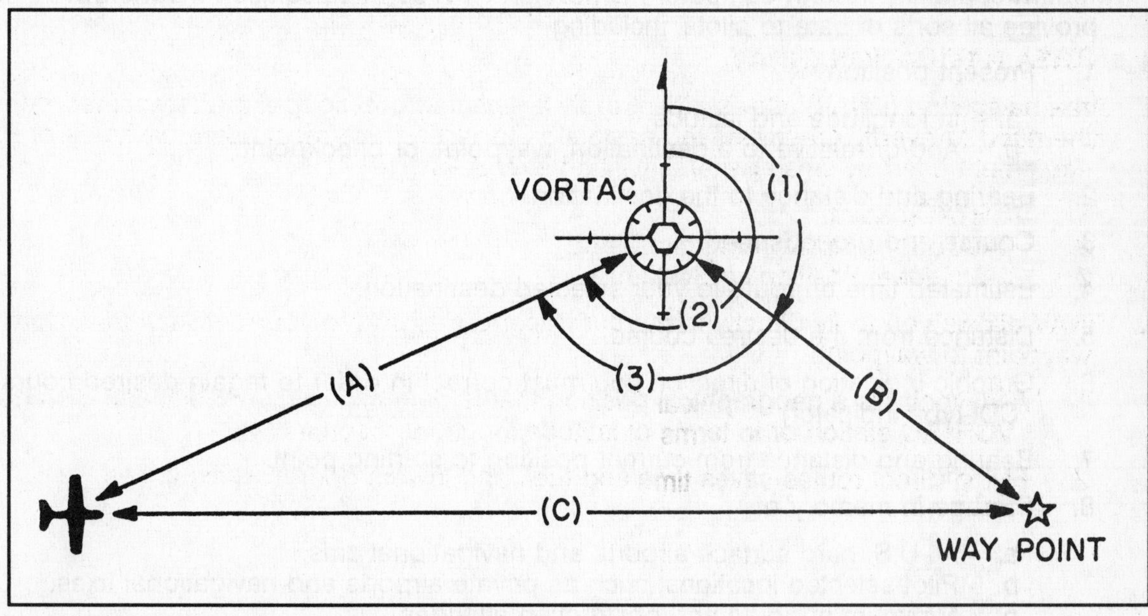


D. The advantages of the VORTAC RNAV system stem from the ability of the airborne computer to locate the waypoint whenever the airplane is within reception range of the VORTAC.

## 11.7 LONG RANGE NAVIGATION (LORAN)

A. LORAN operates on the principle of time measurement.

1. The airplane's LORAN receiver determines its position relative to a chain of transmitting stations.
2. The chain consists of three to five transmitting stations separated by several hundred miles.
   a. Within the chain, one station is designated as the master station (M).
   b. The other stations in the chain are secondary: Whiskey (W), Xray (X), Yankee (Y), and Zulu (Z).
   c. The master station and the secondary stations transmit synchronized pulses at precise time intervals.
   d. The LORAN receiver measures the slight time difference (TD) that it takes for these pulsed signals to reach the airplane.
   e. The LORAN computer calculates the airplane's position based on these time differences.
3. The LORAN system provides signal coverage throughout the continental U.S. and much of Alaska.
4. Only the groundwave signals are used for air navigation.
   a. Within the groundwave range, the accuracy of LORAN is 0.25 NM or better.

B. Modern capability in both computer memory and speed of calculation means LORAN can provide all sorts of data to pilots, including

1. Present position
   a. In longitude and latitude,
   b. And/or relative to a destination, waypoint, or checkpoint.
2. Bearing and distance to the destination.
3. Course and groundspeed.
4. Estimated time en route to your selected destination.
5. Distance from the desired course.
6. Graphic indication of direction you must correct in order to regain desired course (i.e., a CDI-type indicator).
7. Bearing and distance from current position to starting point.
8. Storage in memory of
   a. All U.S. hard surface airports and navigational aids.
   b. Pilot-selected locations, such as private airports and navigational fixes.
   c. Minimum en route and obstruction altitudes.
   d. Readout for any specified routes.
9. Continuous computation of bearings and distances to the nearest airports for use in emergencies.
10. Computation of wind direction and velocity at altitude (when you input your magnetic heading and TAS).

11. Combination or add-on capability with ELTs to transmit exact location to search-and-rescue parties.
12. Combination or add-on capability with fuel flow analyzers to estimate fuel usage to destination, alternates, etc.
13. Reprogrammable computers to upgrade old LORAN software libraries with new features, locations, names, and frequencies of navigation facilities and airports.
14. An alert function to warn you of an impending penetration of Class B (formerly a TCA) or Class C (formerly an ARSA) airspace.

C. While LORAN is excellent when it works, it is not always perfect.
   1. Since it uses a low-frequency radio signal, electrical disturbances such as lightning and static electricity can cause interference.
      a. When flying near areas of thunderstorm activity and/or heavy precipitation, it is not unusual to experience a loss of the LORAN signal.
   2. Antenna installation is crucial to good performance.
      a. The antenna must be kept away from sources of precipitation-induced static and other aircraft-generated interference.

## 11.8 GLOBAL POSITIONING SYSTEM (GPS)

A. GPS is a satellite-based navigation system developed and operated by the Department of Defense (DOD).

B. Like LORAN, GPS is a navigation system that precisely measures the arrival time of radio signals from transmitters at known locations to calculate position.
   1. Orbiting satellites transmit coded pulses containing their position and the precise time the pulse was broadcast.
      a. A GPS receiver listens for each satellite's signal and measures the elapsed time between the satellite's broadcast and its reception.
      b. This establishes the distance between the satellite and the GPS receiver.
      c. By measuring distance to several satellites, a GPS receiver establishes its position through triangulation.
   2. Because radio waves travel at immense speeds, the smallest clock error in a GPS system would result in enormous errors in range calculations.
      a. Thus, a GPS receiver must use the precise clock time broadcast by the satellites to calibrate its clock.
      b. This requires the use of an additional satellite, so three are actually required for a two-dimensional (2-D) position fix.
      c. When four or more satellites are in view of the GPS receiver, both position and altitude (i.e., 3-D) can be determined.
   3. If the receiver's altitude is known, it can be substituted for the range input from one of the satellites.
      a. Thus, most GPS receivers also receive input from the transponder's altitude encoder.
      b. Knowing altitude also allows certain GPS receivers to issue warnings if you are about to encroach on regulated airspace (e.g., Class B) without a clearance, and to avoid issuing a false warning if you are above or below these areas.

C. GPS receivers can be built with databases containing navigational fixes and even runway thresholds.

1. This allows GPS to provide you with the same types of data that LORAN does, as explained in the previous module.

2. Some receivers even have a TV-type moving map display, and can draw an airport diagram complete with runway numbers.

3. Since GPS receivers can compute altitude as well as position, it is reasonable to assume that precision approaches based on GPS will eventually be possible.

D. GPS navigation is not affected by precipitation or thunderstorms, only by the number of satellites in view.

1. Typically, a GPS receiver is tracking five or more satellites, and occasionally as many as eight.

   a. The maximum error is usually 100 meters, or .05 NM.

2. However, the full constellation of satellites is not yet in orbit, resulting in gaps in continuous coverage.

   a. Until the gaps have been closed, no GPS will be approved for use as the primary IFR navigation instrument.

   b. IFR certification is also dependent upon assuming the integrity of GPS signals and the ability to warn the pilot promptly if GPS becomes unusable.

3. GPS is usable world-wide, as long as the receiver's database is programmed with the appropriate navigational fixes and airports.

# CHAPTER TWELVE
# FLIGHT COMPUTERS



This chapter explains how to use E6-B flight computers and also introduces you to electronic flight computers. You will need a flight computer for the cross-country phase of your flight training, and to study for and take the FAA written exam.

We suggest that you begin by purchasing a manual E6-B, rather than an electronic one. A manual flight computer is as fast or faster than an electronic one, costs much less, and never needs new batteries. As your abilities and needs progress, you can always upgrade to an electronic computer as your budget allows.

## 12.1 THE MANUAL FLIGHT COMPUTER

A. The flight computer is used to solve navigational problems and compute some aircraft performance. Some of the possible calculations are
   1. Time, speed, or distance to reach a destination.
   2. Fuel required to reach a destination.
   3. True airspeed.
   4. True altitude.
   5. Effect of wind on heading and groundspeed.
   6. Changing nautical miles into statute miles and vice versa.
   7. Changing Fahrenheit into Celsius and vice versa.

B. The flight computer can also be used to multiply, divide, convert mach numbers (mach numbers are speeds in terms of multiples of the speed of sound) to true airspeed, and various other computations beyond the scope of this book.
   1. The instruction manual included with your flight computer will include all these computations.

C. The illustrations in the following outline are reproduced with permission from Flight Computer Manual copyright © 1972, 1976 by Jeppesen Sanderson, Inc.

1. This is an instruction book prepared for Piper Aircraft Co. by Jeppesen. Jeppesen also produces the same computer with its own "label," i.e., Jeppesen.
2. The E6-B flight computer (which costs about $30) is illustrated in this chapter.
3. In addition to the E6-B slide rule flight computer, there are other designs and models of slide rule flight computers. One series is called the CR type. They are round and do not have a sliding wind grid like the E6-B.

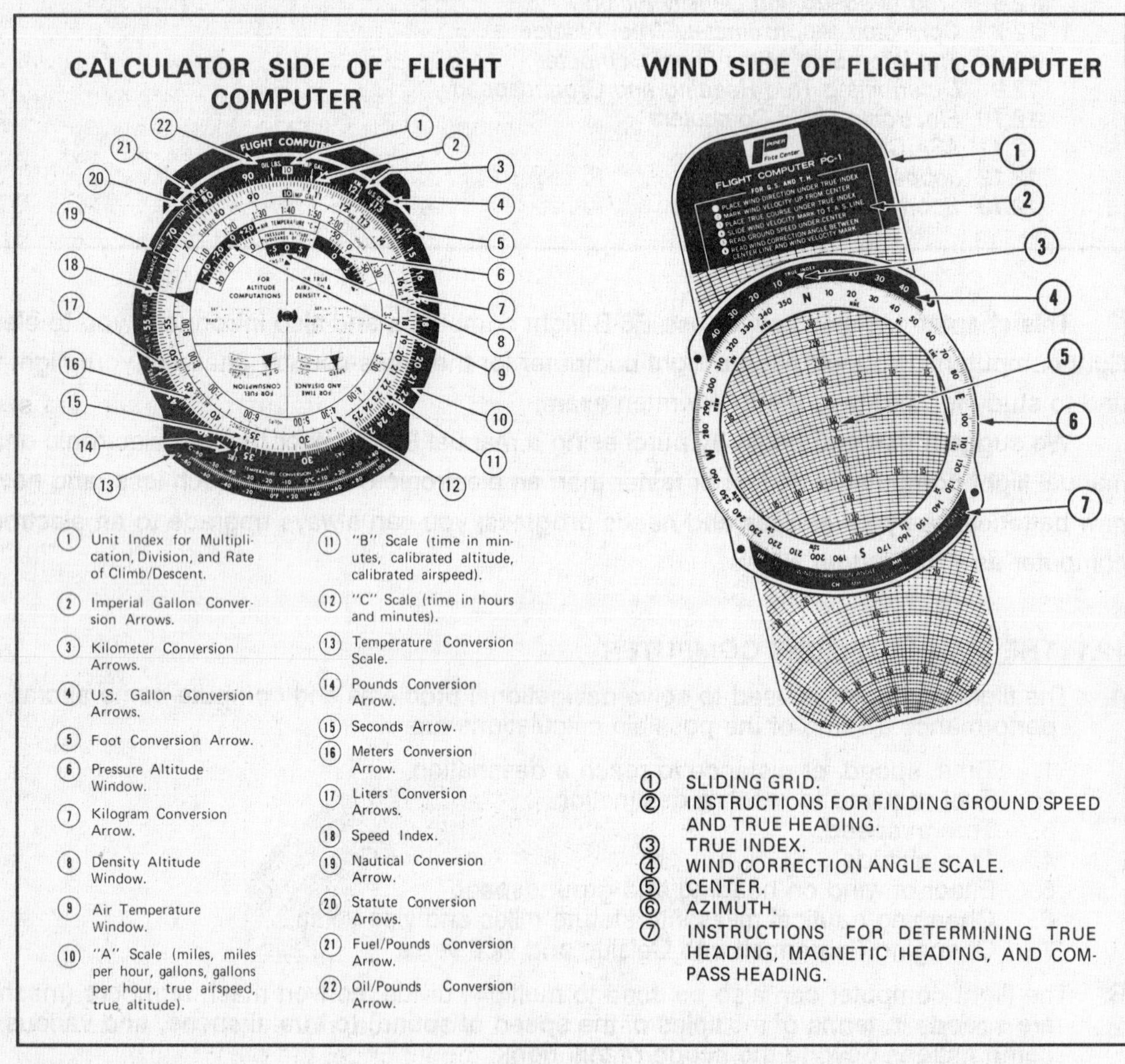


D. A flight computer has two sides: a calculator side and a wind side, as shown in the figure above.

1. Note that the calculator side has many more features than you really need for the computations covered in this book. You should focus on items 6, 8, 9, 10, 11, 12, 13, 18, 19, and 20. These will be explained in the next seven modules.
2. Note that the "sliding grid" for the wind side has two sides. One is for high speed, which you generally will not need, and one is for low speed, used by most private pilots for small planes.

## 12.2 THE CALCULATOR SIDE OF THE FLIGHT COMPUTER

A. The calculator side consists of a stationary portion with a flat circular portion attached. The circular portion can be turned.

1. The numbers along the outside of the stationary portion are referred to as the OUTER SCALE in this chapter. In the figure on page 318, this scale is referred to as scale "A" (item 10).

   a. This scale will represent miles, gallons, groundspeed, true airspeed, or altitude, depending on the calculation being performed.

2. The numbers on the edge of the rotating portion are referred to as the INNER SCALE in this chapter. There are actually two scales here. In the figure on page 318, these scales are referred to as scales "B" and "C" (items 11 and 12).

   a. At the edge of the rotating portion is scale "B", which will represent minutes or indicated airspeed or altitude, depending on the calculation being performed.

   b. Just inside scale "B" (see the figure on page 318) is scale "C" which corresponds directly to scale "B" but represents hours and minutes (instead of only minutes).

3. In the center of the rotating portion are three "holes" (windows). These are used to compute true altitude, density altitude, and true airspeed.

B. As is the case with any slide rule, there are no decimal markings on any of the scales.

1. Thus, 80 could mean .8, 8, 80, 800, etc.
2. When using the calculator side of the flight computer, you must use common sense to put the decimal in its proper place.
3. You must also take care to assign their proper value to the graduations between numbers.

C. The next six modules contain instruction in the basic uses of the calculator side of the flight computer.

## 12.3 CONVERSION OF NAUTICAL MILES TO STATUTE MILES AND VICE VERSA

A. The outer scale has two arrows near each other. One is labeled NAUT. (NM) and the other STAT. (SM).

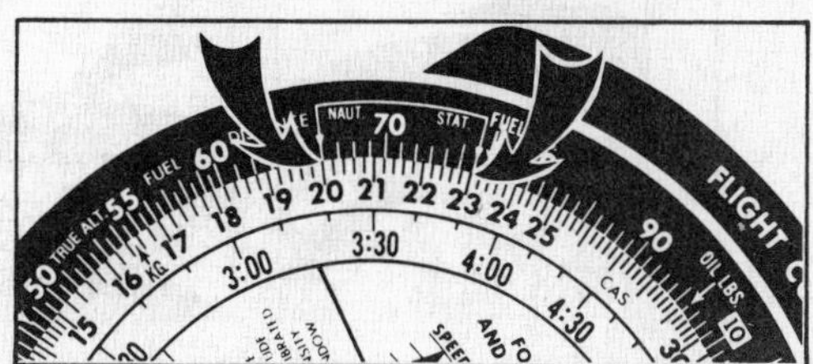


B. When converting NM (or kt.) to SM (or mph) or vice versa, place the number being converted under its arrow, and read the corresponding amount under the other arrow.

C. For example (as illustrated above), 20 NM equals 23 SM or 20 kt. equals 23 mph.

D. Use your flight computer to solve these practice problems (answers on next page).

| | NM | SM |
|---|---|---|
| 1. | 107 | ___ |
| 2. | 139 | ___ |
| 3. | ___ | 181 |
| 4. | ___ | 78 |
| 5. | 320 | ___ |

E. Answers to Practice Problems

1. 123 SM
2. 160 SM
3. 157 NM
4. 68 NM
5. 368 SM

## 12.4 SPEED, DISTANCE, AND TIME COMPUTATIONS

A. Speed, distance, and time are three interrelated elements. With any two of these elements, you can compute the third (missing) element.

1. The computations are:
   a. Speed = distance ÷ time
   b. Distance = speed x time
   c. Time = distance ÷ speed
2. You can use your flight computer to make the above computations.
   a. Note that in any problem both the speed and distance must be in either SM or NM.
   b. You can convert SM to NM or vice versa easily as explained in the preceding module.

B. Determining Time En Route

1. Refer to the figure below.
   a. Turn the rotating portion so that the speed index (solid triangular pointer) is under your groundspeed.
   b. Find the distance on the outer scale and read the time en route on the inner scale.
2. As illustrated below, if your groundspeed is 140 kt., the time to travel 210 NM is 90 min. or 1 hr. 30 min.

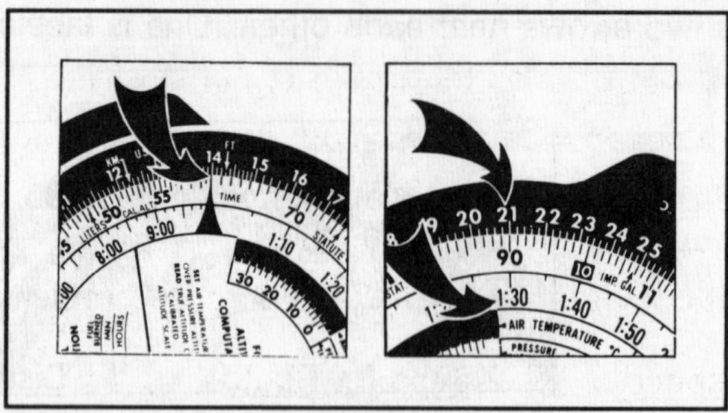

3. Use your flight computer to solve these practice problems (answers on next page).

| | Groundspeed | Distance | Time En Route |
|---|---|---|---|
| a. | 80 mph | 300 SM | ______ |
| b. | 95 mph | 19 SM | ______ |
| c. | 105 mph | 8 SM | ______ |
| d. | 143 kt. | 225 NM | ______ |
| e. | 92 kt. | 142 NM | ______ |

4. Answers to practice problems
   a. 225 min. or 3 hr. 45 min.
   b. 12 min.
   c. 4½ min.
   d. 94 min. or 1 hr. 34 min.
   e. 93 min. or 1 hr. 33 min.

C. Determining Groundspeed

1. Refer to the previous figure.
   a. Turn the rotating portion so the time en route between two points (on the inner scale) is below the distance between those two points.
   b. Find your groundspeed on the outer scale over the speed index.
2. As illustrated in the previous figure, if you traveled 210 NM in 90 min., your groundspeed was 140 kt.
3. Use your flight computer to solve these practice problems (cover the answers below).

| | Distance | Time En Route | Groundspeed |
|---|---|---|---|
| a. | 275 SM | 90 min. | _____ mph |
| b. | 76 SM | 32 min. | _____ mph |
| c. | 111 SM | 56 min. | _____ mph |
| d. | 19 NM | 8 min. | _____ kt. |
| e. | 54 NM | 31 min. | _____ kt. |

4. Answers to practice problems
   a. 183 mph
   b. 143 mph
   c. 119 mph
   d. 143 kt.
   e. 105 kt.

D. Determine the distance traveled in a given time and at a given groundspeed.

1. Use the example in B.2. (on the opposite page) of 140 kt. and 90 min.
   a. Move the speed index under your groundspeed (e.g., 140 kt.).
   b. Find the time en route on the inner scale (e.g., 90 min.) under the distance traveled on the outer scale (e.g., 210 NM).
2. Use your flight computer to solve these practice problems (cover the answers below).

| | Groundspeed | Time En Route | Distance |
|---|---|---|---|
| a. | 107 mph | 207 min. | ____ SM |
| b. | 135 mph | 7 min. | ____ SM |
| c. | 86 mph | 22 min. | ____ SM |
| d. | 127 kt. | 65 min. | ____ NM |
| e. | 164 kt. | 19 min. | ____ NM |

3. Answers to practice problems
   a. 369 SM
   b. 16 SM
   c. 31.5 SM
   d. 138 NM
   e. 52 NM

## 12.5 FUEL COMPUTATIONS

A. Similar to the speed/distance/time computations, you may compute either fuel burned, fuel consumption rate, or time remaining.

1. The computations are:

   a. Fuel burned = fuel consumption rate x time
   b. Time (available) = fuel to burn ÷ fuel consumption rate
   c. Fuel consumption rate = fuel burned ÷ time

2. These computations are made on the flight computer in the same way as time and distance computations, except that gallons are used in place of miles.

B. Determine the total fuel used.

1. Refer to the figure below.

   a. Move the speed index under the fuel consumption rate on the outer scale.
   b. The fuel burned will be on the outer scale over the time on the inner scale.

2. As illustrated below, if the fuel consumption rate is 8.5 gal./hr. and the time en route is 2 hr., the total fuel used will be 17 gal.

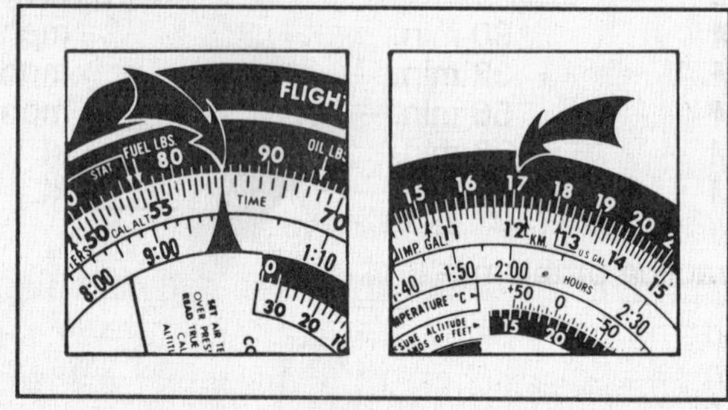


3. Use your flight computer to solve these practice problems (cover the answers below).

| | Consumption Rate | Time En Route | Fuel Burned |
|---|---|---|---|
| a. | 17 gal./hr. | 1 hr. 10 min. | ______ |
| b. | 28 gal./hr. | 90 min. | ______ |
| c. | 7 gal./hr. | 2 hr. 35 min. | ______ |
| d. | 11 gal./hr. | 3 hr. 20 min. | ______ |
| e. | 12 gal./hr. | 270 min. | ______ |

4. Answers to practice problems

   a. 19.8 gal.
   b. 42.0 gal.
   c. 18.1 gal.
   d. 36.7 gal.
   e. 54.0 gal.

C. Determine the fuel consumption rate.

1. Refer to the previous figure.

   a. Move the time elapsed on the inner scale under the fuel burned (17 gal.) on the outer scale.

   b. Find the fuel consumption rate (8.5 gal./hr.) on the outer scale over the speed index.

2. Use your flight computer to solve these practice problems (cover the answers below).

| | Time En Route | Fuel Burned | Consumption Rate |
|---|---|---|---|
| a. | 246 min. | 86 gal. | ______ |
| b. | 54 min. | 17 gal. | ______ |
| c. | 1 hr. 15 min. | 34 gal. | ______ |
| d. | 140 min. | 20 gal. | ______ |
| e. | 2 hr. 10 min. | 23 gal. | ______ |

3. Answers to practice problems

   a. 21.0 gal./hr.
   b. 18.9 gal./hr.
   c. 27.2 gal./hr.
   d. 8.6 gal./hr.
   e. 10.6 gal./hr.

D. Determine available flight time in terms of fuel.

1. Refer to the example in B.2. on the opposite page.

   a. Move the speed index under the fuel consumption rate (8.5 gal./hr.) on the outer scale.

   b. Find the time available (2 hr.) on the inner scale under 17 gal. of fuel on the outer scale.

2. Use your flight computer to solve these practice problems (cover the answers below).

| | Consumption Rate | Fuel Burned | Time En Route |
|---|---|---|---|
| a. | 18 gal./hr. | 60 gal. | ______ |
| b. | 22 gal./hr. | 42 gal. | ______ |
| c. | 9 gal./hr. | 33 gal. | ______ |
| d. | 16 gal./hr. | 50 gal. | ______ |
| e. | 12 gal./hr. | 30 gal. | ______ |

3. Answers to practice problems

   a. 3 hr. 20 min. or 200 min.
   b. 1 hr. 55 min. or 115 min.
   c. 3 hr. 40 min. or 220 min.
   d. 3 hr. 08 min. or 188 min.
   e. 2 hr. 30 min. or 150 min.

## 12.6 TRUE AIRSPEED AND DENSITY ALTITUDE

A. Air density affects the indications of the airspeed indicator and the performance of the airplane.

1. Density altitude is the theoretical altitude in the standard atmosphere where the density is the same as the actual density you are experiencing in flight.
   a. Density altitude is found by correcting pressure altitude for nonstandard temperature.
   b. See Chapter 3, Airplane Performance, beginning on page 61 for further discussion.
2. True airspeed (TAS) is the actual speed of the airplane through the air.
   a. TAS is found by correcting calibrated airspeed (CAS) for density altitude.
   b. See your airplane flight manual to determine CAS based on indicated airspeed.
      1) Generally, there is little error at cruise speeds, i.e., CAS equals indicated airspeed (IAS).
      2) Thus, as a practical matter, you may usually use IAS rather than CAS to determine true airspeed.
   c. See Chapter 4, Airplane Instruments, Engines, and Systems, on page 77 for further discussion.

B. To find TAS and density altitude, rotate the inner portion of the flight computer until the inner and outer scales are matched.

1. Using the inner window on the right side of the flight computer, set the outside air temperature (OAT) over the pressure altitude.
   a. OAT is in °C, and may be above (+) or below (–) 0°C.
   b. To find pressure altitude in flight, set your altimeter to 29.92.
      1) Make a note of the altimeter setting before turning it to 29.92.
      2) Remember to reset the altimeter afterward.
2. Find your CAS (or IAS) on the inner scale, and read TAS directly above it on the outer scale.
3. Read density altitude in the small center window.
   a. One some flight computers the density altitude is read at the bottom of the "airspeed" window.

C. Note: Most performance charts do not require you to compute density altitude because they provide for adjustment for pressure altitude and temperature on the chart itself.

1. Many airspeed indicators have a built-in true airspeed scale. The pilot puts temperature over pressure altitude and the airspeed indicator points to true airspeed on the outer scale.

D. As illustrated below, if the OAT is –10°C at a pressure altitude of 10,000 ft. and you are indicating 130 kt., put –10°C over 10,000 ft. and find 150 kt. TAS over 130 kt. CAS (or IAS).

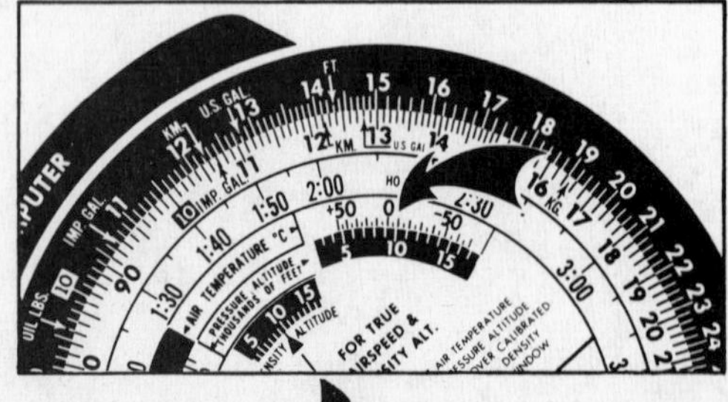

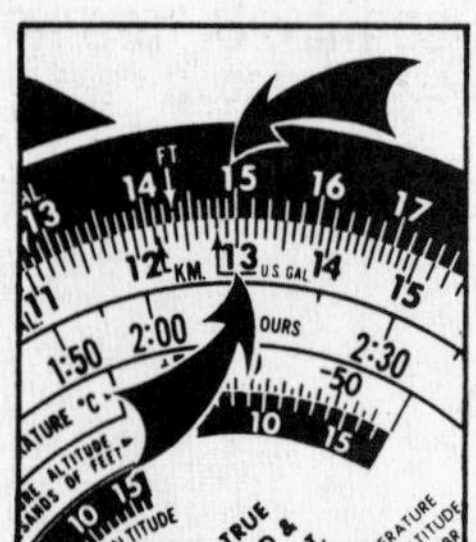

1. Find density altitude of approximately 9,500 ft. in the center (density altitude) window.

E. Use your flight computer to solve these practice problems (cover the answers below).

| | Temperature | Pressure Altitude | CAS (or IAS) | TAS | Density Altitude |
|---|---|---|---|---|---|
| 1. | −30°C | 10,000 ft. | 120 kt. | ____ | ____ |
| 2. | +10°C | 8,000 ft. | 130 kt. | ____ | ____ |
| 3. | −10°C | 12,000 ft. | 140 kt. | ____ | ____ |
| 4. | +10°C | 4,000 ft. | 150 kt. | ____ | ____ |
| 5. | +20°C | 5,000 ft. | 160 kt. | ____ | ____ |

F. Answers to Practice Problems

| | | |
|---|---|---|
| 1. | 133 kt. | 6,800 ft. |
| 2. | 149 kt. | 9,200 ft. |
| 3. | 168 kt. | 11,800 ft. |
| 4. | 160 kt. | 4,300 ft. |
| 5. | 177 kt. | 6,700 ft. |

## 12.7 CORRECTED (APPROXIMATELY TRUE) ALTITUDE

A. Because temperature affects air density, variations in temperature will affect the indications of the altimeter.

1. True altitude is the actual altitude of the airplane above mean sea level (MSL).
2. Indicated altitude is the altitude read directly from the altimeter after it is set to the current altimeter setting.
3. Corrected (approximately true) altitude is found by correcting indicated altitude for nonstandard temperature.

B. To find corrected altitude, rotate the inner portion of the flight computer until the inner and outer scales are matched.

1. Using the inner window on the left side of the flight computer, set the pressure altitude under the OAT.
   a. OAT is in °C, and may be above (+) or below (–) 0°C.
   b. To find pressure altitude in flight, set your altimeter to 29.92.
      1) Make a note of the altimeter setting before turning it to 29.92.
      2) Remember to reset the altimeter afterward.
2. Find your indicated altitude on the inner scale, and read corrected altitude directly above it on the outer scale.

C. Note that corrected altitude is significantly different from indicated altitude only at higher altitudes.

1. Corrected (or true) altitude is dangerously (i.e., hundreds of feet) lower than indicated altitude only at high-elevation airports when the temperature is significantly lower than standard (e.g., wintertime).

D. As illustrated below, given an OAT of –20°C, a pressure altitude of 12,000 ft., and an indicated altitude of 12,500 ft., put –20°C over 12,000 ft. in the inner-left window and find the indicated altitude of 12,500 ft. on the inner scale. Look directly above this value and find the true altitude of 12,000 ft.

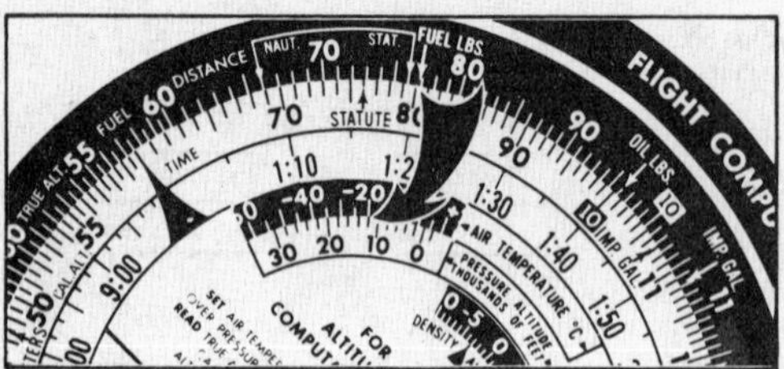


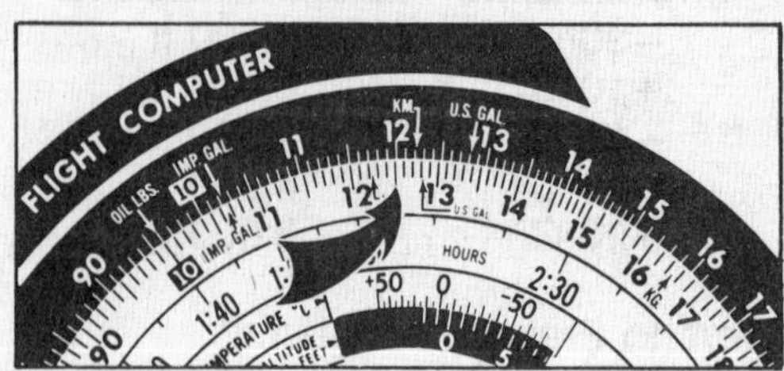


E. Use your flight computer to solve these practice problems (cover the answers below).

| | Pressure Altitude | Temperature | Indicated Altitude | True Altitude |
|---|---|---|---|---|
| 1. | 16,000 ft. | +5°C | 14,000 ft. | ______ |
| 2. | 10,000 ft. | −30°C | 11,500 ft. | ______ |
| 3. | 8,000 ft. | 0°C | 8,000 ft. | ______ |
| 4. | 6,000 ft. | +15°C | 6,500 ft. | ______ |
| 5. | 9,000 ft. | −15°C | 8,500 ft. | ______ |

F. Answers to Practice Problems

1. 15,000 ft.
2. 10,400 ft.
3. 8,050 ft.
4. 6,800 ft.
5. 8,100 ft.

## 12.8 THE WIND SIDE OF THE FLIGHT COMPUTER

A. The wind side consists of a rotating scale and a sliding rectangular grid. Refer to the figure on page 318.

1. The rotating scale is marked with the 360 degrees of the compass.
   a. The inside of the scale is transparent plastic that can be marked with a pencil.
   b. The exact center of the scale has a small center hole, or grommet.
2. The sliding grid is marked with vertical lines and horizontal arcs.
   a. The vertical lines represent degrees left or right of the centerline.
   b. The horizontal arcs represent speed.
      1) The grid has two sides; on one the speed arcs represent 30 to 260, on the other, 150 to 650.
      2) You should use the side with the low range of speeds for most general aviation airplanes.

B. The wind side of the computer is used to determine the effect of wind on the airplane in terms of heading and groundspeed.

## 12.9 DETERMINING TRUE HEADING AND GROUNDSPEED

A. In order to track a desired true course, you must determine and apply a wind correction angle to your true heading.

1. The wind correction angle required depends upon three factors.
   a. True course of your planned flight as plotted on your sectional chart.
   b. True airspeed as determined from the performance chart(s) in your *POH* for your planned cruising altitude and power setting.
   c. Wind direction and speed derived from the winds aloft forecast for your cruising altitude.
2. Be sure that you are using the same units of direction and speed throughout your computations.
   a. Since winds aloft are forecast in knots, you must convert your TAS if it is in mph.
   b. If your course has been determined in magnetic direction (e.g., you are using a VOR radial), you must convert the wind direction to magnetic.

B. To determine your wind correction angle, proceed as follows using the wind side.

1. Rotate the inner scale so the wind direction is under the true index.
2. Slide the grid up or down so the center hole is over one of the heavy arcs.
3. Using the speed gradations to measure knots, mark the wind velocity up from the center hole with a pencil.
4. Rotate the scale so the true course is under the true index.
5. Slide the grid until your pencil mark is on the true airspeed arc.
6. Your pencil mark's position relative to the vertical centerline determines your wind correction factor. Count the number of degree lines your pencil mark is to the left or right of the centerline.
   a. If the mark is to the left of the centerline, subtract the wind correction angle (WCA).
   b. If the mark is to the right of the centerline, add the WCA.
7. Read your groundspeed through the center hole.

C. As illustrated below and on page 328, find true heading and groundspeed given the following conditions:

| | |
|---|---|
| True course | 030° |
| True airspeed | 170 kt. |
| Wind | 080° at 20 kt. |

1. Rotate the scale to put the wind direction of 080° under the true index.
2. Slide the grid to put the center hole over a convenient reference arc (e.g., 160 kt.) and mark the wind velocity up 20 kt. from the center.

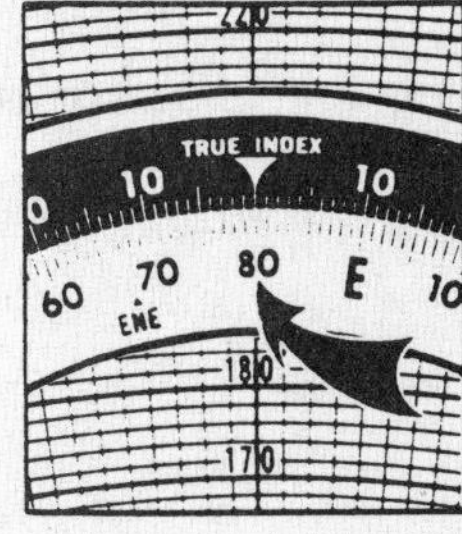


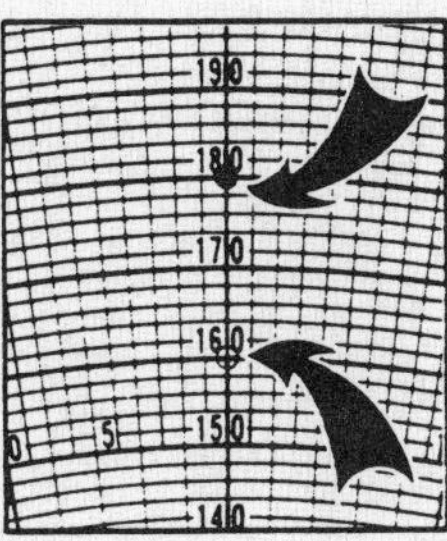

3. Rotate the scale to put the true course of 030° under the true index.
4. Slide the grid to put the pencil mark on the 170-kt. true airspeed arc.

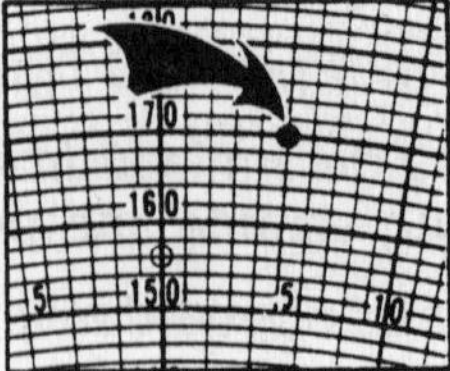

5. Since the WCA is 5° to the right, you must add this to your true course to find your true heading of 035°.
6. Read your groundspeed of 156 kt. under the center hole.

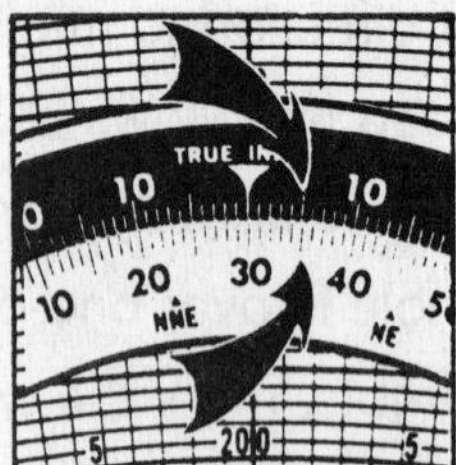
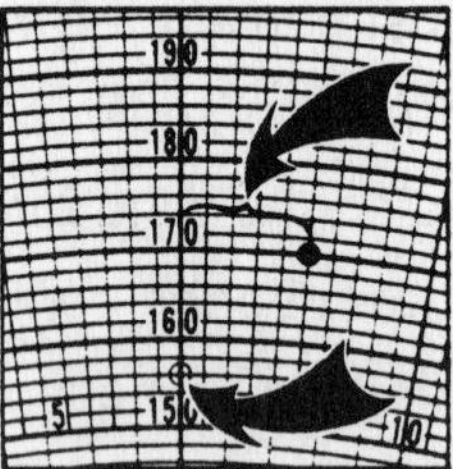

D. Use your flight computer to solve these practice problems (cover the answers below).

| | Wind Direction | Wind Speed | True Course | True Airspeed | Wind Correction Angle | True Heading | Groundspeed |
|---|---|---|---|---|---|---|---|
| 1. | 215° | 20 mph | 260° | 130 mph | ____ | ____ | ___ mph |
| 2. | 050° | 33 mph | 260° | 150 mph | ____ | ____ | ___ mph |
| 3. | 330° | 45 kt. | 350° | 150 kt. | ____ | ____ | ___ kt. |
| 4. | 300° | 45 kt. | 100° | 150 kt. | ____ | ____ | ___ kt. |
| 5. | 220° | 30 kt. | 130° | 150 kt. | ____ | ____ | ___ kt. |

E. Answers to Practice Problems

| | WCA | True Heading | Groundspeed |
|---|---|---|---|
| 1. | 6°L | 254° | 115 mph |
| 2. | 6°R | 266° | 178 mph |
| 3. | 6°L | 344° | 107 kt. |
| 4. | 6°L | 94° | 191 kt. |
| 5. | 12°R | 142° | 147 kt. |

## 12.10 ELECTRONIC FLIGHT COMPUTERS

A. Electronic flight computers perform the functions of manual flight computers in a fashion similar to the way pocket calculators perform the functions of slide rules.

1. They perform all the functions of both sides of the manual computer through prompted entries of required variables on a keypad.

   a. The results of the desired computations are then shown on an LCD display.

2. Electronic flight computers are also capable of weight and balance calculations.

B. There are certain advantages of the electronic over the manual flight computers.

1. Greater precision of computations
2. Automatic placement of decimal points
3. Greater ease of performing multi-part problems
4. Much faster on wind correction problems
5. Capable of weight and balance calculations

C. Some disadvantages of the electronic flight computers are:

1. Cost is two to three times that of a manual flight computer.

2. The greater precision of the electronic computers can be misleading because values such as fuel consumption or winds aloft are usually imprecise.

D. As a student pilot you should probably first learn how to use the manual E6-B (explained and illustrated on page 318).

1. You will learn more about navigation.

2. Thereafter you will be in a better position to use and appreciate an electronic flight computer.

E. These calculators may be used on the FAA written tests and at computer testing centers such as AVTEST, DRAKE, PLATO, and SYLVAN, and during flight tests.

1. However, no instructional material (e.g., operating or instruction manuals for the computers) may be taken to the test site or used during the test.

2. If you plan to use an electronic flight computer during your FAA written test, practice with it on all of the practice problems in this chapter and in Chapter 11, Navigation, in Gleim's *Private Pilot and Recreational Pilot FAA Written Exam*.

F. Three companies currently produce the most widely used electronic flight computers: ASA, Jeppesen, and Sporty's.

1. Each computer retails for under $100.

2. The instruction booklets provided with each model are easily understood and illustrate each operation.

3. Each of the three computers is described in the following modules.

## 12.11 ASA CX-1a

A. The ASA CX-1a "Pathfinder" calculator has a menu of 20 functions, and can perform 31 aviation calculations.

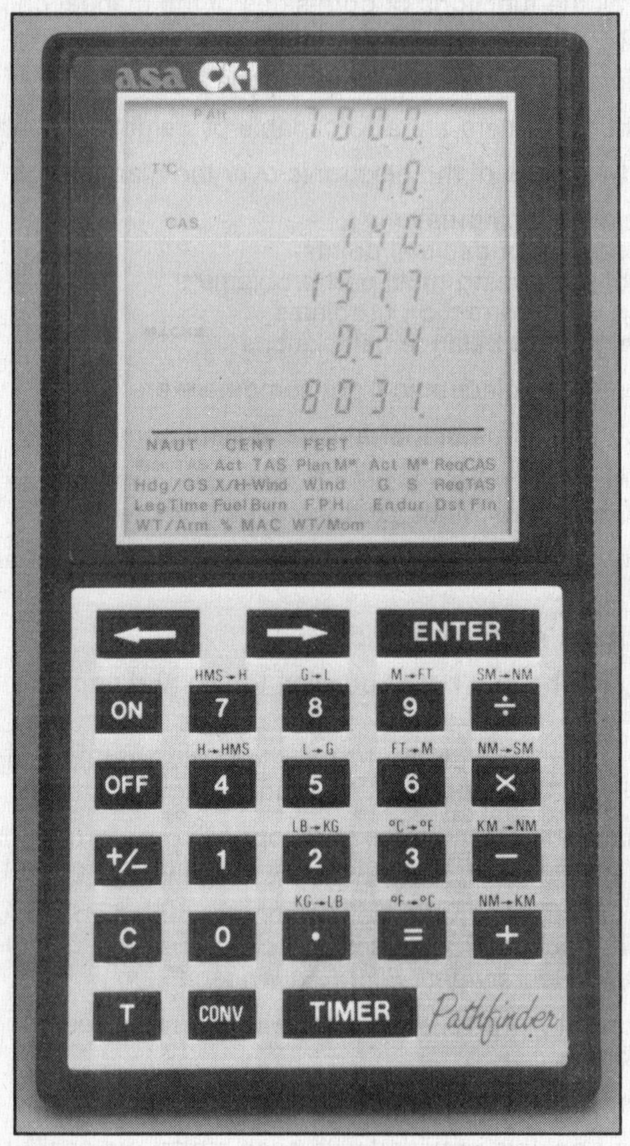

1. The keyboard is simple, which makes it very user-friendly.
   a. The 26 keys on the keyboard are logically arranged and accessible.
      1) Fourteen of the keys have a dual function, which is used to convert values to various units of measure (e.g., SM to NM and vice versa).
2. Up to six lines of numbers are displayed, with inputs and results shown together, and each line clearly labeled.
   a. After you have spent a few minutes reading the manual, the on-screen prompts become fairly self-explanatory.
3. Menu selection of the 20 aviation functions is performed with two cursor buttons. It is quickly obvious that any function can be selected with one to six strokes of the appropriate cursor button.
4. All functions are interactive, which allows "chain" calculations, in which the answer to a previous problem can easily be entered into a subsequent one.

B. The varying functions are also user-friendly.
   1. The conversion function is straightforward.
   2. The built-in timer gives you the choice of counting either up or down.
      a. The "count up" feature will count from zero (or another preset time) to 99:59:59 and can be used to keep track of elapsed time for the flight.
      b. The "count down" feature will run from a preset value to zero and can be used to determine the missed approach point on a non-precision instrument approach.
   3. The weight and balance function allows you to add or subtract weight at will, and always keeps a running total of gross weight and CG.
      a. Either arms or moments may be used, but they must be consistent throughout a calculation.
      b. Loaded CG may also be expressed in % MAC (mean aerodynamic chord).

C. The ASA CX-1a Pathfinder has a 3-year limited warranty, and at the time of this printing, lists for $99.95, including batteries.
   1. Ordering information may be obtained from:

      ASA
      7005 132nd Place SE
      Renton, WA 98509-3153
      (800) 426-8338

## 12.12 JEPPESEN TECHSTAR

A. The Jeppesen TechStar has a menu of five operating modes, capable of performing over 100 aviation and conversion problems.

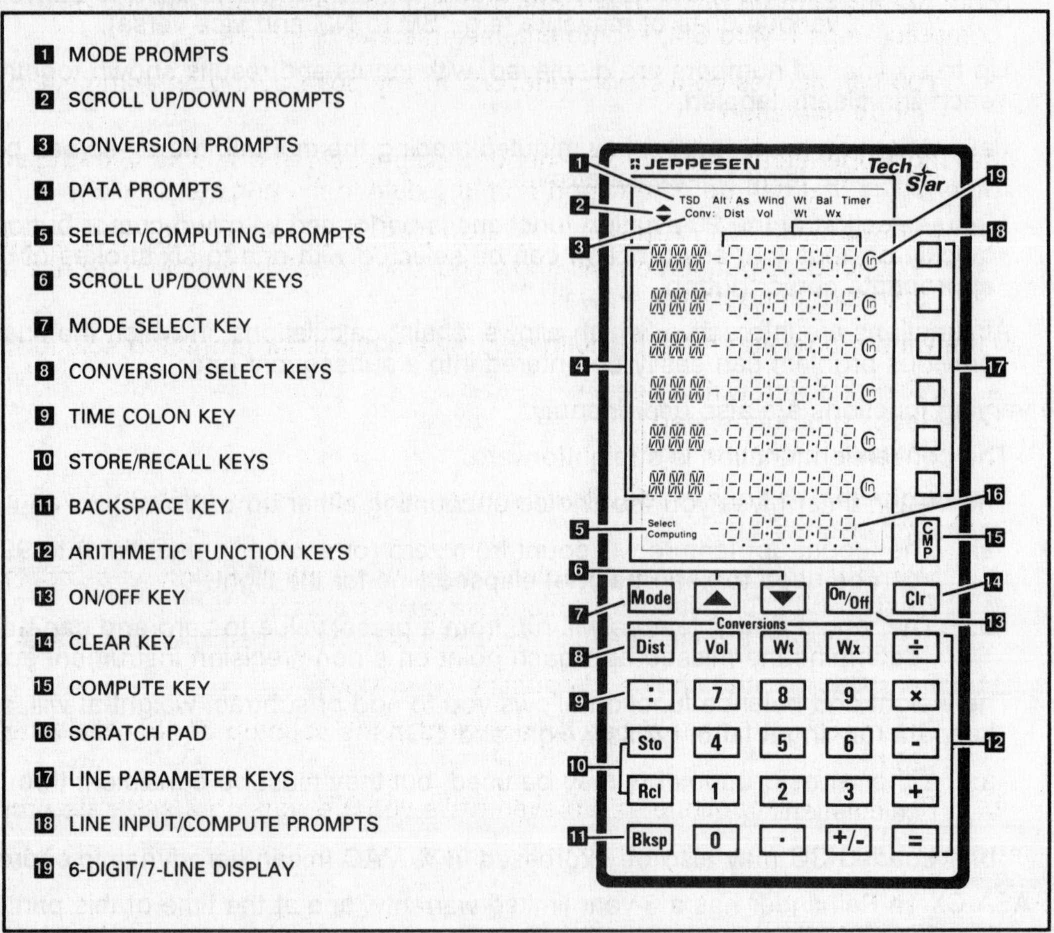


1. The 30 primary keys function in much the same manner as any advanced calculator.
   a. The line parameter keys, arranged vertically along the right side of the display, allow you to select a variety of computations from each mode, as well as input data in any order desired.
   b. Items can be entered in any order and changed at any time without going through the entire problem again.
2. The TechStar is the only one of the three flight computers with a memory function.
   a. It has six user memories that can be accessed without affecting any mode or arithmetic operation in progress.
   b. The six memories can be viewed simultaneously so the user does not need to memorize where (s)he stored material.
3. The manual begins by leading you through a sample problem, after which you will have little trouble accessing the many other available operations.

B. The TechStar has the greatest number of available operations.

1. The on-screen prompter uses over 80 abbreviations.
2. There are many more unit conversions that can be made than with any other flight computer, e.g., NM to SM, kilometers, feet, meters, or inches.
   a. You can access conversion functions at any point during an arithmetic or aviation mode operation.
3. After most operations, there is an extended output screen available showing virtually every other value that can be determined from the data in the original problem.
   a. For example, if you compute TAS from CAS, pressure altitude, and temperature, the extended output screen will show you Mach number, temperature rise, and standard temperature as well.
4. In the wind mode, you have the following three choices for prompted solutions:
   a. Wind direction/wind speed
   b. Heading/groundspeed
   c. Crosswind component
5. The weight and balance mode allows you to enter up to nine items, their weights and moments or arms.
   a. Moments and arms may be entered interchangeably throughout a problem.
   b. Weight and CG shift computations are also available.
   c. CG can be determined as a percent of mean aerodynamic chord (MAC).
6. The timer gives you the choice of counting up or down.
   a. The maximum time that can be activated in the countup or countdown timers is 25 hr.
   b. The timer will continue to run even while you are working a separate problem.

C. The Jeppesen TechStar has a 3-year limited warranty, and at the time of this printing lists for $65.95.

1. Ordering information may be obtained from:

Jeppesen Sanderson, Inc.
55 Inverness Drive East
Englewood, CO 80112
(800) 525-7379

## 12.13 SPORTY'S E6B

A. The Sporty's E6B has a menu of 19 functions, plus calculator and timer, and can perform a variety of aviation computations and conversions.

1. The 29 keys are clearly labeled and accessible.
    a. Fourteen of the keys serve a dual function which is used to convert values to various units of measure.
    b. The four cursor buttons make mode selection simple.
2. The display is clear and easy to use.
    a. Up to six lines of numbers appear on the display screen. Each line has several names for the prompts and the results of your calculations.
    b. After you have spend a few minutes reading the manual, the on-screen prompts become fairly self-explanatory.
3. The E6B stores the products of previous calculations and many prompted inputs in memory, then carries them into subsequent calculations automatically, making chain calculations smooth and uncomplicated.

B. The E6B offers a variety of practical functions.

1. There are three clocks which run continuously and display ZULU and any two other times.

   a. The clocks can be synchronized after being set.

   b. The timer can count up and down. When counting down, the timer will start flashing after zero.

2. The E6B will compute pressure and density altitude, given indicated altitude and altimeter setting.

3. The weight and balance function allows you to add or subtract weight at will and always keeps a running total of gross weight and CG.

   a. Either arms or moments may be used, but they must be consistent throughout a calculation.

   b. Loaded CG may also be expressed in % MAC.

4. Other calculations available are

   a. Various airspeed readings,
   b. Heading and groundspeed,
   c. Leg time,
   d. Fuel required and fuel per hour,
   e. Wind, including crosswind, headwind, and tailwind,
   f. Distance flown.

C. The Sporty's E6B has a 3-year limited warranty, and at the time of this printing, lists for $69.95.

1. Ordering information may be obtained from:

   Sporty's Pilot Shop
   Clermont Airport
   Batavia, OH 45103
   (800) 543-8633

# CHAPTER THIRTEEN
# CROSS-COUNTRY FLYING



Cross-country flight means flying the airplane from one airport to another, often over considerable distances. Most pilots take pride in their ability to navigate with precision. To execute a flight which follows a predetermined plan directly to the destination and arrive safely with no loss of time because of poor navigation is a source of real satisfaction. Lack of navigational skill could lead to unpleasant and sometimes dangerous situations in which adverse weather, approaching darkness, or fuel shortage may force a pilot to attempt a landing under hazardous conditions.

Air navigation is not limited, however, to actually guiding an airplane from one place to another. Navigation begins and ends on the ground. The major planning concerns of cross-country flight are preflight preparation, weather procurement and analysis, and navigation.

## 13.1 PREFLIGHT PREPARATION

A. Plan your flight in stages, well ahead of time.

1. Determine your route of flight.
    a. Estimate the time en route.
2. Determine fuel management and stops en route.
    a. VFR fuel requirements. FARs require that there be sufficient fuel (based on forecast wind and weather conditions) to fly to the intended destination at normal cruise speed
        1) AND be able to continue on for 30 min. in daytime
        2) AND be able to continue on for 45 min. at night.
3. Check the runway lengths and facilities at the airports you intend to use, and compare them to the requirements of your airplane.
4. Check available weather forecasts for a general outlook for the day of your flight.

B. Determine that the airplane has been properly maintained and is airworthy.

1. The maintenance requirements on aircraft that are used in commercial operations (i.e., flight training, charter, etc.) are more stringent than on non-commercial Part 91, which requires maintenance only on an annual basis.
   a. All aircraft must undergo an annual inspection by a Certified Airframe and Powerplant (A&P) mechanic who also possesses an Inspection Authorization (IA).
   b. Aircraft used for compensation or hire must also undergo an inspection every 100 hr. of flight time.
      1) Based on the specific make and model aircraft, further checks beyond the 100-hr. check may be necessary to comply with the FARs. This additional maintenance may be required at the 50-, 150-, or 250-hr. point.
   c. You may not use an ATC transponder unless it has been tested and inspected within the preceding 24 calendar months.
   d. The emergency locator transmitter (ELT) battery must be replaced after half its useful life has expired, or after 1 hr. of cumulative use.
   e. Examine the engine logbooks and the airframe logbook of your airplane.
2. Check to see that all necessary documents are aboard. The word ARROW will help you to remember the required documents:

**A** irworthiness Certificate
**R** egistration Certificate
**R** adio station license
**O** perating limitations, or FAA Approved Airplane Flight Manual
**W** eight and balance information (also in the Flight Manual)

   a. Airworthiness Certificate. Your airplane must have an airworthiness certificate as illustrated below.
      1) An airworthiness certificate is issued to an aircraft by the FAA at the time of manufacture. It remains in force as long as all maintenance, airworthiness directives, and equipment FARs are complied with.

UNITED STATES OF AMERICA
DEPARTMENT OF TRANSPORTATION - FEDERAL AVIATION ADMINISTRATION

**STANDARD AIRWORTHINESS CERTIFICATE**

| 1. NATIONALITY AND REGISTRATION MARKS | 2. MANUFACTURER AND MODEL | 3 AIRCRAFT SERIAL NUMBER | 4. CATEGORY |
|---|---|---|---|
| N66421 | BEECH AIRCRAFT CORP. - V35B | D-10267 | UTILITY |

5. AUTHORITY AND BASIS FOR ISSUANCE
**This airworthiness certificate is issued pursuant to the Federal Aviation Act of 1958 and certifies that, as of the date of issuance, the aircraft to which issued has been inspected and found to conform to the type certificate therefor, to be in condition for safe operation, and has been shown to meet the requirements of the applicable comprehensive and detailed airworthiness code as provided by Annex 8 to the Convention on International Civil Aviation, except as noted herein.**
**Exceptions:**

NONE

6. TERMS AND CONDITIONS
**Unless sooner surrendered, suspended, revoked, or a termination date is otherwise established by the Administrator, this airworthiness certificate is effective as long as the maintenance, preventative maintenance, and alterations are performed in accordance with Parts 21, 43, and 91 of the Federal Aviation Regulations, as appropriate, and the aircraft is registered in the United States.**

| DATE OF ISSUANCE | FAA REPRESENTATIVE | DESIGNATION NUMBER |
|---|---|---|
| June 22, 1979 | D. M. Porteous | DOA, PC#8 |

**Any alteration, reproduction, or misuse of this certificate may be punishable by a fine not exceeding $1,000, or imprisonment not exceeding 3 years, or both. THIS CERTIFICATE MUST BE DISPLAYED IN THE AIRCRAFT IN ACCORDANCE WITH APPLICABLE FEDERAL AVIATION REGULATIONS.**

**FAA Form 8100-2** (7-67) FORMERLY FAA FORM 1362 U S Government Printing Office — 1970-675-526

b. Registration Certificate. Your airplane must have a certificate of registration as illustrated below. A registration is issued to the current owner of an aircraft as registered with the FAA.

UNITED STATES OF AMERICA
DEPARTMENT OF TRANSPORTATION — FEDERAL AVIATION ADMINISTRATION
CERTIFICATE OF AIRCRAFT REGISTRATION

This certificate must be in the aircraft when operated.

NATIONALITY AND REGISTRATION MARKS N 66421

AIRCRAFT SERIAL NO. D-10267

MANUFACTURER AND MANUFACTURER'S DESIGNATION OF AIRCRAFT
BEECH V35B

ISSUED TO
GLEIM IRVIN N
UNIVERSITY STATION PO BOX 12848
GAINSVILLE FL 32604

INDIVIDUAL

This certificate is issued for registration purposes only and is not a certificate of title. The Federal Aviation Administraton does not determine rights of ownership as between private persons.

It is certified that the above described aircraft has been entered on the register of the Federal Aviation Administration, United States of America, in accordance with the Convention on International Civil Aviation dated December 7, 1944, and with the Federal Aviation Act of 1958, and regulations issued thereunder.

DATE OF ISSUE
JUNE 04, 1980

Langhorne Bond
Administrator

DEPARTMENT OF TRANSPORTATION UNITED STATES OF AMERICA

AC Form 8050-3 (5-77)

c. Radio Station License

1) The Federal Communications Commission (FCC) is responsible for regulating the types of aircraft radios.

SHIP/AIRCRAFT RADIO STATION LICENSE
FEDERAL COMMUNICATIONS COMMISSION
WASHINGTON, D.C. 20554

| [x] AIRCRAFT | FAA NUMBER OR FCC CONTROL NUMBER: N66421 | NUMBER AIRCRAFT IN FLEET | EFFECTIVE DATE: 03-08-82 | EXPIRATION DATE: 03-08-87 | |
|---|---|---|---|---|---|
| [ ] SHIP | NAME OF SHIP | | OFFICIAL NUMBER | RADIO CALL SIGN | SELECTIVE CALLING NO. |
| EFFECTIVE DATE | EXPIRATION DATE | ENDORSEMENT DATES | | | |

FREQUENCIES AND CONDITIONS
PRIVATE AIRCRAFT (SECTION 87.201)
TRANSMITTERS: VHF COMM. (118-136 MHZ) EMERGENCY LOCATOR (121.5 & 243 MHZ)
DISTANCE MEASURING EQUIPMENT (DME) (960-1215 MHZ)
TRANSPONDER (1090 MHZ)

THIS LICENSE SUBJECT TO FURTHER CONDITIONS SET FORTH ON THE REVERSE SIDE

NOT TRANSFERABLE

(Must be posted aboard aircraft or ship)

IRVIN N GLEIM
POB 12848 UNIVERSITY STATION
GAINESVILLE FLA
32604

FCC Form 556
March 1980

2) When any type of radio (e.g., communication, transponder) is used aboard an aircraft for transmitting, that aircraft is a radio station.

a) The FCC requires a *radio station license* for radio transmitters used for aviation purposes.

b) This is an FCC requirement, not an FAA requirement.

3) A *restricted radiotelephone operator permit* is required by the FCC for pilots who use high frequency (HF) radios or those who fly internationally.

a) This permit is obtained by filling out an FCC application form.
b) This is normally not required for most pilots.

d. Operating Limitations, or FAA Approved Airplane Flight Manual

1) Your airplane *POH* must be accessible to you during flight. This includes instruction books for all added equipment, e.g., autopilots.

e. Weight and balance information (also in the Flight Manual)

f. Flotation gear should be available if the flight is to be conducted over water.

3. Check to see that all required safety equipment, flashlight, extra batteries, etc., are aboard.

C. On the day of your flight, obtain a complete weather briefing.

1. Based on the information you receive, you may either

a. Be able to proceed with the flight as planned,

b. Need to adjust your route of flight, plan different alternate airports, plan extra fuel stops, or

c. Cancel the flight altogether.

2. Complete a flight log as explained in Module 13.2, Navigation, below.

3. Be sure to have your pilot and medical certificates in your possession.

a. A student pilot is also required to carry his/her logbook.

4. Thoroughly preflight your airplane and make sure it is appropriately fueled and that all equipment is operational.

5. Complete a weight and balance computation.

## 13.2 NAVIGATION

A. There are three major types of navigation in use today.

1. Pilotage and Dead Reckoning

a. Pilotage is the navigation of your airplane using your sectional chart to fly from one visible landmark to another.

1) Pilotage becomes difficult in areas which lack prominent landmarks, or under conditions of low visibility.

2) During your flight, you will use pilotage in conjunction with dead reckoning to verify your calculations and keep track of your position.

b. Dead reckoning is the navigation of your airplane by means of computations based on true airspeed, course, heading, wind direction and speed, groundspeed, and elapsed time.

1) Simply, dead reckoning is a system of determining where the airplane should be on the basis of where it has been.

a) Literally, it is deduced reckoning, which is where the term came from, i.e., ded. or "dead" reckoning.

2) The dead reckoning procedure is done during the preflight planning, as discussed below and while en route.

a) During the preflight, you determine the true course, wind correction angle, true heading, variation, magnetic heading, estimated groundspeed, estimated time en route, and estimated fuel consumption.

b) During your flight, you keep track of your actual compass heading and the time.

i) From this you can determine the actual wind conditions, groundspeed, time en route, and fuel consumption.

ii) Thus, you can deduce when you will arrive at your next checkpoint and the amount of fuel that will be used.

3) A good knowledge of the principles of dead reckoning will assist you in determining your position after having become disoriented or confused.

a) By using information from the part of the flight already completed, it is possible to restrict your search for identifiable landmarks to a limited area to verify calculations and to locate yourself.

2. VOR and ADF Navigation

a. This is radio navigation based on, and by reference to, radio transmitters located throughout the U.S.

b. See Chapter 11, Radio Navigation, beginning on page 295.

3. Area Navigation (RNAV)

a. This is radio navigation based on various transmitters located either on the ground or in orbit around the Earth.

1) An on-board computer calculates its present position, thus allowing you to fly directly to any desired point.

b. Some types of area navigation are

1) VORTAC-based RNAV.
2) LORAN.
3) GPS.

c. See Chapter 11, Radio Navigation, beginning on page 295.

B. Assemble the appropriate VFR charts and other available sources for your trip.

1. Be sure to use only the most current charts.

a. The Federal airspace system is changing constantly, and using current sectionals is your only assurance of up-to-date information.

b. See Chapter 9, Navigation Charts and Airspace, beginning on page 271.

2. Consult the *Airport/Facility Directory* and *NOTAM* publication for additional information pertaining to your flight.

a. See Chapter 10, Other Navigation Publications, beginning on page 289.

C. Plan your flight carefully, using a combination of visual and radio navigation checkpoints.

1. Draw a course line from your departure airport to your destination on your sectional chart.
   a. Make sure the line is dark enough to read easily, but light enough not to obscure any chart information.
   b. If a fuel stop is required, show that airport as an intermediate stop, or as the first leg of your flight.
2. Once you have your course line(s) drawn, survey where your flight will be taking you.
   a. Look for available alternate airports en route.
   b. Look at the type of terrain, e.g., mountains, swamps, large bodies of water, that would have an impact if an off-airport landing became necessary.
      1) Mentally prepare for any type of emergency situation and the action to be taken during your flight.
   c. Be sure that your flight will not take you into restricted or prohibited airspace.
3. There is no set rule for selecting a landmark or navigation aid as a checkpoint. Every locality has its own peculiarities.
   a. The general rule to follow is never to place complete reliance on any single landmark.
   b. Use a combination of two or more, if available.
4. After obtaining your weather information (including winds aloft), as discussed in Module 13.4, Obtaining Weather Information, beginning on page 346, you can select the most favorable altitude for your flight.
   a. You must maintain basic VFR weather minimums.
      1) When flying below 10,000 ft. MSL in controlled airspace, you must remain at least 500 ft. below, 1,000 ft. above, and 2,000 ft. horizontally from the clouds, with at least 3 SM flight visibility.
      2) This also applies in uncontrolled airspace above 1,200 ft. AGL and below 10,000 ft. MSL, at night (only 1 SM visibility and clear of clouds is required during the day).
      3) See Chapter 9, Navigation Charts and Airspace, beginning on page 271.
   b. When operating your airplane under VFR in level cruising flight more than 3,000 ft. AGL, you must maintain the appropriate altitude, unless otherwise authorized by ATC.

| VFR CRUISING ALTITUDES | |
|---|---|
| *If your magnetic course (ground track) is:* | *And you are more than 3,000 ft. AGL but below 18,000 ft. MSL, fly:* |
| 0° to 179° . . . . . . . . . . . | Odd thousands MSL, plus 500 ft. (3,500, 5,500, 7,500, etc.) |
| 180° to 359° . . . . . . . . . | Even thousands MSL, plus 500 ft. (4,500, 6,500, 8,500, etc.) |

   c. Ensure that you maintain an altitude appropriate to obstacle or terrain clearance.

d. Ensure that you maintain an altitude to maintain reception of any radio navigation facilities that you will be using.

5. Using your flight computer, determine your time en route, headings, fuel requirements as explained below and in Chapter 12, Flight Computers, beginning on page 317.

D. Use a flight log to assist you in planning and conducting a cross-country flight. The following discussion explains the flight log presented below. (Feel free to photocopy it to use on your cross-country flights.)

1. Note that the top half is the actual "flight log." The bottom can be used for notes about weather, winds, NOTAMs, and radio frequencies.

   a. Write down all the radio frequencies you will need at each airport and for each VOR you will use for navigation. Thus, you will not be frantically fumbling for them during flight. This will give you added confidence.

   b. The left two-thirds of the top is completed prior to your flight (once you have your winds aloft data), and the right third of the top is completed while you are en route.

2. The "From" and "To" columns list the checkpoints between which you are navigating.

   a. The true course is determined relative to true north, as measured by your protractor on your sectional chart.

   b. Wind correction (+R or –L) is computed on the wind side of your flight computer.

   c. Your true heading is your true course adjusted for wind correction.

**FLIGHT LOG**

| PREFLIGHT | | | | | | | | | | | ENROUTE | | | | | |
|---|---|---|---|---|---|---|---|---|---|---|---|---|---|---|---|---|
| From | To | True Course | Wind Corr. | True Head. | Var. | Mag. Head. | Dist. Leg / Total | Est. GS | Time Leg / Total | Est. Fuel | Act'l. Time | Act'l. GS | Dist. Next Pt. | Est. Arrv'L | Fuel Used | Fuel Remain |
| | | | | | | | | | | | | | | | | |
| | | | | | | | | | | | | | | | | |
| | | | | | | | | | | | | | | | | |
| | | | | | | | | | | | | | | | | |
| | | | | | | | | | | | | | | | | |
| | | | | | | | | | | | | | | | | |
| | | | | | | | | | | | | | | | | |
| | | | | | | | | | | | | | | | | |

| Weather Reports | Winds Aloft | Radio and Navigation Frequencies |
|---|---|---|
| | | |
| | | |
| | | |
| **Terminal Forecasts** | **NOTAMS** | |
| | | |
| | | |
| | | |
| | | |

## FLIGHT LOG

| DEPARTURE POINT | VOR IDENT. FREQ. | RADIAL TO FROM | DISTANCE LEG REMAINING | TIME POINT-POINT CUMULATIVE | TIME TAKEOFF | GROUND SPEED |
|---|---|---|---|---|---|---|
| CHECK POINT | | | | | ETA | |
| | | | | | ATA | |
| | | | | | | |
| | | | | | | |
| | | | | | | |
| | | | | | | |
| | | | | | | |
| DESTINATION | | | | | | |
| | | | TOTAL | | | |

## PREFLIGHT CHECK LIST

DATE

EN ROUTE WEATHER/WEATHER ADVISORIES

DESTINATION WEATHER

WINDS ALOFT

ALTERNATE WEATHER

FORECASTS

NOTAMS/AIRSPACE RESTRICTIONS

d. The magnetic heading is the true heading adjusted for magnetic variation.

   1) Magnetic variation is the difference between true north and magnetic north. The amount of variation is identified in your geographic area by red dashed isogonic lines on the sectional charts.

   2) Remember, subtract easterly variation and add westerly variation.

   3) See Chapter 4, Airplane Instruments, Engines, and Systems, beginning on page 77.

e. The distance is measured between the two points on your sectional chart with a navigational plotter. Remember to use the side with the 1:500,000 scale for sectional charts.

3. Remember that if you are using VORs to navigate, the directions of the airways are magnetic; i.e., they are adjusted for local magnetic variation.

   a. The same is true for the compass rose encircling each VOR.

   b. Thus, when using VORs, you should start with the magnetic course (unadjusted for wind) directly from the sectional chart. Then compute the wind correction angle (after you convert wind from true to magnetic) and adjust the magnetic course to determine the magnetic heading.

4. When you compute the wind correction on your flight computer, also note your estimated groundspeed.

   a. Based on the distance and groundspeed, you can determine your estimated time for this leg and the cumulative estimated time for the flight.

   b. Given the estimated time en route and your planned fuel consumption, determine the fuel to be used on that leg.

5. Once en route, you should mark down the time over every checkpoint. Then you can compare your estimated groundspeed to actual groundspeed and revise your estimated fuel (used and remaining).

E. Note that the preceding procedures are not mandatory. There are many possible shortcuts. On very routine flights, you may not even use a flight log.

   1. For your training flights and your first real cross-country flights, however, you should work up a complete flight log.

   2. After you gain experience, you may want to use an abbreviated flight log. A sample is reproduced on page 344. Feel free to photocopy it for your own use.

## 13.3 WEIGHT AND BALANCE

A. Weight and balance calculation must be reviewed prior to each flight. On local training flights without baggage and even with full fuel, weight and balance should not be a problem. On cross-country flights, weight and balance data warrant more attention.

B. Weight and balance calculations involve the following factors:

1. Limitations and data:
   a. The maximum weight
   b. The empty weight and center of gravity (CG) location
   c. The useful load
   d. The composition of the useful load, including the total weight of oil and fuel with full tanks
2. Load distribution

C. Operation in excess of the maximum weight or outside CG limits is extremely dangerous and prohibited.

D. Use the airplane's certified weight and balance information (normally located in the *POH*) to calculate the weight and balance.

1. Make sure you are within maximum weight and CG limits.
2. See Chapter 6, Weight and Balance, beginning on page 153, for explanation of weight and balance calculations.

## 13.4 OBTAINING WEATHER INFORMATION

A. On all cross-country flights, the pilot is required to determine that the existing and forecast weather conditions are appropriate for the flight (FAR 91.103).

1. Until you have an instrument rating, you are allowed to fly cross-country only when visual flight rules (VFR) weather prevails along the route and at the destination.
   a. However, as a relatively new pilot, you should even avoid marginal VFR (MVFR) conditions.
2. In any case, the following forecast conditions should lead to a No-Go decision:
   a. Thunderstorms
   b. Embedded thunderstorms
   c. Lines of thunderstorms
   d. Fast-moving fronts or squall lines
   e. Flights that require you to cross strong or fast-moving fronts
   f. Reported turbulence that is moderate or greater. (Remember, moderate turbulence in a Boeing 727 is usually severe in a Cessna 152.)
   g. Icing
   h. Fog. Unlike when in a ceiling, you usually cannot maintain visual references with ground fog. This is especially important if sufficient fuel may be a concern.

B. Flight Service Stations (FSSs) are the primary source for obtaining preflight briefings and in-flight weather information.

1. Prior to your flight, you should visit or call the nearest FSS for a complete briefing.

2. There are four basic types of preflight briefings to meet your needs.
   a. Standard briefing:
      1) Should be requested any time you are planning a flight and have not received a previous briefing.
      2) The briefer will provide the following information in sequence.
         a) Adverse Conditions -- significant weather and aeronautical information that might influence you to alter the proposed flight; e.g., hazardous weather conditions, runway closures, NAVAID outages, etc.
         b) VFR Flight Not Recommended. When VFR flight is proposed and conditions are present or forecast, surface or aloft, that in the briefer's judgment would make flight under VFR doubtful, the briefer will describe the conditions, affected locations, and announce, "VFR flight is not recommended."
            i) This is advisory in nature.
            ii) You are responsible to make a final decision as to whether the flight can be conducted safely.
         c) Synopsis. A brief statement describing the type, location, and movement of weather systems and/or air masses which may affect the proposed flight.
         d) Current Conditions. Reported weather conditions applicable to the flight will be summarized from all available sources.
            i) This is omitted if the proposed time of departure is over 2 hr., unless requested by you.
         e) En Route Forecast. Conditions for the proposed route are summarized in logical order; i.e., departure/climbout, en route, and descent.
         f) Destination Forecast. At the planned ETA, any significant changes within 1 hr. before and after the planned arrival are included.
         g) Winds Aloft. Forecast winds aloft will be summarized for the proposed route and altitude.
         h) NOTAMs. Information from any NOTAM (D) or NOTAM (L) pertinent to the proposed flight, and pertinent FDC NOTAMs within approximately 400 mi. of the FSS providing the briefing.
            i) NOTAM (D) and FDC NOTAMs which have been published in the *Notices to Airmen* publication are not included, unless requested by you.
         i) ATC Delays. Any known ATC delays and flow control advisories which might affect the proposed flight.
         j) The following may be obtained on your request.
            i) Information on military training routes (MTR) and military operations area (MOA) activity within the flight plan area and a 100 NM extension around the flight plan area
            ii) Approximate density altitude data
            iii) Information regarding such items as air traffic services and rules, customs/immigration procedures, ADIZ rules, etc.
            iv) LORAN-C NOTAMs
            v) Other assistance as required

b. Abbreviated Briefing:

1) Request when you need information to supplement mass disseminated data (e.g., TWEB, PATWAS, TIBS, etc.), update a previous briefing, or when you only need one or two specific items.

2) Provide the briefer information regarding the

a) Appropriate background information,
b) Time you received the previous information, and/or
c) The specific items needed.

3) Sequence will be the same as in the Standard Briefing, to the extent possible.

4) If you requested one or two specific items, the briefer will advise you if adverse conditions are present or forecast.

a) Details will be provided only at your request.

c. Outlook Briefing:

1) Request whenever your proposed time of departure is 6 hr. or more from the time of the briefing.

2) You will be provided available forecast data applicable to the proposed flight.

3) This type of briefing is for planning purposes only.

a) Obtain a Standard or Abbreviated Briefing prior to departure.

d. In-flight Briefing:

1) In situations where you need to obtain a preflight briefing or an update by radio, you should contact the nearest FSS to obtain this information.

2) After communications have been established, advise the FSS of the type of briefing you require.

3) You may be advised to shift to the flight watch frequency (122.0) when conditions indicate that it would be advantageous.

3. Ask for any information that you or the briefer may have missed.

a. Save your questions until the briefing is complete.

C. FAA Flight Service Stations (FSSs) have primary responsibility for

1. Preflight pilot briefing
2. En route communications with VFR flights
3. Assisting lost VFR aircraft
4. Broadcasting aviation weather information
5. Accepting and closing flight plans
6. Operating the weather teletypewriter or computer systems
7. Taking local weather observations
8. Issuing airport advisories

D. See Chapter 7, Aviation Weather, beginning on page 165, for an explanation of the various weather reports and forecasts, as well as the use of DUAT and the AM Weather service.

## 13.5 VFR FLIGHT PLAN

A. VFR flight plans are not mandatory but they are highly recommended as a safety precaution. In the event you do not reach your destination as planned, the FAA will institute a search for you. This process begins 30 min. after you were scheduled to reach your destination.

B. Flight plans can be filed in person at FSSs, in which case you give them a completed flight plan form.

1. Flight plans may also be called in by telephone or by radio while in flight.
2. The flight plan form below may be photocopied for your own use. It is also available at FSSs and other FAA offices.

| U.S. DEPARTMENT OF TRANSPORTATION FEDERAL AVIATION ADMINISTRATION **FLIGHT PLAN** | (FAA USE ONLY) ☐ PILOT BRIEFING ☐ VNR ☐ STOPOVER | | | | | TIME STARTED | SPECIALIST INITIALS |
|---|---|---|---|---|---|---|---|
| 1. TYPE: VFR / IFR / DVFR | 2. AIRCRAFT IDENTIFICATION | 3. AIRCRAFT TYPE/ SPECIAL EQUIPMENT | 4. TRUE AIRSPEED KTS | 5. DEPARTURE POINT | 6. DEPARTURE TIME PROPOSED (Z) | ACTUAL (Z) | 7. CRUISING ALTITUDE |
| 8. ROUTE OF FLIGHT | | | | | | | |
| 9. DESTINATION (Name of airport and city) | 10. EST. TIME ENROUTE HOURS | MINUTES | 11. REMARKS | | | | |
| 12. FUEL ON BOARD HOURS | MINUTES | 13. ALTERNATE AIRPORT(S) | 14. PILOT'S NAME, ADDRESS & TELEPHONE NUMBER & AIRCRAFT HOME BASE | | | | 15. NUMBER ABOARD |
| | | | 17. DESTINATION CONTACT/TELEPHONE (OPTIONAL) | | | | |
| 16. COLOR OF AIRCRAFT | CIVIL AIRCRAFT PILOTS. FAR Part 91 requires you file an IFR flight plan to operate under instrument flight rules in controlled airspace. Failure to file could result in a civil penalty not to exceed $1,000 for each violation (Section 901 of the Federal Aviation Act of 1958, as amended). Filing of a VFR flight plan is recommended as a good operating practice. See also Part 99 for requirements concerning DVFR flight plans. | | | | | | |

C. As illustrated above, a flight plan requires the following 17 points of information:

1. Type -- VFR, IFR, DVFR (DVFR refers to defense VFR flights. They are VFR flights into air defense identification zones which require a VFR flight plan to be filed.)
2. Airplane identification
3. Airplane type/special equipment
4. True airspeed (kt.)
5. Departure point
6. Departure time -- You supply the proposed (Z) and FSS will fill in actual (Z) when you activate the flight plan after takeoff.
7. Cruising altitude
8. Route of flight
9. Destination (name of airport and city)
10. Estimated time en route -- hours and minutes
11. Remarks

12. Fuel on board -- hours and minutes
13. Alternate airport(s)
14. Pilot's name, address, and telephone number, and airplane home base
15. Number of people aboard
16. Color of aircraft
17. Destination contact/telephone (NOTE: This is optional and is not required.)

D. Your FSS specialist will be glad to assist you and answer any questions. Occasionally you may have to file a flight plan without an FAA form in front of you. Ask the specialist to prompt you for the required information.

E. CLOSE YOUR FLIGHT PLAN: REMEMBER! REMEMBER!
   1. Add "Close your flight plan" to your after-landing checklist.
   2. If you do not close your flight plan, the FAA will have to devote its limited and valuable resources attempting to determine if you did in fact arrive safely.
      a. If they cannot locate you or your airplane, they will contact the appropriate Rescue Coordination Center which will institute a "Search and Rescue" mission, the cost of which you may be responsible for.
   3. Thus, it is particularly important to notify any FAA (FSS or ATC) facility when you are late (over 30 min.) or have diverted to an alternate route or destination.
   4. While en route, you can identify yourself and your location to FSSs along your route (especially convenient if you are obtaining weather information), which will assist the FAA if they have to look for you.
   5. If you cannot reach the FSS to close your flight plan, call any ATC (Air Traffic Control) facility, which will relay the message.

## 13.6 DIVERSION TO AN ALTERNATE AIRPORT

A. Among the aeronautical skills that you must have is the ability to plot courses in flight to alternate destinations when continuation of the flight to the original destination is impracticable.
   1. Reasons include
      a. Low fuel,
      b. Bad weather,
      c. Your own or passenger fatigue, illness, etc.,
      d. Airplane system or equipment malfunction, and
      e. Any other reason that causes you to decide to divert to an alternate airport.
   2. The diversion may be accomplished by means of pilotage, dead reckoning, and/or radio navigation aids.

B. Most diversions to alternates are weather induced because VFR cross-country flight is so susceptible to weather changes.
   1. Learn to recognize adverse weather conditions.
      a. Adverse weather conditions are those conditions that decrease visibility and/or cloud ceiling height.
      b. Understanding your preflight weather forecasts will enable you to look for signs of adverse weather (e.g., clouds, wind changes, precipitation).
      c. Contact the nearest FSS or en route flight advisory service (EFAS) for updated weather information.

d. At the first sign of deteriorating weather, you should divert to an alternate. Attempting to remain VFR while the ceiling and visibility are getting below VFR minimums is a dangerous practice.

e. In order to remain VFR, you may be forced to lower altitudes and possibly marginal visibility. It is here that visibility relates to time as much as distance.

2. Plan to get your instrument rating.

C. Diversion is easiest when you know your present location and are aware of alternate airports.

1. You should continuously monitor your position on your section chart and the proximity of useful alternate airports.

2. Check the maximum elevation figure (MEF) in each latitude-longitude quadrant of your route to determine the minimum safe altitude.

   a. MEF is expressed in ft. MSL, which will enable you to make a quick determination by checking your altimeter.

3. Determine that your alternate airport will meet the needs of the situation.

   a. If the diversion is due to weather, ensure your alternate is in an area of good weather; otherwise, you may be forced into the same situation again.

D. Divert on a TIMELY basis. The longer you wait, the fewer advantages or benefits there are to making the diversion.

1. In the event diversion to an alternate airport results from an emergency, it is important for the pilot to divert to the new course as early as possible.

   a. Consider the relative distance to all suitable alternates.

   b. Select the alternative most appropriate to the emergency at hand.

   c. Change your heading to establish the approximate course immediately.

   d. Later, wind correction, actual distance, and estimated time and fuel required can be computed.

2. Courses to alternates can be estimated with reasonable accuracy using a straightedge and the compass roses shown surrounding VOR stations on the sectional chart.

   a. The VOR radials and airway courses (already oriented to magnetic direction) printed on the chart can be used satisfactorily for approximation of magnetic bearings during VFR flights.

   b. Remember that the VOR radial or printed airway heading is **outbound** from the station. The course **to** the station is the reciprocal of the parallel radial or airway.

   c. Distances can be determined by using the measurements on a plotter, or by marking the appropriate place on the straight side of a piece of paper with a finger or pencil and then measuring the approximate distance on the mileage scale at the bottom of the chart.

3. If radio aids are used to divert to an alternate, the pilot should

   a. Select the appropriate facility,
   b. Tune to the proper frequency,
   c. Positively identify the station,
   d. Determine the course or radial to intercept or follow.

4. Once established on your new course, use the known (or forecast) wind conditions to determine an estimated groundspeed, ETA, and fuel consumption to your alternate airport.

   a. Update as you pass over your newly selected checkpoints.

## 13.7 LOST PROCEDURES

A. Nobody wants to get lost, especially in an airplane, but all pilots occasionally find themselves disoriented. The skill needed is to recognize disorientation quickly and then implement corrective action to become reoriented.

B. Steps to avoid becoming lost:

1. Always know where you are.
2. Always know what your next landmark will be and look for it.
   a. Similarly, anticipate the indication of your radio navigation aids.
3. If your radio navigation aids OR your visual observations of landmarks do not confirm your expectations, become concerned and take action.

C. As soon as you begin to wonder where you are, remember the point at which you last were confident of your location.

1. Watch your heading. Know what it should be and keep it constant.
2. Do not panic. You are not "lost" yet.
3. Recompute your expected radio navigation indications and visual landmarks.
   a. Reconfirm your heading (compass and heading indicator).
   b. Confirm correct radio frequencies and settings.
   c. Review your sectional chart, noting last confirmed landmark.
   d. Attempt to reconfirm your present position.
4. You should use all available means to determine your present location. This includes asking for assistance.
5. The best course of action will depend on factors such as ceiling, visibility, hours of daylight remaining, fuel remaining, etc.
   a. Given the current circumstances, you will be the only one to decide the best course of action.
   b. Understand and respect your own and your airplane's limitations.

D. If you cannot determine your position and you are within range of at least two VORs or NDBs, use the following procedure.

1. Tune and identify the VOR or NDB nearest where you think you are, and determine the radial or outbound bearing you are on.
   a. Draw a line on your chart outbound from the VOR or NDB in the proper direction.
2. Select a second station in your vicinity, and determine your location relative to it.
   a. Draw an appropriate line on your chart.
3. Where the two lines intersect is your position.

E. If you are equipped with a two-way radio and a transponder, call the nearest FSS for the ATC frequency in your area.

1. ATC will be able to determine your position on radar if you are within their coverage.

F. If neither of the procedures previously noted is available, plot the estimated distance and compass direction flown from your last noted checkpoint as though there were no wind. The point so determined will be the center of a circle within which your airplane's position may be located.

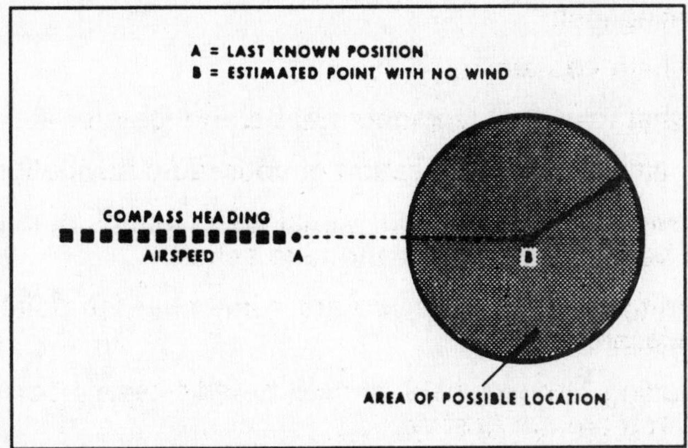


1. This is often called a "circle of error."
   a. If you are certain the wind is no more than 30 kt., and it has been less than 30 min. since the last known checkpoint was crossed, the radius of the circle should be approximately 15 NM.
2. Continue straight ahead and check the landmarks within this circle.
   a. Your most likely position will be downwind from your desired course.

G. If all else fails to identify your position, you should change course toward the nearest concentration of prominent landmarks visible to you.
1. If you have a very long known landmark, e.g., coastline, interstate highway, etc., you need to proceed toward it.
2. Maintain the minimum safe altitudes.
3. When a landmark is recognized, or a probable fix obtained, you should at first use the information both cautiously and profitably.
   a. No abrupt change in course should be made until a second or third landmark is positively identified to corroborate the first.

H. If you are able to reach someone on your communications radio, ask for help.
1. There is nothing wrong with asking for assistance.
2. The important point is to ask for help before other problems develop, e.g., low fuel, panic, nightfall, adverse weather, etc.
3. Remember frequency 121.5 for emergencies.

# CHAPTER FOURTEEN
# FLIGHT PHYSIOLOGY



All airplane pilots must possess valid and appropriate medical certificates issued by an Aviation Medical Examiner. Although a history of certain medical conditions may disqualify a pilot from flying, most pilots who do not meet medical standards may still be qualified under certain conditions. You should visit an Aviation Medical Examiner as soon as possible in your flight training in order to determine that you meet the medical standards.

You should also review your fitness for each flight. Additionally, you should be aware of a number of potential medical problems that may arise during flight.

## 14.1 FITNESS FOR FLIGHT

A. Pilot Personal Checklist

1. Aircraft accident statistics show that pilots should conduct preflight checklists on themselves as well as their aircraft.
   a. Pilot impairment contributes to many more accidents than do failures of aircraft systems.
2. **I'M SAFE** -- I am NOT impaired by

**I** llness
**M** edication
**S** tress
**A** lcohol
**F** atigue
**E** motion

B. Illness

1. Even a minor illness can seriously impair your performance as a pilot.
   a. Fever and other distracting symptoms can impair judgment, memory, alertness, and the ability to make calculations.
   b. Also, any medication you may be taking to combat these symptoms may itself decrease your performance as a pilot.
2. The safest rule is not to fly while suffering from any illness.

C. Medication

1. Pilot performance can be seriously impaired by both prescribed and over-the-counter-medications.

   a. Many medications have primary or side effects that may impair judgement, memory, alertness, coordination, vision, and the ability to make calculations.

   b. Any medication that depresses the nervous system can make you more susceptible to hypoxia.

2. The safest rule is not to fly while taking any medication, unless approved by the FAA.

D. Stress

1. Stress from the pressures of everyday living can impair pilot performance, often in very subtle ways.

   a. Difficulties can occupy thought processes so as to decrease alertness.
   b. Distraction can so interfere with judgment that unwarranted risks are taken.
   c. Stress and fatigue (see below) can be a deadly combination.

2. When you are under more stress than usual, you should consider delaying flight until your difficulties have been resolved.

E. Alcohol

1. As little as 1 oz. of liquor, 1 bottle of beer, or 4 oz. of wine can impair flying skills.

   a. Even after your body has completely destroyed a moderate amount of alcohol, you can still be impaired for many hours by hangover.

   b. Alcohol also renders you much more susceptible to disorientation and hypoxia.

2. The FARs prohibit pilots from performing cockpit duties within 8 hr. after drinking any alcoholic beverage or while under the influence of alcohol.

   a. An excellent rule is to allow at least 12 to 24 hr. "from bottle to throttle," depending on how much you drank.

F. Fatigue

1. Fatigue can be treacherous because it may not be apparent to you until serious errors are made.

   a. It is best described as either acute (short-term) or chronic (long-term).

2. Acute fatigue is the everyday tiredness felt after long periods of physical or mental strain.

   a. Consequently, coordination and alertness can be reduced.

   b. Acute fatigue is prevented by adequate rest and sleep, as well as regular exercise and proper nutrition.

3. Chronic fatigue occurs when there is not enough time for full recovery between episodes of acute fatigue.

   a. Performance continues to fall off, and judgment becomes impaired.
   b. Recovery from chronic fatigue requires a prolonged period of rest.

G. Emotion

1. Certain emotionally upsetting events can render you unable to fly an airplane safely.

   a. The emotions of anger, depression, and anxiety not only decrease alertness but also may lead to your taking self-destructive risks.

2. If you experience such an event, you should not fly until you have recovered from it.

## 14.2 HYPOXIA

A. Hypoxia is a state of oxygen deficiency in the body sufficient to impair functions of the brain and other organs.

1. Although a deterioration in night vision occurs at a cabin pressure altitude as low as 5,000 ft. MSL, other significant effects of altitude hypoxia usually do not occur in the normal, healthy pilot below 12,000 ft. MSL.
2. From 12,000 to 15,000 ft. MSL (without supplemental oxygen), judgment, memory, alertness, coordination, and ability to make calculations are impaired.
3. Headache, drowsiness, dizziness, and either a sense of well-being (euphoria) or belligerence occur.

B. The effects appear after increasingly shorter periods of exposure to increasing altitude.

1. Pilot performance can seriously deteriorate within 15 min. at 15,000 ft. MSL.
2. At altitudes above 15,000 ft. MSL, the periphery of the visual field turns gray. Only central vision remains (tunnel vision).
3. A blue color (cyanosis) develops in the fingernails and lips.
4. You lose the ability to take corrective and protective action in 20 to 30 min. at 18,000 ft. MSL.
   a. This happens in 5 to 12 min. at 20,000 ft. MSL, followed soon by unconsciousness.

C. Significant effects of hypoxia can occur at even lower altitudes given one or more of the following factors:

1. Carbon monoxide inhaled in smoking or from exhaust fumes.
2. Small amounts of alcohol and low doses of certain drugs (e.g., antihistamines, tranquilizers, sedatives, and analgesics).
3. Extreme heat or cold, fever, and/or anxiety.

D. Hypoxia is prevented by understanding the factors that reduce your tolerance to altitude and by using supplemental oxygen above 10,000 ft. during the day, and above 5,000 ft. at night.

1. Corrective action if hypoxia is suspected or recognized includes
   a. Use of supplemental oxygen.
   b. An emergency descent to a lower altitude.

## 14.3 HYPERVENTILATION

A. Hyperventilation, which is an abnormal increase in the volume of air breathed in and out of the lungs, can occur subconsciously when you encounter a stressful situation in flight.

1. As hyperventilation "blows off" excessive carbon dioxide from the body, you can experience symptoms of lightheadedness, suffocation, drowsiness, tingling in the extremities, and coolness. Often, you may react to these symptoms with even greater hyperventilation.
2. Incapacitation can eventually result from incoordination, disorientation, and painful muscle spasms.

B. The symptoms of hyperventilation subside within a few minutes after the rate and depth of breathing are consciously brought back under control.

1. The buildup of the appropriate balance of carbon dioxide in your body can be hastened by controlled breathing in and out of a paper bag held over your nose and mouth.

C. It is important to recognize that early symptoms of hyperventilation and hypoxia are similar.

1. Also, hyperventilation and hypoxia can occur at the same time.
2. If you are using an oxygen system when symptoms are experienced, set the oxygen regulator immediately to deliver 100% oxygen. This is to make sure you are not experiencing hypoxia.
3. If it is not hypoxia, give attention to rate and depth of breathing.

## 14.4 CARBON MONOXIDE POISONING

A. Carbon monoxide is a colorless, odorless, and tasteless gas contained in exhaust fumes and tobacco smoke.

1. When breathed even in minute quantities over a period of time, it can significantly reduce the ability of the blood to carry oxygen.
2. Consequently, effects of hypoxia occur.

B. Most heaters in light aircraft work by air flowing over the exhaust manifold.

1. Using these heaters when exhaust fumes are escaping through manifold cracks and seals is responsible every year for both nonfatal and fatal aircraft accidents from carbon monoxide poisoning.
2. If you detect the odor of exhaust or experience symptoms of headache, drowsiness, or dizziness while using the heater you should suspect carbon monoxide poisoning and immediately shut off the heater and open the air vents.
   a. If symptoms are severe, or continue after landing, medical treatment should be sought.

C. Tobacco does more than deprive the body of oxygen because of the carbon monoxide content in smoke.

1. Tobacco smoke lowers the sensitivity of the eye and cuts night vision by approximately 20%.
   a. Nicotine increases the body's heat production 10% to 15% above normal, creating added oxygen demands.
   b. Ironically, the same cigarette that increases the demand for oxygen also reduces the supply.
2. Careful tests have shown that the carbon monoxide in tobacco smoke can lower the pilot's tolerance to altitude by as much as 5,000 to 6,000 ft. because the blood is saturated with carbon monoxide.
   a. Thus, pilots who smoke are already at altitude before they ever leave the ground and may need supplemental oxygen at a lower altitude than nonsmokers.

## 14.5 DECOMPRESSION SICKNESS AFTER SCUBA DIVING

A. If you or one of your passengers intends to fly after scuba diving, you should allow the body sufficient time to rid itself of excess nitrogen absorbed during diving.

1. If this is not done, decompression sickness due to evolved gas (bubbles in the bloodstream) can occur at low altitudes and create a serious in-flight emergency.

B. The recommended waiting time before flight to flight altitudes of up to 8,000 ft. is at least 12 hr. after a dive which has not required controlled ascent (nondecompression diving).

1. You should allow at least 24 hr. after diving which has required controlled ascent (decompression diving).

2. The waiting time before flight to flight altitudes above 8,000 ft. should be at least 24 hr. after any scuba diving.

C. These recommended altitudes are actual flight altitudes above mean sea level (MSL), not pressurized cabin altitudes. This takes into consideration the risk of decompression of aircraft during flight.

## 14.6 MOTION SICKNESS

A. Motion sickness is caused by continued stimulation of the tiny portion of the inner ear which controls your sense of balance. The symptoms are progressive.
   1. First, the desire for food is lost.
   2. Then saliva collects in the mouth and you begin to perspire freely.
   3. Eventually, you become nauseated and disoriented.
   4. The head aches and there may be a tendency to vomit.

B. If suffering from airsickness, you should
   1. Open the air vents.
   2. Loosen clothing.
   3. Use supplemental oxygen.
   4. Keep the eyes on a point outside the airplane.
   5. Avoid unnecessary head movements.
   6. Cancel the flight and land as soon as possible.

C. Although motion sickness is uncommon among experienced pilots, it does occur occasionally.
   1. Most important, it jeopardizes your flying efficiency, particularly in turbulent weather.
   2. Student pilots are frequently surprised by an uneasiness usually described as motion sickness.
      a. This is probably a result of combining anxiety, unfamiliarity, and the vibration or jogging received from the airplane. These sensations are usually overcome with experience.
   3. Pilots who are susceptible to airsickness should NOT take the preventive drugs which are available over the counter or by prescription.
      a. Research has shown that most motion sickness drugs cause a temporary deterioration of navigational skills or ability to perform other tasks demanding keen judgment.

## 14.7 SINUS AND EAR BLOCK

A. During ascent and descent, air pressure in the sinuses equalizes with aircraft cabin pressure through small openings that connect the sinuses to the nasal passages.
   1. An upper respiratory infection (e.g., a cold or sinusitis) or nasal allergies can produce enough congestion around one or more of these small openings to slow equalization.
      a. Then, as the difference in pressure between the sinus and cabin mounts, the opening may become plugged.
      b. This "sinus block" occurs most frequently during descent.
   2. Sinus block is prevented by not flying with an upper respiratory infection or nasal allergic condition.
      a. Adequate protection is usually not provided by decongestant sprays or drops to reduce congestion around the sinus openings.
      b. Oral decongestants have side effects that can impair pilot performance.

B. As the cabin pressure decreases during ascent, the expanding air in the middle ear pushes the eustachian tube open and escapes down it to the nasal passages, thus equalizing ear pressure with the cabin pressure.

1. During descent, the pilot must periodically reopen the eustachian tube to equalize pressure.
   a. This can be accomplished by swallowing, yawning, tensing muscles in the throat, or if these do not work, by the combination of closing the mouth, pinching the nose closed, and attempting to blow through the nostrils (Valsalva maneuver).
2. Again, an upper respiratory infection (e.g., a cold or sore throat) or nasal allergies can produce enough congestion around the eustachian tubes to make equalization difficult.
   a. The difference in pressure between the middle ear and the airplane's cabin can build to a level that will hold the eustachian tube closed, making equalization difficult if not impossible. This problem is commonly referred to as "ear block."
3. Ear block produces severe ear pain and loss of hearing that can last from several hours to several days.
   a. Rupture of the ear drum can occur in flight or after landing.
   b. Fluid can accumulate in the middle ear and become infected.
4. Ear block is prevented by not flying with an upper respiratory infection or nasal allergic condition.

## 14.8 ILLUSIONS IN FLIGHT

A. Many different illusions can be experienced in flight.

1. Some can lead to spatial disorientation.
2. Others can lead to landing errors.
3. Illusions frequently contribute to fatal aircraft accidents.

B. Illusions Leading to Spatial Disorientation

1. Various complex motions and forces and certain visual scenes encountered in flight can create illusions of motion and position.
   a. Spatial disorientation from these illusions can be prevented only by visual reference to reliable, fixed points on the ground or to flight instruments.
   b. Read and be aware of the following illusions. You need a general understanding of their nature and cause, but you do not need to be able to explain each one.
2. *The leans* -- An abrupt correction of a banked attitude, which has been entered too slowly to stimulate the motion sensing system in the inner ear, can create the illusion of banking in the opposite direction. The disoriented pilot will roll the aircraft back into its original dangerous attitude, or if level flight is maintained, will feel compelled to lean in the perceived vertical plane until this illusion subsides.
3. *Coriolis illusion* -- An abrupt head movement in a prolonged constant-rate turn that has ceased stimulating the motion sensing system can create the illusion of rotation or movement in an entirely different axis. The disoriented pilot will maneuver the aircraft into a dangerous attitude in an attempt to stop rotation. This most overwhelming of all illusions in flight may be prevented by not making sudden, extreme head movements, particularly while making prolonged constant-rate turns under IFR conditions.
4. *Graveyard spin* -- A proper recovery from a spin that has ceased stimulating the motion sensing system can create the illusion of spinning in the opposite direction. The disoriented pilot will return the aircraft to its original spin.

5. *Graveyard spiral* -- An observed loss of altitude during a coordinated constant-rate turn that has ceased stimulating the motion sensing system can create the illusion of being in a descent with the wings level. The disoriented pilot will pull back on the controls, tightening the spiral and increasing the loss of altitude.

6. *Somatogravic illusion* -- A rapid acceleration during takeoff can create the illusion of being in a nose up attitude. The disoriented pilot will push the aircraft into a nose-low, or dive, attitude. A rapid deceleration by a quick reduction of the throttles can have the opposite effect, with the disoriented pilot pulling the aircraft into a nose-up, or stall, attitude.

7. *Inversion illusion* -- An abrupt change from climb to straight-and-level flight can create the illusion of tumbling backwards. The disoriented pilot will push the aircraft abruptly into a nose-low attitude, possibly intensifying this illusion.

8. *Elevator illusion* -- An abrupt upward vertical acceleration, usually caused by an updraft, can create the illusion of being in a climb. The disoriented pilot will push the aircraft into a nose-low attitude. An abrupt downward vertical acceleration, usually caused by a downdraft, has the opposite effect, with the disoriented pilot pulling the aircraft into a nose-up attitude.

9. *False horizon* -- Sloping cloud formations, an obscured horizon, a dark scene spread with ground lights and stars, and certain geometric patterns of ground light can create illusions of not being aligned correctly with the actual horizon. The disoriented pilot will place the aircraft in a dangerous attitude.

10. *Autokinesis* -- In the dark, a static light will appear to move about when stared at for many seconds. The disoriented pilot will lose control of the aircraft in attempting to align it with the light.

C. Illusions Leading to Landing Errors

1. Various surface features and atmospheric conditions encountered in landing can create illusions of incorrect height above and distance from the runway threshold.

    a. Landing errors from these illusions can be prevented by anticipating them during approaches, aerial inspection of unfamiliar airports before landing, using VASI systems when available, and maintaining optimal proficiency in landing procedures.

    b. Study the following five illusions, and anticipate and observe them when and if they occur.

2. *Runway width illusion* -- A narrower-than-usual runway can create the illusion that the aircraft is at a higher altitude than it actually is. The pilot who does not recognize this illusion will fly a lower approach, with the risk of striking objects along the approach path or landing short. A wider-than-usual runway can have the opposite effect, with the risk of leveling out too high and landing hard or overshooting the runway.

3. *Runway and terrain slopes illusion* -- An upsloping runway, upsloping terrain, or both, can create the illusion that the aircraft is at a higher altitude than it actually is. The pilot who does not recognize this illusion will fly a lower approach. A downsloping runway, downsloping approach terrain, or both, can have the opposite effect.

4. *Featureless terrain illusion* -- An absence of ground features, as when landing over water, darkened areas, and terrain made featureless by snow, can create the illusion that the aircraft is at a higher altitude than it actually is. The pilot who does not recognize this illusion will fly a lower approach.

5. *Atmospheric illusions* -- Rain on the windscreen can create the illusion of greater height, and atmospheric haze the illusion of being at a greater distance from the runway. The pilot who does not recognize these illusions will fly a lower approach. Penetration of fog can create the illusion of pitching up. The pilot who does not recognize this illusion will steepen the approach, often quite abruptly.

6. *Ground lighting illusions* -- Lights along a straight path, such as a road, and even lights on moving trains can be mistaken for runway and approach lights. Bright runway and approach lighting systems, especially where few lights illuminate the surrounding terrain, may create the illusion of less distance to the runway. The pilot who does not recognize this illusion will fly a higher approach. Conversely, the pilot overflying terrain which has few lights to provide height cues may make a lower than normal approach.

## 14.9 VISION

A. Of the body senses, vision is the most important for safe flight. It is important for you to understand your eye's construction and how the eye is affected by darkness.

1. Two types of light-sensitive nerve endings called "cones" and "rods" are located at the back of the eye, or retina, which transmit messages to the brain via the optic nerve.

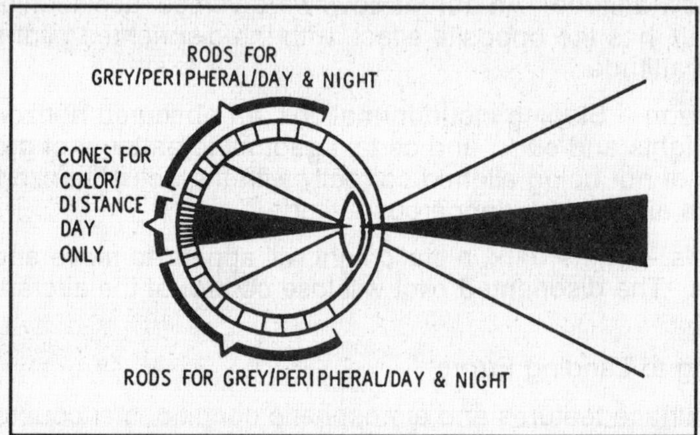


a. The cones are located in the center of the retina, directly behind the pupil.

1) Their function is to detect color, details, and distant objects.
2) They function both in daylight and in moonlight.

b. The rods are concentrated in a ring around the cones.

1) Their function in daylight is to detect objects, particularly those in motion, out of the corner of the eye (i.e., peripheral vision), but they do not give detail or color, only shades of gray.
2) They function in daylight, in moonlight, and in darkness.

2. The fact that the rods are distributed around the cones and do not lie directly behind the pupils, makes "off center" viewing (i.e., looking to one side of an object) important during night flight.

a. During daylight an object can be seen best by looking directly at it.

b. At night, you will find after some practice that you can see things more clearly and definitely by looking to one side of them, rather than straight at them.

1) Remember, rods do not detect objects while your eyes are moving, only during the pauses.

B. Adapting your eyes to darkness is an important aspect of night vision.

1. When entering a dark area the pupils of the eyes enlarge to receive as much of the available light as possible.

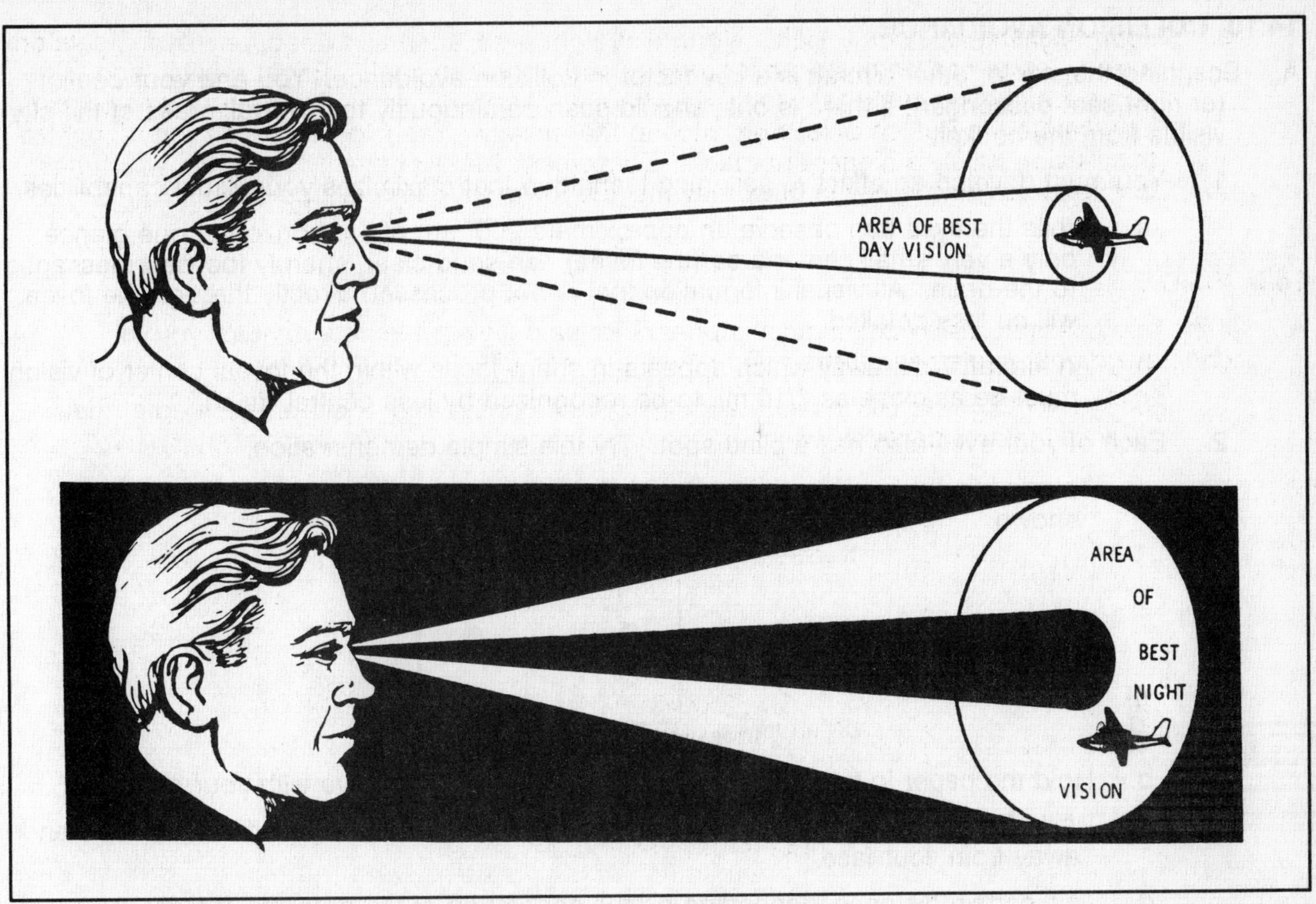


2. It will take approximately 5 to 10 min. for the cones to become adjusted to the dim light, and your eyes become 100 times more sensitive than they were before you entered the dark area.
   a. In fact, the cones stop working altogether in semidarkness.
   b. Since the rods can still function in light of 1/5,000 the intensity at which the cones cease to function, they are used for night vision.
3. After about 30 min., the rods will be fully adjusted to darkness and become about 100,000 times more sensitive to light than they were in the lighted area.
4. The rods need more time to adjust to darkness than the cones do to bright light. Your eyes become adapted to sunlight in 10 sec., whereas they need 30 min. to fully adjust to a dark night.

C. The eyes are the first part of your body to suffer from low oxygen at altitude because the capillaries are very small and have a limited capacity to carry oxygen.
   1. Night vision may be adversely affected above 5,000 ft. MSL.
      a. Fly low and/or use oxygen at night.
   2. Good vision depends on your physical condition. Fatigue, colds, vitamin deficiency, alcohol, stimulants, smoking, or medication can seriously impair your vision.
      a. EXAMPLE: Smoking lowers the sensitivity of the eyes and reduces night vision by approximately 20%.

## 14.10 COLLISION AVOIDANCE

A. Scanning the sky for other aircraft is a key factor in collision avoidance. You and your copilot (or right seat passenger), if there is one, should scan continuously to cover all areas of the sky visible from the cockpit.

1. You must develop an effective scanning technique that maximizes your visual capabilities.
   a. While the eyes can observe an approximate 200° arc of the horizon at one glance, only a very small center area (the fovea) can send clear, sharply focused messages to the brain. All visual information that is not processed directly through the fovea will be less detailed.
   b. An aircraft 7 mi. away which appears in sharp focus within the foveal center of vision must be as close as 7/10 mi. to be recognized by less central vision.
2. Each of your eyes also has a blind spot. Try this simple demonstration.
   a. Take a blank piece of paper, lay it sideways, and mark a dot on each side as shown.

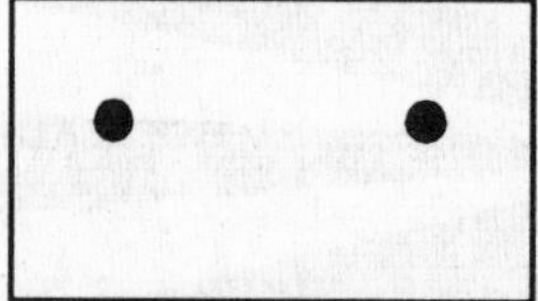

   b. Hold the paper in front of your face and cover your right eye with your hand.
   c. While focusing your left eye on the right dot, move the paper alternately toward and away from your face.
   d. At a certain distance, depending on the separation of the dots, the left dot will seem to disappear.
   e. If another aircraft were in this blind spot, and blocked from view of the other eye by a part of your airplane, the other aircraft would essentially be invisible.
3. Effective scanning is accomplished with a series of short, regularly spaced eye movements that bring successive areas of the sky into the central visual field.
   a. Each eye movement should not exceed 10°.
   b. Each area should be observed for at least 1 sec. to enable detection.
4. Visual tasks inside the cabin should represent no more than 1/4 to 1/3 of the scan time outside, or no more than 4 to 5 sec. on the instrument panel for every 16 sec. outside.
   a. You must realize that your eyes may require several seconds to refocus when switching view from items in the cockpit to distant objects.
5. Effective scanning also helps avoid "empty-field myopia."
   a. When flying above the clouds or in a haze layer that provides nothing specific to focus on outside the aircraft, the eyes tend to relax and seek a comfortable focal distance which may range from 10 to 30 ft.
   b. For you, this means looking without seeing, which is dangerous.

B. Collision avoidance

1. Determining Relative Altitude -- Use the horizon as a reference point. If you see another aircraft above the horizon, it is probably on a higher flight path. If it appears to be below the horizon, it is probably flying at a lower altitude.

2. Taking Appropriate Action -- You must be familiar with the rules of right-of-way, so that if an aircraft is on an obvious collision course, you can take the appropriate evasive action.

3. Consider Multiple Threats -- The decision to climb, descend, or turn is a matter of personal judgment, but you should anticipate that the other pilot may also be making a quick maneuver. Watch the other aircraft during the maneuver, but begin your scanning again immediately. There may be even more aircraft in the area!

4. Collision Course Targets -- Any aircraft that appears to have no relative motion and stays in one scan quadrant is likely to be on a collision course. Also, if a target shows no lateral or vertical motion, but increases in size, take evasive action.

5. Recognize High Hazard Areas

    a. Airways and especially VORs and airport traffic areas are places where aircraft tend to cluster.

    b. Remember, most collisions occur on days when the weather is good.

6. Cockpit Management -- Study maps, checklists, and manuals BEFORE flight, along with other proper preflight planning (e.g., noting necessary radio frequencies). Also, organizing cockpit materials can reduce the time you need to look at them during flight, permitting more scan time.

7. Windshield Conditions -- Dirty or bug-smeared windshields can greatly reduce your ability to see other aircraft. Keep a clean windshield.

8. Visibility Conditions -- Smoke, haze, dust, rain, and flying toward the sun can also greatly reduce the ability to detect other aircraft.

9. Visual Obstructions in the Cockpit

    a. You may need to move your head to see around blind spots caused by fixed aircraft structures, such as door posts, wings, etc. It may even be necessary occasionally to maneuver your airplane (e.g., lift a wing) to facilitate seeing.

    b. Check that curtains and other cockpit objects (e.g., maps that glare on the windshield) are removed and stowed during flight.

10. Lights On

    a. Day or night, exterior lights can greatly increase the visibility of any aircraft.
    b. Keep interior lights low at night so that you can see out in the dark.

11. ATC Support -- ATC facilities often provide radar traffic advisories (e.g., flight following) on a workload-permitting basis. Use this support whenever possible or when required.

    a. But being in a radar environment (i.e., where traffic is separated by radar) still requires vigilance to avoid collisions. Radar does not relieve you of this responsibility.

# APPENDIX A
# YOUR FLIGHT REVIEW



The purpose of this appendix is to guide you through the steps you must take to remain current once you have received your Private Pilot Certificate. As a student pilot, you were probably flying fairly often, practicing precision maneuvers, and receiving regular critiques from your CFI. Now that you are on your own as a private pilot, you may be flying less often, flying more for pleasure and less to practice precision maneuvers. You must make a conscious effort not only to maintain, but progress beyond the standards to which you flew as a student pilot.

FAR 61.56 requires every pilot to accomplish a flight review every 2 years. (See Chapter 8, Federal Aviation Regulations Outlined, on page 219.) This flight review (commonly referred to as a biennial flight review or BFR) must consist of a review of the current operating and flight rules of FAR Part 91, and any maneuvers and procedures which the CFI giving the review feels are necessary for you to demonstrate that you can safely act as a private pilot. The flight review may be given by any appropriately rated CFI. In addition, the FAA (and your author) recommend that you maintain some sort of personal currency program.

The FAA has in the past proposed to require recreational and non-instrument-rated private pilots with less than 400 hr. to successfully complete a flight review every 12 months. This requirement has been at least deferred, if not eliminated. A pending change to the flight review regulations is the requirement that the flight review consist of a minimum of 1 hr. ground and 1 hr. of flight instruction for all pilots.

## PERSONAL CURRENCY PROGRAM

A. You should consider designing a currency program tailored to the specific needs of the type of flying you will be doing.
   1. You might take an hour or so of instruction every few months from a local CFI.
      a. Each periodic lesson might cover a different set of maneuvers such as stalls, pattern work, hoodwork, etc.
   2. You may be able to integrate practice with normal flights.
      a. For example, you might make a few short- or soft-field takeoffs and landings at the end of a cross-country flight.

B. You may wish to participate in the FAA's Pilot Proficiency Award Program (commonly known as the Wings Program), and to attend pilot safety seminars conducted through the FAA Accident Prevention Program.
   1. You may complete one phase of the Wings Program per year.

a. You must attend at least one of the following:
   1) FAA-sponsored or FAA-sanctioned aviation safety seminar,
   2) Industry-conducted recurrent training program, or
   3) Physiological training course.

b. Obtain 3 hr. of training from a CFI.
   1) 1 hr. of flight training to include basic airplane control, stalls, turns, and other maneuvers directed toward mastery of the airplane.
   2) 1 hr. of flight training to include precision approaches, takeoffs and landings, including crosswind, soft-field, and short-field techniques.
   3) 1 hr. of instrument training in an airplane, instrument simulator, or training device.

c. All of these requirements must be completed within 12 months after you begin the training for a phase of the Wings Program.

2. For more information on the Wings Program, obtain a copy of AC 61-91F, *Pilot Proficiency Award Program*, dated 3/6/91. Use the order form on page 291 in Chapter 10, Other Navigation Publications.
3. Completing a phase of the Wings Program satisfies the flight review requirement.

C. Explore the wide range of publications and other commercially developed materials which are available for use in personal currency programs.
   1. Sources for these materials include
      a. Pilot examiners
      b. Flight schools
      c. Individual CFIs
      d. Accident Prevention Program Managers
      e. Accident Prevention Counselors
   2. For information regarding the sources, contact the Accident Prevention Program Manager at the nearest FAA Flight Standards District Office (FSDO).
   3. To ensure staying up to date in regulatory changes and flying techniques, you should also regularly read aviation periodicals of your choice.

D. Consider adding a new rating onto your Private Pilot Certificate.
   1. An instrument rating is an obvious choice for a private pilot.
      a. The training will greatly improve your technical skill in flying.
      b. More importantly, your cross-country navigation skills will be greatly enhanced.
      c. You will become a safer pilot all around.
   2. Earning a new rating (or certificate) satisfies the flight review requirement.

## STRUCTURE AND INTENT OF THE FLIGHT REVIEW

A. You must accomplish a flight review within 2 years after your last flight review or checkride for a rating or certificate.
   1. A flight review can be conducted by any appropriately rated CFI.

B. The basic purpose of the flight review is to provide a periodic check and assessment of your aviation knowledge and flying skills.
   1. Hopefully, this will bring to light any weaknesses that might adversely affect your flying safely.

2. The flight review should encompass and meet the following factors and goals.
   a. Provide an evaluation of your flying ability and of you as an overall pilot.
   b. Provide a learning experience rather than a pressure "test" atmosphere.

C. The flight review should be tailored to meet your needs, based on the types of flying you generally do.
   1. The primary purpose is to assess your knowledge and ability to fly safely.
      a. Thus, the FAA does not have standard guidelines or a list of maneuvers.
   2. You should be assessed on your broad awareness of regulations, procedures, and good practices.

D. Consider many factors in selecting a CFI.
   1. Presumably, you are in regular contact with a CFI for advanced training, checkouts at a local FBO for rentals, or a similar reason.
      a. This is probably the CFI you will use for your flight review.
   2. You may, however, wish to use another CFI for your flight review to:
      a. Benefit from the experience of another CFI,
      b. Avoid waiting for your CFI,
      c. Gain rental privileges at another FBO, etc.
   3. The CFI (and you) must be rated in the category and class of aircraft you wish to use.
      a. If you want to take your flight review in a multiengine airplane, the CFI must hold a multiengine rating on his/her pilot and flight instructor certificates.
      b. If you complete a flight review in one category and class of aircraft, you are considered proficient in all categories and classes in which you are rated. You do not have to take a flight review in each one.
   4. Consider your compatibility with the CFI in terms of personality and experience.
      a. You and the CFI should take a similar approach to the flight review.
      b. Taking a flight review with a CFI who has much more experience than you can be a tremendous learning experience.
         1) On the other hand, a newly rated CFI will be extremely knowledgeable on regulations and airspace.

E. A flight review is valid for 24 calendar months.
   1. If you took your last flight review on July 15, 1992, another flight review will be due July 31, 1994.
   2. If you do not accomplish your flight review in 24 calendar months, it does not mean your certificate is invalid.
      a. A pilot certificate is valid until it is suspended, revoked, or surrendered.
   3. If you do not accomplish the flight review, you are not allowed to act as pilot in command until you have done so.
      a. You are allowed, however, to act as a second in command or to act as a safety pilot for others.
      b. Solo flight is not allowed because, even though you are not carrying passengers, you are acting as the pilot in command.

## THE PREFLIGHT REVIEW INTERVIEW

A. Before undertaking the flight review, the CFI you have chosen should interview you to determine the nature of your flying and operating requirements.

1. This discussion will provide you both with an opportunity to assess each other and determine what each expects to encounter and gain during the flight review.
2. In addition, you and your CFI should review all the necessary paperwork, including all required aircraft documents.

B. During the interview, your CFI will consider the following elements in formulating a plan for your flight review.

1. The Type of Aircraft You Fly
   a. A flight review in a twin-engine airplane should be different from one conducted in a small, two-seat tailwheel airplane with no radios.
   b. Your CFI may recommend that you take the flight review in the airplane you usually fly, in the most complex airplane you fly, or perhaps in more than one category/class of airplane.
2. The Type of Flying You Do
   a. If you usually conduct long-distance flights into large airports, you may need a review on classes of airspace, radio navigation, and high-density airport operations, rather than soft-field landing techniques.
   b. Conversely, if you only fly locally out of a sod field, you should have a review of uncontrolled airport procedures, short- and soft-field techniques, rather than clearance delivery procedures.
   c. If you are anticipating making a flight that is significantly different from the type of flying you usually do, you might ask for some review on that different type of flying.
3. The Amount and Recency of Your Flight Experience
   a. If you have not flown in several years, you may require an extensive review of basic maneuvers and FARs, including recent changes in airspace and other requirements.
      1) Your CFI may even recommend that you undertake a complete refresher course.
   b. If you are upgrading to a newer or faster airplane, your CFI might emphasize knowledge of aircraft systems and performance, or in cross-country procedures appropriate to a faster airplane.
   c. In any case, your CFI will ensure that you review all the areas in which (s)he determines that you should receive training in order to operate safely.

C. At the end of the interview, you and your CFI should reach an understanding based on the above considerations regarding how the flight review will be conducted.

1. Your CFI may provide you with reading materials or recommend publications for study before actually undertaking the flight review.
2. (S)he should also review with you the criteria for satisfactory completion of your flight review.

## THE ORAL REVIEW

A. Your CFI should tailor the review of general operating and flight rules to your needs.

1. The objective is to ensure that you are aware of the applicable regulations and procedures to operate safely in various classes of airspace under an appropriate range of weather conditions.

2. The review should be broad enough to meet this objective, yet provide you with a more comprehensive review in those areas in which your knowledge is weaker.

B. Although the FARs only specify a review of FAR Part 91, your CFI may wish to review other topics, such as those listed below. (Refer to the appropriate chapters in this book.)

1. Regulations
   a. Pilot certificates and other FAR Part 61 requirements
   b. Aircraft documents and records
   c. Air traffic control and airspace

2. *Pilot's Operating Handbook* (*POH*)
   a. Aircraft performance and limitations
   b. Weight and balance
   c. Aircraft systems and operating procedures
   d. Emergency procedures
   e. Preflight inspection

3. Cross-Country Flying
   a. Flight planning and obtaining weather information
   b. Avoidance of hazardous weather (including wake turbulence)
   c. The interpretation of aeronautical charts

## THE FLIGHT REVIEW

A. The maneuvers and procedures covered during the flight review will be those which, in the opinion of your CFI, are necessary for you to perform in order to demonstrate that you can safely exercise the privileges of your Private Pilot Certificate.

1. This may include a flight to the practice area or to another airport with maneuvers accomplished while en route.

2. It could also include simulated instrument flight.

3. Regardless of your experience, your CFI may wish to review at least those maneuvers considered critical to safe flight, such as stalls, slow flight, and takeoffs and landings.

B. Your CFI will construct a review sequence which closely resembles your typical flight, including maneuvers and procedures such as those listed below.

1. Airport Operations
   a. Preflight inspection
   b. Use of checklist and cockpit resource management
   c. Radio communication
   d. Collision avoidance
   e. Ground and traffic pattern operations
   f. Takeoffs and landings (normal, crosswind, short- and soft-field)
   g. Go-arounds

2. Maneuvers
   a. Stalls
   b. Maneuvering during slow flight
   c. Constant altitude (steep) turns

3. Emergency Procedures
   a. Simulated forced landings
   b. Flight by reference to instruments
   c. Systems failure
4. Cross-Country Flying
   a. Radio navigation (if airplane equipped)
   b. Navigation by pilotage and dead reckoning

C. The flight review need not be limited to evaluation purposes.
   1. Your CFI may provide additional instruction in weak areas or, if you wish, defer this instruction to a follow-up flight.

## COMPLETING THE FLIGHT REVIEW

A. A flight review should always be concluded with a helpful, positive discussion and suggestions for improvement.
   1. In order for the flight review to be of any real value, you must receive this appraisal with an open mind.
   2. You should receive an objective picture of your current ability to fly safely, as demonstrated during the flight review.

B. Your CFI will not endorse your logbook indicating an unsatisfactory flight review, but (s)he may, if you wish, sign your logbook to record instruction given.
   1. (S)he will then recommend additional training or practice in the areas of the flight review that were unsatisfactory.
   2. If 24 months have not yet elapsed since your last flight review, you may continue to fly and practice on your own.
      a. If your 24 months have expired, you must take instruction or be accompanied by a current pilot in order to practice.
   3. If you feel your CFI has unfairly judged you, you do have the option of completing the flight review with another CFI.
      a. However, a different CFI will not be familiar with your strengths and weaknesses, and will probably wish to conduct another complete review.

C. When you successfully complete a flight review, your logbook must be endorsed as shown below by the CFI who gave the review.
   1. Endorsement for completion of flight review: FAR § 61.56

      *Mr./Ms. ___________, holder of pilot certificate # ___________, has satisfactorily completed the flight review required by FAR § 61.56 on (date).*

      | ________ | ____________ | ________ | ____________ |
      |---|---|---|---|
      | *Date* | *Signature* | *CFI No.* | *Expiration Date* |

   2. The logbook endorsement is the only record you have of the flight review.

D. Most flight reviews are logged as dual, i.e., flight instruction.

# BOOKS AVAILABLE FROM GLEIM PUBLICATIONS, Inc.

## WRITTEN EXAM BOOKS

Before pilots take their FAA written tests, they want to understand the answer to every FAA written test question. Gleim's written test books are widely used because they help pilots learn and understand exactly what they need to know to do well on their FAA written test.

Gleim's books contain all of the FAA's airplane questions (nonairplane questions are excluded). We have unscrambled the questions appearing in the FAA written test books and organized them into logical topics. Answer explanations are provided next to each question. Each of our chapters opens with a brief, user-friendly outline of exactly what you need to know to pass the written test. Information not directly tested is omitted to expedite your passing the written test. This additional information can be found in our flight maneuver and reference books and practical test prep books described below.

***PRIVATE PILOT AND RECREATIONAL PILOT FAA WRITTEN EXAM*** **($12.95)**

The FAA's written test for either certificate consists of 60 questions out of the 710 questions in our book.

***INSTRUMENT PILOT FAA WRITTEN EXAM*** **($16.95)**

The FAA's written test consists of 60 questions out of the 898 questions in our book. Also, those people who wish to become an instrument-rated flight instructor (CFII) or an instrument ground instructor (IGI) must take the FAA's written test of 50 questions from this book.

***COMMERCIAL PILOT FAA WRITTEN EXAM*** **($14.95)**

The FAA's written test will consist of 100 questions out of the 564 questions in our book.

***FUNDAMENTALS OF INSTRUCTING FAA WRITTEN EXAM*** **($9.95)**

The FAA's written test consists of 50 questions out of the 180 questions in our book. This is required of any person to become a flight instructor or ground instructor. The test only needs to be taken once. For example, if someone is already a flight instructor and wants to become a ground instructor, taking the FOI test a second time is not required.

***FLIGHT/GROUND INSTRUCTOR FAA WRITTEN EXAM*** **($14.95)**

The FAA's written test consists of 100 questions out of the 859 questions in our book. To be used for the Certificated Flight Instructor (CFI) written test and those who aspire to the Advanced Ground Instructor (AGI) rating for airplanes. Note that this book also covers what is known as the Basic Ground Instructor (BGI) rating. However, the BGI is **not** useful because it does not give the holder full authority to sign off private pilots to take their written test. In other words, this book should be used for the AGI rating.

***AIRLINE TRANSPORT PILOT FAA WRITTEN EXAM*** **($23.95)**

The FAA's written test consists of 80 questions each for the ATP Part 121, ATP Part 135, and the flight dispatcher certificate. This first edition contains a complete answer explanation to each of the 1,304 airplane ATP questions (111 helicopter questions are excluded). This difficult FAA written test is now made simple by Gleim. As with Gleim's other written test books, studying for the ATP will now be a learning and understanding experience rather than a memorization marathon -- at a lower cost and with higher test scores and less frustration!!

---

## FAA PRACTICAL TEST PREP AND REFERENCE BOOKS

Our new Practical Test Prep books are designed to replace the FAA Practical Test Standards reprint booklets which are universally used by pilots preparing for the practical test. These new Practical Test Prep books will help prepare pilots for FAA practical tests as much as the Gleim written exam books prepare pilots for FAA written tests. Each task, objective, concept, requirement, etc., in the FAA's practical test standards is explained, analyzed, illustrated, and interpreted so pilots will be totally conversant with all aspects of their practical tests.

| | | | |
|---|---|---|---|
| | *Private Pilot FAA Practical Test Prep* | 538 pages | ($16.95) |
| **NOW** | *Instrument Pilot FAA Practical Test Prep* | 514 pages | ($17.95) |
| **AVAILABLE!** | *Commercial Pilot FAA Practical Test Prep* | 426 pages | ($14.95) |
| | *Flight Instructor FAA Practical Test Prep* | 626 pages | ($17.95) |

***PRIVATE PILOT HANDBOOK*** **($12.95)**

A complete private pilot ground school text in outline format with many diagrams for ease in understanding. A complete, detailed index makes it more useful and saves time. It contains a special section on biennial flight reviews.

***RECREATIONAL PILOT FLIGHT MANEUVERS*** **($11.95)**

Contains, in outline format, pertinent information necessary to be a skilled recreational pilot. An excellent reference book to begin your flight training endeavors.

**MAIL TO:** **GLEIM PUBLICATIONS, Inc.**
P.O. Box 12848
University Station
Gainesville, FL 32604
**OR CALL:** **(800) 87-GLEIM, (904) 375-0772, FAX (904) 375-6940**

**THE BOOKS WITH THE RED COVERS**

Our customer service staff is available to take your calls from 8:00 a.m. to 7:00 p.m., Monday through Friday, and 9:00 a.m. to 2:00 p.m., Saturday, Eastern Time. Please have your VISA/MasterCard ready.

## WRITTEN TEST BOOKS

|  |  |  | |
|---|---|---|---|
| *Private/Recreational Pilot* | Sixth (1992-1994) Edition | $12.95 | ____ |
| *Instrument Pilot* | Fourth (1992-1994) Edition | 16.95 | ____ |
| *Commercial Pilot* | Fourth (1992-1994) Edition | 14.95 | ____ |
| *Fundamentals of Instructing* | Fourth (1991-1993) Edition | 9.95 | ____ |
| *Flight/Ground Instructor* | Fourth (1991-1993) Edition | 14.95 | ____ |
| *Airline Transport Pilot* | First (1991-1993) Edition | 23.95 | ____ |

## HANDBOOKS AND PRACTICAL TEST PREP BOOKS

|  |  |  | |
|---|---|---|---|
| *Recreational Pilot Flight Maneuvers* | (First Edition) | 11.95 | ____ |
| *Private Pilot Handbook* | (Fourth Edition) | 12.95 | ____ |
| *Private Pilot FAA Practical Test Prep* | (First Edition) | 16.95 | ____ |
| *Instrument Pilot FAA Practical Test Prep* | (First Edition) | 17.95 | ____ |
| *Commercial Pilot FAA Practical Test Prep* | (First Edition) | 14.95 | ____ |
| *Flight Instructor FAA Practical Test Prep* | (First Edition) | 17.95 | ____ |

Shipping 3.00

Add applicable sales tax for shipments within the State of Florida — Sales Tax ____

*Please call or write for additional charges for out-of-the-U.S. shipments*

**Printed 04/93. Prices subject to change without notice. We ship latest editions.** — **TOTAL $____**

1. *We process and ship orders within 1 day of receipt of your order. We generally ship via UPS for the Eastern U.S. and U.S. mail for the Western U.S.*
2. *Please PHOTOCOPY this order form for friends and others.*
3. *No CODs. All orders from individuals must be prepaid and are protected by our unequivocal refund policy.*

*Library and company orders may be on account. Shipping and handling charges will be added to the invoice, and to prepaid telephone orders.*

Name ____________________
(please print)

Shipping Address ____________________
(street address required for UPS)

____________________

City ________ State ____ Zip ________

☐ MasterCard/VISA ☐ Check/Money Order Telephone ( ) ________

MasterCard/VISA No. ________ Expiration Date *(month/year)* __/__

__ __ __ __ - __ __ __ __ - __ __ __ __ - __ __ __ __

Signature ____________________

*011C*

**GLEIM PUBLICATIONS GUARANTEES**
**THE IMMEDIATE REFUND OF ALL RESALABLE TEXTS RETURNED IN 30 DAYS**
**SHIPPING AND HANDLING CHARGES ARE NONREFUNDABLE**

P.S. We presume your local FBO or bookstore does not stock the books you are ordering from us directly. If you provide us with a name and address, we will invite them to do so.

## INSTRUCTOR CERTIFICATION FORM
## PRIVATE PILOT WRITTEN TEST

Name: ______________________________________________

I certify that I have reviewed the above individual's completion of the *PRIVATE PILOT FAA WRITTEN EXAM* home-study course by Irvin N. Gleim for the FAA Private Pilot written test [covering the topics specified in FAR 61.105(a)(1) through (6)]. I find that (s)he has satisfactorily completed the course and find him/her competent to pass the written test.

| Signed | Date | Name | CFI Number | Expiration Date |
|---|---|---|---|---|

* * * * * * * * * * * * * * * * * * * * * * * * * * * * * * * * * * * * * * * * * *

## INSTRUCTOR CERTIFICATION FORM
## RECREATIONAL WRITTEN TEST

Name: ______________________________________________

I certify that I have reviewed the above individual's completion of the *RECREATIONAL PILOT FAA WRITTEN EXAM* home-study course by Irvin N. Gleim for the FAA Recreational Pilot written test (covering the topics specified in FAR 61.97). I find that (s)he has satisfactorily completed the course and find him/her competent to pass the recreational pilot (airplane) written test.

| Signed | Date | Name | CFI Number | Expiration Date |
|---|---|---|---|---|

## AUTHOR'S RECOMMENDATION

**The Experimental Aircraft Association, Inc.** is a very successful and effective nonprofit organization that represents and serves those of us interested in flying, in general, and in sport aviation, in particular. I personally invite you to enjoy becoming a member:

$35 for a 1-year membership
$20 per year for individuals under 19 years old
Family membership available for $45 per year

Membership includes the monthly magazine *Sport Aviation*.

*Write to:* Experimental Aircraft Association, Inc.
P.O. Box 3086
Oshkosh, Wisconsin 54903

*Or call:* (414) 426-4800
(800) 843-3612 (in Wisconsin: 1-800-236-4800)

**The annual EAA Oshkosh Fly-in** is an unbelievable aviation spectacular with over 10,000 airplanes at one airport! Virtually everything aviation-oriented you can imagine! Plan to spend at least 1 day (not everything can be seen in a day) in Oshkosh (100 miles northwest of Milwaukee).

*Convention dates:* 1993 - July 30 through August 5
1994 - July 29 through August 4
1995 - July 28 through August 3

# INDEX

Please forward your suggestions, corrections, and comments concerning typographical errors, etc., to **Irvin N. Gleim • c/o Gleim Publications, Inc. • P.O. Box 12848 • University Station • Gainesville, Florida • 32604**. Please include your name and address so we can properly thank you for your interest. Also, please refer to both the page number and the FAA question number for each item.

1. ________________________________________

2. ________________________________________

3. ________________________________________

4. ________________________________________

5. ________________________________________

6. ________________________________________

7. ________________________________________

8. ________________________________________

9. ________________________________________

10. ______________________________

11. ______________________________

12. ______________________________

13. ______________________________

14. ______________________________

15. ______________________________

16. ______________________________

17. ______________________________

Name: ______________________________

Address: ______________________________

City/State/Zip: ______________________________

Telephone: ______________________________